The *Skeptic*
Encyclopedia of Pseudoscience

A B C ● C L I O

Santa Barbara, California   Denver, Colorado   Oxford, England

THE *SKEPTIC* ENCYCLOPEDIA of PSEUDOSCIENCE

Michael Shermer, Editor

Pat Linse, Contributing Editor

VOLUME TWO

Michael Shermer, Skeptics Society, *Skeptic* magazine, P.O. Box 338, Altadena, CA 91001
URL: http://www.skeptic.com, email: skepticmag@aol.com
(626) 794-3119 (phone), (626) 794-1301 (fax)

Library of Congress Cataloging-in-Publication Data
The *Skeptic* encyclopedia of pseudoscience / edited by Michael Shermer.
p. cm.
Includes index.
ISBN 1-57607-653-9 (set : hardcover : alk. paper) — ebook ISBN 1-57607-654-7
1. Pseudoscience—Encyclopedias. I. Shermer, Michael.   II. Skeptic.
Q172.5.P77 S44 2002
503—dc21
2002009653

02 03 04 05 06 10 9 8 7 6 5 4 3 2 1

This book is also available on the World Wide Web as an e-book.
Visit abc-clio.com for details.

ABC-CLIO, Inc.
130 Cremona Drive, P.O. Box 1911
Santa Barbara, California 93116-1911

This book is printed on acid-free paper.
Manufactured in the United States of America

To James "the Amazing" Randi,
our hero, colleague, friend, and inspiration

Contents

SECTION 2
INVESTIGATIONS FROM
SKEPTIC MAGAZINE

Volume Two

The *Skeptic*
Encyclopedia of Pseudoscience

3
CASE STUDIES IN PSEUDOSCIENCE
FROM SKEPTIC MAGAZINE

The Alien Archetype

The Origin of the "Grays"

JOHN ADAMS

In the aftermath of the Heaven's Gate mass suicide, the task of debunking erroneous and unwholesome notions of the "alien" acquires a previously unanticipated level of seriousness. By "alien" I mean the now-classic and ever-popular "Gray," the alien archetype that was depicted on the Heaven's Gate web site, and featured in nearly every film, television program, book and magazine article, from *Communion* to *The X-Files*, and even recently satirized on *The Simpsons*. While artistic and theatrical productions often use this image, the Gray has been popularized even more by those who wish to create the belief that aliens actually exist (e.g., reported abductees and peddlers of "autopsy" footage). Given the absence of any clarity or consistency in UFO folklore concerning the exact origins or motives of the Grays, the striking consistency between purported eyewitness reports of their physical appearance is perhaps the greatest comfort to those preoccupied with proving their authenticity.

I would like to argue that the historical context of those who envision aliens is not only crucial to establishing how they should look but is also quite plausibly the sole basis of popular extraterrestrial stereotypes. Two centuries ago, aliens were often visualized as Native Americans or Blacks in both eyewitness recollection and in straightforward fiction accounts. In the past century, with the advent of Darwinism, a new stereotype of the alien began to take shape. Space invaders were recurrently both "witnessed" and artistically represented as hairless, with enormous, potent eyes, enlarged craniums, and light complexions. The Gray may reveal little about any actual world beyond Earth but a great deal about the imaginative content of the human mind in the western world at this point in our history.

In the summer of 1996, NASA revealed compelling evidence that Mars may once have sustained life. In the spring of 1997, a mass suicide occurred at the Heaven's Gate Temple in California, inspired, at least to some degree, by a longing for communion with alien beings. The juxtaposition of these two events shows that the spectre of extraterrestrial life looms forth both as an object of serious inquiry and as a catalyst to morbid delusion.

In such an atmosphere, the task of dealing with the subject of extraterrestrial life demands a level of seriousness previously unneeded. As the Heaven's Gate example attests, some characterizations of aliens formed in the absence of any actual contact are far less wholesome than others. To address the issue of life beyond Earth sensibly, we should demystify some common conceptions of the anatomy of extraterrestrials by exploring their historical and cultural roots.

One particular image of the alien currently dominates popular culture in both abduction testimonials and science fiction accounts. Dr. John E. Mack, professor of psychiatry at

Harvard and well-known advocate of alleged abduction victims, uses the widely known term *Grays* when referring to these alien visitors, describing them as "by far the most common entity observed" (Mack, 1995, 22). They are typically pale, hairless, and genderless, with prominent eyes and enormous heads balanced on diminutive bodily frames. While there is no hint of agreement concerning precise alien origins or motives, the consensus on their physical appearance in many separate reports is so broad that UFO enthusiasts often cite it as corroborative proof of authenticity.

Common sense calls for us to challenge these testimonies from the get go: Why come so far across the vast distances of interstellar space merely to gather, probe, and traumatize a few humans (although some believers put the number into the millions), and then why bother—ever so discreetly—to return them? Is overexposure to *Star Trek* and *X-Files* a likely culprit here, and don't the abductions seem to be straight out of the late night horror show? Believers may counter such swipes with their own, inquiring: But what of the degree of concurrence among so many eyewitnesses? Since this cannot be denied, why should it be ignored? They may also propose that Hollywood is not inspiring a collective fantasy, but rather quietly employing knowledgeable researchers to assure the authenticity of sci-fi productions like the historical consultants who inform the directors of the great epics.

In demystifying the Gray the first issue to address is the matter of color. "Little green men" was the color of choice for some B-movie aliens, but serious believers all agree that actual ETs lack skin pigmentation. Much closer to white than to charcoal, a Gray is by definition a traveler whose scientific competence vastly surpasses humanity's. In considering this, we should not ignore the European genealogy of modern science fiction, which was once steeped in racial prejudice.

Few consistencies in alien appearance have endured since the cultures that accepted the Copernican model of the universe first began to speculate about how extraterrestrials should appear. One of the only assumptions lasting over the centuries is that the voyagers capable of making the trip must have lighter skin than the awe-stricken spectators who greet their arrival. From early modern Europe, representative interplanetary fantasies include Francis Godwin's *The Man in the Moone* (1638) and Ralph Morris' *A Narrative of the Life and Astonishing Adventures of John Daniel* (1751). In such narratives, first contact is achieved through the genius and initiative of European aeronauts inspired by the exploits of Christopher Columbus and Sir Francis Drake (Adams, 1995, 71–73). Until the 1890s it was taken for granted that the aliens would not come to Earth, but instead be "discovered." True to the Columbian legacy, they are envisioned in early modern European fantasy narratives as American Indians or Africans (Adams, 1995, 70, 73–81). Testimony about actual contact, it should be emphasized, closely conformed to fictional stereotypes. In 1758 Emanuel Swedenborg, a foremost scientist and theologian of the Enlightenment (and founder of the Swedenborgian Church), chronicled aliens inhabiting his own solar system which he encountered in a trance state reportedly bestowed upon him by the grace of God (Adams, 1995, 78; Swedenborg, 1787, 1). Martians resembled the dark-skinned races of his own world and clothed themselves in tree bark (Adams, 79; Swedenborg, 107). On Jupiter, the aliens lived in conical tents (Adams, 80; Swedenborg, 63). His eyewitness account bears the title "De telluribus in mundo nostro solari, quae vocanter planetae," or "The Earths in our universe which are called planets."

Nineteenth century German racists not surprisingly imagined that Martian invaders capable of subduing the Nordic states must be more white than Europeans. In 1897, the year that H. G. Wells' *War of the Worlds* first ap-

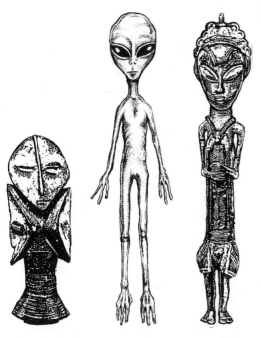

The geneaology of the Gray may be found in the earth's historical or cultural past. (left to right) A lega sculpture from the Congo (Thompson, 1974, 120). The familiar gray (Rosenblatt, 1996, 44). Yoruba Earth cult brass figure from Nigeria (Thompson, 1974, 70).

Occultist Aleister Crowley claimed he had contacted Lam, an alien, and drew this picture of him. Note the uncharacteristically small eyes (Grant, 1980, 160–161).

peared as a magazine serial, a book was published in Germany titled *Auf Zwei Planeten* or *Two Planets*. Its author Kurd Lasswitz was an acclaimed science fiction writer in his own country. While Wells' invaders perish shortly after their arrival (from exposure to common germs), Lasswitz's aliens survive Earth's microorganisms and conquer the planet. Regarded as heroic imperialist problem-solvers by the author, they are similar to humans, especially (not surprisingly) to Germans (Lasswitz, 1971, 27; 55). They privilege Europeans in their global colony with coveted positions as collaborators. The book contains revealing images. The Martians have "large heads" and "large shining eyes." Their hair is noteworthy solely because "nearly all" of them had "very light, nearly white hair" (Lasswitz, 1971, 16, 25). (Blondness taken to the next level, perhaps?) Strolling down a German lane, a lightly

veiled Martian who knew the ranges of Earth's climactic conditions notes with apparent relief (Lasswitz, 1971, 323): "And how pleasantly one can walk here in the sunshine without being burnt!"

A vast proportion of the aliens portrayed in every form of mass media since the genre of science fiction became popular have had light skin. Those who currently perpetuate the image in artistic endeavors or through other forms of self-expression are by now almost certainly oblivious to the possible roots of this conception in the social and political context of the times when images of aliens first permeated popular culture.

Another prominent feature of the Gray is the bulbous, hairless head. Not surprisingly, this too is traceable to European history. One of the first famous Europeans of the 20th century to lay claim to privileged communication

Science fiction writer Hugo Gernsback's imaginative conception of how an alien might look, illustrating an article from December 1937 bearing the title "Can We Signal Mars by Short Wave?" The "Hugo" Awards for science fiction are named after Gernsback (Dick, 1993, 101).

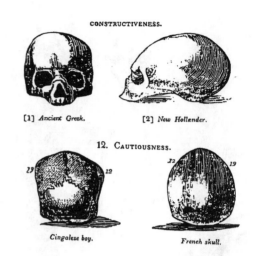

CONSTRUCTIVENESS.

[1] *Ancient Greek.*   [2] *New Hollander.*

12. CAUTIOUSNESS.

Cingalese boy.   *French skull.*

The concept that the Western skull's supposed rounder forehead shape and larger forehead size is directly correlated with preferred traits is illustrated in this comparison between Western skulls and skulls from groups considered more primitive. From George Combe's *Lectures on Phrenology* (Combe, 1854, 173; 185).

with aliens was occultist Aleister Crowley. Crowley claimed contact with Lam, an extra-terrestrial being that he believed functioned as a "link" between Sirius and the Andromeda constellations (Grant, 1980, 281). He himself drew Lam between 1918 and 1919 as a humanoid closely resembling a white man with a grossly expanded bald head (Grant, 1980, 95, 160, 281). The piercing eyes which gaze upon the viewer so knowingly, however, are far too small to match the current Gray model. Perhaps this disparity accounts for the absence of the portrait in the standard evangelistic UFOlogy tracts.

Just as it is no surprise that Swedenborg saw Indians, it is to be expected that an Englishman of the early 20th century would visualize Lam. Over the past few generations those immersed in the culture of the West, whether they reside in its bosom or view its images in movie houses, are likely to have some familiarity with Darwinism. The idea that "bigger is better" insofar as the brain is concerned, though prone to some ridicule in scientific cir-

cles in recent times, gained wide exposure and appeal even before Darwinism and still maintains some credibility in the general populace today. We have all seen the famous Time-Life book "march of progress" diagram, reproduced countless times in numerous ways: as the incarnations of pre-human typologies "advance" over time, the skull becomes more bulbous and prominent while the jaws and nasal passages recede. The body diminishes as the hair thins to reveal a typical Caucasian man.

Sculptures of Newton and Voltaire that embellished the Victorian drawing rooms of Crowley's world often seem to grossly accentuate the prominence of the forehead. In marked contrast to these white marble busts were living displays of large muscular Blacks afflicted with microcephalism presented as "missing links" in the 1860s by P. T. Barnum. As purported evolutionary throwbacks, the latter would signify a virtual inversion of the Gray ideal.

The celebration of the expanded cranium has a long history in western history. Jean-

Professor Cavor, an English adventurer from H. G. Wells's 1901 novel, *The First Men in the Moon*, is captured by moon-dwelling Selenites. This story, as well as Wells's better-known *War of the Worlds*, was first published in popular magazines before the turn of the 20th century. Illustrated by lavish and imaginative paintings, they provided prototypes in the public mind for aliens more than a hundred years ago. The illustrator of these particular aliens seems to have mixed traits of both high and low cast moon-dwellers from Wells's text.

Jacques Rousseau (Rousseau, 1915, 150), Charles Darwin (Darwin, 1974, 452–3), Lewis Henry Morgan (Morgan, 1967, 25), Friedrich Engels (Engels, 1990, 138), and Franz Boas (Boas, 1974, 232–3) would only commence a list of influential thinkers who either unequivocally affirmed a correlation between the measure of brain size and the quality of the intellect or at some point seriously toyed with the notion as a significant issue worthy of serious scientific consideration. *The First Men in the Moon*, written by H. G. Wells in 1901, conformed to the expectations of its age by making a direct correlation between large cranial

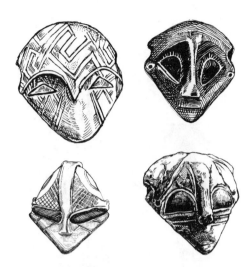

Ancient representations of mythic spirit beings: Vinca figures from the Balkans. Such spiritual art dates back to the fifth millennium B.C.E. (Gimbutas, 1992, 63, 124).

size and natural superiority. The moon was populated by Selenites—humanoids of varied anatomies organized according to a caste system in which cranial magnitude determined moral and political authority. After violent encounters with brutish lower-caste cattle herders, an earthling observes: "But presently I came upon a body of Selenites led by two who were curiously different, even in form, from any of those we had seen hitherto, with larger heads and smaller bodies and much more elaborately wrapped about." The moon is ruled by a creature called the Grand Lunar, surrounded by a retinue of worthy advisors with "swollen heads." The Grand Lunar is in certain respects the ultimate Gray. Having "no face," his head is several yards long, reposed upon a tiny "shriveled" body. While Wells has little to say concerning the complexion of the majority of the aristocratic Selenites and places their eyes to the sides, comparing them to hens, the Grand Lunar is described as "white," with "little eyes" that "stared down at" the narrator (Wells, 1901, 133, 140, 145, 150–151).

The connection between cranial size and

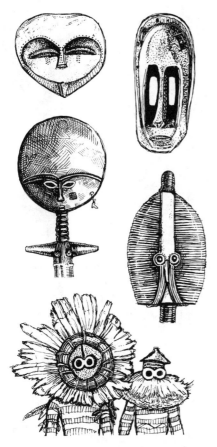

A sixth-century Christ. Byzantine artists exaggerated the eyes in portrayals of human subjects, particularly in representations of heroes and saints.

In Asia sacred buddhist monuments known as stupas dot the landscape. They are often painted with two large human eyes which are unaccompanied by any other sensory organs.

The eyes have it. African folk art often exaggerates eyes over other facial features when depicting the spiritual. (Top left) Bakwele dance mask, Congo; (Top right) Dogan dance mask, Mali; (Middle left) Ashanti fertility doll, Ghana; (Middle right) Bakota reliquary, Gabon; (Bottom) Bapended masked dancers, Congo. (Redrawn from Trowell, N.D., 23, 46, 50, 92, 152).

genius lost favor in the latter half of this century. Quack anthropology and racist biology were silenced by disgust and embarrassment over the Nazi legacy. Among the topics of concern for scientific professionals in Nazi Germany was "the persistence of the 'Cromagnon' racial type in certain populations" (Proctor, 1988, 41). It is amusing to imagine that an abductee some day may claim to be spirited away by furry pin-headed aliens with compact brains that surpass bulkier models. But we should not hold our breath.

An examination of the belief systems of the past two centuries may suggest the origins of the light skin color and large head, but it is not as useful in explaining the size of the eyes. While a Darwinian imagination would not likely posit minuscule eyes on any creature evolved beyond human capacities, to banish ears, noses, and mouths from the visage would make even less sense. While some insights into the riddle may be found in the modern history of the West, others are equally or best addressed by turning to representations of spiritually superior beings from the ancient world. (Spiritual associations may also explain the depictions of baldness, which may have been inspired by Darwinism but also seems rooted in more universal and global conceptions. "Wild men" are universally by definition hirsute beasts. Tonsuring is quite common in monastic settings as a mark of spiritual advancement; note the practice at Heaven's Gate.)

The idea that extraordinary beings should see rather than hear, smell, touch, or taste is one that is universal and widespread. All-seeing presumes all-knowing—a capacity widely hoped for in god-like beings. In Western culture, too,

God is described as "all-seeing" rather than "all-hearing." A quest for terms that pertain to the remaining four senses as powerful as the English words "visionary," "illumination," and "enlightenment" would entail quite a scavenger hunt. These associations of the visual with all-knowing god-like wisdom could provide an explanation for the tendency to depict spiritually superior beings with enlarged eyes.

A wide variety of cultures depict gods or goddesses as hairless beings with huge eyes but no other distinct facial sensory organs. Exaggerated eyes are found in such diverse sources as primitive African art, Byzantine mosaics, Buddhist sacred sites and prehistoric icons from the Balkans. Although they confirm nothing more than the certainty that many societies have accentuated the eyes of their divinities, one look at some of them would almost necessarily prompt an association with the Gray (Thompson, 1974, 70, 120; Gimbutas, 1992, 63, 124, 126, 182).

The alien as Gray, like the other parts of the alien abduction and UFO belief system, clearly has a terrestrial rather than extraterrestrial origin. It would be interesting to come back in another century or two to read what historians have to say about the UFO/alien craze that swept America in the latter half of the 20th century.

References:

Adams, J. 1995. "Outer Space and the New World in the Imagination of Eighteenth-Century Europeans." *Eighteenth-Century Life*. 19 (1): 70–83.

Boas, F. 1974 (1894). "Human Faculty as Determined by Race." In *The Shaping of American Anthropology: 1883–1911. A Franz Boas Reader*. George Stocking (ed.). New York: Basic Books.

Booth, W., and W. Clailborne. 1997. "Group's Leader among 39 Cult Suicides: Families Get News of Members Lost Many Years Ago." *Washington Post*, March 29. A: 1, 9.

Combe, G. 1854. *Lectures on Phrenology*. New York: Fowlers and Wells.

Dart, J., J. Rainey and L. Stammer. 1997. "Tract Offers Clues about Group's Theology, Motives." *Los Angeles Times*, March 28. A: 1, 15.

Darwin, C. 1974 (1838). "Extracts from the B-C-D-E Transmutation Notebooks." In *Darwin on Man: A Psychological Study of Scientific Creativity*. Howard E. Gruber (ed.). Paul Barrett (trans. and annotated). New York: E.P. Dutton & Co.

Dick, S. 1993. "The Search for Extraterrestrial Intelligence and the NASA High Resolution Microwave Survey (HRMS): Historical Perspectives." *Space Science Reviews*. 64: 93–139.

Engels, F. 1990 (1884). "The Origin of the Family, Private Property and the State." In *Karl Marx & Frederick Engels: Collected Works*. (Vol. 26). New York: International Publishers.

Gimbutas, M. 1992. *The Goddesses and Gods of Old Europe*. Berkeley: University of California Press.

Grant, K. 1980. *Outside the Circles of Time*. London: Frederick Muller, Ltd.

Lasswitz, K. 1971 (1897). *Two Planets*. Carbondale: Southern Illinois University Press.

Mack, John. 1995. *Abduction: Human Encounters with Aliens*. New York: Ballantine Books.

Morgan, L. H. 1967 (1877). *Ancient Society*. New York: World Publishing Company.

Proctor, R. 1988. *Racial Hygiene: Medicine under the Nazis*. Cambridge: Harvard University Press.

Rosenblatt, R. 1996. "Classifying the Unknown: Types of Alien Beings." *Fate*. June: 44–7.

Rousseau, J. J. 1915 (1755). "Discours sur l'origine et les fondements de l'inégalité parmi les hommes." In *The Political Writings of Jean-Jacques Rousseau*. (Vol. 1). Cambridge: Cambridge University Press.

Swedenborg, E. 1787 (1758). "De telluribus in mundo nostro solari, quae vocanter planetae." London: R. Hindmarsh.

Thompson, R. 1974. *African Art in Motion*. Berkeley: University of California Press.

Trowell, M., and Neverman, H. (N.D.). *African and Oceanic Art*. New York: Harry N. Abrams, Inc.

Wells, H. G. 1965 (1901 Publishing Co.). *The First Men in the Moon*. New York: Airmont.

Anastasia

A Case Study in the Myth of the Miraculous Survival

TIM CALLAHAN

"From a word to a word was I led."
—Havamal (The Sayings of the High One),
from the Poetic Edda of Iceland. (The speaker is the god Odin.)

In the process of researching an upcoming book, I came across a passage in the Gospel of John which indicated that the author saw the end of the world as taking place in his own generation. Jesus says (John 5:25–29):

> Truly, truly, I say to you, the hour is coming, and now is, when the dead will hear the voice of the Son of God, and those who hear will live. For as the Father has life in himself, so he has granted the Son also to have life in himself, and has given him authority to execute judgment, because he is the Son of man. Do not marvel at this; for the hour is coming when all who are in the tombs will hear his voice and come forth, those who have done good, to resurrection of life, and those who have done evil to the resurrection of judgment.

As is often the case, an examination of the key words in the original Greek clarifies the meaning of the passage. The Greek word translated as "hour" is *hora*, which if it doesn't mean exactly an hour does mean a fleeting period of time. This is further emphasized in that the form of the verb "to come" (erchomai) is present imperfect, meaning that "is coming" is an exact translation. The word for "now," *nun*, also expresses immediacy. It is not so much "now" as "right now." The word for the dead here is *nekros*, deriving from *nekus*, meaning a corpse. So the dead in question are dead bodies. These bodies will experience resurrection or anastasis, meaning literally to stand again (*ana* again + *stasis* stand), either to life or krisis (judgment or damnation). So John has Jesus saying that the hour or fleeting period of time is coming and in fact is here right now, when dead bodies will come forth from their tombs and stand again at the sound of Jesus' voice to face judgment.

While each of these Greek words is important in conveying the immediacy and physicality of the imminent last judgment—both of which are somewhat less forceful in the English translation—the word *anastasis* in particular stood out for me since it is obviously the source of the name of the famous Princess Anastasia (1901–1918), who alone of all the family of Czar Nicholas II is so often fabled to have survived the Bolshevik firing squad. A name which means "resurrection" or literally to "stand again" is naturally going to be popular among Christians, particularly those of the Eastern Orthodox persuasion, where Greek, rather than Latin, was at least the initial liturgical language. Thus it is not surprising that there are four popes and two Byzantine emperors named Anastasius. Since Russia was Christianized by Greek Orthodox missionaries, several Russian names have Greek origins. Among these are Feodor (Theodore, Gr. *theodoros* "gift of God"), Vassily (Basil, Gr. *basilios* "king") and, of course, Anastasia. It is my contention that the reason the princess bearing this name was chosen by those hoping for a restoration of the Romanovs as the survivor of the firing squad is based, consciously or unconsciously, on the symbolism of her name. There is no other reason for choosing her as the sole survivor.

One might argue that, if what we are dealing with here is myth rather than a tale that is at least possibly historical, the logical survivor would be the Czarevitch Alexis. However, his malady, hemophilia, made it so unlikely that he would survive multiple gunshot wounds, that one of his sisters had to be chosen. It is not surprising that the one chosen to have survived being shot at close range by a firing squad, partially burned, and subsequently buried happened to be named "Resurrection." That there must be a survivor, in spite of the horrendous odds against such a possibility, is demanded by myth as surely as it is militated against by reality. In fact this story has been told over and over from ancient times and is a powerful legend. Anastasia's mythic survival was assured far more by the emotional needs it fulfilled than by the dubious protection the family jewels, supposedly sewn into the bodices of the princesses to conceal them, provided against a hail of bullets. (The deflection of most of the bullets by the bejeweled bodices is the usual explanation of Anastasia's survival.)

Not only is the legend of the miraculous survival of a supposedly murdered royal scion an ancient story, it has a precedent in Russian history, literature and music in the character of False Dmitry from the story of Boris Godounov, which, ironically enough, provides a prelude to the accession of the Romanov dynasty. The story of Boris Godounov was immortalized in an epic poem by Alexander Pushkin, which subsequently became the basis of the opera by Modest Moussorgsky. Boris rose to power on the death of Ivan IV ("the Terrible") in 1584. He was advisor to Feodor, Ivan's eldest surviving son, who was mentally retarded. Even before Feodor died without leaving an heir, Ivan's seven-year old son, Dmitry, died in 1591. Though this seems to have occurred as a result of an epileptic seizure, it was rumored that he was murdered and it was widely held that Boris, who was elected Czar by the Zemsky Sobor (privy council) on Feodor's death in 1598 and who had everything to gain by extinguishing Ivan's line, had ordered the child's assassination. At first popular, Boris had increasing problems because of opposition from the boyars, compounded by crop failures in 1601–2. Many of the common people saw this as a sign of divine wrath for the supposed murder of Dmitry. In 1603 a young monk by the name of Grigory Otrepyev declared that he was Prince Dmitry and that he had in fact survived the "attempted" assassination. Naturally, such a claim was not welcomed by Boris, and Grigory was forced to flee to Poland. There his tenuous claim was taken seriously, since it was to the benefit of Poland to recognize him as pretender to the Russian throne. He married Marina Mniszech, the 15-year old daughter of one of the chief Polish nobles supporting his claim, and returned to Russia with a Polish army in 1604. This force was swelled by various Russian malcontents, and though it was defeated, Boris died in 1605, and "Dmitry" was made czar.

Of course, he had to give considerable territorial concessions to the Poles, and a Polish garrison was established in Moscow. Under the protection of Polish forces, the Roman Catholic church, intent on bringing Orthodox Russia under the sway of the Pope, sent Jesuit missionaries into Russia to convert the people. This and other high-handed policies of the new czar provoked a violent reaction. The Jesuits were murdered, and a period of anarchy called the "Time of Troubles" ensued. Moscow was retaken, and Grigory was put to death in 1606 in a coup led by Vassily Shuisky, who was then elected czar. However, there were many in Russia opposed to Shuisky's rule, and in 1607 another False Dmitry appeared, claiming this time to have survived the coup. Though he did not physically resemble Grigory Otrepyev, the malcontents rallied around him, and Marina even acknowledged him to be her husband. He was eventually killed by his own followers in 1610. But the very next year yet another False Dmitry appeared and held sway until he was captured and executed in Moscow in 1612. The general chaos, including the Polish military presence in Russia, wasn't ended until after the accession of Michael Romanov as Czar in 1613.

The story of False Dmitry echoes the history of another interregnum, this one resulting from the assassination of Nero Caesar in C.E. 68. This is the Nero redivivus legend, the belief that Nero either survived his assassination or rose from the dead afterward and escaped to the east where he was marshaling an army of Parthians with which to invade the Roman Empire. This superstition was strong enough that between C.E. 69 and 88 three different pretenders posing as Nero attempted to seize control of the Roman Empire. It was also a probable source of much of the imagery of the Beast (the Antichrist), and particularly of the Number of the Beast, in Revelation. Since the letters of the Greek alphabet, like those of the Hebrew alphabet, have numerical values,

names can be converted into numbers and numbers into names. The number 666, the number of the beast, converts into "Neron Caesar." In some early manuscripts the number of the beast is 616, which gives us "Nero Caesar" in the Greek alphabet.

Yet another assassinated prince whose death spawned pretenders was Bardiya, son of Cyrus the Great and brother of Cambyses. Cambyses succeeded Cyrus as ruler of the Persian Empire in 529 B.C.E. and had his brother Bardiya murdered before setting out to conquer Egypt in 525. As brutal as such an act was, it was probably also quite prudent in that Bardiya might well have taken the throne in Cambyses' absence. As it was, when Cambyses died on his way back from Egypt in 522, a Mede noble by the name of Gaumata claimed to be Bardiya and seized the throne. Darius, Cambyses' son-in-law, managed to murder Gaumata and lay claim to the throne in 519. Since he was only distantly related to the royal family, the legitimacy of this claim was tenuous at best, and Darius had to put down a series of revolts before he could become Darius I, ruler of the Persian Empire. Among those he had to dispose of was another false Bardiya, this time a Persian noble named Vahyazdata.

Thus it can be seen that Anastasia is among the latest of murdered royal scions whose death gave rise to legends of a miraculous survival. That she is not the last is evidenced in our own legends of the survival of John F. Kennedy, Elvis Presley, and now it appears, even Princess Diana. As trivial as Elvis sightings may make the legend seem, the ancient lineage of the tale shows that it is a myth to be understood rather than merely dismissed out of hand. The irrational hope that the king, kingly line or beloved leader (or even cultural icon) didn't really die a premature sordid death but is waiting for the propitious moment in which to return, avenge his would-be destroyers and dispense justice is related to the myth of the sleeping king of old. This may be

Arthur, who supposedly sleeps with his knights at Avalon, or it might be Charlemagne or even Frederick Barbarosa. In all these cases the great king of old did not actually die but instead lies in a death-like sleep in a cave surrounded by his loyal retainers, waiting by divine mandate for the time of his nation's greatest peril, when he and his knights will awake, ride forth, deliver his land, and possibly even reestablish Camelot. The emotional hold of such legends can be seen from the fact that despite the failure of Charlemagne to drive the Nazis out of France or that Britain owed more to the R.A.F. than to Arthur in repelling Hitler, the myths do not die.

Another variant of this myth is that the heir to the rightful kingly line is in hiding and will one day drive out the invader. Historically this has a bit more validity than the legend of miraculous survival. Alfred the Great (849–899) managed to go from hiding in the swamps to overthrowing the Danes in 871, and Robert the Bruce was likewise able to deliver Scotland from the English invaders at the Battle of Bannockburn in 1314. Both of these situations also recall the plight of David and his outlaw band being pursued by King Saul. For all that, the Stuart cause and that of the Scottish Highlanders died on the field of Culloden in 1746 with the final defeat of Bonnie Prince Charlie (1720–1788). The myth of the king in hiding who rides out of obscurity to claim his rightful throne, drive out the vile invaders, and revive the ancient realm was given new life by that greatest of all modern myth makers, J.R.R. Tolkien, in *The Lord of the Rings* trilogy, the final volume of which is aptly named *The Return of the King*. In Tolkien's modern epic, Aragorn, rightful heir of the kings of the west, wanders the land as the ranger Strider. The other rangers are his knights, and as their title implies, they provide protection from evildoers in the wild lands that have grown up since the fall of the kingdom of the west. When we first meet Strider,

he bears a broken sword. The "Sword that was Broken" has been carried by generations of Aragorn's forbearers and cannot be reforged until the one destined to regain the lost throne is given the proper sign. With the reforging of the sword the king will reclaim his realm.

The sword that is either lost, broken or virtually unattainable is a motif which connects the lost but rightful king to the myth of the hero in general. Arthur proves that he is the rightful heir to the throne of Uther Pendragon by pulling the sword Excalibur from the stone, which none but the rightful king can do. Likewise, in the Icelandic Volsunga Saga only Sigmund can pull the sword Nothung from the sacred oak, Branstock. And just as the stone represents the earth, Branstock represents Yggdrasil, the world tree or axis mundi of Norse myth. At its roots lies the underworld; in its branches are the heavens and the gods; and in its trunk is the world of human beings. At the hero's death Nothung is broken and must be reforged by Sigmund's son Sigurd (the German Siegfried). In Greek myth Theseus, raised in Troezen in the Peloponnesian peninsula, but son of King Aegeus of Athens, must roll a great boulder away to gain the sword and sandals that will establish his identity as the true son of Aegeus. Once again the sword is symbolically held by the earth, which will only yield it up to the rightful heir. In all three of these myths we find the elements of the kingly family that has lost power, the kingdom that must be reclaimed and the rightful heir emerging from obscurity. Since the death of Uther Pendragon, Britain had been divided into warring petty kingdoms. Arthur reunites them and establishes Camelot. The power of the Volsungs has been broken by a treacherous attack. Sigurd reforges the broken sword his father had pulled from the world tree and regains the glory of the Volsungs. While Aegeus hasn't lost his throne, he has been unable to procure an heir from two marriages. Theseus is conceived while Aegeus is visiting Troezen and, being drunk, ends up in the bed of a princess named Aethra, who had originally been promised to another hero. Thus the origin of Theseus, like that of Arthur (the product of Uther deceiving Igraine, wife of the duke of Cornwall), is through an illicit affair. As a result both Arthur and Theseus are raised in obscurity—the same obscurity in which the miraculous survivor exists until he or she remembers that they are in reality Bardiya, Nero, Dmitry or Anastasia. In the final case most women who claimed to be the Romanov princess, including Anna Anderson, the most famous pretender, said that amnesia induced by the trauma of their near assassination prevented them from pressing their claims earlier.

That the hero is commonly ignorant of his true parentage until it is revealed to him at puberty and that he is often raised by humble step-parents or as an illegitimate child was the case with not only Arthur and Theseus, but with Moses, Sargon the Great, Perseus, Romulus and Remus, and a host of others as well. This has been seen in psychoanalytic terms by Otto Rank and Sigmund Freud as a neurotic rejection on the part of the hero of the low station of his true parents or his position of illegitimacy. He claims instead the fantasy of a father who is a king or even a god. In the latter case, though Herakles (Hercules) is raised by his supposed parents, he is in reality the son of Zeus. In the psychoanalytic view, the hero's vain fantasy is that he will prove himself worthy of his divine or kingly father, who will then recognize him as his true son. However, we might just as well turn the psychoanalytic explanation around and see it as a tale which had to be invented by others for the lineages of great men, since their greatness obviously betrayed either kingly or even divine origins. For example, eventually, even great philosophers were given this status. Thus, after his death, Plato was made the son of Apollo, who assumed the guise of Plato's mortal father to impregnate his mother. This was commonly given as the reason the pharaohs of Egypt could seemingly be descendants of mortal fathers, while in reality being the sons of a god. The deity, usually Amon-Re, assumed the likeness of the reigning pharaoh to engender the new crown prince, who as ruler of Egypt was required to have divine parentage. In the case of Moses the situation is seemingly reversed in that he is in reality the child of a people held in bondage and is raised in the Egyptian court. However, as a prince of Egypt, he is fatherless, and the Israelites are God's chosen people, while the Egyptians are destined to be overthrown as a demonstration of God's power. Moses' real royalty in this myth is his position as a Levite, one who does indeed have a real father, and who is as well the chosen deliverer of his people. Another possible source of the hero's recognition at puberty that he is a person of different parentage from what he previously thought may involve a source that is more anthropological than psychological, namely the rite of passage from childhood and ignorance into adulthood and revelation of the tribal secrets, at which time the newly initiated adult often received a new name and as such a new identity.

While there is often a very pragmatic reason for the miraculous survivor to put forth his or her claim—in the case of the false Bardiyas, Nero redivivus and the False Dmitries the rule of a kingdom, in the case of Anastasia a considerable fortune held for the Romanovs in a Swiss bank—there are also powerful emotional, psychological, anthropological and mythic/religious forces which support these recurring claims. The elements common to the myths of the miraculous survival, the sleeping king and the hero in general are as follows:

1. The central character is lost, disinherited, estranged from his kingly or divine father, raised in obscurity and deceived as to his true position or placed under a

spell, such as a deathlike sleep or its modern variant, amnesia.

2. Though they have been wronged and denied their heritage, they are in fact destined for greatness. This will be shown by a supernatural sign, omen or the passage of an ordeal: the recovery of the lost or broken sword, the sign of the burning bush, or even the recovery of a lost memory.

3. Just as the central character begins the story in a state of ignorance and estrangement, so the kingdom or even the world itself is in a state of disorder for lack of the true king. Either a state of anarchy exists or an impostor, possibly even an invader, sits upon the the throne: Sauron menaces Middle Earth; Uther's kingdom is in shambles; the Volsungs are in hiding and denied their rightful lands; the Danes have overrun Wessex; a fratricidal murderer rules Persia; Rome is in chaos; Boris Godounov has usurped the throne of the line of Rurik; the Bolsheviks rule with an iron fist.

That the world or at least the kingdom is in chaos for want of the true king involves not only myth, but the ritual of sacred marriage, in which the king is symbolically married to the goddess who is the earth or at least the land through a ritual sexual union with a priestess representing the goddess. That the true king was reigning was evidenced by the fertility of the land. Thus, the crop failures in the reign of Boris Godounov which convinced the people that he was unfit to rule tapped into a surviving stratum of pre-Christian belief. The chaos of the kingdom in the hero myth is a divine sign that the land awaits the true king. The sacred kings of this ancient belief system were often ceremonial, their power being more symbolic than real. However, attempts to replace them often provoked violent reprisals. Thus when the Germanic war leader Arminius (Herman or "war man"), who had kept the Romans from conquering Germany, attempted to make himself king of the Cherusci, he was summarily assassinated. One of the likely reasons his claim to kingship was seen as invalid might well have been that he was a warrior. The sacred king was often forbidden to profane himself by shedding human blood. The tension between the character of the sacred king who must not go to war and the deliverer of the kingdom who must can be seen in the two titles claimed for Jesus by his followers. In apocalyptic terms the "Son of God," a title previously applied to the Davidic kings (see Psalms 2:7), was a war leader who would drive out the invader and restore the line of David to the throne of Israel. Yet in such apocalyptic works as the Book of Daniel or the non-canonical but extremely influential 1 Enoch, the "Son of man" is a holy king without weapons who, because of his holiness, inherits the millennial kingdom after the apocalyptic destruction of evil and rules it in peace.

4. In a grand climactic confrontation, possibly even an apocalyptic battle between ultimate good and ultimate evil, the king (or even the lost princess) will return and set all things right. By now many readers will have observed that the elements of divine intervention to right a cosmic wrong by the restoration of the rightful king, with justice held in abeyance until that ruler reclaims the throne by way of a final battle, are central to the Christian mythos. Jesus, the divine son, is born and raised in obscurity and humility while his enemy Herod seeks his death. The entire world is in a state of travail, awaiting the

righting of old wrongs when Christ, the true king–variously characterized in terms of the warlike Son of God and the holy Son of man–returns. And so we are brought back to John 5:25–29 with Jesus saying that the hour is coming when the dead will rise and stand again (anastasis) to face judgment.

That the miraculous survival, whether it be of Anastasia, JFK or even Elvis ("the King"), is part and parcel of the same mythos that is the source of the heroic quest in general and Christianity in particular not only establishes its roots deep in the psyche and often beyond the reach of reason, it also has profound political implications. For example, consider Islam. Like Christianity it was initially spread with messianic zeal, but unlike Christianity it did not make even the pretense that conversion should be by peaceful persuasion. Coercion to compel right thinking is not seen by many of the pious as being anything but proper. It also, like Christianity, has a linear view of time, that is that human history has a logical beginning, middle and end, and that the end is divinely ordained. Now let us consider that many of the Islamic states have a national view which mirrors that of the hero or miraculous survivor. That is, they can reasonably see themselves as wrongly deprived of their central position. Geographically located on lands where civilization had its origins and being descendants of the peoples who gave us not only our alphabet but our numerical system as well, they see the world–which is clearly an unjust place–in the grip of largely secular powers, Johnny-come-lately foreigners and infidels who often support corrupt regimes. In other words, the same deep psychological motivations that gave us the hero myth may well operate as the motivating force of a holy war. It is therefore important for us to engage the Islamic world, to work to raise its standard of living and to encourage within it democracy and the free flow of ideas.

That the psychological elements of the hero myth might interact with the sense of injustice in Islamic nations should alert us to the potential danger in general posed by an appeal to its deep and powerful emotional roots. Consider some of the elements common to many totalitarian regimes:

1. The Charismatic Leader, or "the man on the white horse." This is the hero himself or even the sacred king. Whether it be Hitler, Stalin or Mao, he embodies the ruler who will set things right, often by his mere presence. By bringing fertility to the land, the sacred king of ancient times was a cosmic functionary.
2. The Organic State, in which all social functions are subsumed into state organizations. This is usually seen as a requirement to unify the social structure in order to mobilize the nation in service to the great cosmic goal (see # 4).
3. The enemy within and the enemy without. Historically the enemy within has been anything and everything from homosexuals, "liberals" and opposition parties, to any ethnic group which either hasn't been willing to assimilate (such as the Gypsies) or hasn't been allowed to (such as the Jews). The enemy without is whatever power opposes the totalitarian state.
4. The Cosmic Goal: Whether it be the Thousand Year Reich, the eventual "withering away of the state" or even the millennial kingdom, this is the justification and focus for the subordination of the individual and often the basis for external aggression.

Let us consider all of these points together. The mythos of the totalitarian state is essentially as follows: We seek to fulfill a great goal, a world of ultimate good and justice. In order to reach it we must submerge our individual differences and all pull together under the guidance of our great leader. The only reason we cannot immediately achieve our great goal is that the world is an imperfect place, filled with small minded people, some undermining our society within and others attacking it from without. Until these enemies are overcome, we cannot achieve our cosmic goal. This mythos contains within it the noble quest which is nothing short of the restoration of the cosmic ideal, the profound sense of being a victim of injustice and, embodied in both the state and the leader, a semi-divine father figure whose recognition is eagerly sought. This last aspect was noted by the late Wilhelm Reich, who, before he became entangled in his pseudoscientific orgone therapy, had many profound psychological insights. In *The Mass Psychology of Fascism* he noted that the fascist state reproduced in macrocosm the authoritarian patriarchal family. He argued that the lower middle class, from whom the Nazis gained their core support, would have been better served by the political agenda of the Socialists, but that they voted for the Nazi Party based on an emotional appeal which bypassed reason. While Reich concentrated on the patriarchal family, the emotional appeal implicit in the totalitarian mythos is far broader in that it embodies those elements common to the myths of the miraculous survivor, the hero and the sacred king. (Indeed, as representative of the sacred king, the leader must triumph if the cosmos is to function properly.) That is to say that the same grand myth which provided the emotional basis for the high ideals of the Arthurian cycle and the works of J.R.R. Tolkien also helped fuel the rise of the Third Reich.

It is commonly noted by the apologists of religion that, as bad as theocratic states such as Calvin's Geneva or Cromwell's England were, secular states such as Nazi Germany and the Soviet Union have far surpassed them in dehumanizing brutality, the implication being that modern totalitarianism is the logical end of rational humanism. Yet, as I noted above, the emotional appeal of the totalitarian ideal parallels that of myth and religion. It is thus hardly the logical end point of rational secularism. In any case the fact of the matter is that in every country in Europe in which the fascists took power in the 1930s they did so in concert and coalition with religious conservatives. Thus the Catholic church supported, either implicitly or explicitly, Mussolini in Italy, Franco in Spain, Salazar in Portugal, and Ante Pavalic in Croatia. Likewise, the Orthodox church supported Metaxas in Greece, and both Protestants and Catholics supported the rise of Adolf Hitler. Likewise, in Japan the role of the emperor as the focus of national identity was part and parcel of the national religion. Of course the dictatorships of Stalin and Mao were largely anti-religious. Thus it would seem that, while religious authorities can be used to back dictators—particularly those who crusade against "Godless communism"—totalitarianism is less a function of relative belief or disbelief in a god than of the modern technology of mass media married to ancient mythic themes during periods of national crisis.

At the present time, the collapse of the Soviet Union has deprived the Anastasia myth of much of its power by removing the brutal, unjust usurper required by the hero myth. Anna Anderson, the most famous of the Anastasia pretenders, died in 1984, and DNA tests on a portion of intestinal tissue removed before her death and subsequent cremation proved that she could not have been Anastasia. In any case, even had the Russian princess survived, she would be 97 by now. The Romanov romance could conceivably be revived by a son of Anastasia, but such a pretender would not be a miraculous survivor, and even in its present disordered state, Russia is hardly as susceptible now as it was in the Time of Troubles to the appeal of that myth. Nevertheless, the hero myth retains its power even in our largely secularized society, as evidenced by the popularity of the *Star Wars* movies. It is important to know and understand the dynamics of the hero myth as a way of not only understanding the recurring variations of the miraculous survivor but as well to know how to debunk incipient dictators and others of their ilk. Yet, as we have seen over and over again, rational exposure of the falsehood of cherished beliefs often provokes a fierce defense rather than an acceptance of the proof. Witness the response to the appearance of Emily Rosa on Larry Mantle's "Air Talk" show (KPCC 5/7/98). Every one of those who called in supported therapeutic touch and had rationalizations for why Emily's simple and elegant experiment didn't really prove the pseudoscientific practice invalid. At least one caller was incensed.

It would appear then that an emotional basis for opposing the use of the hero myth in the service of a totalitarian ideal must be sought. To some degree this can be achieved by encouraging people to be their own heroes, rather than by subordinating themselves to another hero. However, I would attack the emotional desire for closure as the prime defense against dictators, and I would do this by way of making people comfortable with the chaos and imperfection of the cosmos and the human condition. I would argue that a certain level of chaos is necessary for the dynamic functioning of the universe. In a state of crystalline perfection any change, any level of dynamism must be viewed as evil. One argument against a perfect god is that he, she or it would have no reason to create a universe, since the deity's own perfection would be sullied by the creation. Viewing the deity as an artist, one driven to create, implies imperfection. Fortunately, the idea of the cosmos as necessarily flawed is actually implicit in the hero myth itself in the form of the usurper whom the hero must overcome. The oppression of the kingdom by the evil usurper can be seen in psychological terms as a neurotic failure to deal with a less than ideal world and the focused projection of the

hero's lowly state on the deliberate frustration of his rightful position by a malevolent personage. Yet, once again there is as well an equally valid anthropological reason for the mythic character of the usurper. This is particularly evident in the myth of Osiris and Set, where Set, representing death, kills Osiris the rightful king. Horus, whose magical conception and imperiled infancy are not only classic hero motifs but precursors of the Christian nativity myths, not only avenges his father's death but restores Osiris to life. But this is not the end of the story, for the myth is cyclical. In fact the year is divided between the rule of Osiris and the rule of Set. In short the deity or hero representing the sun or the grain must be destroyed by his rival and be reborn seasonally for the world to function. Thus the usurper is a functionary of a dynamic, cyclic cosmic order. In some variants of the Osiris myth Horus and Set are eventually reconciled. Thus, if understood properly, the hero myth need not be a dangerous source of neurosis and totalitarianism. If, along with the appreciation of the power of myth, we can teach people to strive for improvement of the human condition while still accepting imperfection and chaos, in short lack of final closure, as valid aspects of both the human condition and the cosmos itself, we can greatly diffuse the source of the totalitarian mythos to which the myth of the miraculous survival belongs.

References:

Bury, J. B., S. A. Cook and F. E. Adcock, eds. 1970. *The Cambridge Ancient History*, Vol III. Cambridge and London: Cambridge University Press.

Campbell, Joseph. 1964. *The Masks of God: Occidental Mythology.* New York: Penguin Books U.S.A. Inc.

Ellis Davidson, H. R. 1964. *Gods and Myths of Northern Europe.* Harmondsworth, Middlesex, U.K.: Penguin Books Inc.

Graves, Robert. 1955. *The Greek Myths.* Harmondsworth, Middlesex, U.K.: Penguin Books Inc.

Hastings, James, ed. 1934. *Encyclopaedia of Religion and Ethics*. 4th edition. Edinburgh: T. & T. Clark (New York: Charles Scribner's Sons).

Helms, Randel. 1988. *Gospel Fictions*. Buffalo: Prometheus Books.

Pushkin, Alexander (trans. Alfred Hayes). 1982. *Boris Godounov*. New York: The Viking Press.

Reich, Wilhelm. 1942. *The Mass Psychology of Fascism*. New York: Farrar, Straus and Giroux.

Strong, James. 1890. *Strong's Exhaustive Concordance of the Bible*. Gordonville, TN: Dugan Publishers Inc.

Tolkien, J. R. R. 1965. *The Lord of the Rings*. New York: Ballantine Books Inc.

Ancient Astronauts

Zecharia Sitchin as a Case Study

ERIC WOJCIEHOWSKI

In 1968, Erik von Däniken released his book *Chariots of the Gods?*, which touched off a fire storm of debate between his admirers and those who had found his claims wanting. To refresh your memory, its thesis was that Extraterrestrials had come to planet Earth in ancient times and have been remembered in myths and legends as well as from the architecture they allegedly left behind.

Despite the fact that von Däniken has lost much of his audience (at least in America), he still seems to have left an impression on the public that has not faded. Although academics have spent many hours showing the errors in von Däniken's reasoning, the Ancient Astronaut notion remains alive. Why? Well, for starters, critics have spent most of their time on von Däniken's theory of ancient astronauts and not on the general concept of extraterrestrial visitations. By this, I mean that although Erik von Däniken popularized the idea, the theory itself has largely been defined by a number of other people.

Sadly the usual approach taken against the Ancient Astronaut theory is akin to dismissing the "UFO's are space aliens" theory by only criticizing one of the many authors who have promoted this viewpoint. The skeptical community is very familiar with old claims resurfacing with different packaging. This is why

each case must be addressed separately. It is related to what UFO researcher Jacques Vallee has called "The Ratchet Effect" ("most amateurs of the paranormal never went back to a baseline of normal belief once they had become convinced of a certain weird fact, even if it was later proven to be false," 1991, 85).

This essay is not intended to be an exhaustive critique of everyone who has ever proposed the existence of ancient astronauts. It evaluates instead one author who seems to inspire a continued following even though von Däniken has faded.

Out of all the people who have ever claimed that aliens have been to planet Earth in the distant past, Zecharia Sitchin is the one man who deserves the most attention. To date, he has suffered little or no criticism (except Oberg, 1978). In following the Ancient Astronaut theory for many years (as well as being a member of the Ancient Astronaut Society), I have observed that Sitchin is cited time and again by believers as the definitive "expert" in this field (there are now even "study groups" forming in the hope of the construction of "Sitchin Centers" to continue his legacy).

In 1976, Zecharia Sitchin released the first of his books, *The 12th Planet*. Subsequently, more books followed along the same theme, including *The Stairway to Heaven* (1980), *The Wars of Gods and Men* (1985), *The Lost*

Realms (1990), *Genesis Revisited* (1990), *When Time Began* (1993), and *Divine Encounters* (1995). Taken together, Sitchin has chosen to call his work "The Earth Chronicles." Although all his books should be considered in evaluating his work, the first three are the most important.

Briefly, Sitchin believes that approximately 450,000 years ago an alien race came to Earth from an as-yet-undiscovered 10th planet in our solar system. (The sun and moon were counted as 10 and 11, making this undiscovered planet the "12th" planet. Sitchin displays pictures from the ancient Near East where 11 or 12 orbs or "stars" appear in a circle. He then makes the claim that this, along with speculative references found in ancient scriptures, represents the fact that ancient people knew of all the planets we do now; see Oberg, 1978, for a critique of Sitchin's claims in regards to astronomy.) These beings came here to mine gold and other materials. Approximately 250,000 years ago the aliens interbred with *Homo erectus* to create modern *Homo sapiens*, to be used as slave labor in mines, on farms, and in the homes of the aliens. As time went on, the aliens began to give privileges to humans as well as allowing them to run their own lives and affairs.

During these events, an immense flood of biblical proportions occurred, Egyptian and Near Eastern civilizations were established, wars involving aliens and humans commenced (where flying machines and a nuclear missile were involved), and the pyramids of Giza and other monumental structures (including some of those in the Americas) were built.

According to the blurb on the dust jacket of the hardcover edition of *The 12th Planet*, "Zecharia Sitchin was raised in Palestine where he acquired a profound knowledge of modern and ancient Hebrew, other Semitic and European languages, the Old Testament, and the history and archaeology of the Near East. He attended the London School of Eco-

nomics and Political Science and graduated from the University of London, majoring in economic history. A leading journalist and editor in Israel for many years, he now lives and writes in New York." According to the program of the Ancient Astronaut Society's 16th anniversary world conference, "Mr. Sitchin spent nearly 40 years in gathering and synthesizing the data (for his books). Mr. Sitchin is a member of the Israel Exploration Society, the American Oriental Society, and the Middle East Studies Association of North America." It should also be noted that Sitchin is one of a handful who can read the Sumerian language and cuneiform script. This alone suggests long hours of study in ancient Near Eastern history and culture. It is no wonder that his work is trotted out by believers. He appears to be an educated man who has sided with them. His opinions have weight and therefore deserve attention. So with such credentials, what brought Sitchin to the conclusion that aliens had shaped much of human history?

Sitchin answers this by stating, "It was at school in Tel-Aviv; we reached in our bible studies Chapter VI of Genesis—the story of the Great Flood or Deluge. It begins with several enigmatic verses, undoubtedly the remnant of a longer text, that describe the circumstances on Earth prior to the Deluge. They tell us—in the familiar King James translation":

> when men began to multiply on the face of the earth, and daughters were born unto them, that the sons of God saw the daughters of men that they were fair; and they took them wives of all which they chose.... There were giants in the earth in those days, and also after that, when the sons of God came in unto the daughters of men and they bear children to them, the same became mighty men who were of old, men of renown (Freer, 1987, iii).

But Sitchin was studying the Bible in its original Hebrew and he noticed that the word

"Nephilim" literally meant, "Those who had come down" and not (as translated in the King James version of the Bible) "giants" (Freer, 1987, iii). From this Sitchin began his quest to find out who the Nephilim were, taking their presence in the Bible as a literal truth of existence.

Sitchin traced this word back to the names of ancient Sumerian and Babylonian gods. By concentrating on these and Near Eastern texts Sitchin concluded that the Nephilim were really an alien race that literally "came down" to Earth thousands of years ago.

So let us begin where Sitchin did and see if his claims bear out. Our starting point is in the ancient Near East, with the Sumerian words and pictographs they left behind to describe their gods.

According to Sitchin, if we trace back the word *Nephilim* we come to the Sumerian equivalent of DIN-GIR. The first syllable, DIN, according to Sitchin, means "righteous," "pure," or "bright" (Sitchin, 1976, 169); the second syllable, GIR, "was a term used to describe a sharp-edged object" (Sitchin, 1976, 168). Expanding on this, Sitchin states that by putting these syllables together, "DIN-GIR as 'gods' or 'divine beings' conveyed the meaning of 'the righteous ones of the bright, pointed objects' or more explicitly, 'the pure ones of the blazing rockets'" (Sitchin, 1976, 169). What is important here is how Sitchin came to his final translation. A literal translation of the word DIN-GIR should read (based on Sitchin's translation) "pure sharp-edged object" or "bright sharp-edged object." This should lead one to the conclusion that the DIN-GIR was one object. But Sitchin claims that DIN-GIR should be read as "pure ones of the blazing rockets," which insinuates two things: the "pure ones" and the "blazing rockets." This part of Sitchin's rendition does not justify his final translation. So why did Sitchin go from the DIN-GIR being only one object to two? And why did he choose to translate the syllable

GIR from the more accurate description of "sharp-edged object" to the rather dramatic "blazing rockets"? It seems he was influenced by the pictorial signs for each syllable.

According to Sitchin (Sitchin, 1976, 170), the pictorial signs for DIN and GIR, which resemble a multistage rocket ship, combined with the textual references to gods roaming and flying from heaven to Earth leads to the conclusion that they were indeed rocketships: "Sumerian and Akkadian texts leave no doubt that the peoples of the ancient Near East were certain that the Gods of Heaven and Earth were able to rise from Earth and ascend into the heavens, as well as roam Earth's skies at will" (Sitchin, 1976, 128). Attentive readers will notice that Sitchin interprets the DIN to be two things at once: the "pure ones" (aliens) and part of the multistage rocket. This despite his pointing out that the word and the pictograph are supposed to represent one and the same thing! This shows that Sitchin is finding and using many unfounded meanings as well as creating double ones for each of these words and pictographs.

All we can really say is that we are dealing with a "pure" or "bright" "sharp-edged object." All the other elements Sitchin applies to the DIN-GIR, like making each word stand for two things at once, are not justified. The pictograph for DIN-GIR does not necessarily represent a rocket ship from antiquity. This only occurs through speculation.

It has been noted that DIN-GIR is somewhat like the Egyptian word for god which is *Neter* (Morenz, 1960, 19). It is clear that although many different interpretations have been given for Neter, none are absolute. However, the most likely explanation seems to be that the Neter (complete with its own pictograph) could be nothing more than a sort of flag (Morenz, 1973, 9). This would then suggest a clear sign of totemism, a sort of "banner" which stood for each group of people who rallied around it. If DIN-GIR can be said to be similar in meaning to Neter, then it is possible that the word and its pictograph are of the same sort. Only in this case, the "banner" would be a "bright" or "pure" sharp-edged object somewhat akin to an obelisk or spear-like construction. Sumerologist Samuel Noah Kramer states that the peoples of the ancient Near East thought of their gods as the assumed powers which operate behind the natural order of the world (Kramer, 1981, 77–78). Thus it is possible that the DIN-GIR was a totem used to symbolically represent these assumed forces and nothing more.

Sitchin repeatedly argues throughout his work that the aliens were anthropomorphic and human-like in design. And it is true that some cylinder seals reveal the gods in this type of form. But aside from the difficulties in explaining how two species, separated on different planets, came to be so similar (so similar that they were able to interbreed), the engravings which display the anthropomorphism of the gods are not the oldest forms. The majority of the oldest existing drawings show us the ancient Near Eastern gods are more animalistic in design. It was only in later times that the gods began to be drawn as erect-standing, two-armed, two-legged beings with a body and a head (Jacobsen, 1976, 9). If the aliens were really the gods, and if they were human-like in characteristics, then the oldest drawings should bear this out. They do not. (Jacobsen does state that in the early periods the human forms may have been a competing characterization of the gods. Regardless, this was not the dominant form. Some may say that this is purely a metaphorical way of expressing the attributes of real historical beings. But the error in this thinking is easily discerned. By claiming such, one would have already concluded that these beings did exist. But since we are dealing with a multitude of forms, we must treat them as a whole when attempting to evaluate the religious aspects of the ancients.)

To fully understand Sitchin's claims about aerial objects, we must also examine his interpretation of the Sumerian word *MU*. According to Sitchin, this word (equal to the Hebrew word *shem*) should be properly translated as a "skyborne vehicle" (Sitchin, 1976, 139–167). He spills much ink telling the reader that the MU was described as "lights up as a fire" and of an enclosure specifically created to "protect" the MU "which in a fire comes forth." He also quotes from a text which describes the goddess Inanna flying in her MU (Sitchin, 1976, 42). He then shows how the word MU evolved in later times to describe obelisk-type structures and believes that the obelisks were erected in memory of multistage rocket ships that humans once saw when the aliens were here. However, as with the DIN GIR, Sitchin has not made a very strong case. We do not have to assume that just because the gods were said to have been flying in their MU's or because the MU's looked like rocket ships (notice that an obelisk gives such an appearance) that they actually were. We must ask, how were the MU's perceived to have been used by the ancients? Were they used in connection with rituals performed to create symbolic flights as shamans worldwide have been known to conduct? Or were they really technological wonders? The fact remains that until the spade of an archaeologist uncovers the corroded remains of a buried rocket, a more mundane, orthodox interpretation should be sought in connection with the DIN, GIR, and MU.

We can now move on to some of Sitchin's other reworkings of the historical texts to reveal his other blunders. The biggest problem with Sitchin's work is that although he lists an extensive bibliography at the end of his books, he rarely gives specific references to individual works when he quotes a particular text. I have attempted to track down many of his references to see if his retelling of the tales matches what was actually written. For those that I have found, some of the texts that Sitchin uses seem to have been taken out of context, or abbreviated, leading to a loss of the intended meaning.

As with other Ancient Astronaut theorists Sitchin carefully selects evidence that matches his preconceived notions. He documents the texts that seem to support his claims but fails to mention those that contradict them. For instance, in *The 12th Planet* Sitchin argues that the extraterrestrials genetically created modern humans for slave labor from the already existing *Homo erectus*. He quotes from various texts to show that the ancients believed that the gods created man and then launches into more word play as he substitutes modern technological terms for the descriptions of the actions of the gods who performed this alleged feat of genetic engineering. What Sitchin fails to mention is that many different versions of how mankind came to be exist among the ancient sources. There is not one coherent belief system working here. Religious scholar Mircea Eliade has noted, "There are at least four Sumerian narratives that explain the origin of man. They are so different that we must assume a plurality of traditions" (1978, 59). Not only do we have stories that humans were created by gods, we also have stories that suggest that humans sprouted from the Earth like plants! Also, within the Babylonian creation story known as the Epic of Creation, also known as the Enuma Elish, it is said that the god Ea (Enki) created humans from the blood of the god Kingu. In Sitchin's discussion of the Enuma Elish, he considers Kingu to be our present day moon.

Additional texts reveal Sitchin's short-comings for lack of attention to detail. There is a tale from the ancient Near East entitled the Etana myth. It begins where the gods are looking for some human worthy of sitting on the throne of the city of Kish. A man by the name Etana is chosen for such an honor. The tale then takes a strange turn when an eagle and a snake make an oath not to operate outside the rules and laws handed down by the sun god Shamash. Shortly after, the eagle breaks this part of the bargain and snatches the snake's young to feed his own babies. Because of this crime, the eagle is punished by being imprisoned in a deep pit until its natural death. The story then returns to the life of Etana. He pleads to Shamash, asking that the god help him procreate, for what concerns Etana most is his inability to have children. This is where the two, seemingly independent, stories converge. Shamash tells Etana where to find the entrapped eagle. With the eagle's help, Etana may journey to heaven to obtain the "plant of birth." As they travel higher and higher, the eagle repeatedly asks Etana to look back and see how the land and the sea look smaller. As can probably be guessed, Sitchin argues that the eagle was actually a spacecraft that took Etana to the god's planet. His proof seems to come from Etana's observation, preserved in the texts, of how the land and sea seem to grow smaller with distance (Sitchin, 1976, 161–163). What is most interesting is that Sitchin completely ignores the fact that the eagle is never described as anything other than an actual eagle. No references appear in the Etana myth to indicate anything technological. For instance, when Etana "boards" the eagle and prepares for flight, the eagle instructs Etana and Etana follows. The eagle states: "put your chest over my breast, put your hands over the quills of my wings, put your arms over my sides." And Etana follows, "He puts his chest over its breast, put his hands over its feathers. . . ."

It is not difficult to see that Etana supposedly travels into space on the outside of the eagle! What about Etana's observation of the appearance of the receding land and sea as he flew higher? Well, so what? The peoples of the ancient Near East were surely aware that as something moved further away, it appeared to be smaller. The writer (or writers) of the Etana myth probably assumed (correctly) that the same illusion would occur if one were to travel skyward. This observation of distance is no proof of an actual journey to the sky.

Finally, Sitchin's blatant "pick and choose" method is illustrated by his silence about the serpent's role in the story, as well as the conflict between it and the eagle. The story must be dealt with by examing all elements of it. And this story presents us with a very poetic account of Etana and the snake-eagle oath which is purely a mythological-poetic account, not a historical one.

In Sitchin's book *The Stairway to Heaven*, we see another example of his selective methods. Sitchin charts what he thinks was the journey and final destination Egyptian Pharaohs believed they would undertake after death. He uses the Egyptian writings and texts and concludes that Pharaohs believed they would exit their tombs, travel east and then proceed through an underground base made up of 12 levels and end up aboard a rocket ship bound for the "Imperishable Star" (which Sitchin identifies as the aliens' home planet). In one instance Sitchin quotes Utterance 422 from the Egyptian Pyramid Texts. When I checked this quote against the one found in R. O. Faulkner's book, *The Ancient Egyptian Pyramid Texts* (which Sitchin lists in his bibliography and which is known to be the best English translation of these writings), the actual Utterance 422 is almost five times as long as Sitchin's quote! He never reveals that he is abbreviating. From reading both versions, it can be shown that Sitchin's lack of attention to detail damages his position. Within the original Utterance 422, it is proclaimed to the king, "may he do what he was wont to do among the spirits, the Imperishable Stars." Note that the "Imperishable Stars" appears in plural form. This would suggest that the king is to be among the many Imperishable Stars (or the stars we see in the sky today) and not on any particular star. In fact, many of the Utterances speak of a plurality of Imperishable Stars. This detail, which Sitchin fails to document, com-

pletely changes where the Pharaoh was believed to go after death. Sitchin's claim that Pharaohs envisioned themselves boarding a rocket ship to fly to space is also flawed. In Utterance 508, it states, "O Re, I have laid down for myself this sunshine of yours as a stairway under my feet on which I will ascend to that mother of mine, the living Uraeus which should be upon me. . . ." Here Re is clearly identified as the sun and the sun's rays are what the Pharaoh plans to use to get to him. Where was the king believed to go among the stars? Part of Utterance 471 states, "and I (Pharaoh) ascend the sky, I will go aboard this bark of Re, it is I who will command on my own account those gods who row him. Every god will rejoice at meeting me just as they rejoice at meeting Re when he ascends from the eastern side of the sky in peace. . . ." In other words, Re (the sun) is said to go from east to west, carried on a boat. It is this mythological boat that Pharaohs are said to have gone to, not another planet. These concepts are purely mythological and nothing more.

We should also note that despite Sitchin's interpretation, the 12 levels of underground passages through which Pharaoh supposedly traveled after death were most likely not a real place. The main reason for this is that we clearly have not uncovered such an immense underground base nor have we found any rocket launch pads or anything of the sort.

This points out the most damaging flaw in Sitchin's theory—the lack of physical evidence. Not one trace of evidence exists anywhere in the world for such a high technology in the not too distant past. Some have claimed that since all this supposedly happened a long time ago it is no wonder that this technology has probably eroded away or been destroyed by the natural process of time and the deeds of men. However, Sitchin has argued in *The 12th Planet* that our alien visitors arrived here approximately 450,000 years ago and in his book *The Wars of Gods and Men*, he argues that the aliens were still on Earth at the time of Alexander the Great, circa 333 B.C.E. Even if our visitors left around 300 B.C.E., that means that they were here for about 448,000 years! Yet there is none of the "waste" one would expect to find from such a highly advanced civilization residing on this planet for so long. By comparison, we have only had a space program since the 1960s and hundreds of pieces of junk material remain in orbit around the Earth. We have only been a technological society for about 100 years and we can see the scars upon the planet from the extensive mining, farming and building. If a technological society existed on this planet for about 448,000 years and left a mere 2,000 years ago, we would know it from more than rock pyramids and legendary tales.

Some other fine points to note are Sitchin's interpretations of various pictures and art from the ancient sites. On page 93 of his book *The Stairway to Heaven* he remarks that the picture labeled Figure 49 displayed on page 94 is that of the sun, sky, and the aliens' home planet. However, it probably better represents the sun, sky and the moon instead. On page 35 of *The 12th Planet*, in referring to Figure 15 on page 36, Sitchin claims that this is a picture of "a man lying on a special bed; his face is protected by a mask, and he is being subjected to some kind of radiation." There really is no proof that this is what is occurring. Not only that, but the picture does not suggest a "mask" but suggests instead that the man lying on the table has two heads!

Although Zecharia Sitchin is an educated man in a different category from most authors promoting the Ancient Astronaut theory, he still employs the same faulty logic as the rest. Sitchin's work delves into astronomy, archaeology, anthropology, ancient history, geology, genetics, biology, mythology, linguistics and more. I have chosen to deal particularly with Sitchin's use of legend and myth and other texts because he quotes them extensively as "proofs" of his thesis. The elements I have examined, specifically the lack of physical evidence to support Sitchin's claims, demonstrate the pseudoscientific nature of his work.

References:

Anthes, Rudolf. "Mythology in Ancient Egypt." 1961. In Kramer, Samuel Noah (ed.) *Mythologies of the Ancient World.* New York: Doubleday.

Dalley, Stephanie (trans.). 1989. *Myths from Mesopotamia.* New York: Oxford University Press.

Eliade, Mircea. (Willard R. Trask, trans.). 1978. *A History of Religious Ideas,* Vol. I. Chicago: University of Chicago Press.

Faulkner, R. O. (n.d.). *The Ancient Egyptian Pyramid Texts.* Oak Park: Bolchazy Carducci Publishers.

Freer, Neil. 1987. *Breaking the Godspell.* Phoenix: New Falcon Publications.

Harrold, Francis B., et al. 1995. "Cult Archaeology and Creationism in the 1990's and Beyond." In Harrold, Francis B. and Eve, Raymond A. (eds.). *Cult Archaeology and Creationism: Understanding Pseudoscientific Beliefs about the Past.* Iowa City: University of Iowa Press.

Jacobsen, Thorkild. 1976. *The Treasures of Darkness.* Westford: Murray Printing Company.

Kramer, Samuel Noah. 1981. *History Begins at Sumer.* Philadelphia: University of Pennsylvania.

Morenz, Siegfried. 1960. (Ann E. Keep, trans.). *Egyptian Religion.* New York: Cornell University Press.

Oberg, James E. 1978. "*The 12th Planet* book review." *Skeptical Inquirer.* Spring/Summer pp. 116–118.

Sitchin, Zecharia. 1976a. *The 12th Planet.* Santa Fe: Bear & Company, Inc.

——. 1976b. *The 12th Planet.* New York: Avon Books.

——. 1980. *The Stairway to Heaven.* New York: Avon Books.

——. 1985. *The Wars of Gods and Men.* New York: Avon Books.

——. 1990. *The Lost Realms.* New York: Avon Books.

Vallee, Jacques. 1991. *Revelations.* New York: Ballantine Books.

Holistic Medicine

The Case of Caroline Myss

PHIL MOLÉ

Philosopher Paul Kurtz, in his masterful book *The Transcendental Temptation*, identified two traits common to all types of supernormal thinking: (1) All varieties of magical thinking thrive when there is ignorance of the natural causes responsible for a phenomenon; (2) This ignorance leads the magical thinker to hypothesize the existence of unknown, miraculous causes (1986, 455).

This type of thinking is especially prevalent in alternative medicine, where practitioners with poor understanding of physiology or standards of medical evidence offer mystical explanations for diseases and therapies. The defining traits of alternative, or holistic, models of health are their untestability, their abundant use of metaphor in lieu of scientific evidence, and their belief in intuition as a means of obtaining medical knowledge.

Caroline Myss is currently one of the most prominent authors in this lucrative field. Thanks to the success of her 1996 book *Anatomy of the Spirit*, Myss has been virtually impossible to ignore. She commands top dollar for her workshops and appearances, and has promoted her teachings on *Oprah*. Her most recent book, *Why People Don't Heal and How They Can*, has been an overwhelming best-seller in both its hardcover and paper-

back editions. Obviously, a large number of people like what Caroline Myss has to say.

Myss draws upon several strains of spirituality, including Roman Catholicism and Judaism, but her teachings have three distinct characteristics. First, she uses a hypothetical system of energy centers in the human body to explain the development of disease, and to link each illness with a specific emotional issue. Second, she maintains that her unaided intuition can provide detailed and accurate diagnoses of a subject's illnesses, even if the subject is not physically present in the room with her. Third, she stresses a vague type of holism that champions the very duality it claims to transcend, and ultimately wishes for the subservience of all other viewpoints to her own. This article will closely examine each of these characteristics, and assess the merits of Myss's teachings through the perspective of conventional medicine.

Chalking It up to Chakras

Caroline Myss bases most of her teachings on her belief in seven energy centers, or chakras, located within the human body. In traditional Tantric practice, the chakras are represented as lotus flowers positioned along the spinal cord. Specifically, the chakras are thought to correspond with the following anatomical positions:

1. First chakra—between the anus and genitals
2. Second chakra—lower abdomen
3. Third chakra—solar plexus
4. Fourth chakra—chest cavity
5. Fifth chakra—throat
6. Sixth chakra—center of the forehead
7. Seventh chakra—top of the head

The vertical arrangement of the seven chakras represents a hierarchy of increasing spiritual awareness, and each chakra is thought to be activated by a particular set of emotions. For example, the energy of the first chakra is activated by base feelings of tribal affiliation, while the seventh chakra resonates to our quest for spiritual wisdom. However, negativity can cause our chakras to lose energy. This, she says, is how we become sick. When we fail to be as positive and spiritually aware as we should be, we withdraw energy "directly from the basic energy level we need to run our physical bodies." This depletion "is the mechanism through which the physical body becomes weakened" (Shealy and Myss, 1988, 93).

Not surprisingly, Myss also maintains that imbalances in the chakras always manifest themselves as afflictions in very specific parts of the body. Since the chakras themselves are thought to respond to particular emotions, this essentially assigns each illness a unique emotional cause. Myss dubs this model of the body the "human energy system." In this system, heart attacks are caused by excessive guilt and fear, AIDS is attributed to having a "victim consciousness," and syphilis is chalked up to feelings of hostility toward oneself (Shealy and Myss, 1988). Thus, illnesses are the cumulative history of our emotional lives or, as Myss repeats with mantra-like purpose, "our biography becomes our biology."

All of the above claims are completely unfounded scientifically. First, the chakra system, while undoubtedly a valuable component of a cultural and religious practice, has no proven relationship with the anatomy or physiology of the human body. Nothing resembling the energy of the chakras has ever been detected, despite the exquisite sensitivity of modern instruments. Myss tries to brush past this detail by alluding to the mysterious nature of this energy, assuring us that "conventional medical tests have no way of measuring energy loss" (1996, 10). This waffling won't do: Energy is energy, and if it has discernible physical effects, it should also be measurable.

To make matters worse, there is no agreement about how many chakras there are. The traditional kundalini yogic system recognizes seven major chakras (Campbell, 1974, 331), and this remains the most widely accepted number. However, some mystics recognize other minor chakras, and some maintain there are other major ones as well. Myss takes the latter position. In *Why People Don't Heal and How They Can*, she claims to have learned of an eighth chakra external to the physical body while doing intuitive readings during the 1980s (Myss, 1997, 89). This begs the question of why this bonus chakra wasn't mentioned in *Anatomy of the Spirit*, published in 1996. Why did Myss take so long to discover this chakra, and even longer to incorporate it into her teachings? One may also ask why she doesn't mention the additional four external chakras recognized in some yogic systems (Dale, 1996, 47). Is there an objective criterion Myss used to exclude these chakras? If so, what is it?

If this inconsistency doesn't trouble you, imagine what would happen if conventional medicine showed a similar absence of objective guidelines. Imagine, for instance, that your physician couldn't decide if you had one kidney or two. Flabbergasted, you'd go to another doctor. What if he informed you that there is a third kidney floating outside your body? If you're anything like me, you'd be out of there faster than you can say "muladhara chakra."

Even if we could agree how many chakras there are, there's no guarantee that we'd understand the origins of our illnesses any better. In much of her writings, Myss stresses that unresolved emotional issues often lead directly to illness. "Refusing to let go of past events, whether positive or negative, means throwing away some part of your daily energy budget. If you start losing energy and don't do anything about it, you'll inevitably develop a weakness in your physical body" (1997, 19). From this perspective, disease develops because of our inability to accept life's lessons—it is at least partly our own creation. Yet, this emotional model of illness fails to account for how a person who's perfectly content with life can suddenly collapse from heart failure, or how a happy, innocent child can be diagnosed with cancer. In situations like these, Myss assures us it is simply the will of God, who wants us to learn "certain lessons that our soul needs to discover" (1997, 28). But how do we know if an illness is our fault or God's? Myss offers no clear guidelines. Furthermore, unresolved emotional issues can hardly explain how disease develops in animals and plants. Only the conventional medical model can account for these anomalous data.

Myss also fails to explain—in terms other than reckless metaphor—how her hypothetical human energy system is understandable in terms of our knowledge of modern medicine. This deficiency is particularly apparent in *The Creation of Health*, her collaboration with Dr. Norman Shealy. In one chapter, Myss supplies "energy analyses" of illnesses to complement Shealy's traditional medical descriptions. But the two authors rarely find a tangible intersection; Myss cannot reconcile her system's untestable mystical claptrap with the established

canon of medical thought. Here is her explanation for blocked arteries (Shealy and Myss, 1988, 161):

> Blocked arteries, as a rule, are created through the warehousing of guilt feelings and fears related to disappointing the expectations of others. Guilt weighs heavily on a person's consciousness, and like cement being poured slowly into someone's body, eventually hardens.

This comes just two pages after Shealy describes coffee and cigarette use, high fat diets, high density lipoproteins (HDLs) and other agents with at least partially understood causal mechanisms leading to blocked arteries. We are not told what, if anything, these mechanisms have to do with Myss's explanation.

When discussing AIDS in another section of the same book, Myss speculates that "the AIDS virus has spontaneously emerged into our global atmosphere in response to the massive victimization of all forms of life, including the planet itself" (1988, 200). She goes on to explain, in a particularly ridiculous passage, that the Earth itself is showing symptoms of AIDS. Her reasoning goes like this: (1) AIDS usually results in diseases such as pneumocystis and Kaposi's sarcoma which affect the lungs; (2) Forests around the world are being destroyed; (3) Forests can be considered "the lungs of the earth;" (4) The "lungs of the earth" are thus being destroyed; Therefore (5) the Earth has AIDS. Conspicuous by their absence are any discussions of HIV, intravenous drug use, or any other known mode of contracting AIDS.

As these examples show, Myss makes almost no attempt to incorporate medical knowledge into her chakra system, and seems unaware that this kind of synthesis is the only way she could possibly validate her theory. The burden of proof is on Myss to demonstrate how her ideas improve on our established understanding of illnesses, and how the chakras can add to the study of human physiology. Theories which provide no new information are useless. Unless Myss can establish the objective existence of chakras, prove they have measurable energy, and establish unambiguous mechanisms for how this energy affects the body, her ideas will remain empty of content.

Energy Analysis: The Power of Intuitive Diagnosis

When you imagine you've developed a whole new model for explaining illnesses and the human body, it's only natural to offer a new methodology for working with your model. For Myss, this new methodology takes the form of intuitive diagnosis, an ability she claims to have honed nearly to perfection over years of practice.

Myss alleges that, using nothing but pure intuition, she can "see" the energy shortages in a person's chakras and accurately diagnose their illnesses. She claims to have discovered this ability in the autumn of 1982, while working at Stillpoint Books—a publishing company she co-founded to publish books about alternative medicine. Myss, mind you, didn't actually believe in all of that metaphysical hocus pocus; she was a skeptical materialist who "smoked while drinking coffee by the gallon" and "developed an absolute aversion to wind chimes, New Age music, and conversations on the benefits of organic gardening" (1996, 1).

Nonetheless, Myss could not hide her gifts from the world for much longer. Soon, she discovered she had an uncanny ability to gain insights about the causes of her friends' illnesses. She describes them as being "like impersonal daydreams that start to flow as soon as I receive a person's permission, name and age. Their impersonality, the nonfeeling sensation of the impressions, is extremely significant because it is my indicator that I am not

manufacturing or projecting these impressions" (1996, 2). Why was Myss chosen to receive this magical ability? Here are her thoughts on this question:

> While I can teach you up to a certain point about how to become intuitive, I'm actually not sure how I learned it myself. I suspect that I became extremely intuitive as a consequence of my curiosity about spiritual matters, combined with a deep frustration I felt when my life didn't unfold according to plan. On the other hand, it's equally possible that my medical intuition was simply the result of something I ate. Knowing how the gods work, I would not find it surprising in the least (1997, 5–6).

This passage, with its profound mixture of silliness (in considering her ability the possible result of something she ate) and arrogance (in claiming to be privy to divine knowledge), is a fine example of the intellectual value to be found in Myss's books.

Myss claims to be most accurate in her diagnoses when she has no information about the medical subject except for her name and birthdate. She explains that this method allows her to "receive information that a more personal connection would otherwise tend to block," such as information about the spread of cancer in a subject's body (Shealy and Myss, 1988, 85). She claims to accomplish this by projecting "emotional energy" toward a patient by intensely concentrating on her name and age.

How accurate is Myss? It depends on what standard of evidence you demand. If you need almost no evidence you can embrace the statement by her collaborator, Dr. Norman Shealy, that she is 93% accurate (Shealy and Myss, 72). Those of us who need good reasons for believing medical statements, however, may find Shealy's statement—and the evidence it's based on—a tad unconvincing.

Let's consider how Shealy "tested" his colleague's accuracy. According to Shealy, he would speak to Myss on the telephone while he had a patient in his office. He allegedly would inform Myss only of the patient's name and age, record her impressions, and compare them against his own "traditional" medical diagnosis.

There are valid reasons not to accept results obtained using Shealy's methodology. First, there did not seem to be any control for experimenter bias. Shealy spoke to Myss during her process of intuitive diagnosis; we have no way of knowing that he did not subconsciously provide clues to lead Myss to the right answer. This possibility seems especially important to control for because of indications that Shealy believed in Myss's alleged ability immediately upon meeting her at a conference in 1985, and he never seemed to question the validity of her claims. "Norm never tested me from the position of wanting me to prove to him that this skill existed. He already knew it was possible to develop exceptional perceptual abilities, and thus his interest in my work was from the position of whether or not I could be accurate enough for his purposes" (Shealy and Myss, 1988, 86). What "accurate enough for his purposes" means is open to interpretation, especially when the accuracy is determined by an experimenter who already assumes that the phenomenon under investigation exists, and fails to control for his bias. How accurate would Myss have been if Shealy had given her a written list of the patients and their ages, sequestered her in a room until she decided on her diagnoses, and then compared her diagnoses with those made by impartial physicians? Alas, we do not know, for no experiment like this appears to have been performed.

Second, we do not know what criterion of accuracy Shealy used to assess Myss's abilities, or the total number of tests he performed. For example, did Myss always give the specific diagnosis of a patient (e.g., "blocked arteries") or

did she sometimes merely state a vague impression couched in symbolism (e.g., "I see an energy blockage in the fourth chakra")—with Shealy translating into medical terms? Would an unbiased physician have read Myss's diagnoses the same way Shealy did? And how many readings did Shealy base his accuracy estimate upon? Could he have subconsciously kept a record of "hits" and ignored the "misses"? These are not trivial questions; any reputable medical journal would require this information before even considering Shealy and Myss's claims for publication.

In the absence of evidence for her abilities, Myss tries to establish proof indirectly by claiming a historical precedent for intuitive diagnosis. She and Shealy discuss the emergence of intuitive medicine through such pioneers as Franz Mesmer and Edgar Cayce. We are told that Mesmer—a German physician who founded an odd pseudoreligion based on the mysterious properties of "animal magnetism" in the late 18th century—"laid the foundations for psychiatry and psychology" and helped later practitioners to learn the value of intuition (1988, 62). Cayce, a would-be prophet who thought himself the reincarnation of an angel who graced the Earth before Adam and Eve (Randi, 1995, 42), is said to have "laid the groundwork for all intuitive diagnosticians to follow" by giving thousands of mystically divined diagnoses during his lifetime (66).

The average person, reading about Mesmer and Cayce for the first time in *The Creation of Health*, would have no way of knowing that both men have been almost universally recognized as quacks. Mesmer was investigated in 1784 in France by a Royal Commission containing, among others, Benjamin Franklin and Antoine Lavoisier. The commission ingeniously and conclusively demonstrated that "animal magnetism" did not elicit the physiological effects Mesmer had claimed—the power of suggestion had done it all (see Mesmerism entry in section 5). Cayce, similarly, has been shown to have erred very significantly in many of his diagnoses, and his reputation was built entirely through anecdotal evidence and the faith of true believers (Gardner, 1952). The fact that Myss has foisted off this pair of known charlatans as genuinely important contributors to medical science does not speak highly of her scholarship—or her intentions.

Mindless Mergers: The Holistic Hodgepodge

Insignificant evidence and unrestrained speculation cannot stand on their own; the careful self-help guru must also provide a philosophy comprehensive and uncritical enough to support even her wildest metaphysical musings. And what philosophy could possibly be as intimidatingly encompassing or as thoroughly accepting of any and every vaguely pleasing notion as New Age holism?

"Holism," as usually described in popular metaphysical books, is more than just the well-known wisdom that "the whole is greater than the sum of its parts." Rather, the most common and virulent strains of holism state that any distinction between the whole and its parts is unfathomable because we simply cannot obtain any real understanding about something by taking it apart into smaller units and analyzing it. In other words, the traditional scientific method of reductionism is a big no-no, and we are fools to think otherwise. We should simply accept the universe in all its glorious infinity, and realize that such an immense whole cannot ever be truly subordinated to rational investigation. If we could overcome the confinement of reason, we would see that categories are meaningless, opposites are illusory, and—as Myss is fond of saying—"all is one."

Myss ushers in the new era of holism with great enthusiasm, explaining that we've been living in the Age of Pisces for the last 2000 years, an age characterized by categorical thinking. "The Piscean age was a time of dualism," she writes, "when human consciousness divided in a powerful way into polarities, such as those between Western and Eastern culture, church and state, body and spirit (in a split epitomized by Manicheanism), the science of magnetics, even political polarities of left and right" (Myss, 1997, xiv). However, the coming millennium will mark the beginning of the Age of Aquarius, and we'll put an end to all of this typological silliness. "The energy of this emergent age pulls us to create a culture in which spirit and energy have a higher priority than matter and the body, and to understand that the energy within our minds, bodies, and spirits is the same as that of God or the greater divinity" (Myss, 1997, xv). In this new system, we'll finally understand the body as an energy system, and "healing will then be a much gentler process of delicately manipulating the etheric body through the use of crystals, sound and color" (Shealy and Myss, 1988, 370).

To the uncritical, all of this may seem as harmless and pleasing as a Yanni album. However, there are glaring deficiencies in Myss's holistic philosophy. First, her historical justification for considering the last 2000 years an age of dualism is a gross oversimplification. And as far as "the science of magnetics" goes: It's true that we've learned that all magnets maintain a type of "duality," since every magnet has a "north" and "south" pole. However, the study of magnets also led the great physicist James Clerk Maxwell to show that light, magnetism, and electricity were related electromagnetic phenomena. This was a substantial step toward unity in the laws of nature, not dichotomy.

Second, Myss's holism is far too unselective to ever be of any scientific use. It seems as if Myss will incorporate just about anything into her philosophy if it sounds pleasing enough and has sufficient superficial similarity to other components of her philosophy. For example, in *Anatomy of the Spirit*, she links the Christian sacraments to her chakras—apparently because (could you guess?) there are seven of each. In both *The Creation of Health* and *Why People Don't Heal and How They Can*, she assigns great value to astrology, a pseudoscience boasting a long and spectacular history of failure. What's her reason for putting stock in such a worthless practice?

> For me, astrological influences are authentic, but not as commonly thought of by people who assume that astrology is a form of fortune telling. It is not. It is the study of the influences of the energies of the planets on the entire system of life, including human life. That we are part of a whole is a given. That individual parts of that whole radiate certain qualities is natural. Astrological influences do not control one's life; they merely indicate potentials and possibilities (Shealy and Myss, 365–366).

So the stars influence us because we're all inseparable parts of a whole. Why, then, can't the magnet here on my desk fetch the can of Foster's I left upstairs on the counter? Because it's too far away, you say, and my magnet doesn't exert enough force? But the planets and stars are also much too far away to exert a measurable gravitational force on us. Why does Myss predict that planets and stars will influence us, but she doesn't seem concerned that my magnet cannot retrieve my cold beverage? This holism stuff is really confusing.

Third, the more Myss talks about holism, the more she reveals the hopeless categorization in her own thinking. Myss has a rather novel conception of holism; she seems to think that her system is different from dualism because she ultimately forces all phenomena to be arbitrarily subordinated to a single philosophical outlook. Yet, there is no such difference, because Myss is really a strict dualist who ruthlessly imposes her self-made categories on the world. Much of her philosophy is phrased

in terms of opposing pairs: "energy" versus "matter," "mind" versus "body," and "holistic" medicine versus "allopathic" medicine. Myss generally holds the first term in each of these pairs in higher esteem, and predicts it will triumph over its assigned adversary. Her distinction between matter and energy is almost trivially easy to discredit, since Einstein did all the work for us at the beginning of this century. However, her other two dichotomies indicate important failures in logic.

Myss clearly considers mind to be composed of a different substance than the physical body, but simultaneously seems to think that our mind permeates every cell of our body, as new age physiologist Candace Pert has often stated (Myss, 1996, 35). This "mind" is considered closely allied with "an energy field that extends as far out as your outstretched arms" which acts as "an information center and a highly sensitive perceptual system" (33). Thus, the mind-body dichotomy is linked with the "energy-matter" dichotomy Einstein so elegantly debunked long ago.

This system is essentially identical to the dualistic theories of mind promulgated centuries ago by philosophers such as Descartes. However, Descartes did not have access to the knowledge of neuroscience we have today. In the light of work by thinkers like Paul and Patricia Churchland and Nobel Laureate Francis Crick, we are beginning to understand the mysteries of consciousness in terms of the relationships between neurons. In this perspective, consciousness is an emergent property resulting from the functions of these neurons, and there is no need to postulate a transcendental material as the underlying "stuff" of thought. Consciousness is a process, as Ian Stewart and Jack Cohen remind us, and can best be understood through a contextual analysis of its functions (1998, 211). Emotions are an important part of this context, but only when included in testable hypotheses about the psychology and neurology of thought. Myss's vague mystical notions clearly do not belong in this developing model.

The presented dichotomy between alternative and conventional medicine is even more spurious, and potentially damaging. Myss claims she has no dislike for conventional medicine, and repeatedly stresses her desire to see holistic medicine incorporated into mainstream practice, but she does not hide her preference to see the latter system subordinated to the former. "Holistic and conventional medicine take two different attitudes toward power: active and passive," she tells us. On the same page she observes that "the language of conventional medicine sounds more military than that of energy medicine: 'The patient was attacked by a virus' or 'A substance contaminated the cell tissue, resulting in a malignancy'" (1996, 48). The implication is clear: mainstream medicine is cold-spirited and trivializes the patient's power to heal, while holistic medicine is gentle and celebrates autonomy in the face of sickness.

Myss also assures us that holistic medicine has its own methodology and standards, and should not be subject to the rigid appraisal afforded mainstream medicine.

> The traditional medical community, which includes physicians, nurses, psychiatrists and psychologists, has specific professional standards and requirements. Within the holistic field, there are numerous forms of therapy that do not require the same intense periods of education. The training needed to become a massage, color or polarity therapist, for instance, is not as formal a process as is medical or nursing school training. That is not to say the work therapists do in these alternative fields is not of immense value or that the training they receive is inadequate. The training involved for several categories of holistic therapies, however, is not as formally organized in traditional academia, and that difference is cause for much of the lack of apprecia-

tion for the work of holistic practitioners (Shealy and Myss, 1988, 24).

Unfortunately, the reason so many of these holistic therapies aren't "formally organized in traditional academia" is that they are utterly without merit. Without some method of separating effective therapies from useless therapies and strict training standards from lax standards, there is simply no way to perform medicine competently.

The best antidote for Myss's brand of holistic doublespeak has been provided by *Journal of the American Medical Association (JAMA)* editors Phil B. Fontanarosa, M.D. and George D. Lundberg, M.D. In a special issue of *JAMA* dedicated to alternative medicine, the editors issued the following statement: "There is no alternative medicine. There is only scientifically proven, evidence-based medicine supported by solid data or unproven medicine, for which scientific evidence is lacking" (1998). It doesn't matter what the origin of a therapy is, or whether we choose to think of it as "holistic" or "allopathic." We are concerned only with its effectiveness and safety.

This attitude directly contradicts the viewpoint of holists like Myss, who continually stress that Western medicine is averse to "natural" remedies. However, a close look at the evidence clearly shows that the holists are wrong. Treatments derived from nature or passed down through folklore are subjected to the same experimental evaluations as treatments engineered in the laboratory, and history records the careful integration of worthy therapies. For instance, one of the most effective cancer treatments used today is derived from a plant found in Madagascar (Morell, 1999, 17). The heart medicine digoxin was extracted from the foxglove plant, aspirin was obtained from a compound in the bark and leaves of willow trees, and antimalarial drugs have been taken from the bark of the cinchona tree (Mestel, 1999, 74). And as bacteria develop increasing resistance to antibiotics, scientists are searching every habitat from the ocean floors to the sediments of coastal mangrove forests for the next generation of antibacterial agents.

Many alternative medicine practitioners, including Myss, seem unaware of the importance naturally obtained remedies have held in the history of medicine. They imagine a kind of warfare between themselves and the medical establishment. They prefer to dig their trenches, crouch out of sight, and make the occasional sneer at their adversary. As a result, many people are misled into unfair judgments about the attitudes of modern medicine, and are compelled to uncritically accept the "alternatives" offered by holistic practitioners. This situation should not and cannot continue. Medicine is far too important to be turned into a game of pernicious accusations in which the truth is obscured. The smokescreen of holism must be cleared, and alternative treatments must be exposed to the light of critical scrutiny. As the editors of *JAMA* concluded, "for patients, for physicians and other health care professionals, and for alternative medicine practitioners—indeed, for all who share the goal of improving the health of individuals and of the public—there can be no alternative" (Fontanarosa and Lundberg, 1998, 1619).

The Healing Power of Truth

Caroline Myss offers no tangible evidence to support any of her claims. Her hypothetical energy system cannot be detected, her intuitive diagnostic abilities are unproven, and her holistic philosophy is riddled with inconsistencies and unsubstantiated judgments. I predict medical progress will continue quite nicely without even the slightest help from Myss or her ideas.

Myss, undaunted, will undoubtedly press on in search of spiritual insights into the nature of healing. On May 4, 2000, she and some of her faithful will travel on a "healing journey" to Peru to visit the Incan ruins, where they will "fully experience the healing nature" of these sacred sites. May I offer some advice for those going? First, ask yourself this: If these sites had so much sacred, healing power, why aren't there still Incas there? Next, read a few books about the history of the Incas, and consider the very likely possibility that their civilization was destroyed by poor understanding of their environment's capacity to support their population density (Shermer, 1997, 76–77). Despite their amazing cultural accomplishments, the Incas' religious beliefs and practices couldn't provide the knowledge needed to keep their society intact.

Is Caroline Myss really offering factually based claims, or is she simply appealing to mysticism? What would the consequences be if mainstream medicine adopted her standards of evidence? The results, you may well conclude, would be disastrous; but that is a fate we are empowered to avoid. We can counter mystical claims with objective evidence, and use modern scientific inquiry to guide us through troubled times. In fact, it is our responsibility to do so. To follow Myss and to forsake scientific knowledge for a haphazard system of unwarranted speculations is to choose the road to ruin.

References:

Appleton, Elaine. 1997. "Solo Flight: Medical Intuitive Caroline Myss Teaches Spiritual Healing." *Natural Health.* 27:1, 84–89.

Campbell, Joseph. 1974. *The Mythic Image.* New York: MJF Books.

Chambers, Veronica. 1997. "Heal Thyself: New Age Author Caroline Myss Hits the Big Time." *Newsweek,* December 22.

Churchland, Patricia S., and Churchland, Paul M. 1998. *On the Contrary: Critical Essays, 1987–1997.* London: MIT Press.

Cohen, Jack, and Stewart, Ian. 1998. *Figments of Reality: The Evolution of the Curious Mind.* New York: Cambridge University Press.

Crick, Francis. 1994. *The Astonishing Hypothesis.* New York: Touchstone.

Dale, Cyndi. 1996. *New Chakra Healing: The Revolutionary 32-Center System.* St.Paul: Llewellyn.

Fontanarosa, Phil B., and Lundberg, George D. 1998. "Alternative Medicine Meets Science." *Journal of the American Medical Association.* 280:18, 1618–1619.

Gardner, Martin. 1952. *Fads and Fallacies in the Name of Science.* New York: Dover.

Kurtz, Paul. 1986. *The Transcendental Temptation.* Buffalo: Prometheus Books.

Mestel, Rosie. 1999. "Drugs from the Deep." *Discover.* 20:3, 70–75.

Morell, Virginia. 1999. "The Variety of Life." *National Geographic.* 195:4, 6–32.

Myss, Caroline. 1996. *Anatomy of the Spirit: The Seven Stages of Power and Healing.* New York: Harmony Books.

——. 1997. *Why People Don't Heal and How They Can.* New York: Harmony Books.

Randi, James. 1995. *An Encyclopedia of Claims, Frauds and Hoaxes of the Occult and Supernatural.* New York: St. Martin's Press.

Shealy, C. Norman, and Myss, Caroline. 1988. *The Creation of Health: The Emotional, Psychological and Spiritual Responses that Promote Health and Healing.* Walpole: Stillpoint Publishing.

Shermer, Michael. 1997. "The Beautiful People Myth: Why the Grass Is Always Greener in the Other Country." *Skeptic,* Vol. 5, No. 1.

Police Psychics

Noreen Renier as a Case Study

GARY P. POSNER

On April 3, 1996, the skeletal remains of 76 year-old Norman Lewis, missing for two years, were recovered from the murky waters of a limestone quarry in the tiny Florida town of Williston, located just southwest of Gainesville. The April 5 Associated Press story, as headlined in the *St. Petersburg (Florida) Times*, revealed: "Psychic tip leads to missing man's body." Although she was not present during the search or recovery, the "tipster" was Florida "psychic detective" Noreen Renier, who boasts of a successful history of assisting in hundreds of police investigations into unsolved homicides and missing-person cases.

Before specializing as a "psychic detective," Renier, age 60, was credited with having predicted the 1981 assassination attempt on President Ronald Reagan, and the assassination of Egyptian President Anwar Sadat later that year. Through the years, she has appeared on numerous national television programs including the *Joan Rivers Show, Geraldo, Sightings*, and even the CBS newsmagazine *48 Hours*. In the classic textbook *Practical Homicide Investigation*, used by the FBI and many other police academies, the author identifies Renier as "a psychic and recognized authority on the phenomena of extrasensory perception."

According to press accounts, on March 24, 1994, after telling his girlfriend that he would be right back, the elderly Mr. Lewis drove off from home, leaving behind his wallet and respiratory inhaler, and (along with his truck) was never seen or heard from again. In its April 11, 1994, edition, the *Ocala (Florida) Star-Banner* quoted Williston Police Chief Olin Slaughter as observing, "It's like he fell off the edge of the earth."

After spending more than a year following up on "hundreds" of leads and conducting numerous land and aerial searches, all to no avail, the Williston police, and the Lewises, decided to enlist the aid of a psychic. Investigator Brian Hewitt suggested Noreen Renier, having previously been impressed by a performance of hers. The Lewis family reportedly provided the $650 fee for her services (the police department was said not to have had sufficient funds).

On July 17, 1995, three weeks after Hewitt's initial phone call to her, Renier performed her "psychic" reading, at her home. Clutching one of Mr. Lewis' possessions, she tuned into his "vibrations" and provided a number of specific clues intended to help lead the police to his body. The *Williston Pioneer* (on April 4 and June 27, 1996) quoted Chief Slaughter as saying that Renier indicated Lewis had traveled "east from his home to an area where there is . . . water in something like a pit." The *Chiefland (Florida) Citizen* (April 11, 1996) quotes Slaughter: "She could see he was surrounded by metal. . . . She could see a cliff wall, and loose bricks, a railroad track, and a bridge." The numbers "45" and "21" were also said to have been offered as helpful clues.

A subsequent look by the police into several bodies of water proved as fruitless as the earlier searches. But because of Renier's reading, the police called in a team of Navy divers from Jacksonville to search one particular limestone quarry among many scattered throughout the area. Although about eight months elapsed before the team could arrive, on April 3, 1996, with the assistance of a $70,000 detection device, the divers did indeed locate the missing truck containing Lewis' remains, submerged in 20 feet of murky water.

When the Williston police announced that the case had been solved largely as a result of Renier's psychic clues, the story quite naturally captured the attention of the media. In addition to regional newspapers and television, the Associated Press and national radio icon Paul Harvey reported upon it, and the TV show *Sightings* devoted a segment to it in November 1996. The "Williston Case" quickly became the pinnacle of Renier's storied career.

Enter the Skeptic

My involvement in the Williston case began in May 1996, when I received a telephone call from a researcher for Towers Productions, which was producing a series called *The Unexplained* for the A & E Network. Their program on "Psychic Detectives" (which first aired in January 1997) would feature several individuals, including Renier, and would specifically cover Williston. My participation was requested to insure a balanced presentation.

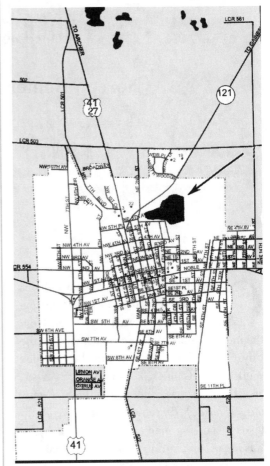

Figure 1

Two months later, the police and I were interviewed for the show (in Williston), as was Renier the following day (at her Orlando home). By then, I had accumulated a number of newspaper articles and maps and had come to an unexpected and provocative conclusion: Norman Lewis' remains appeared to have been found not because the police had the Navy divers search the body of water best fitting Renier's psychic clues, but because they had the Navy search the wrong watery pit!

Scanning my roadmap of Williston, I immediately noticed its most striking feature—a blue body of water nearly in the heart of town, less than one mile east of Mr. Lewis' home. (Figure 1) This limestone quarry, when approached from the west, is located adjacent to the inter-

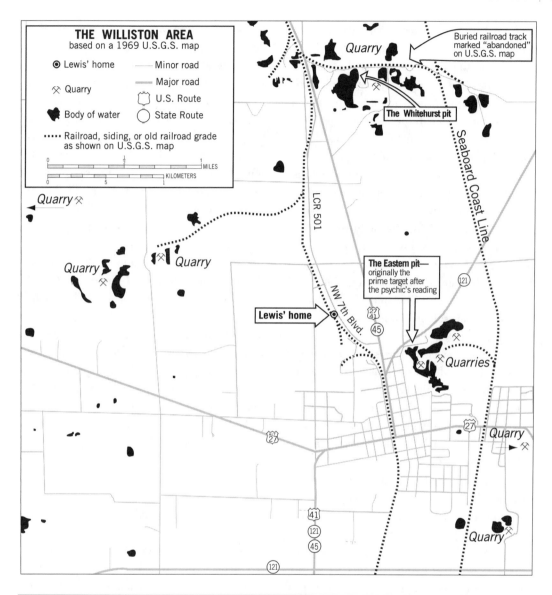

Figure 2

section of U.S. 41 and State Route 121. Flipping that map over I saw that the map on the opposite side reveals that U.S. 41 is also known in Williston as State Route 45. If Lewis had indeed traveled east from his home to a watery pit, as Chief Slaughter indicated Renier had seen in her psychic vision, he would have encountered such a quarry just beyond the junction of State Routes 45 and 121. Renier's two numerical clues were reportedly "45" and "21"—had she offered "45" and "121," someone might have cynically accused her of having researched the case and consulted a map!

The U.S. Geological Survey's "Williston Quadrangle" map, which I purchased at a Tampa map store, shows this clearly marked "Quarry" area in more detail. (Figure 2) Of note is the Seaboard Coast Line's north/south railroad track 3/4 of a mile east of the quarry's eastern circumference, with a branch directed westward into the heart of the quarry area. One of Renier's clues was "railroad track."

As I told the Towers producer, I cannot be certain if Renier's clues were the result of "psychic" power or some other, purely natural, process. But, I added, forget about "psychic" power for a moment and just employ "ordinary" detective-style reasoning and common sense. Consider that the intensive ground and aerial searches had turned up nothing. If Mr. Lewis and his truck were somewhere within the potential reach of the Williston police, where could they possibly be? In the middle of a densely wooded area? In an abandoned building? (Either, perhaps, if only a body was missing. But a truck?) Only one possibility even comes to mind—submerged in a body of water.

Chief Slaughter, it seems, had had the right idea all along, even if he was not consciously aware of it. It did indeed appear "like [Lewis] fell off the edge of the earth"—and into a bottomless, or at least very deep, watery pit. A quick glance at the Williston roadmap revealed an obvious potential site, as confirmed by the U.S.G.S. map.

One minor problem: The logical site, the one that Renier's clues seem tailored to—the limestone quarry less than a mile east of Lewis' home, at the junction of State Routes 45 and 121, serviced by a railroad track—was not where Lewis' truck and remains were ultimately found! Rather, they were located in a different limestone pit, one nearly due north of Lewis' home and more than twice as far away! The recovery site, known as the White-hurst pit, is also located adjacent to State Route 45, but not Route 121.

Renier's "21" clue, in fact, played no beneficial role whatsoever in assisting in the location of Lewis' body. Yet, this clue has been hailed by the police as perhaps her most eerily precise of all. Why? Because, after Lewis' body had been recovered, it was announced that he had been found "2.1" miles from his home—even though, as the crow flies, the distance ap-

pears to measure only about 1.6 miles on the U.S.G.S. map.

Nor was her "railroad track" clue of any value in deciding which of these two quarries to have the Navy divers search. Although the U.S.G.S. map clearly shows an "abandoned" track traversing the Whitehurst quarry east/west, the police did not become aware of the buried track until a portion of it was unearthed after the divers had already been called in.

Nor did her "bridge" clue offer any assistance in targeting this particular pit, or in helping narrow down the search area within the 30-acre Whitehurst quarry. But, as WTVT-TV 13 (Tampa) reported on April 19, 1996, "Another clue that amazed [Chief] Slaughter was that the psychic saw a bridge nearby. Turned out [after the fact] that he'd passed it countless times and never saw it—on the access road to the quarry—an old, wooden truck scale that smacks for all the world of a bridge, if you take the time to stare at it."

And as for her apparently precise State Route "45" clue, read on.

"Hits" and Misses

In July 1996, a skeptical Tampa attorney made a Florida Public Records Act request of the Williston police department to provide him with a copy of its entire file on this case, which he then forwarded to me. Investigator Hewitt responded by sending copies of all the paperwork, which included two items of immediate interest: a May 12, 1995, report (supplemented on June 15) filed by Hewitt, and the "clues" jotted down by Hewitt from Renier's July 17, 1995, "psychic" reading. In his two-page May 12/June 15 report (I have corrected a few spelling errors), Hewitt notes that a

handyman . . . had recently told [a client] that [Lewis] had told him that if [Lewis] were not able to take care of himself because of illness, he would find a river or pit rather than the [retired] sailors home. . . . Four days before his disappearance, [Lewis] told [the handyman] that if his health were failing, he would never be cared for by relatives or submit to the sailors home, that there were too many pits and canals. . . . [The handyman later] arrived at the police station . . . and he related [to Hewitt] the last conversation he had with Norman Lewis . . . indicating it [actually] took place approx. three weeks before his disappearance. He stated Norman seemed agitated and dissatisfied with . . . his life [including having] problems at the house with his girlfriend, relating she did not make him feel needed. . . . Told [handyman] not to get old, and made some reference to knowing every rock pit in the county. . . . (Figure 3.)

This "smoking gun" document had been previously unknown to me and to the A & E producer. But it was now apparent that as a result of his failing health and other personal problems (an early newspaper article had also described him as "despondent" over financial matters), Lewis had threatened to commit suicide in a "river" or a "rock pit." Further, word of this had begun to spread through his tiny community and had become known to the police two months prior to their session with Renier. Might Renier have actually learned of this, in advance, from the police?

The Tampa attorney had also specifically requested any video/audiotapes of Renier's reading. After inquiring as to why only written records were released, Hewitt advised him that an audiotape did in fact exist and would be provided. As for a videotape, Hewitt wrote: "As I have advised you in several telephone conversations, the only [video]tape contained in the requested file . . . is of the recovery, which you indicated you did not want."

When even the promised audiotape failed to arrive, the attorney threatened a lawsuit "if a copy of the [audio]tape is not presented to us within seven (7) days." Hewitt finally responded by delivering what he termed "a copy of the field audiotape [which] contains portions of the session with Noreen Renier." To my dismay, upon playing the tape, it was evident that there was a cut/edit after nearly every sentence spoken by Renier (and often in mid-sentence or mid-word). Further, the entire tape runs for a mere five minutes and forty-three seconds. Yet, it does contain some "clues" worth discussing:

- "A lot of rocks. . . . Swallowed up [down there in the water] but there's hardness higher up. . . . We have a lot of things that go straight down. No one really knows what's down there because it's so hazardous and dangerous and people don't go down there. . . . There's a railroad track that goes through there." [Did she know about the suicide threat? Or consult maps, as I did?]
- "Let me have a starting place. . . . We want to get you in the quadrant from 9 to 12 . . . into that pie-shaped area." And from Hewitt's handwritten notes from Renier's reading: "Where do you want me to start? At his house. . . ." [Starting from Lewis' house, his body was found in the 12:00 to 3:00 quadrant, not "9 to 12."]
- "Speedometer is zero in front of the house. . . . Maybe 4, maybe 5. If it's 45 miles, if it's 4.5 miles. I want to go to my left. I want to go to 9. . . . I feel 45, 45 degrees. You know how they have that little baby circle up there? [i.e., 45°]. . . . Looking for H and 45." [This is the "45" clue being credited as a "hit" because Lewis was found near State Route 45!]
- "Must be still somehow in the vehicle. I feel the metal very, very strongly." [Renier had been told in advance that Lewis' truck was also missing.]
- "We're not too far from an old bridge. Either it's been decayed or it's broken or it's not

WILLISTON POLICE DEPARTMENT ⁚ Continuation ✕ REPORT A
✕ Supplement ⁚ REPORT B

1. CASE REPORT #	94 1 01581
	Yr. Mo. Day No

| 2. CRIME TYPE MISSING PERSONS | 3. LOCATION OF OCCURRENCE 752 NW 7TH BLVD | 4. DATE OF ORIG. REPORT 03-25-94 | 5. DATE OF THIS REPORT 05-12-95 |

7. NAME (First, Middle, Last) NORMAN LEWIS

8. YES NO UK ☒ JUVENILE INVOLVED ☒ SUSPECT NAMED
YES NO ☒ SUSPECT VEHICLE DESCRIBED ☒ ADDITIONAL PROPERTY LISTED

9. YES NO CRIME TYPE ☒ RECLASSIFIED

10. DISPOSITION
A ☐ CBA/SWORN D ☐ INA.
B ☐ EX. CL. E ☐ C/C
C ☐ UNF. ☒ INV. CONT

11. BLOCK NO.   INDICATE BLOCK NUMBER IN LEFT MARGIN

ON 05-12-95, AT APPROXIMATELY 1143 HRS, RECEIVED MESSAGE VIA DISPATCH TO PHONE VIRGINIA LEWIS. ATTEMPTED CONTACT

A CONVERSATION SHE HAD WITH SHIRLEY YAGER (⎯⎯⎯) IN WHICH SHE WAS TOLD BY A BLACK MAN WHO WAS INTRODUCED TO SHIRLEY BY NORMAN TO DO SOME HANDYMAN WORK FOR HER. HAD RECENTLY TOLD HER NORMAN HAD TOLD HIM THAT IF HE WERE NOT ABLE TO TAKE CARE OF HIMSELF BECAUSE OF ILLNESS HE WOULD FIND A RIVER OR PIT RATHER THAN THE SAILORS HOME. THANKED JOE FOR.

AND THAT THE AFOREMENTIONED BLACK MAN (ED ROBINSON) HAD ALSO BEEN CLOSE WITH NORMAN. SHE RELATED THAT ROBINSON HAD RECENTLY TOLD HER THAT FOUR DAYS BEFORE HIS DISAPPEARANCE HE TOLD ROBINSON THAT IF HIS HEALTH WERE FAILING HE WOULD NEVER BE CARED FOR BY RELATIVES OR SUBMIT TO THE SAILORS HOME THAT THERE WERE TO MANY PITS AND CANALS TO MET WITH. SHE ALSO

06-15-95 AT APPROXIMATELY 1240 HRS, MR. ROBINSON ARRIVED AT THE POLICE STATION. I BROUGHT HIM INTO MY OFFICE AND HE RELATED THE LAST CONVERSATION HE HAD WITH NORMAN LEWIS, INDICATING IT TOOK PLACE APPROX. 3 WEEKS BEFORE HIS DISAPPEARANCE. HE STATED NORMAN SEEMED AGITATED AND DISSATISFIED WITH THE THINGS GOING ON IN HIS LIFE. THAT WAS THE GIST OF HIS CONVERSATION WHICH WAS VERY ERRATIC AS HE JUMPED FROM TOPIC TO TOPIC. HE RELATED TO PROBLEMS AT THE HOUSE WITH HIS GIRLFRIEND, RELATING SHE DID NOT MAKE HIM FEEL NEEDED. HOW HE HAD MARRIED THE SAME WOMAN THREE TIMES, AND WOULD NEVER MARRY AGAIN. MR. ROBINSON STATED THAT NORMAN HAD LIVED PART OF THE YEAR NORTH AND PART IN FLORIDA AND HE WAS RELATING HE WAS DISSATISFIED WITH BOTH LOCATIONS, AND WOULD NEVER COME BACK TO FLORIDA AGAIN. STATED HE WAS NOT GOING TO DEPEND ON ANYBODY AGAIN. TOLD ME ROBINSON NOT TO GET OLD AND MADE SOME RE-FENCE TO KNOWING EVERY ROCK PIT IN THE COUNTY. (THE AFOREMENTIONED RECOLLECTIONS ARE IN NO PARTICULAR ORDER OR SEQUENCE ACCORDING TO ROBINSON) MR. ROBINSON STATED HE HAD BEEN FRIENDS WITH NORMAN FOR APPROX. THE LAST 5 OR 6 YEARS AND RELATED HE HAD NOT SEEN HIM THAT TROUBLED BEFORE

| 12 REPORTING OFFICER E. Brian Hurtt | ID # 6044 | SHIFT 1 | 13. SUPERVISOR | I.D.# | YES NO ⁚ ⁚ REPORT APPROVED ⁚ ⁚ FOLLOW-UP NEEDED | PRIORITY 1 2 3 4 5 |

Figure 3

used. . . . It's called the old bridge or is an old bridge." [The old truck scale was nearby, although it was certainly not known as "the old bridge."]

- "One point, or one-one point two. I see two-two-I [the letter "I"]. I believe a very strong H, 'Ha'-sounding or an H in it." And from Hewitt's notes: "221 . . . 22 . . . 21 . . . 2I . . . H . . . EML . . . E . . . 11.2" [Renier was credited with an eerily accurate "hit" because Lewis was supposedly found "2.1" miles from his home! But what about "45 miles" and "4.5 miles"?]

Among the pages in the police file is a map of Williston with a 90° (L-shaped) area from 11:00 to 2:00 (not "9 to 12") drawn on it and labeled "Noreen's quadrant." The point of convergence of the two lines is correctly marked "Norman's House," and the quadrant includes the northern Whitehurst pit where the body was found (at about 1:00) but not the eastern pit that her clues appear to more closely fit (at about 3:30–4:00).

In stark contrast to A & E's balanced coverage of the case on *The Unexplained*, the Sci-Fi Channel's *Sightings* coverage included no skeptical input. The *Sightings* narrator asks, but is not able to answer, the question: "Why did Norman disappear?" No mention is made of Investigator Hewitt's report, filed two months prior to Renier's "psychic" reading, regarding Lewis' "rock pit" suicide plan. But in fairness to *Sightings*, the police had also withheld this crucial information from the A & E producer.

In Renier's re-created reading for the *Sightings* cameras, with her eyes closed, feigning a trance-like state, she strays from her original reading so as to now specifically associate the number "21" with miles: "Numbers—21. I feel miles." On the edited audiotape, there is no mention of "21" in any context (although, as shown earlier, "21" does appear in Hewitt's notes in the midst of a stream of numbers/let-

ters with no particular regard to mileage), and the only numbers associated with "miles" are "45" and "4.5." Nor is there a "21" clue on the edited videotape (yes, it did finally materialize—see below).

The "45 miles" clue is especially puzzling, as Renier has been credited with correctly determining that Lewis would be found a short distance from his home. From her *Sightings* re-creation: "I'm driving for a short distance, and then something happens, and I see him in the air, going downward." And from the edited videotape of her original reading:

"Norman's house is here [gesturing to the right with her right arm]. Here's the road [gesturing straight ahead with her left arm]. We go this way [pointing straight ahead with her left hand]. . . . But we don't go very far that way, we're going to veer off here [pointing left with her left hand] . . . towards the river. And for some reason the river is down below [as if describing Lewis' arrival at the pit/quarry's sheer cliff]."

This passage on the videotape appears to be a second "smoking gun," this time with regard to the particular body of water to which Renier's directions actually lead. As I earlier indicated, Renier's clues (as I understood them even before receiving this video) seemed to lead not to the Whitehurst pit (located north of Lewis' home) where the body was ultimately found, but rather to another rock pit much closer to, and nearly due east of, his home.

During my two visits to Williston, I viewed the former Lewis residence, located on N.W. 7th Blvd. With the home on the right side of the street, proceeding straight ahead (as per Renier's "psychic" vision) leads southeasterly for approximately one-third mile, at which time the road curves left to a due east bearing, until N.W. 7th Blvd. ends at its intersection with U.S. 41, approximately one-half mile from the Lewis home. Another quarter-mile or so due east, dead ahead (no pun intended), is the massive "eastern" rock quarry, the most prominent feature on the Williston roadmap.

Summarizing Renier's role in this case, the *Sightings* narrator says, "Investigator Hewitt put all of Renier's clues together, used some gut instinct of his own, and came up with one word—'Quarry.'" But we now know that Hewitt had actually learned two months earlier of Lewis' plans for ending his life in a quarry. And in the edited video of Renier's actual reading, she refers to the body of water not as a "pit" or "quarry," but as a "river" (although she appears puzzled as to why it goes "down" such a sheer cliff). The word "quarry" is heard once on the videotape, not after Hewitt has a chance to digest all of Renier's clues and apply his "gut instinct," but in the midst of the session, by an unidentified male questioner present with Hewitt in Renier's living room: "Now look at that quarry. As you're looking at it and looking at it from the entrance there. . . ."

Following Renier's reading, did the police zero in on one quarry to which Noreen's directions pointed? Hewitt says on *Sightings* that he "walked around probably 30 quarries" before deciding that the Whitehurst pit most closely matched the totality of Renier's clues. Perhaps that was his reason for having the Navy divers scour that one pit, which did result in Lewis' body and truck being recovered. But his initial rationale for concentrating on the Whitehurst pit was described this way in his report filed six days after Renier's reading: ". . . the Whitehurst pits are an obvious first impression . . . being the closest and the most accessible from the Lewis residence." (Although the "eastern" pit was fenced off by this time, it had been easily accessible when Lewis disappeared, and it is half as far from Lewis' home as is Whitehurst.)

As for this "eastern" pit, a person with some inside knowledge of the police investigation (who allowed me to tape our conversation but requests anonymity) told me that this had been the "prime target for the investigation"

immediately following Renier's reading. "They didn't think there was a [railroad] track [at Whitehurst]."

At the conclusion of the *Sightings* report, the narrator explained how Renier's "22" clue (remember that stream of numbers?) had also been remarkably accurate: When Lewis' body was recovered, "the calendar date on Norman's diving watch was stopped on the number 22." For the record, he had disappeared and presumably committed suicide on the 24th of March, 1994. As a clue to the location of Mr. Lewis' missing body, "22" was utterly useless.

The Videotape's Curious Arrival

The ultimate arrival of the edited videotape came as a complete surprise. When the audiotape turned out to have been heavily and crudely edited, the attorney wrote back to Hewitt requesting "a complete copy of the audiotape." Hewitt's reply explained that the tape "is the only audio tape I have regarding Noreen Renier's session [and] was expressly made [from a more lengthy original] for field use with regard to the location of Mr. Lewis." Most curiously, the letter continued: "You are requesting additional material. . . . We are under no obligation to provide you with any material without prepayment. Therefore, with your payment of [an additional $14.00] . . . I will forward to you the only remaining tape I have regarding this case."

The attorney assumed that the "only remaining tape" was a video of the recovery of the truck and body, as Hewitt had previously indicated. Nonetheless, he decided to fork over the $14.00. Incredibly, a month later, he received from Hewitt the videotape which, despite having been edited down to about 14 minutes, still contained the "smoking gun" segment.

In a letter accompanying the videotape, Hewitt informed the attorney that he had "filed for mediation with the State Attorney General's office . . . to assure you [that] we are in full compliance under the Florida Public Records Act." Through the mediator, the attorney then posed several questions, including these: "Why did the police department initially deny having a videotape and thereafter send us one?" "One map . . . depicts an area labeled 'Noreen's quadrant.' Who drew this quadrant on the map?" [see earlier discussion]. "What is the personal relationship, if any, between Detective Hewitt and Noreen Renier?"

This third question was prompted by two peculiar circumstances—the apparent initial withholding of information by Hewitt, and a stunning move by Renier: After living in Orlando for more than 20 years, she has now packed her bags and relocated to Williston!

Another question relates to an undated police report, filed by Hewitt, which does not appear to comport with Renier's reading, at least as excerpted on the tapes. Writes Hewitt, "She picked out [L]CR 501 on local map which I provided, indicating it was the road Lewis had traveled after leaving his residence, in a northerly direction." LCR 501 is the northern extention of Lewis' street, but according to the video's "smoking gun" segment, Renier actually indicated that he headed south.

But the answers to these questions have not been forthcoming. The mediator has written back informing the attorney that the Public Records Act does not compel Hewitt to re- spond. And the City Attorney for the town of Williston has sternly weighed in: "[Y]ou have [already] received all public records in possession of the City relating to [this] investigation."

After-the-Fact Reasoning

Two final questions, fundamental to the very nature of "psychic" phenomena, require consideration. In my chapter on Renier for the book *Psychic Sleuths* (edited by Joe Nickell, Prometheus Books, 1994), I showed at the time how Renier (like the rest of the psychics profiled in the book) had yet to convincingly demonstrate genuine "psychic" power under proper observing conditions. Has Renier now become the first psychic to successfully do so? Or might her "success" in the Williston case be explainable in more mundane terms, perhaps as the result of a combination of factors such as advance research, common sense/intuition, feeding back information gleaned from the police themselves, and "retrofitting"—interpreting ambiguous clues, after the fact, as having been remarkably accurate and valuable "hits"?

To those who believe in "psychic" power and other supernatural phenomena, the answers to these two questions no doubt remain "crystal ball" clear. And they remain equally clear, though through quite another prism, to those skeptics of the paranormal who demand extraordinary proof of such extraordinary claims.

Pseudoarchaeology

Native American Myths as a Test Case

KENNETH L. FEDER

A little less than 15 years ago, I was invited to participate in a radio talk show at a local station in Hartford, Connecticut. I was a last-minute addition to a panel that included a local museum curator and three Native Americans. The curator's museum housed a collection of ancient Indian artifacts including material related to at least one human burial that was on display. The curator originally had agreed to be the lone spokesperson on the broadcast arguing for the importance and legitimacy of the excavation, analysis, display, and curation of archaeological objects. However, sensing an "ambush," the curator had requested that an archaeologist be included on the panel. I was available and agreed, perhaps naively, to participate.

Like most of us conducting field archaeology of prehistoric sites in the United States, I had been attracted to the discipline because of an abiding interest in the human past. Also, like most North American prehistorians, though I am not an Indian, I became an archaeologist equally because of a fascination with and intense admiration for the cultures of Native America.

Knowing this, it was a terrible irony to me, that, even 15 years ago, the relationship between Native Americans and archaeologists could be characterized as an uneasy and eroding truce. Many Native Americans viewed archaeologists as interlopers from the dominant culture, outsiders who exploited native peoples for their own purposes. The common, and often reasonable perspective of many Indians was that archaeologists were scientists who studied Indian ancestors, but who had little interest in and no accountability to the descendants of the people who had produced the cultures and sites upon which these scientists focused. Many Native Americans believed that archaeologists had merely updated, to a degree, the old racist saw: "The only good Indian is a dead (i.e., prehistoric) Indian." Many Native Americans believed, often justifiably, that archaeologists were concerned about only the ancient ancestors of Indians, and cared little or nothing about living native peoples or those peoples' perspectives of their own history. For many, as archaeologist Randall McGuire (1997) points out, archaeology represented yet another instance in which outsiders had appropriated something that belonged to Native Americans—their history: ". . . the archaeologist's authority over Indian pasts is simply one other aspect of their lives that has been taken from their control" (McGuire 1997, 65). Archaeologist Larry Zimmerman goes even further, indicating that to some Native Americans, the pursuit of archaeology is a kind of "scientific colonialism" (1997, 108).

I had agreed to participate in the radio panel for two fundamental reasons. I felt some level of general responsibility for the bad behavior of some members (by no means all or even a majority) of my discipline and I believed, innocently I suppose, that I could expiate my personal feeling of guilt and exonerate my field of study if only I could explain my work and the work of most of my fellow archeologists.

Unfortunately, my museum colleague had foreseen the scenario of the radio panel correctly. It was a set up; the goal all along had been to exploit the growing controversy within Native American communities about archaeology. No real dialogue took place. None had been intended. The museum curator and I had been invited to serve as effigies of our disciplines. We were the representatives of evil western culture, ghouls of science who desecrated and then displayed the graves of Native Americans for fun and profit.

As depressing as this was 15 years ago, the relationship between at least some Native Americans and some archaeologists has deteriorated, if anything, since that radio broadcast. It is a shame and is based more on political issues and less on any genuine conflict between what archaeologists actually do and what some natives find objectionable.

Archaeologists as Desecrators of the Sacred

Archaeologists are sometimes depicted as exploiters and despoilers of native culture. There is a popular perception that archaeologists spend much of their time looking for and then desecrating tombs, looting them of their fabulous and sacred treasures placed there to accompany the deceased to the afterlife, all in the name of museums willing to spend huge sums of money for such objects. But is this really what archaeologists do? Certainly it conforms to a commonly held stereotype, but does this reflect the kind of archaeology conducted by anthropologically trained archaeologists in the late 20th century?

In fact, it does not. Certainly I could understand the Indians on the radio panel objecting strenuously to the excavation of the bones of their immediate ancestors, but I have never excavated a human burial and know of very few archaeologists who have. The passage at the federal level in 1990 of the Native American Graves Protection and Repatriation Act (NAGPRA) has resulted in the removal of large collections of human remains and their associated grave goods from museums and laboratories and has made excavation and curation of the human remains of Native Americans all but impossible. State regulations are also in place to control quite rigorously the excavation of human remains. Archaeologists may debate the wisdom of this policy and many may decry the inestimable loss to science that accompanied NAGPRA (Haederle 1997; Meighan 1994), while others feel that the obligation is to the sensitivities of the people most directly concerned and not some idealized notion of "science" (Zimmerman 1994), but the argument is moot. These days, burials most often come to light only as the result of natural erosion or construction, and most municipalities have rules that tightly regulate the disposition of human remains so exposed. In many places these rules were drawn up with substantial input from native peoples.

This is not to say that conflicts do not arise, but, again, it seems that this occurs because of misunderstandings on both sides of the issue, and such conflicts are exacerbated by the degree of animosity that has developed as a result. For example, in an interview in the *New York Times* (Johnson 1996), noted archaeologist Rob Bonnichsen recounted the following horror story. Bonnichsen was excavating at the 10,000 year old Mammoth Meadow site in Montana when, much to his surprise and delight, human hair turned up in the most ancient levels. I am aware of, at most, one other example of human hair from a site of this age in North America, and the potential for DNA analysis must have been terribly exciting to the researchers.

One might have reasonably assumed that only an archaeologist or paleoanthropologist could get all that worked up over a handful of ancient hair. However, when word got out about the hair, two local Indian tribes demanded that the research stop and that the hair be returned for reburial under the provisions of NAGPRA! As of October 1996, the hair was still in limbo, research on an important site had been held up for two years, but at least the final regulations of NAGPRA now exclude "portions of remains that may reasonably be determined to have been freely given or naturally shed by the individual from whose body they were obtained" (NAGPRA regulations, section 10.1 (d) (1)). In the Lewis Carroll world (or is it Franz Kafka?) of federal regulations regarding archaeology, this new wording can be viewed as a major step forward. As attorney Alan Schneider (1996) points out, now archaeologists can legally hold on to and analyze human hair, toenail clippings, and coprolites (ancient, preserved feces) without the wrath of NAGPRA being visited upon them.

Of course, it isn't only hair, toenails, and the like that divides Indians and archaeologists. Not just the intentional excavation but even the analysis of human remains exposed by natural processes has become a point of contention. The most recent and unfortunate example of this is the so-called Kennewick skeleton found in Washington state. Before word got out about the remains, radiocarbon dating was performed and the bones turn out to be more than 9,000 years old. This date surprised researchers because the skeleton exhibited gross morphological characteristics more in line with a European rather than a Native American population. Subsequent to the dat-

ing, however, the local Umatilla tribe demanded it be returned to them for reburial and they further demanded that no additional analysis be conducted on this well-preserved skeleton. The disposition of the skeleton is still up in the air (it has spawned a court case), but in another instance, in Idaho, the Shoshone-Bannoks allowed the radiocarbon dating of a skeleton found in their historical territory—it was 10,600 years old—but the tribe then vetoed DNA analysis (Johnson 1996).

Neither the Umatilla nor the Shoshone-Bannoks can prove any direct or intimate biological connection with these very ancient skeletons. The irony here is that with the analysis of mitochondrial DNA (if any is preserved in the skeletons) it might be possible to prove that, indeed, these modern Indians are the lineal descendants of the individuals represented, strengthening their demand for stewardship of the remains. Of course, this is a two-edged sword—it might also turn out that the modern Indians claiming stewardship are not closely related to the ancient person, thereby reducing the strength of their claim. In the case of the Shoshone-Bannoks, for example, the ancestors of these modern Indians probably migrated into their current territory less than a thousand years ago, so their connection to the person represented by the skeletal remains found in their modern territory is weak.

Many Indians, however, seem unconcerned with such historical particulars, asserting kinship with and demanding control over any Indian remains found in their modern territory. From a scientific perspective, this makes no sense. We end up with remarkable instances in which modern natives assert stewardship of ancient bones of their ancestral enemies simply because those bones are now located within the recently demarcated boundaries of their reservation. Concern for the bones of immediate ancestors might be understandable, but desiring control over the very ancient bones of individuals who were not immediately ancestral is perplexing. I count among my ancestors Germans, Russians, and Poles, but I feel no great kinship with or reverence for the bones of Upper Paleolithic people unearthed in those modern nations.

Nevertheless, it is understandable from an anthropological perspective how members of different segments of a beleaguered minority, often treated as a monolithic group by the majority, might feel a broad solidarity with members of their larger group, transcending economic, political, tribal, or even temporal boundaries. For example, we do not hear of African Americans expressing solidarity only with other descendants of the particular African tribes from which they can trace their ancestors taken into slavery. Ordinarily, they draw their boundaries more broadly, to include all people in a similar circumstance—the descendants of people taken into slavery, originating anywhere on the African continent. It is not surprising, therefore, that Native Americans do the same, even claiming kinship with and demanding stewardship of enormously ancient human remains that can be connected only in the most tenuous way to any particular modern tribe. When good science meets legitimate emotionalism there seems little room for compromise, with archaeologists and Indians possessed of fundamentally different and equally defensible perspectives. The law now stands on the side of Native Americans and, like it or not, archaeology in North America has changed as a result.

Though archaeologists are adjusting to the restrictions of NAGPRA's rules concerning human remains, there is a broader and potentially more devastating issue. A low point in the radio dialogue mentioned above had to have been when one panel member informed me that everything buried in the ground had been placed there for a spiritual reason by his ancestors, and I had no right to disturb these "sacred objects." If this were true, archaeology faces extinction, but what "sacred objects"

could he have meant? Gnawed on deer bones? Sherds of a shattered cooking pot? A spear point snapped in two when it struck an animal? Minuscule flakes shattered off a stone core or a simple, sharp-bladed utilitarian tool? These are the materials most commonly recovered during archaeological excavations in North America; these are the "treasures" we most commonly unearth, not anything that can possibly be construed as "sacred."

Beyond the mundane nature of the vast majority of the material archaeologists regularly excavate, it should be added that most of this material has not been intentionally hidden away by ancient people but consists, instead, of objects that have simply been abandoned and that have, through any combination of entirely natural processes—alluviation, soil formation through organic decay, etc.—simply been covered up. The vast majority of what we excavate is "garbage" in the literal sense; food remains, waste products from manufacturing processes (for example, unusable flakes of stone produced when stone tools were made), or pieces of tools that had broken, been used up, worn out, and then simply discarded.

Those who assert that everything we excavate was sacred to ancient people have bought into the romantic, popular media caricature of archaeologists mentioned above where we dig up mostly treasures intentionally hidden away under the ground for ceremonial reasons. In reality, most of what we dig up is stuff ancient people cared so little about they simply tossed it on the ground, in a trash pit, or on a pile of other garbage. Native Americans might have a reasonable argument when they complain that archaeologists care more for what trash can tell them about Indian history than what their own oral history tells them. Most archaeologists are convinced that garbage represents objective truth and that self-conscious histories—oral and written—often are far more subjective and biased. Nevertheless, the claim that we regularly and intentionally extract objects from the ground that the ancestors of modern Indians placed there with the intention that these things remain buried is a gross exaggeration and a distortion. This belief is untenable from either a scientific or emotionalist perspective. What can sometimes result is the paradox that material not sacred to a people in antiquity becomes so in the present simply because archaeologists dug it up! How else can we explain the recent case in Florida where, not pursuant to NAGPRA but following state regulations, the excavated paleontological remains of an extinct elephant (a mastodon) were "returned" to a local Native American group for reburial (as cited in Lepper 1996)?

Indian Origins

Just when I thought the radio panel discussion was proving to be a waste of everyone's time, I spotted a book brought along by one of the Native Americans. The book was titled *American Genesis*, written by Jeffrey Goodman (1981), a writer who advertised himself as an academically trained anthropologist, fully armed with a Ph.D.

Trying to deflect the conversation from archaeology and museums, I asked the others on the panel what they thought about Goodman's book—which, coincidentally, at the time I was in the process of reviewing (Feder 1983b) and also for which I was writing a detailed and scathing deconstruction (Feder 1983a). I was, again rather naively, shocked at the response: "It's a great book. Dr. Goodman recognizes that we Indians didn't come from somewhere else. We've always been here. Not like you archaeologists. You think we are foreigners. You claim we were latecomers."

Until that moment I had no idea that Goodman had garnered some interest among Indians as the result of the major theme of *American Genesis*. Archaeologists believe that the

ancestors of modern Native Americans originated in northeast Asia and migrated across the Bering Land Bridge sometime toward the end of the Pleistocene epoch. They accomplished this during a period when sea level was depressed as a result of the binding up of an enormous quantity of the earth's seawater in ice fields called glaciers that covered much of the higher latitudes and altitudes of North and South America, Europe and Asia. *American Genesis* represented a categorical rejection of this scientific orthodoxy.

It seemed to me that Indian support for Goodman's thesis was yet another irony in an already spectacularly ironic situation since it was based on an ignorance of what Goodman had stated explicitly about the origins of Native Americans in his previous book. Though Goodman made a major issue of disputing the accepted Bering Land Bridge migration scenario in *American Genesis*, and while the title of that book itself seemed to indicate it, he did not explicitly support the claim that Indians had originated in the New World, as the Native American on the radio panel seemed to believe. In fact, in a previous book (*Psychic Archaeology*), Goodman (1977) had been quite explicit. Based on information provided to him by a self-proclaimed psychic, Goodman claimed that New World native peoples had not originated in the New World but, instead, had migrated from, of all places, the Lost Continent of Atlantis, thus creating a rather remarkable nexus of pseudoscientific claims about the human past.

After the radio broadcast we all went our separate ways. Goodman's work lost much of its sheen—or, at least, its currency—and I heard little or nothing of him. Also, controversy about the Bering Land Bridge migration scenario seemed to disappear. Specific versions and especially the timing of the migration or migrations certainly have been argued: was an interior route across the land bridge more significant than a coastal route; did the initial influx of people occur around 12,000 years ago, 15,000 years ago, or before even 20,000 years ago? However, the general notion of a movement of human beings from northeast Asia across the land bridge into North America has not been disputed in the popular media or professional journals in the last two decades. I thought, or at least, hoped that this point of contention between Indians and archaeologists had been disposed of and that more important issues could be discussed. Unfortunately, this assumption and hope were in vain. The issue of the origin of Native Americans has again become a topic of popular debate. And, interestingly, not just where they came from but, even more fundamentally, how we should approach the question and, essentially, how we can know anything about their past (including their origins) are now subject to debate.

A recent book, *Red Earth, White Lies: Native Americans and the Myth of Scientific Fact*, by Indian activist, scholar, writer, and university professor Vine Deloria Jr., attacks archaeology rather viciously and in particular assails those who support the Bering Land Bridge scenario. It compounds the irony to report that (if my small personal sample is representative) many of us who went into archaeology in the 1960s and 1970s read and applauded one of Deloria's (1969) previous books, *Custer Died for Your Sins*. We likely are more sensitive to the issues being discussed here at least in part because of having read it. In a recent compendium of papers (Biolsi and Zimmerman 1997; see especially Grobsmith 1997), a number of anthropologists agree that the anthropological study of Native Americans as it is practiced today is partially a result of Deloria's criticisms of the discipline in *Custer*.

With the publication of *Red Earth, White Lies*, however, not just a few of us have taken lately to scraping the remnants of our "Custer Died for Your Sins" bumper stickers off of our aging automobiles (see Whittaker [1997] for a review of *Red Earth, White Lies*). Deloria re-

jects any claim that the ancestors of modern American Indians came from somewhere else and proposes, instead, that, based on Native American creation stories, American Indians have always been in the New World since the time of their creation.

One must understand Deloria's rejection of the almost certainly historically accurate land bridge scenario within a broader historical context. The belief that Native Americans must have come from somewhere in the Old World can be traced back to almost immediately after it was recognized that Columbus had not made landfall on Cathay (China) or Cipangu (Japan). It must be admitted that this belief was based on biblical exegesis and not on any particular scientific evidence or reasoning. In 1537 Pope Paul III had decreed that "the Indians are truly men and that they are not only capable of understanding the catholic faith but, according to our information, desire exceedingly to receive it" (as cited in Hanke 1937, 72). Therefore, as Spanish clerics Gregoria Garcia and Joseph de Acosta (see Huddleston 1967) pointed out in their works written barely one hundred years after Columbus's voyages, the Indians must be traceable to one of Noah's three sons because all other people had been killed in the flood. Because the ark landed on "the mountains of Ararat" in southwest Asia, the descendants of Noah who were to become the ancestors of Native Americans must have traveled to the New World, either by ocean-going vessels (Garcia) or by traversing on foot a land connection between the Old and New Worlds (Acosta).

Beyond simply accounting for Native Americans in a way that conformed to the Bible, some 16th-century writers cited biological evidence for an Old World source for the native peoples of the Americas. For example, Giovanni de Verrazzano, an Italian navigator sailing for France in 1524, made landfall at what is today the border of North and South Carolina and then traveled north, looking for a sea route to the west and, it was hoped, a way past the New World and to Asia. He entered Delaware Bay and the mouth of the Hudson River, sailed along Connecticut's coast, entered and explored Narragansett Bay, followed the shore of Cape Cod and then went home, unsuccessful in his attempt to find a passage to the west. Verrazzano spent several weeks exploring the interior of Rhode Island and had an opportunity to examine local natives closely. He concluded: "They tend to be rather broad in the face. . . . They have big black eyes. . . . From what we could tell in the last two respects they resemble the Orientals."

Today, this kind of gross, morphological comparison is no longer the only biological datum on which we base the assertion of a connection between Asians and Native Americans. For example, based on his analysis of 200,000 teeth, physical anthropologist Christy Turner (1987) has shown the clear affiliation of northeast Asians and Native Americans; their teeth share far more in common than either group's teeth share with the dentition of Africans, Europeans, or native Australians. More recently, analysis of mitochondrial DNA (mtDNA) has reaffirmed what Turner's analysis of teeth indicated (Gibbons 1993; Stone and Stoneking 1993). These researchers have shown that four mtDNA variants are found among Native Americans. All four of these variants are found in Asia, and they are not found in Europe, Africa, or Australia.

So, how can Native Americans question these seemingly indisputable data and why would they want to? After all, what does it matter that science can show that neither the ancestors of Native Americans nor anyone else's ancestors are truly "native" to the New World—or, for that matter, to Europe, Asia, or Australia? The hominid family and the species of anatomically modern *Homo sapiens* are native to Africa. We are all, ultimately, natives of Africa; everywhere else in the world, people are immigrants. So what?

At the same time that Europeans were attempting to trace the source of New World native peoples, there also was a great and transparent desire to somehow diminish the legitimacy of the claim of these natives to the lands of the Western Hemisphere. One way in which this was done was to deny the depth of the antiquity of their presence here. As writer Robert Silverberg (1989, 48) puts it, it was "comforting to the conquerors" to believe that, though the Indians may have had some temporal priority, they hadn't really made it to the New World all that long before Columbus.

One major challenge to this belief was the seemingly ancient ruins found in Central America and, especially, the remnants of a geographically extensive, technologically sophisticated culture of "mound builders" who had been responsible for the construction of thousands of burial tumuli and enormous, truncated pyramids of earth that were nearly ubiquitous throughout the Ohio, Illinois, Missouri, and Mississippi River valleys. European thinkers responded to this challenge by denying any cultural or biological connection between Indians and the mound builders, asserting, instead, that the "Moundbuilder" civilization had been the product of a greatly ancient, pre-Indian migration of perhaps even Europeans to the New World. In this historical fantasy, the peaceful and complex Moundbuilder culture had been wiped out before the arrival of Europeans in the 16th century, almost certainly by an only slightly pre-European influx of marauding, aggressive, and warlike savages. These latecoming savages were the ancestors of, of course, American Indians.

One can understand and empathize with a negative reaction on the part of some modern Indians to the more recent scientific assertion that Native Americans arrived here from somewhere else in the measurable past. The claim that the native peoples of the New World came from someplace else was viewed by the Native American on the radio panel and, I believe, is viewed by Vine Deloria Jr. and many other modern Indians, as just another attempt in a history of attempts to contradict or somehow reduce the rightful native claim to the New World. As Randall McGuire (1997, 77) puts it, the archaeological view of Indian origins represents, to many natives, the self-serving "viewpoint of the conquerors of the continent."

My response to this today is the same as it was 15 years ago. Modern archaeology shows that, by the most conservative of estimates, the ancestors of American Indians arrived in the New World 13,000 years ago and, in all likelihood, made the trek across the Bering Land Bridge 15,000 or, perhaps, 20,000 years ago. That would be a minimum of 650 and as many as 1000 generations (at 20 years per generation) of a human presence in the New World. By any definition, that would make quite firm any hypothetical claim of ownership of the New World by American Indians. No archaeologist disputes this; American Indians were here first, and their roots run very deep, orders of magnitude deeper than Europeans.

Deloria's perspective on Native American origins is unabashedly creationist, but not the fundamentalist Christian variety that most of us are familiar with. This should not be surprising, and scientists have long seen this coming. In debating creationists, scientists have often pointed out the fact that the so-called two-model approach of evolution on the one hand and creationism on the other is predicated on a false dichotomy. Of course, there is no such thing as the "creation model," because this presupposes that there is a single—i.e., Judeo-Christian—creationist view. As scientists have constantly pointed out to creationists, there are as many creationist perspectives as there are cultures that have pondered the origins of the universe, the world, life, and people—and very few cultures have not so pondered. We have used this fact to argue against a "two-model" approach in education, because this, in reality, establishes the Judeo-Christian

origin myth as the single representative of creationism when, by the very argument of the creationists for fairness, we ought to be devoting equal time in our biology classrooms to Hindu, Navajo, Azande, Egyptian, Iroquois, etc., creation views as well.

There is, of course, a significant contradiction within Deloria's variety of Native American creationism. Deloria is a Standing Rock Sioux and, I presume, the creation story he personally accepts comes from his culture. Fair enough. However, in the Outline of World Cultures of the Human Relations Area Files (HRAF), a broad but by no means exhaustive database of ethnographic studies covering the world, about 250 separate and distinct native culture groups in North and Middle America are inventoried and close to an additional 250 separate and distinct culture groups in South America are listed. The federal government officially recognizes more than 550 Indian tribes and native Hawaiian groups. Some linguists argue that there were close to 1500 different languages and dialects in the Americas aboriginally, so one could argue that there may have been about that many cultural groups.

Examining the HRAF database for New World origin stories or myths, we find literally hundreds of very different stories concerning the creation of people. To compound the problem, as a member of a tribal group, in *Red Earth, White Lies* Deloria expresses solidarity with other tribal peoples elsewhere in the world. These tribal groups also have their own creation stories, adding further to the variety. Michael Shermer (1997, 129–130) presents a taxonomy of some of these myriad creation stories: slain monster version, primordial parents version, cosmic egg version, spoken edict version, sea or water version, and even the no creation/the world and people have always been here version. There is as much disagreement among these many stories as there is between any one of them and scientists adhering to evolution in general and to the Bering Land

Bridge migration scenario specifically in the case of Native Americans.

Under most prosaic patterns of thought and reasoning, one would assume that these stories can't all be right. Either the scientific conclusion based on evidence and logic is correct, or one of the origin myths based on faith and oral history must be correct. Nevertheless, Deloria appears to take the opposite approach. In his view, only one of the explanations is wrong— that is, of course, the explanation given by science—and all of the others, regardless of the fact that they are contradictory—are correct.

(Deloria rejects the assertion that the ancestors of the American Indians migrated to the New World from Asia partially because none of their origin stories say that they did so. Considering that this migration likely involved a small number of people at least 13,000 years ago, I am perplexed why this should be significant. For example, I doubt that many modern Parisians have had stories of painting the fabulous images on the walls of Lascaux cave passed down in their families. Nevertheless, it is almost certainly the case that some of the direct ancestors of some modern Parisians were the actual Lascaux artists.)

Deloria recognizes this apparent flaw in his reasoning. In response, he is explicit about his rejection of the notion of objective historical or scientific fact: "Tribal elders did not worry if their version of creation was entirely different from the scenario held by a neighboring tribe. People believed that each tribe had its own special relationship to the superior spiritual forces which governed the universe. . . . Tribal knowledge was not fragmented and was valid within the historical and geographical scope of the people's experience" (Deloria 1995, 51–2).

Remember, Deloria sub-titles his latest book *Native Americans and the Myth of Scientific Fact*. Deloria is not merely accusing scientists of making up myths about Native Americans (though, certainly, he does this). More significantly, he asserts that the very concept of scientific fact itself is a myth. So, we are left with

Deloria's apparent belief that each tribal or traditional culture's reality is different, yet each is "valid" or correct, and that this is a useful and legitimate way to view the world.

Much of this confusion can be traced to the fact that Deloria ignores the reality that myth and science are two different things and approach explanation in entirely different ways. As scientists, rationalists, and even Pope John-Paul II have pointed out, the creation stories of religion instruct people in what their relation is to the "creator" and how, flowing from that, they should live good and moral lives. The Lakota story of the ancestral Buffalo People emerging from the Earth's interior, no less so than Genesis, tells people "how one goes to heaven," but not literally "how heaven was made" (Pope John-Paul II, referring to the Bible, as cited in Lieberman and Kirk 1996). Maintaining that the Lakota creation story is historical truth is no different from claiming that Genesis is literally true and makes inevitable an otherwise avoidable clash between religion and science.

Is There a Future for the Science of the Past?

It is easy to be pessimistic about the future of American archaeology. The rift between myth and science, between emotionalism and rationalism, seems so great, so fundamental, so defining, that it would appear that there is very little common ground possible on which both Indians and archaeologists can stand together.

However, there is at least some hope, of not only a rapprochement, but cooperation. Some natives have written in support of archaeological research, recognizing its contribution to the history of their tribes (see the volume edited by Swindler et al. 1997). Furthermore, there is a small, but dedicated cadre of anthropologists and archaeologists who are, in fact, Native Americans. Those who find themselves straddling both worlds may be the discipline's best hope to communicate to Indian people the significance, potential, and rationale of what we do and for natives to communicate their concerns to archaeologists.

For example, Dorothy Lippert (a Choctaw working on her Ph.D. in anthropology) has written in a wonderfully eloquent piece: "For many of our ancestors, skeletal analysis is one of the only ways that they are able to tell us their stories . . . these individuals have found one last way to speak to us about their lives" (1997, 126). Though many Indians might disagree, Lippert feels "appropriate reverence" for her ancestors can be maintained while scientists study their physical remains to enable her ancestors to use their "voice made of bone."

Even for the many natives who would disagree with Lippert, the excavation, analysis, and curation of demonstrably non-sacred objects are possible in many circumstances. For example, Rose Kluth and Kathy Munnell (both Chippewa) make an absolute distinction between burial and non-burial sites and agree that: "Archaeological sites contain the history of our people, in different stages of their lives, according to the seasons of the year. I believe that useful information can be recovered from these types of sites that will be helpful and interesting to Native Americans" (1997, 117).

Beyond this, some tribes have sponsored their own programs of archaeological research on their reservations. The Navajo, Zuni, and Hopi are good examples. A particularly positive example of Indian recognition of the benefits of archaeology comes from Connecticut where the Pequot tribal nation initiated its own archaeology program (McBride 1990). This tribe obtained federal recognition only recently and with the enormous revenues generated by their wildly successful casino, sought to reconstruct their history and recognized the value of archaeology in that pursuit. Archaeological excavations are nearly continuous on Pequot reservation land and the tribe is currently building a state of the art museum in which the archaeology they have sponsored will be a major element.

It might be suggested that at least part of the success of the relationship between the Pequot and archaeology rests in this simple fact: the archaeology of the Pequot is something that the Pequot wanted, initiated, paid for, and control. In terms of access to sites as well as who signs the checks, the archaeologists necessarily are accountable to them. This is a situation unlikely to be repeated terribly often elsewhere in North America, but it is a clear reflection of the significance of Indian control of their own past in the dispute between Indians and archaeologists.

Conclusions

Many Native Americans may find the pursuit of archaeology unnecessary, redundant, trivial, and, at best, a "necessary evil" for complying with federal regulations (Johnson 1996). They may view the results of our research as antagonistic to their personally held religious beliefs. They may find insulting the very notion that ancient trash may be more accurate than their oral histories. Nevertheless, archaeology may survive anyway, only because, though they may feel they have no use for it, many Indians do not find at least some of our activities to be fundamentally objectionable. This may be the best we can currently hope for. The suspicion some Native Americans feel about archaeology is thoroughly understandable, but this does not diminish the irony that the people whose cultures archaeologists hope to illuminate and, in fact, celebrate may find the entire thing at worst a desecration and at best a peculiar waste of time.

References:

Biolsi, T., and L. Zimmerman, eds. 1997. *Indians and Anthropologists: Vine Deloria Jr. and the*

Critique of Anthropology. Tucson: University of Arizona Press.

Deloria Jr., Vine. 1969. *Custer Died for Your Sins: An Indian Manifesto*. New York: Macmillan.

——. 1995. *Red Earth, White Lies: Native Americans and the Myth of Scientific Fact*. New York: Scribners.

Feder, Kenneth L. 1983a. "Absurdist Archaeology: A Review of Jeffrey Goodman's *American Genesis*." *Bulletin of the Archaeological Society of Connecticut* 45:89–92.

——. 1983b. "American Disingenuous: Goodman's *American Genesis*—A New Chapter in Cult Archaeology." *The Skeptical Inquirer* 7(4):36–48.

Gibbons, A. 1993. "Geneticists Trace the DNA Trail of the First Americans." *Science* 259:312–313.

Goodman, Jeffrey. 1977. *Psychic Archaeology: Time Machine to the Past*. New York: Berkley.

——. 1981. *American Genesis*. New York: Berkley.

Grobsmith, Elizabeth. 1997. "Growing up on Deloria: The Impact of His Work on a New Generation of Anthropologists." In *Indians and Anthropologists: Vine Deloria Jr. and the Critique of Anthropology*. T. Biolsi and L. J. Zimmerman, eds. Pp. 35–49. Tucson: University of Arizona Press.

Haederle, Michael. 1997. "Burying the Past." *American Archaeology* 1(3):14–18.

Hanke, L. 1937. "Pope Paul III and the American Indians." *Harvard Theological Review* 30:65–102.

Johnson, George. 1996. "Indian Tribes' Creationists Thwart Archaeologists." *New York Times*. Pp. C1, C13. October 22.

Kluth, Rose, and Kathy Munnell. 1997. "The Integration of Tradition and Scientific Knowledge on the Leech Lake Reservation." In *Native Americans and Archaeologists: Stepping Stones to Common Ground*. N. Swindler, K. E. Dongoske, R. Anyon, and A. S. Downer, eds. Pp. 112–119. Walnut Creek, California: Altamira.

Lepper, B. T. 1996. "Hidden History, Hidden Agenda. A Review of Hidden History of the Human Race." *Skeptic*, Vol. 4, No. 1: 98–100.

Lieberman, Leonard, and Rodney C. Kirk. 1996. "The Trial Is Over: Religious Voices for Evolution and the 'Fairness' Doctrine." *Creation/Evolution* 16(2):1–9.

Lippert, Dorothy. 1997. "In Front of the Mirror: Native Americans and Academic Archaeology." In *Native Americans and Archaeologists: Stepping Stones to Common Ground*. N. Swindler, K. E. Dongoske, R. Anyon, and A. S. Downer, eds. Pp. 120–127. Walnut Creek, California: Altamira.

McBride, Kevin. 1990. "The Historical Archaeology of the Mashantucket Pequots, 1637–1900." In *The Pequots in Southern New England: The Fall and Rise of an American Indian Nation*. L. M. Hauptman and J. D. Wherry, eds. Pp. 96–116. Norman: University of Oklahoma Press.

McGuire, Randall. 1997. "Why Have Archaeologists Thought the Real Indians Were Dead and What Can We Do About It?" In *Indians and Anthropologists: Vine Deloria Jr. and the Critique of Anthropology*. T. Biolsi and L. J. Zimmerman, eds. Pp. 63–91. Tucson: University of Arizona Press.

Meighan, Clement W. 1994. "Burying American Archaeology." *Archaeology* 47(6):64, 66, 68.

Schneider, Alan L. 1996. "Recent NAGPRA Developments." *Current Research in the Pleistocene* 13:9.

Shermer, Michael. 1997. *Why People Believe Weird Things*. New York: W. H. Freeman.

Silverberg, Robert. 1989. *The Moundbuilders*. Athens: Ohio University Press.

Stone, Anne C., and Mark Stoneking. 1993. "Ancient DNA From a Pre-Columbian Amerindian Population." *American Journal of Physical Anthropology* 92:463–471.

Swindler, Nina, Kurt E. Dongoske, Roger Anyon, and Alan S. Downer, eds. 1997. *Native Americans and Archaeologists: Stepping Stones to Common Ground*. Walnut Creek, California: Altamira Press.

Turner, Christy G. 1987. "The Tell-Tale Teeth." *Natural History*. January, 6–10.

Whittaker, John C. 1997. "Red Power Finds Creationism." *Skeptical Inquirer* 21(1):47–50.

Zimmerman, Larry J. 1994. "Sharing Control of the Past." *Archaeology* 47(6):65, 67, 68.

——. 1997. "Anthropology and Responses to the Reburial Issue." In *Indians and Anthropologists: Vine Deloria Jr. and the Critique of Anthropology*. T. Biolsi and L. J. Zimmerman, eds. Pp. 92–112. Tucson: University of Arizona Press.

Pseudoarchaeology

Precolumbian Discoverers of America as a Test Case

RONALD FRITZE

Who discovered America? It seems like an innocuous question. We all know that Columbus "discovered" America, in the sense that Europeans first heard about a New World through him. And we all also know that the Indians were here first, and thus they "discovered" America before anyone, if one considers migrating peoples discoverers.

A 1992 CNN poll, however, revealed that only 20% of Americans thought that Columbus was the first to discover America. An overwhelming majority of the respondents (70%) thought that other people had preceded Columbus in reaching the Americas, while 10% did not know. The problem is that a question which simply asks—who first discovered America?—is badly posed. Among that 70% of people who deny Columbus's priority in the discovery of the Americas are undoubtedly many people who possess a sophisticated understanding of the pre-Columbian history of the Americas. They are right. Columbus was not first. The prehistoric hunters who were the ancestors of the Native Americans and crossed the Bering Land Bridge some 15,000 years ago were the true discoverers of the Americas. Furthermore, Leif Ericsson and other Norse seafarers reached the Americas in the decades after 1000 CE (Common Era). The testimony of the Norse sagas has been confirmed by the discovery of a genuine Norse archaeological site at L'Anse aux Meadows on Newfoundland which may have even been Leif Ericsson's own camp.

Unfortunately many other people who deny the priority of Columbus are not thinking of either the prehistoric wanders who crossed the Bering Land Bridge or Leif Ericsson. Instead, they credit the first discovery of the Americas to various peoples from the ancient and medieval eras, including: Egyptians, Phoenicians, Africans, Trojans, Carthaginians, Romans, Arabs, Irish, Welsh, Germans, Poles, and various groups of Jews such as the wandering Hebrews, one or more of the Ten Lost Tribes, and refugees from the Bar Kokhba revolt. All of these people have been proposed as having crossed the Atlantic Ocean well before 1492. On the other side of the world various Chinese, Japanese, Hindu, Polynesian, and Mongol explorers, and travellers along with a lost fleet of Alexander the Great, all supposedly crossed the Pacific and found the Americas prior to Columbus.

Numerous books and articles have been published which advocate one or more of these dubious theories of pre-Columbian contacts between the Old World and the Americas. In 1990 the Foundation for Ancient Research and Mormon Studies published *Pre-Columbian Contact with the Americas across the Oceans: An Annotated Bibliography*, edited by John L. Sorenson and Martin

Raish. This massive two volume work lists 5,613 items and is not exhaustive. New works are being published all the time. Sadly, the vast majority of these works are poor pieces of scholarship in which the same errors of method and fact keep appearing again and again, year after year. It is a situation that professional anthropologists, archaeologists, and historians all find to be quite discouraging. Furthermore, these professional scholars often find their own writings and opinions rejected and disdained by these advocates of various pseudo-histories of the pre-Columbian Americas. The distinguished anthropologist Robert Wauchope described the situation as follows:

> Lay writers on these subjects [pre-Columbian contacts] have one great bias in common: they all scorn, ridicule, and complain bitterly about the professional anthropologists of American museums and universities, whom they regard variously as stupid, stubborn, hopelessly conservative, and very frequently plain dishonest.

It is a claim all too familiar to skeptics, who are frequently told by pseudoscientists that those who oppose them are ignorant or fraudulent. At the same time, these very same people profess to be following the strictest scholarly standards in their own work. That claim is not true. The following is a survey of the types of errors committed by the adherents of various pre-Columbian contact theories. While it covers most of the main ones, it is by no means comprehensive, let alone exhaustive. (See my book *Legend and Lore of the Americas before 1492*.)

Diffusionism Made Simple

1. *Diffusionism and Hyper-Diffusionism.* Diffusionism is an anthropological concept that seeks to explain cultural change on the basis of unilateral or reciprocal borrowing between different cultural groups that occurs as a result of trade, migration, or conquest. All theories that explain the rise of higher civilizations and their various cultural traits primarily on the basis of supposed contacts with the Old World are inherently diffusionist.

Anthropologists universally accept the phenomenon of diffusion as a partial explanation for cultural change. Some advocates of diffusionism, however, have been extreme in their claims about the extent of cultural exchanges between different societies. As a result they have been labeled hyper-diffusionists. Hyper-diffusionists deny that parallel evolution or independent invention of tools or ideas took place to any great extent at all throughout prehistory. They claim that humans were remarkably uninventive and that history never repeats itself. During the early 20th century, the British anthropologist W. J. Perry and the anatomist Grafton Elliot Smith took hyper-diffusionist theory to its ultimate extreme by tracing the origins of all higher civilizations throughout the world back to one source—ancient Egypt. Both men wrote numerous books and articles postulating the influence of ancient Egyptian culture on various societies throughout the world. Though hyper-diffusionist theories never dominated anthropological and archaeological thinking, moderate diffusionism did in the early 20th century. Therefore, it is not surprising that various fringe theories postulating visits to the New World by one or another group from the Old World (e.g., the Ten Lost Tribes of Israel, Mongols) found support in the rise of diffusionist concepts. After all, Grafton Elliot Smith's theory that Egypt was the source of all other ancient civilizations was simply a somewhat more restrained version of Augustus Le Plongeon's earlier theories about the ancient Maya being the mother culture of world civilization including the Egyptians.

The development of radiocarbon dating after 1946, and its calibration using correlations with dendrochronology (tree-ring dating) during the 1960s, completely undermined the hyper-diffusionist reconstructions of prehistory. These techniques revealed that cultures once thought to be the beneficiaries of cultural diffusion from ancient Egypt were actually as old or older than the oldest Egyptians. Archaeological thinking was revolutionized. The independent invention of various cultural traits had obviously taken place far more frequently than diffusionists had supposed. But hyper-diffusionists have refused to give up and continue to revive the same flawed evidence, demonstrating that they are really doing pseudohistory, not scientific history.

2. *Pyramids and Statues.* Egypt is famous for its pyramids but so is Central America with its great pyramids at Teotihuacán, Chichén Itzá, and other places. A casual observer might easily conclude that the ancient Egyptians and Americans were in contact because these great structures look so much alike. Indeed, the general similarity of the pyramids, and the "negroid-like" features of the Olmec statues of Mexico, have led extreme Afrocentrists to conclude that black Africans (they also claim the Egyptians were all black) were the first to discover America. Unfortunately two basic problems make any Egyptian-American contacts impossible. The first objection is chronology. Many centuries separated the Pyramid Age of Egypt from the time when the pyramids of Teotihuacán and Chichén Itzá were constructed. Second, while the form of the pyramids may be similar, the functions are totally different. Egyptian pyramids primarily served as tombs while the American pyramids were temples. Furthermore, archaeological research has reconstructed the independent evolution of the pyramids in both regions, leaving no room for diffusionist explanations. Finally, while features on Olmec statues do indeed resemble those of African peoples, they also look similar to those of native Americans. What one "sees" in a statue, however, is hardly historical evidence of origin, since one can easily see what one wants or expects to see, especially in such generalized forms as artwork.

3. *Supposed Pre-Columbian Diffusion of Plants.* If a cultivated plant of Old World origin could be traced to the Americas before 1492 or vice versa, it would be strong evidence for human contact between the two hemispheres. Many such claims are associated with cotton, maize, and the sweet potato, but they have proven in most cases to be fallacious.

There are over 20 species of cotton of which four are cultivated for their fibers. Two of the cultivated species are *Gossypium arboreum* and *Gossypium herbaceum*, which have 13 chromosomes in their cells and are known as the Old World cottons. The other two species, *Gossypium hirsutum* and *Gossypium bardadense*, possess 26 chromosomes and are known as the New World cottons. Genetically, the two cultivated New World cottons are hybrids that contain the 13 chromosomes of another wild species of New World cotton and the 13 chromosomes of the cultivated Old World cottons. The wild New World cottons are not capable of producing useful fibers. But when these two sets of chromosomes are combined, a cotton plant is created that produces lush clumps of useable fibers. Obviously somehow and sometime in the past the cultivated Old World cottons came into contact with the wild New World cottons and the result was the hybrid, cultivated cottons of the New World. The mystery is whether this process occurred naturally or was assisted by humans.

The creation of the cultivated New World cottons definitely took place a long time ago. Archaeologists have found remains of cotton at Mohenjo-Daro in the Indus River valley dating from 3,000 BCE. In the Americas, cotton fabrics dating from 2,000–3,000 BCE have been recovered from archaeological sites at the Tehuacán Valley in Mexico. Obviously the creation of

Gossypium hirsutum and *Gossypium bardadense* took place in the distant past. So distant, in fact, that human assistance by means of transoceanic contact between the Old World and the Americas seems very unlikely. Instead, natural means seem to have produced the cultivated New World cottons. Scholars have developed two possibilities for how this process occurred. First, they suggest that the cultivated Old World cottons *Gossypium arboreum* and *Gossypium herbaceum* had grown in the Americas at one time but became extinct sometime before 1492. No archaeological evidence has yet been found to support this theory. Second, they suggest that the unopened cotton bolls of the Old World cottons are capable of floating across the oceans. The prolonged exposure to salt water will not always destroy the seeds' ability to germinate successfully. Either of these scenarios brings Old World cottons into contact with wild New World cottons so that hybridization can take place. Neither depends on human travellers to carry the seeds.

Maize, or corn as it is more commonly known in North America, is almost universally accepted by the scholarly world to have originated in ancient America and later spread throughout the world after Christopher Columbus's voyage of 1492. At the same time, many diffusionist writers have suggested that maize actually originated in Asia or that it was of American origin but travelled to Africa, Asia, and Europe before 1492, thus indicating the existence of pre-Columbian contacts between the Americas and the Old World. George F. Carter, the distinguished geographer, has made such claims for pre-Columbian maize in China. Extensive research into the voluminous and detailed botanical literature of pre-Columbian China, however, has failed to reveal any evidence of the cultivation of maize before the early 16th century. The archaeological and historical record for South Asia also has provided no indication of the existence of maize in that region prior to 1492. The same

observation applies to Europe where maize first received notice in 1532 in a herbal written by Jerome Buck. From that point onward, maize appeared regularly on the pages of European herbals and botanical works from the 16th century. No such mentions occurred in European botanical works written during the 14th and 15th centuries. This omission would be highly suspicious if maize had already reached Europe before 1492, which it apparently did not do. The literature concerning pre-Columbian maize in Africa is extensive, although the chief exponent of that theory is the South African anthropologist M. D. W. Jeffreys. Jeffreys believes that Arabic–Black African contacts with the Americas took place about 900 CE and after. But as Paul Mangelsdorf, the leading authority on the evolution and history of maize/corn, has suggested, the ambiguities in the terminologies used by Jeffreys' historical sources appear to have caused a confusion between maize and the similar sorghums that did grow in pre-Columbian Africa.

Mangelsdorf has also pointed out that the most telling evidence for the post-Columbian introduction of maize into the Old World is the total absence of pre-Columbian corn cobs outside of the western hemisphere. Pre-Columbian corn cobs are very commonly found in archaeological sites throughout the Americas. They survive readily under many climates and conditions, but so far none that can be convincingly dated to before 1492 have been found in the Old World. Maize cannot be cited as evidence that pre-Columbian contacts took place between the Old World and the Americas because no pre-Columbian maize appears to have existed in the Old World.

There are two divergent claims regarding the sweet potato as evidence for pre-Columbian contact between the Americas and the Old World. One theory is that the sweet potato originated in Africa and was carried to the Americas. The other places the origin of the sweet potato in the Americas but claims that it was carried into Polynesia during the era before European contact.

The sweet potato (*Ipomoea batatas*) is considered by the vast majority of scholars to be a native of the Americas. It is a member of the morning glory family of plants, and research indicates that it evolved from a wild plant in tropical Central America with the scientific name of *Ipomoea trifida*. In 1954, the botanist Elmer Drew Merrill speculated about a possible African origin for the sweet potato, although other botanists have either rejected his idea as unfounded or ignored it. That has not stopped some diffusionist writers from occasionally using Merrill's theory of an African origin for the sweet potato to bolster their own ideas about African voyages to pre-Columbian America. It should be remembered, however, that the botanical and archaeological evidence overwhelmingly puts the original home of the sweet potato in the Americas.

Except for a few Spanish landings in the 16th century, sustained European contact with Polynesia began in the 18th century with Jacob Roggeveen's discovery of Easter Island in 1722, and Captain James Cook's visits to the Hawaiian Islands in 1778 and New Zealand in 1769. When the Europeans arrived, the natives of these islands were all cultivating the sweet potato. Obviously the plant came from the Americas, but how and when did it get to Polynesia? Some people have suggested that a natural transfer occurred in which a sweet potato seed or tuber floated from the Americas to the various Polynesian islands by accident. Most experts, however, feel that the sweet potato's seeds or tubers were not capable of floating such vast distances across the Pacific Ocean. Furthermore, prolonged exposure to salt water would also destroy the fertility of the seeds and tubers. As a result, the presence of sweet potatoes in Polynesia would seem to indicate that Polynesian-American contacts similar to Thor Heyerdahl's *Kon Tiki* voyage occurred during the pre-Columbian era.

Besides the physical presence of the sweet potato in Polynesia, supporters of Polynesian-American contacts also cite linguistic evidence. They claim that in the Lima region of Peru, the native Quechua word for sweet potato is *kumar* or *kumal*. The Polynesians know the sweet potato by variations of these Quechua words so that it is called *uwala* in Hawaii, *kumara* in New Zealand and Easter Island, *umara* in Tahiti, and *unala* in Samoa. Unfortunately, this impressive linguistic evidence is inaccurate. *Kumar* or *kumal* was not the Quechua word for sweet potato. In reality, the Quechua word for sweet potato is *apichu*. Kumar does not refer to sweet potato anywhere along the coastal region of Peru. So, the best linguistic evidence does not support the occurrence of Polynesian-American contacts.

Donald D. Brand, a geographer from the University of Texas, has advanced a subtle theory that claims that the spread of the sweet potato occurred entirely during the post-Columbian times. According to his scenario, Spanish settlers carried the sweet potato home to Spain. From there it reached Portugal in 1500. The Portuguese then carried it to their trading stations in India before 1505. From there Asian traders—Persians, Arabs, and Hindus—took the sweet potato into the Moluccas, or the Spice Islands. At that point, the sweet potato entered a trading network connected to Melanesia. After spreading quickly across these islands, the sweet potato then reached Polynesia before any Europeans set foot on those islands.

Flawed Methodologies

1. *The Wordlist Game.* In 1846 the future historian Francis Parkman made the following observation while travelling on the great plains:

The Indians raised in concert their cries of lamentation over the corpse, and among [which was] . . . clearly distinguished those strange sounds resembling the word "Hallelujah," which together with some other accidental coincidences, has given rise to the absurd theory that the Indians are descended from the ten lost tribes of Israel.

What seemed an "accidental coincidence" or "absurd" to Parkman, however, has seemed to be sound evidence to many, more credulous theorists of pre-Columbian contacts between the Americas and the Old World. Algonquins and Irish, Maya and Egyptians, or Peruvians and Polynesians are among the groups for which fallacious wordlists have been compiled. Countless other lists of similar sounding words with similar meanings between one Native American language and another Old World language have appeared to prove various theories of pre-Columbian contacts.

Unfortunately the compiling of such wordlists is an overly simplistic form of comparative linguistics. Linguistic scholars consider the study of grammar to be the more reliable way to make comparisons between different but possibly related languages. Grammatical structures tend to change slowly. In comparison, the words used in any language change over time, often quite rapidly. If two languages contained significant numbers of words borrowed from each other, it would indicate a fairly recent contact. Otherwise, wordlists are fairly useless as evidence of contact in the more distant past.

It is possible to compile lists of similar sounding words with similar meanings for every language in the world with every other language in the world. These lists can be larger or smaller depending on how generously one allows the words to sound alike or have similar meanings. In the end, however, all these lists really prove is that there are a limited number of sounds (phonemes) or combinations of sounds that human beings can make to form words. That number may be a large one but when compared to the vastly larger number of words in all the languages of the world that exist or have existed, there will be many cases where the same sounds have roughly the same meaning in two different languages even though there are no historical connections between those two languages. The similarity is not merely a coincidence but one that has a high probability of happening one way or another. Truly significant connections between words in different languages can only be determined by studying the etymology (the changing history of a word's usage) of the individual words. When proper linguistic methods are applied to the problem of pre-Columbian contacts between the Americas and the Old World they invariably show that nothing significant took place.

2. *Inscription Mania and Illegitimate Epigraphy.* Epigraphy is the study of inscriptions left by ancient peoples. It is one of the major sources of information that historians use to study the ancient Mediterranean world. Various ancient cultures in Central America, notably the Maya, also produced large numbers of inscriptions of use to epigraphers. Outside of Central America, the various cultures of Native Americans did not possess systems of writing and so would have left no inscriptions for epigraphers. Recently, however, the Harvard marine biologist and amateur archaeologist Barry Fell has theorized that various ancient Celtic peoples and other groups of Mediterranean people colonized North America in the pre-Christian era. He claims that numerous inscriptions in the ancient Celtic script called Ogam are scattered throughout New England and other regions. He and his supporters are constantly on the lookout for such inscriptions and they claim to have been quite successful. The problem is that Ogam script basically consists of combinations of straight lines. So what Fell and his supporters claim is an ancient

Celtic inscription looks like natural scratching and wear on rocks to mainstream archaeologists. Fell's case is further compromised by his regarding such proven archaeological frauds as the Davenport Tablets as a genuine artifact left by his "ancient colonists." Basically Fell and other amateur epigraphers are guilty of seeing what they want to see among the weathered rocks of New England. Their unquestioning belief in the existence of these pseudo-inscriptions has been labeled "inscription mania" by professional archaeologists.

3. *The Game: Patolli-Pachesi Parallels.* A frequently discussed and superficially compelling evidence for pre-Columbian contacts between Asia and America is the similarities between the Aztec game of patolli and the Hindu game of pachesi. In both games the players move pieces around boards with cross-shaped tracks divided into segments. The number of moves a piece can make is determined by throwing lots; the Hindus used cowrie shells while the Aztecs used beans. Similarities between these and other games have been noted as early as 1724. Later in 1879 the great English anthropologist E. B. Tylor (1832–1917) wrote a paper suggesting that patolli has actually been derived from pachesi as a result of ancient contacts between Asia and the Americas. Tylor added the authority of probability to his argument in 1896 and stated that it was highly improbable that two such similar games could have been invented independently.

Tylor's contemporaries, the American scholars Stewart Culin and Daniel Brinton, rejected his conclusion that patolli came to ancient America as a result of cultural diffusion from Asia. They stressed that it was independently invented in the Americas without any Asian influences and went on to cite evidence of geographical distribution and variations to bolster their contention. On the other hand, in the next generation of scholars A. L. Kroeber (1876–1960), the doyen of American anthropology, supported Tylor's conclusions for many years although not because of any particularly sound reasons.

Some anthropologists have developed a theory of limited possibilities to explain similarities between different cultures as an alternative to diffusion. Basically, this theory states that the number of cultural choices may not be large in some cases. Seemingly complex and similar institutions and artifacts could develop independently because the probabilities against it happening are not all that great. In the case of patolli and pachesi, the dice or lots must have at least two flat sides to be functional, while the cross shape of the board is really quite a common and universal shape. Furthermore, with cultures all over the world engaged in gaming, it is not surprising for similar games to appear independently. The anthropologist John Charles Erasmus has cautioned against the facile calculating of possibilities or probabilities for the development of similar cultural traits. Large numbers of people at all times and all over the world are engaged in the process of cultural evolution. That variable, however, is seldom taken into consideration when the probabilities of independent invention are discussed. Furthermore, patolli is the only aspect of Aztec culture that shows any indication of possible Hindu contact. The absence of other Mexican cultural traits of probable Hindu origin is another strong evidence against any pre-Columbian contacts between Mexico and India.

4. *Coin Finds.* Over the years, 41 documented reports have appeared of Old World coins with pre-Columbian dates being found in the Americas, particularly North America. There may be others. These finds have been used to argue for pre-Columbian visits by Canaanites, Phoenicians, Hebrews, Greeks, Romans, and Norse sailors although so far only the Norse find has managed to stand up to scholarly scrutiny.

Lucio Marineo Siculo (1460–1533), a somewhat credulous Italian humanist, in 1533 reported the finding of a Roman coin from the time of Caesar Augustus in a gold mine in Panama. He concluded that the presence of this coin proved that the Romans had reached the Americas before the Spanish. Gonzalo Fernandez d Oviedo y Valdes touched on Siculo's story in his *Historia general y natural de las Indias* of 1535 and showed that it was ridiculous.

Significantly, no one found any more pre-Columbian coins in the Americas until several Roman coins from the imperial era were found in the Fayetteville area of Tennessee between 1818 and 1823. The early archaeologist Caleb Atwater was immediately skeptical and suspected that the coins were deliberate plants. The Tennessee antiquarian John Haywood, however, considered the find to be authentic. It is interesting that even Haywood reported that after a Mr. Colter, a man known to possess Roman coins, left Tennessee for Alabama in 1823 that no more coins have ever been found in Tennessee. Modern archaeologists generally agree with Atwater's original assessment and think that the Tennessee coins were part of a hoax.

Only one other documented coin find took place in the 19th century. It occurred in 1880 on an Illinois farm and involved the finding of a Seleucid Greek coin from c. 173–64 BCE. Otherwise all of the remaining 32 coin finds took place in the 20th century, and of that number, 24 were found after 1945. With the exception of the Norse penny found in Maine, all of these coins appear to have been brought to the Americas after 1492. Some of the coins have actually turned out to be forgeries such as the three Bar Kokhba coins found at various places in Kentucky in 1932, 1952, and 1967.

Other genuine ancient coins have been located in archaeological situations that indicate they may be losses from modern collections rather than remains from the distant past. Many coins have been found on the surface of the soil rather than having been dug up. The most common natural tendency for a coin on the ground would be slowly to sink down into the soil rather than to work its way up to the surface after it was buried. It is estimated that some one million Roman coins are in the coin collections of the late 20th century United States. Most of those were brought back from Europe after World War II. Many of these Roman coins are only worth $10.00 or less and so are not looked after all that carefully. The possibility of accidental losses is quite real, and that appears to be what has happened in most of these 20th century finds of pre-Columbian coins.

Jeremiah F. Epstein's 1980 study of coin finds basically concluded that none of them provide legitimate evidence for pre-Columbian contacts. One exception to his conclusion, however, is the Norse penny from the reign of Olav Kyrre (1066–1093) of Norway found in Maine in 1957. Tests have established that it is genuine. But since no one now denies that the medieval Norse reached Newfoundland, it is not implausible that they visited Maine as well.

Fake Artifacts

1. *Kensington Rune Stone.* This famous but fraudulent Norse artifact was first discovered in Minnesota in 1898 and still has supporters of its authenticity in spite of considerable debunking scholarship to the contrary.

In 1898, Olof Ohman "discovered" the Kensington Rune Stone while clearing trees from his farm in Douglas County, near the town of Kensington, Minnesota. It contained an inscription in runic characters, the ancient alphabet of Scandinavia. Unfortunately, the physical appearance of the inscription belied its supposed antiquity; e.g., its cuts showed none of the weathering associated with a stone carving over 300 years old. It has even been suggested that the inscription was added after Ohman first unearthed the stone.

The Rune Stone's inscription told of a party of Norse making its way through the wilderness during 1362 and suffering the loss of 10 of its members from attacks by hostile Indians. Such a find would have been of immense interest to the Scandinavian immigrant community of the Upper Midwest. In 1898 they were anxious to find proof of Norse precedence over Christopher Columbus in the European discovery of America. The World Columbian Exposition at Chicago during the 1890s had aroused their ethnic ire. Scandinavian Americans wanted to believe that the Kensington Rune Stone was authentic so local support was strong. The scholarly reception of the Kensington Rune Stone, however, was negative from the start on the basis of anachronistic usages of both runic characters and Norse words. Eventually enthusiasm for the Rune Stone stalled and Ohman took it back to his farm where he used it as a steppingstone. True believers in the Scandinavian community, however, continued to claim the Kensington Rune Stone was genuine.

In 1907 Hjalmar R. Holand, a young researcher, came to Douglas County to gather material on the Norwegian immigration to the United States. During his researches, the locals told him about Ohman's rune stone and a curious Holand went to see it. Rejecting earlier scholarly opinion, Holand decided it was a true Norse artifact and Ohman even gave it to him. Starting in 1908, for the rest of his life, Holand attempted to prove that the Kensington Rune Stone was really a medieval Norse inscription. He even got the Minnesota Historical Society so interested that when they issued a report on the stone's authenticity, they ignored additional scholarly opinions to the contrary and pronounced it genuine. Efforts by Holand in 1911 to secure favorable judgments from European scholars met with failure as they all considered the stone to be a hoax. But

Holand remained undaunted. In 1932 he published his first book, *The Kensington Stone*, which defended the stone's authenticity. The stone travelled to the Smithsonian Institute in 1948 for further scholarly investigation which again produced negative results. Holand, however, continued to believe that the Kensington Rune Stone was a true medieval Norse artifact.

The 1950s saw the beginning of a wave of scholarly publications denying the authenticity of the Kensington Rune Stone. The two most devastating attacks came from books by experts on Norse studies—Erik Wahlgren in 1958 and Theodore C. Blegen in 1968. Their studies convincingly showed that the Kensington Rune Stone was a fake. Blegen even suggests how Olof Ohman may have collaborated with his neighbor Sven Fogelbad to produce the inscription. None of this scholarly activity has managed to stop some true believers from continuing to have faith in the Kensington Rune Stone. For the vast majority of historians and archaeologists, the Kensington Rune Stone is no more than one of the most persistent hoaxes in the history of American archaeology.

2. *Paraiba Stone.* In 1872, the most enigmatic of the supposed Phoenician artifacts in the Americas came to light—the Paraiba Stone. A man named Joaquim Alves da Costa claimed to have found, "near the Paraiba" river, a broken stone which had an inscription in a strange alphabet carved on it. After transcribing the inscription, Costa sent the copy to Rio de Janeiro for study. But Brazil had no experts in ancient semitic languages. Instead the conscientious naturalist Ladislau Netto took up the assignment, learned Hebrew, and ultimately determined that the writing on the stone was Phoenician and then translated it. His translation described how 10 Phoenician ships were blown by storms to the coast of Brazil in 534 BCE. Immediately the French scholar Ernest Renan attacked the Paraiba inscription as a fake and others soon joined him. By 1885 the hapless Netto felt compelled to

publish a retraction of his original conclusions and even suggested five possible suspects who might have engineered the hoax. Meanwhile Costa disappeared with the stone and no accredited scholar ever saw it first hand. Even the original location of the find was in great doubt since Brazil had two different Paraiba regions. During the 1960s, Cyrus Gordon, a professor of semitic languages and an ardent diffusionist, revived the Paraiba Stone's claims to authenticity. Basically, Gordon had asserted that the Paraiba inscription contains Phoenician grammatical constructions that were unknown in 1872. Other equally qualified specialists in semitic languages disagree with his conclusions and continue to declare the Paraiba Stone to be a hoax. That judgment is the opinion of archaeologists and prehistorians in general.

Historical Fallacies

1. *Portuguese Policy of Secrecy or Silence.* This controversial historical thesis, formulated in the first quarter of the 20th century by various historians, primarily Portuguese, states that Portugal made many voyages and discoveries in the Atlantic Ocean, including the discovery of the Americas sometime before 1492, but chose to keep those discoveries secret.

Before the 19th century, the historical record contains many gaps and breaks. This condition certainly applies to the surviving records from the Great Age of Discovery. None of the original logs for Christopher Columbus's four voyages survived, although a partial transcript exists for the first voyage. John Cabot's voyages to North America in 1497 are practically without any contemporary documentation and the same situation applies to Bartolomeu Dias's discovery in 1487 of the Cape of Good Hope. Such losses of primary sources

are tragic but all too common and they usually occur quite innocently as the result of accidents or neglect. Some historians, however, have questioned whether the gaps in the Portuguese records are all that random. They suggest that some design or policy may lie behind the disappearance of some documents.

The thesis of a deliberate and systematic Portuguese government policy of secrecy concerning overseas exploration is a product of 20th-century historians. Jaime Cortesao, a Portuguese historian, first formulated the thesis in 1924. He contended that the surviving Portuguese chronicles about overseas explorations show definite signs of truncation and censorship.

If one is inclined to believe Cortesao, quite a lot of information was suppressed, including a Portuguese discovery of America prior to 1448. Jaime Cortesao was not alone in his support for the existence of a policy of secrecy. In Portugal the thesis has become a historical orthodoxy and a pillar of national pride. School textbooks at all levels teach it as fact. Lisbon's city government has even decorated its Avenida de Liberdade with a mosaic inscription which reads "Descoberta da America 1472 Joao Vaz Corte-Real Descobridor da America."

Outside of Portugal, historians, including Samuel Eliot Morison, generally reject Cortesao's thesis of a policy of secrecy and its various claims of monumental but previously uncredited Portuguese achievements during the 15th century. Dissent exists even in the Portuguese historical community where the respected historian Duarte Liete attacked Cortesao's theory as early as 1936. But in spite of all the controversy, the thesis of a Portuguese policy of secrecy still possesses enthusiastic supporters, and so continues to attract equally determined opponents.

The basic complaint of skeptical historians concerning the policy of secrecy is the almost complete absence of solid evidence for its existence. Historians admit that monarchs and countries throughout history have attempted to protect their overseas commerce by maintaining secrecy about the how and the where of their sources. But ultimately these efforts have failed. Supporters of the policy of secrecy reply that the lack of evidence is in itself evidence of the existence of a policy of secrecy that was extremely effective. Of course, their opponents, particularly Samuel Eliot Morison, find such an argument both circular and ridiculous. Ultimately Morison feels that Cortesao's thesis requires the Portuguese to maintain their secrets apparently for the sake of secrecy alone and often against their own best interests. He rightly argues that the Portuguese government's pursuit of a policy of secrecy needs to make sense and be of benefit to the national interests. If Portugal already knew about the Americas before 1492, why did Joao II abdicate virtually all of that new land to Spain in the Treaty of Tordesillas?

Another argument repeatedly brought to bear against the existence of such a policy of secrecy is the well-documented and sustained participation of a substantial number of foreigners in Portugal's overseas explorations. Martin Behaim of Germany and Christopher Columbus of Genoa are simply the best known of a host of foreigners who served in Portugal's overseas ventures. With so many foreigners involved in Portugal's overseas enterprises, it would have been impossible to keep important discoveries a secret. Details of Portugal's jealously guarded African trade leaked out with amazing rapidity. Furthermore, little attempt was made to keep secret Bartolomeu Dias's discovery of the Cape of Good Hope in 1487 or Vasco da Gama's voyage to India in 1497. Why did the Portuguese let these important discoveries become public knowledge if they had such an effective policy of secrecy? Not surprisingly, outside of Portugal, the thesis of the policy of secrecy and its accompanying suppression of information about various discoveries, most notably a pre-Columbian discovery of America, has found little support among historians.

2. *White God Legends.* This group of Native American myths purportedly describes vague memories of pre-Columbian visitors from the Old World. Most of these legends supposedly relate to peoples from the ancient Mediterranean or Western European cultures. Some adherents of pre-Columbian contacts between the Old World and the Americas claim that these same legends actually refer to visitors from Africa or China, which would more accurately make them yellow or black god legends.

The Native American gods commonly identified as white gods are Quetzalcoatl, Kukulcan, Itzamna, Votan, Viracocha, and Sume. According to various popular writers, all of these deities were bearded, white-skinned, departed from the Americas with a promise to return, and established civilization and higher humanitarian values during the time they ruled over the various indigenous tribes and kingdoms. It is claimed that these legends of white gods are almost universal among the aboriginal peoples of both North and South America. These legends supposedly aided the Spanish conquest of the Aztecs, the Incas, the Mayas, the Chibchas, and various other peoples since they mistakenly took the Spanish conquistadors to be their returning white gods.

Although there were many supposed white gods among the various groups of Native Americans, there are even more candidates to serve as the inspiration for the white god legends among the supposed pre-Columbian visitors to the Americas. The list includes St. Thomas, St. Brendan, Prince Madoc of Wales, and even Jesus Christ.

The problem with all of these theories is that they are not based on original and authentic Native American legends. Most of the so-called white gods are actually humans who filled the role of being culture-heroes. Like the Greek culture-hero Prometheus who brought civilizing fire to humanity, the Native American culture heroes brought the benefits of agriculture, writing, the calendar, and true religion to their peoples. Generally these gods are described as bearded but that is no proof of their being white. Native Americans can sometimes grow beards, and these beards, such as the Aztec emperor Moctezuma II's, were observed by the Spanish. The problem is that many versions of these legends have been contaminated with post-Columbian additions by the Spanish. The whiteness of these white gods is not mentioned in the most authentic versions of the culture-hero legends. Quetzalcoatl is actually described as having a black or a black and yellow striped face. It also appears that the white god's departure from and promise to return to the Americas are usually post-Columbian additions. In the case of Quetzalcoatl, some historians, such as Nigel Davies, think that the belief that Hernán Cortés was the returned Quetzalcoatl was a delusion concocted by the nervous Aztec emperor Moctezuma II. There was no general belief among the Aztecs that Quetzalcoatl would return. David Carrasco, a historian of religion, disagrees and instead claims that during its final years the Aztec empire lived in dread anticipation of Quetzalcoatl's return. But in the case of the other Native American gods—Votan, Viracocha, and Sume—the legend of the white gods was a Spanish fraud.

Other problems with linking white god legends to historic persons or peoples are chronological. Quetzalcoatl lived sometime during the years 900–1100 CE, which eliminates most of the supposed ancient pre-Columbian visitors, including Jesus Christ, as candidates for inspiring his legend. Furthermore, the white god legends, like most tales of pre-Columbian visitors to the Americas, lack a convincing foundation in the archaeological and documentary evidence. Close study of the Native American myths simply makes the white god legends seem less and less credible.

Why Pseudohistory?

Why do people continue to believe in dubious theories about pre-Columbian contacts between the Old World and the Americas? One reason is that it is a common characteristic of human nature to have a fascination with the strange and fantastic and these theories are, for the most part, very strange and utterly fantastic. They also claim to be based on lost or even suppressed knowledge which provides yet a further source of fascination. There are hints and even outright claims of some sort of conspiracy to suppress such knowledge. Ultimately pre-Columbian contact theorists and their adherents can believe that they are embattled intellectual heroes. Since it is difficult, if not impossible, to disprove a secret conspiracy (it is, in essence, a nonfalsifiable claim), adherents are fairly safe in their belief.

Sadly, there is also an element of racism inherent in many of the theories of pre-Columbian contact. The 19th-century supporters of the theory of a lost white race of moundbuilders were basically denying that the Native Americans possessed the ability to create a higher civilization. But any modern theory that attributes the fundamental development of higher civilization in the Americas to visiting Egyptians, Hebrews, Phoenicians, Romans, Africans, Chinese, Japanese, or some other ancient Old World peoples is also unfairly downplaying the manifest creativity and intelligence of the Native Americans. Such theories ignore a substantial archaeological record which fully documents the achievements of the Native Americans. Too many theorists of pre-Columbian contacts have their own racial or ethnic agenda which ignores the legitimate achievements of the pre-Columbian

Native Americans and is insensitive to the feelings of their descendants.

In spite of their logical and scholarly problems, theories about pre-Columbian contacts between the Americas and the Old World continue to thrive, while books supporting those theories are steadily proliferating. Sloppy and inappropriate methodologies and inadequate or non-existent evidence have never stood in the way of the concoction or the survival of the most preposterous theories about pre-Columbian contacts. Just in the past few years several new books concerning this realm of pseudohistory have appeared or are scheduled to appear. In 1992 two books appeared which surveyed the whole gamut of theories about pre-Columbian contacts: Patrick Huyghe, *Columbus was Last: From 200,000 B.C. to 1492, A Heretical History of Who Was First* (Hyperion), and Gunnar Thompson, *American Discovery: The Real Story* (Misty Isles Press). Apparently the various theories of pre-Columbian contacts can mutually coexist in relative peace with each other, at least in the pages of these two tomes. Meanwhile in the same year R. J. Jairazbhoy published *Rameses III: Father of Ancient America* (Karnak House) which continues his earlier efforts to establish the role of travellers from ancient Egypt in the rise of higher civilization in the Americas. Publication of two additional books is expected at any time. Ivan Van Sertima, the author of *They Came before Columbus: The African Presence in Ancient America* (Random House, 1977), is supposed to be close to publishing *African Voyages before Columbus*. Even more imminent is Jim Bailey's *Sailing to Paradise: The Discovery of America in 5,000 B.C.* (Simon & Schuster, forthcoming) which appears to extend the theories he first put forward in *The God-Kings and the Titans: The New World Ascendancy in Ancient Times* (St. Martin's, 1973). But in spite of all the hype, these books are all plowing or will be plowing the same old, tired, and infertile fields of evidence. It is truly a never ending story.

References:

Nigel Davies, *Voyagers to the New World* (1979).

Kenneth L. Feder, *Frauds, Myths, and Mysteries: Science and Pseudoscience in Archaeology* (1990).

Ronald Fritze, *Legend and Lore of the Americas before 1492.* (1993).

Robert Wauchope, *Lost Tribes and Sunken Continents: Myth and Method in the Study of American Indians* (1962).

Stephen Williams, *Fantastic Archaeology: The Wild Side of North American Prehistory* (1991).

Pseudoscience and the Paranormal

JAMES RANDI

I am in a very peculiar business. I appear on stages around the world as a conjurer. The American term for it is magician. It's not a good expression because if you look in the dictionary the strict definition of a magician is one who uses magic. And magic, at least by the definition I prefer from a leading dictionary, is the attempt to control nature by means of spells and incantations. Now, ladies and gentlemen, in my time, as you might have guessed, I have tried spells and incantations. No good. You can spell and incant all you want; the lady will still be on the couch, waiting patiently to float into the air, or will be imprisoned in the box with the saw blade descending upon her unprotected midriff, and in some danger of being severely scratched, if not worse! Spells and incantations don't work. You have to use skuldug-gery. And let me make it very clear what the magical trade—the conjuring trade—is with a precise definition. It is the approximation of the effect of a true magician using means of subterfuge and trickery.

The magician, in the American usage, is an actor playing the part of a wizard. We are entertainers. I don't think that there are many folks—but there are some out there by David Copperfield's own admission to me—who still believe that they really can do the things they purport to do. After a magical performance we've all undergone the same experience, all of us in the trade; you get people coming to you afterwards and saying: "I really enjoyed

what you did; thank you so much for coming." And you say, "Well, it's great to be here. I'm happy that you were pleased with it." Then they say, "You know, the business with the bottles that multiplied. Obviously, that's a trick. And the one where you did the thing with the rings and the ropes. That's a trick too. But the one where you told the lady what word she'd chosen out of the newspaper—that, of course, can't be a trick." I'd say, "Yes, that's a trick, too, but it's disguised as a miracle of a semi-religious nature." And they wink at you and they say, "Sure." Then they walk away and tell their friends afterwards, "Well, he won't admit it, but we all know."

There is a hunger, a very strong hunger, within us all to believe there is something more than what the laws of nature permit. I'm not just saying audiences that watch the magician. I mean within us all. We'd like to have a certain amount of fantasy in our lives, but it's a very dangerous sort of temptation to immediately assume that it must be supernatural or occult or paranormal if we don't have an explanation for it. I can tell you that in my life I've spent a great deal of time investigating and observing and carefully noting and making use of psychology. I am not a psychologist; I have no academic credentials whatsoever, so I come to you today absolutely unencumbered by any responsibilities of that nature. There is no dean who will call me on the carpet tomorrow morning and say, "You shouldn't have said that." You see, I'm in the business of giving opinions from an uninformed point of view, except from the point of view of a skeptical person who knows how people's minds work and often don't work.

Historians of science have calculated that at the current rate of scientific growth, in a certain number of years scientists will consist of every human being on earth, as well as all the animals—the donkeys, the burros, the whole thing. Well, my friend David Alexander remarked to me, in a cruel aside, that even today certain parts of certain horses have become scientists. And that is quite true; I have met many of them and though they have Ph.D.s, you'd hardly know it. I've just come back from a project that's ongoing at the moment and I've seen that principle at work. I must share with you another thing in passing. I have a theory; this is only a theory, and it is at present unproven. But observations so far tend to support its possible validity, with my advance apologies to Ph.D.s in the room. I have a theory about Ph.D.s and the granting of the degree itself. I am outside the field, not an academic, so as a curious observer I have many times seen films of, and in a couple of cases actually attended, ceremonies where Ph.D.s are created. They are created, you know. The Ph.D. itself is earned, of course, but then the person who has passed all the tests and done all the right things in the right way and has been approved doesn't become a Ph.D. until one significant moment where a roll of paper, usually with a red or a blue ribbon around it, is pressed into his or her hand. At that moment that person becomes a very special class of being known as Ph.D.

Now, I have noted at those ceremonies, and perhaps you have observed it as well, that the man who gives out those rolls of paper wears gloves. Why? Why would he want to wear gloves? Is the paper dirty? I don't think so. Is there something about that roll of paper, or perhaps the ribbon, that he doesn't want to contaminate him, and he doesn't want to touch

his skin? I'm going to postulate—just an idea—that perhaps there is a secret chemical that has been genetically engineered which is on the surface of that paper so that when the Ph.D. candidate receives that roll of paper this chemical is absorbed by the skin, goes into the bloodstream and is conducted directly to the brain. This is a very carefully engineered chemical which goes directly—please don't laugh; this is science—goes directly to the speech center of the brain and paralyzes the brain in such a way that two sentences from then on, in any given language, are no longer possible to be pronounced by that person. Those two sentences are "I don't know" and "I was wrong."

I honestly don't know about that; however, my observations of the situation are that I have never heard any Ph.D. utter either one of those sentences. I have never heard them say, "I'd like to marry a lobster" either, but that doesn't mean they can't say it. But those two sentences never seem to pass their lips.

I am being exceedingly facetious, of course. I have every respect not only for science, but for those who pursue the various disciplines of science. It takes a great deal of courage, application, study, sacrifice, and in many cases, some outrageous attacks on your integrity and your ability in order to maintain a point of view in science which may or may not be popular. I have been with many prominent scientists who have, from time to time, had to stick their professional necks out, and sometimes their necks get pretty badly beaten up in the process. It's not an easy thing to speak against what is generally accepted.

What then is generally accepted? I'm afraid, due to the media impact on our civilization, that a great number of things are easily swallowed because they are repeated so often. They are endlessly presented to the public, and eventually make their way to the academic community as well. Any number of times I have spoken to scientists who, when I ask them a critical question about some belief in some sort of parapsychological, supernatural or occult claim, have said, "You know, I hear a good deal about it and Professor so-and-so did make a statement about it. Perhaps, Professor so-and-so, based upon the small amount of data which he has presently gathered, compared to what should be gathered, in order to establish a satisfactory statistical picture, an amount of data on which conclusions could be drawn by one of the various statistical pictures available to him, has come upon conclusions that are prematurely expressed. Therefore, furthermore, and moreover, on further examination. . . ." That's the academic's reply. When they ask me, I simply say, "In my layman's non-academic opinion, I think that Professor so-and-so is not rowing with both oars in the water." It's simple, direct, and an honest expression of my opinion.

I am presently faced with a situation, again unnamed, where I am going to have to show a number of dedicated, honest, hard-working people that they have made a colossal error of judgment. I have to do this in a resounding manner, simply because to not do so could result in a great deal of personal damage, grief, and considerable heartbreak and discomfort to a great number of people who are already laboring under certain disadvantages and burdens that they did not bring upon themselves. I hate to be so mysterious about it, but it is an ongoing work of investigation. I am not often involved in that serious a situation. Usually my circumstances are more open—I am looking into an astrologer's claims or into some sort of pseudoscientific thing. But I always have to remember an experience that occurred to me.

It is easy, when faced with an apparently supernatural phenomenon, to say "I guess it's a ghost" or "It must be paranormal," or "It could be poltergeists," and we walk away from it because we can't or won't look a little further into it. Some years ago, when I lived in New Jersey my house was a sort of a wayside

stop for itinerant magicians, conjurers, mountebanks—various characters of ill repute who would come by to visit for a while. One time I came home after a couple of days away, very tired, and came in on my foster son, Alexis, who was in the kitchen helping a couple of magicians drink up the beer. I walked in and said, "Guys, I'm very, very tired; I'm going to bed. I'll see you in the morning."

I guess they carried on until late that night. I fell asleep, woke up the next morning, came staggering into the kitchen in time to see them eating up more of my groceries in the form of breakfast at this time. I sat down, got a half cup of coffee into me and straightened up the table. Alexis looked at me and said, "What's with you?" I said, "I think last night I might have actually had a classic example of the O.B.E." That's the out-of-body experience. It means that somehow you find yourself out of your body and looking down on it or from a distance. Alexis looked at me and said, "Sure. You?" I said, "Yes, I have to be honest. It appears to me as if I did undergo such an experience."

"OK, give us a description," they replied. The two magicians at the table leaned closer over their bacon and eggs and wanted to hear what I had to say. "Well, I remember waking up in the middle of the night—I couldn't get to sleep at first because I was so tired, so I turned on the television. The program went on and on and I eventually fell asleep. I remember waking up in the middle of the night, and I felt that I was spread-eagled against the ceiling of my bedroom, looking down at the bed. Alice, my black cat, was curled up in a ball in the exact center of the bed so that I had to be way over to one side. And I was, of course, trying not to disturb the cat! As I was up against the ceiling I noticed that the room was lit in sort of a grayish light. I looked down toward the television set and saw nothing but static on the screen and heard nothing but white noise. What I saw was startling. I saw myself, in bed, scrunched over to one side, a chartreuse bed-spread on it, with Alice the cat in the middle. I noted that as she opened her eyes they were green. It almost looked like two holes punched through her head. She looked at me and went, 'hmmph' and went right back to sleep."

Now that was a very strong experience for me. I really believed, from the evidence presented to me, that I had an out-of-body experience that matches the description that we've all heard about so many times. But, fortunately for me, I'm not really dead-set against having my belief structure disturbed or having new facts come in that would disturb my previous convictions. And, fortunately, I am able to tell you what actually happened. Alexis looked at me and said, "I've got two things to show you." He went to the foot of the stairs and came up with a big, transparent laundry bag. He had taken it half way down to the laundry room. He brought it all the way up the stairs, and inside noted sheets, pillowcases, and the chartreuse bedspread. He said, "That's been there since yesterday." The bedspread hadn't been on the bed last night! I dashed to the bedroom door, looked in, and the spread I used when the other one was in the laundry lay on the bed. They looked nothing alike. Alexis then called my attention to the patio, noting that he had put Alice outside yesterday afternoon because one of the magician guests was highly allergic to cats. She had remained outside, very unhappily, through the night and into this morning. She could not have been curled up in the middle of the bed last night.

It was a dream—a hallucination, if you will. I had two very good pieces of evidence that it could not have happened. That's important in that if I did not have one or both of those pieces of evidence, I would now have to say to you that, to the best of my knowledge, I had an out-of-body experience. But, all the other out-of-body experiences we hear of, we have to wonder. Those folks are not quite as skeptical about the subject as I am, in most cases. If they

don't have some convincing evidence to the contrary, what's to stop them from saying, "I'm absolutely certain I've had an out-of-body experience?" There is no other explanation for it except the possible and rather parsimonious conclusion that they were either dreaming or had a hallucination. It might have been a bad pork chop, for all we know. Please consider that carefully, and don't forget it, because it's a good example of how even the arch-skeptic could possibly have been taken in.

I have had a number of small experiences like that, including the déjà-vu type experiences that so many people have had. (I love the line from the fellow who says, "I keep having the same déjà-vu, over and over again.") But I have resisted the temptation to merely say, "Well, at last I've got proof of it." I'm highly skeptical, but what is that skepticism based on? If you're skeptical as well, have you asked yourself, "Upon what do I base my skepticism?" Are you just plain ornery? Do you just not want to go along with the status quo? Do you know some people who believe in it who are really pretty dense and you don't want to join their group?

You must have a reason, I think, for yourself and for others as to why you are skeptical. These things are not likely to be true; therefore, you need proof of them. We're not required to prove a negative; we can't do that. I can't prove telepathy doesn't exist. I remember getting a question years ago. A lady stood up in the audience and said, "Can you prove to me that ESP doesn't exist?" I said, "No, I can't." She sat down with her arms folded and replied "Ah ha." That was a victory for her. I went on to explain that I can't prove a negative. My question is, "Do you believe in it?" She said, "Absolutely." I asked if she could prove that it is so. She said, "Well, I'm quite convinced of it."

"That's not my question," I responded. "Can you prove that it is so? You're the one making the claim." We skeptics, as Michael Shermer clearly pointed out, are not in the business of debunking. If I were in the business of debunking, and I've often had that label pinned on me and I've always resented it and denied it—it means I would go into an investigation convinced that "this ain't so and I'm going to show you that it isn't." I'm not a lawyer; I don't have an advocacy position to take. I go into a situation as an investigator. To be perfectly fair, I can't prove a negative, but I go into this thing prepared to be shown. Am I prejudiced against it? Oh, yes! I have to admit that. But if you've been sitting by a chimney for 63 years on the evening of December 24 and a fat man in a red suit has never bounced down that chimney, you can say, "One hundred percent of my evidence shows me that this claim is not necessarily so. I cannot prove that it isn't, but it's not very likely to be true, based on what we know."

The Santa Claus example may seem trivial and a little inappropriate, but it is actually a good metaphor for so many paranormal and pseudoscientific claims. Another is flying reindeer. This one we can actually test. (Please don't tell the SPCA about this.) I don't really want to do the experiment, but let's walk through it as if I were doing it. It's a thought experiment. Let's select, by some randomizing process, a thousand reindeer. We'll number them and get them all together in a reindeer truck (I don't know what you put reindeer in) and take them to the top of the Empire State Building in New York. We are going to test whether or not reindeer can fly. You have your reindeer all lined up, a video-camera operator standing by, lots of pads of paper and pens at work. The time is now ten past ten in the morning. OK, first experiment. Number one reindeer, please, up to the edge. Camera going? Good. Push. Uhh, write down "no." Really NO! Number two. Push. I don't know what the result of the experiment will be; I suspect strongly what it will be, based upon my meagre knowledge of the aerodynamics of the average

reindeer, though I'm not an expert on it. But based upon previous accounts of what reindeer can and cannot do, I think we are going to end up with a pile of very unhappy and broken reindeer at the foot of the Empire State Building. And probably a couple of policemen will be standing by a squad car saying, "I don't know, but here comes another one."

What have we proven with this experiment? Have we proven that reindeer cannot fly? No, of course not. We have only shown that on this occasion, under these conditions of atmospheric pressure, temperature, radiation, at this position geographically, at this season, that these 1000 reindeer either could not or chose not to fly. (If the second is the case, then we certainly know something of the intelligence of the average reindeer.) However, we have not, and can not, prove the negative that reindeer cannot fly, technically, rationally, and philosophically speaking. People will often look at this example and say, "Well, how many reindeer would you have to test?" I'm not going to get into the statistics of the argument; I will only tell you that you cannot prove a negative. The other folks who claim that something is so are required to prove it. It is what we call the burden of proof. In this case, if it's so it's very easy to prove. Just show me one flying reindeer. Then they rationalize, saying, "Oh, no. It's only the eight tiny reindeer that live at the North Pole who can, and will, on the evening of December 24, fly to do that specific job." In that case you have to throw up your hands and say, "Well, I don't think your hypothesis is very testable." Don't spin your wheels!

Thought experiments like this one only go so far. As an example of a real experiment testing unusual claims, I just came back from Hungary where I was invited to Budapest by the Academy of Sciences. They are very concerned about the fact that now that many of these countries are freed from the burdensome and onerous yoke of Communism and have the freedom to receive all kinds of scientific information in the form of journals and lectures, nonsense comes in as well. The astrologers, the faith healers, the ESP artists, the people with the pendulums, the water dowsers—they're lined up and pouring across the border because they see a new market. The scientists of Hungary were concerned about this. A well-known member of parliament who is also a well-respected brain scientist of international repute said to me, "Mr. Randi, have you seen any of the publicity on the magnetic ladies?" I had.

In case you're not familiar with the magnetic ladies of Hungary, I will relieve you of that ignorance immediately. You may have seen a picture that made all the wire services in this country last year, of the magnetic man from (then) Leningrad. There was a picture of a middle-aged man standing like this, naked from the belt up, with a flatiron stuck here, a hammer there, nails, razor blades—all kinds of metal clinging to his body. The caption said that he attracted these things. They just jumped, willy nilly, onto his body. He was somehow magnetic. I'll bet his wristwatch was a mess! Don't bring him near your computers! I can just imagine him going through a steel door. Bam! Right into it!

Well, I took that with the proverbial grain of salt about the size of a basketball, and just put it in the scrapbook and forgot about it. But the professor asked me about the magnetic ladies of Hungary, and he said, "Their reputation is such that objects, not necessarily metallic ones, cling to their bodies with such tenacity that a strong man cannot tear them loose." Now, wait a minute! Suppose you have some instant glue, and we take a tennis ball and stick it on the lady's neck, on the side. If a strong man can't tear it off, he's going to tear her skin off—or her head! Something has to give! My scientist friend and sponsor of this trip looked at me and said, "How can they make claims like this?" I said, "Well, show me the magnetic ladies." He said that the following day, after the press conference, they were scheduled to arrive. I could hardly wait.

One of the parapsychologists had suggested that he could bring me some instrumentation for detection of their magnetism. He promised that we'd take the two ladies down to the laboratory (hand in hand, clinging to one another, no doubt). I declined to go to the laboratory because the laymen reading the report in the newspaper wouldn't understand "laboratory." What are you going to do? Put a cyclotron on her ear? No. I equipped myself with a scientific device and I went along. The device was called a compass. It's a scientific instrument and an easy way to perform the test. If a woman is magnetic, the compass is going to point right at her. The two ladies showed up. I told my friend in advance that he must understand that the claim is one thing; the event itself will often be something totally different. It won't be half as entertaining or amusing, or true, as the actual demonstration.

One lady literally did this: she took her wristwatch off her wrist and did this. [Randi put his watch on his forehead and it stays there without falling.] "How do you explain that?" she said. I looked at both ladies, who were wearing very greasy, high gloss makeup. It was obviously sticky, mixed with a little perspiration. She said, "We have no explanation for it." I said I didn't find it terribly difficult to explain.

The second lady had an even better demonstration. She took a small ceramic saucer from her purse, stuck it on her forehead, where it remained. "And how do you explain that?" she parroted the other woman. I pulled it off her forehead, and stuck it on the foreheads of the first four people standing on my right. It stuck very effectively to the foreheads of all of them! Then we tested under controlled conditions. (By the way, the compass test failed miserably; it pointed to North, obstinately refusing to point at them.) I asked for soap and water and, through the interpreter, asked the first lady if I could wash her forehead to remove the makeup and any perspiration that might be there. She informed me that if she washed her forehead it wouldn't work because water is absorbed into the skin and water and electricity, or magnetism, don't mix. She denied that that would be a satisfactory test, as did the second lady, and they left. "You've learned your first lesson in the scientific investigation of unusual claims," I told the Professor. "Don't start to give theories on how it might work until you've seen whether it meets the claims of the newspaper account, or is really something much less impressive."

To be fair to these women, I can see how that account might have ended up in a newspaper. I'm sure those ladies didn't say to the newspaper reporters, "A strong man can't pull it away from me." But a reporter is a human being and maybe his story doesn't look all that great when he writes that things cling to their bodies. Then perhaps he thinks: "Um, how about 'with such tenacity that a strong man can't pull them loose'"? Now, he has a story! What I'm saying is that the media are as much to blame for the spread of nonsense and pseudoscience as the claimants themselves. For example, a few years ago the New York Daily News, on page three where they put the "heavy news" and sensational stuff, announced that a student at Duke University had successfully in great detail described not only an aircraft accident 24 hours in advance of the event, he even gave the number of people who would be killed. He was short by only two. He even described the location of the crash in the Canary Islands. That was picked up by news services and was featured on television programs; it was on every newscast for quite some time. It was received by the press as a genuine example of prophecy, and the director of the program in which this was involved at Duke University actually made a statement that he had a sealed envelope 24 hours before in his

safe that was not touched by this gentleman until after the episode had taken place. It was allegedly torn open at that time and it contained the prediction.

To explain this phenomenon I will take you into a different world, for just a moment, so you will understand something. Magicians know how this young man could very easily have done this trick. I won't go into all the details; you can imagine some of them yourself. But the effect is exactly as described—a sealed signed envelope, put into a safe, later carefully opened. Inside you either find a tape cassette or a sealed letter with all kinds of security on it, signed, maybe genuinely notarized, as of the day before. It contains the prediction. A miracle of a semi-religious nature? No, it's a trick. It can be done by any good magician.

Now, let us return to article in the Daily News, first edition. It came out in the afternoon. It had the story on page 3, and a box in the middle of it describing the mechanics of how it had been locked up in a safe and it had a final paragraph which quoted the student at Duke University who made the prediction with this disclaimer: "It's all part of the publicity for my magic show, which is happening tomorrow night. Don't take it seriously." The second and third editions of the Daily News had everything except that one sentence.

Another example of how the media distorts claims comes from a young fellow who lived a few doors down from me when I was living in Rumson, New Jersey. He was one of the local characters who did adventurous things like going out on rafts and sailboats. I thought he was a nice kid. One day on the front page of the New York Times there was a little box showing a map of the Bermuda Triangle with a Maltese Cross on it. The headline read: "Rumson boy lost at sea in Bermuda Triangle." I read the short article, continued on another page, which said he had taken off in his one-man sailboat, sailed into the Triangle carrying a radio transmitter, and hadn't been heard from since. The Coast Guard was searching for him. No sooner had I finished reading this and had called some friends in New York to tell them about it, I went out to pick up the mail and to my shock there was this kid waving hello to me. He was perfectly all right! I said to him, "You're in the *Times* this morning." He said, "Yeah, they picked me up late last night and they brought me in. They want me to be observed in the hospital, but I feel perfectly all right. We had a bit of a storm; I lost the radio overboard and they finally picked me up very, very early, around 2:30 this morning and they flew me in."

Though the first story made a big splash, the followup never appeared in the *New York Times* or any other paper of which I know. It's still part of the mythology about the Bermuda Triangle. So far as we know, from reading accounts that were published in newspapers, that kid is still someplace out in a sailboat in the Bermuda Triangle or perhaps taken off to Mars. You've got to learn that newspaper editors and reporters are subject to the same kinds of pressures that we all are. We all want something successful. Often the choice is between a story and a non-story. We have to realize that we cannot depend on the media to always represent the facts as they actually are. That's not a great deal of news to you, but you must bear it in mind at all times. Be careful about accepting what appears in print; don't let them say to you, "They put it in the paper; it must be so," or "Someone wrote a book on it. It must be so."

Furthermore, books are often published which, before they actually reach the stands and are on sale, have been completely refuted because they are based on false information. Do they immediately withdraw them? No. I'll give you a good example. There's a book called *Learning to Use Extrasensory Perception*. It's published by Charles Tart, a respected psychologist at University of California, Davis. I heard Dr. Tart give a talk in Casper, Wyo-

ming. I'm going to tell you exactly what he said and see if your reaction is the same as mine. I recorded it on tape so I know exactly the words he said; this is not a case of interpretation or faulty recollection. He said, in speaking to the audience:

There was a time, years ago, when I was highly skeptical of any paranormal claims of any kind. One of the things that convinced me that there must be something to this is a strange experience that I personally went through. It was wartime. I was at Berkeley, California, and everybody was working overtime. We worked until very late hours of the night and the young lady who was my assistant at the time worked with me until very late this one night. She finally went home; I went home. Then the very next day she came in, all excited. She reported this event. It was wartime; they did work overtime. They often were very, very tired when they went home. It was understandable they would fall into a deep sleep and get as much sleep as they possibly could during the night. She reported that during this night she had suddenly sat bolt upright in her bed, convinced that something terrible had happened. "I had a terrible sense of foreboding," she said, but she did not know what had happened. "I immediately swung out of bed and went over to the window and looked outside to see if I could see anything that might have happened like an accident. I was just turning away from the window and suddenly the window shook violently. I couldn't understand that. I went back to bed, woke up the next morning and listened to the radio." A munitions ship at Port Chicago had exploded. It literally took Port Chicago off the map. It levelled the entire town and over 300 people were killed. Whether it was an accident or sabotage, no one ever found out. She said she had sensed the moment when all these people were snuffed out in this mighty explosion. How would she have suddenly become terrified, jumped out of bed, gone to the window, and then—from 35 miles away, the shock wave had reached Berkeley and shook the window?

Indeed, she remembered looking at the clock to see what time it was—right to the minute. Well, when I heard this, I said to myself, "There's something wrong here." I see a couple of smiles around the audience; maybe you've spotted the same thing I did. I had a geologist friend sitting three or four seats away; I handed him a note. He winked, smiled, got up and left the room. He came back in, handed it to me, and it just said on it, "8 seconds." What question did I ask him? [Answer from audience: What is the difference in time of propagation over a distance of 35 miles of a shock wave through the air, compared to a shock wave through the ground? The difference is 8 seconds.] So 8 seconds before that window shook, she had been startled by the room itself shaking, not by the airwave, but by the groundwave. My theory is this: the groundwave which shook the bed startled her, she swung out of bed, went over to the window, looked outside, didn't see anything, went to turn away from the window and suddenly the pane shook in front of her.

The next morning I went to Professor Tart where he was having breakfast by himself. I had known him through correspondence and phone conversations but had never met him personally. I went over, introduced myself, sat down for a moment and gave him this bit of theory. I said there would be 8 seconds difference in the time. He didn't look up from his scrambled eggs for the longest time. Finally, when he did, he smiled and said, "Mr. Randi, that may be the explanation that you prefer." I think he had just decided that he wasn't going to entertain that idea very solidly. But I don't know that he ever made that statement subsequent to that, so maybe he did come to the conclusion that what I offered as an explana-

tion was more likely to be true. But it is so typical of the field! Again, I'm involved in some stuff that I can't tell you about, and I apologize for that, where I have a number of prominent scientists who are absolutely ignoring, refusing to look at very good evidence in this case that I'm investigating. They can come up with rationalizations for it that you wouldn't believe, unless you've been through this process before. It is incredible how they can ignore good evidence to show that there is a prosaic, rational, and very probable explanation for what they are observing.

I want to close this presentation with some parallel examples of scientific claims that turned out to be so much nonsense. Let's go back to 1903 in France. You may have heard of this; if not it really is something you should look up. A prominent scientist—a physicist named Rene Blondlot—startled the world of science with his announcement of the discovery of N-rays. A very well respected man who had won many prizes in science and justifiably so, he was doing experiments by today's standards that were very simple—such as finding the speed of electricity in a conductor. It sounds easy today, but in those days it was a very sophisticated experiment and not all that easily done. Blondlot was in his 70s at the time when he discovered N-rays, named after the town of Nancy, where he was head of the Department of Physics at the University of Nancy.

What were N-rays? N-rays were allegedly radiation exhibiting impossible properties emitted by all substances with the exception of green wood (wood not dried out) and anesthetized metal. (Metal that had been dipped in ether or chlorophorm did not give out N-rays!) Within a matter of six to eight months of the announced discovery of N-rays, 30 papers had come in from all over Europe confirming the existence of N-rays. Reports were published in journals despite the fact that there were many laboratories reporting failure after failure in replicating the results. Such acceptance was understandable considering that X-rays, which also exhibited unsuspected properties, were by then firmly established.

What Blondlot had was a basic spectroscope with a prism (not glass, but aluminum) on the inside, and a thread. The narrow stream of N-rays was refracted through the prism and coming out produced a spectrum on a field. The N-rays were reported to be invisible, except when viewed when they hit a treated thread (for example, treated with calcium sulfide). They moved the thread across the gap where the N-rays came through and when it was illuminated that was reported as the detection of the N-rays.

Before long N-rays were established as factual. *Nature* magazine was skeptical of the N-rays since laboratories in England and Germany were unable to find them. (Germany had just discovered X-rays the decade before and the French were annoyed that they didn't have a ray.) *Nature* sent an American physicist named Robert W. Wood from Johns Hopkins University to investigate. Now, I've been accused of skulduggery in my time, but what Wood did was brilliant. When no one was looking he removed the prism from the N-ray detection device and put it in his pocket. Without the prism the machine could not possibly work because it was dependent on the refraction of N-rays by the aluminum-treated prism. Yet, when the assistant conducted the next experiment he found N-rays! He swore they were there.

When the experiment was over Wood knew it was really over. He was prepared to make his report, and when he went to replace the prism back in the machine, one of the other assistants saw him do this and thought he was actually removing it, and he decided to show Wood up. Thinking Wood had removed the prism (when he had actually put it back), he set up the experiment, could find no lines, and opened the box to show that the prism was not there and to his dismay, there it was! The whole incident blew up. Papers were withdrawn, those that were in the mail were retracted, and N-rays disappeared from the scene.

How did this happen? How did over 30 papers get published? Not because the scientists who wrote the papers were stupid. Not because they were lying. But because they were deceiving themselves. Irving Klotz made this observation in *Scientific American:*

> According to Blondlot and his disciples, then, it was the sensitivity of the observer rather than the validity of the phenomena that was called into question by criticisms such as Wood's, a point of view that will not be unfamiliar to those who have followed more recent controversies concerning extrasensory perception.

By 1905, when only French scientists remained in the N-ray camp, the argument began to acquire a somewhat chauvinistic aspect. Some proponents of N-rays maintained that only the Latin races possessed the sensitivities (intellectual as well as sensory) necessary to detect manifestations of the rays. It was alleged that Anglo-Saxon powers of perception were dulled by continual exposure to fog and Teutonic ones blunted by constant ingestion of beer.

Yet science does not always learn from these mistakes. Visiting Nancy recently and speaking on the subject of pseudoscience, I discussed this example and though I was in the city that gave the name to N-rays, no one in the audience had ever heard of them, or of Blondlot, not even the professors from the University of Nancy!

Now let's go to modern Germany, after the fall of Communism, and compare N-rays to the newly discovered "E-rays." They are actually called Erdestrallen, or "Earth-rays," but I've gotten the media all over the world to call them E-rays, a sort of parallel to N-rays. E-rays are even sillier than the N-rays. What are they? First of all they cannot be detected by any known means, except by water dowsers. They cause cancer. They supposedly come from the center of the Earth. The West German government spent over 400,000 marks, or about $200,000, to pay dowsers to go around to hospitals that were federally funded and federal office buildings to move beds and desks that were in the way of these deadly E-rays. I offered to go over for nothing and conduct a very simple two-part test: 1. Can one dowser find the same spot twice? and 2. Can two dowsers find the same spot once? I told them about this and their response was, "We don't need to do the experiment because we know dowsing works. It's been around since the Middle Ages and the historical tradition validates its truthfulness."

I challenge all the dowsers in a similar way. Since 94 percent of the Earth's surface has water within drillable distance my challenge is to find a dry spot! They don't want to do it. Why? Because they only have a six percent chance of success. Dowsing is an idiomotor reaction that is very deceptive. It is an unconscious motion that you cannot detect and it looks for all the world like some mysterious force.

In a similar fashion, a few years ago I was in France investigating the results of experiments done by Jacque Benveniste on water with memory. He managed to get his article published in *Nature*, who put a disclaimer in the middle of the paper that perhaps "vigilant members of the scientific community with a flair for picking holes in other people's work may be able to suggest further tests of the validity of the conclusions." *Nature* sent a team of investigators over to his laboratory, of which I was a part. (The other two were John Maddox and Walter W. Stewart.) We showed that there were serious problems with the protocol, as well as the fudging of data. When controls were tightened, the experimenter could not replicate the results.

Then there is the theory of homeopathy

born in the nineteenth century, the brainchild of one Samuel Hannaman. Medicine was in its infancy. Poor people could not afford doctors and recovered more often than the aristocracy who received all sorts of substances, which often killed them. Samuel Hannaman gave sick poor people water, which was suppose to contain a curative agent. Since these people did not go to doctors, they tended to survive, and this supported his belief in the curative power of his special water.

The first principle of homeopathy is that an extract of some substance in water will help cure you. The second principle is that an attenuated or diluted solution will work even better. How diluted were these? If you take a solution and dilute it with 10 parts of water for every one part of itself, you've got what is called a "one solution." If you take one part of that and put it in 10 parts of water, now one part in 100, it's called a "two solution." If you have a "five solution," you have one part in 100,000. When you get to "Avogadro's limit" there is a chance of there being one molecule in the solution. One more dilution and you have one chance in 10 of there being one molecule in the solution. Well, the homeopathy people start off with a solution of 10 to the power of 50 (a one followed by 50 zeros)! Since there are 10 to the power of 23 stars in the known universe, that's what I call dilute. But that's nothing. They go all the way to 10 to the power of 1500!!!

That is so diluted that I could not conceive of what 10 to the 1500 really means, so I called Martin Gardner and asked for an example with which to illustrate it. He called me back and said that an equivalent is to take one grain of rice, crush it up in a teaspoon and dissolve that powder in a sphere of water the size of the solar system, then repeat that process two billion times!! (The technical problems of mixing such a solution are obvious!)

The critical point of homeopathy—the point of all this diluting—is that every molecule of water that comes into contact with the homeopathy water retains the memory of that special water! Thus a little substance can go a long way. I have a simple question from a layman's perspective. Since water has been around for "billions and billions of years," in this process it must have come into contact with every organic and inorganic molecule on Earth. That being the case, why not just give the patient ordinary tap water?

In fact, these homeopathic waters are so diluted that the homeopathy doctors and scientists can't even tell the difference between the water with iron and the water with gold. Come on folks, let's get real. There is no evidence that this stuff works, yet people go right on believing anyway. Here's a typical response, this from a letter written by Boaz Robinzon of the Faculty of Agriculture: "I want you to know that no matter what the *Nature* investigating committee has written, I am still confident that the phenomenon observed is a real and reproducible one and it is only a matter of time until we shall be proven right."

That's a classic example of someone who does not wish to face reality. I've been going around the world telling people to get real for years. That's the peculiar business that I'm in. I shouldn't have to be in that business but someone has to do it. Will it ever end? Probably not, but perhaps with the efforts of the skeptics and scientists we can "dilute" it a little!

Psi and Psi-Missing

TODD C. RINIOLO AND
LOUIS A. SCHMIDT

hen investigating group results of extrasensory performance, most researchers find chance results (Kurtz, 1985, 508–9). However, a discrepancy exists, as some parapsychologists consistently find results that statistically vary from chance. Consistent variations above chance (i.e., extrasensory perception) and below chance (i.e., psi-missing) are both interpreted as evidence of a psi mechanism (Rhine, 1952, 91; Schmeidler, 1966, 387). Most skeptics believe this discrepancy exists not because of extrasensory influence, but because of poor experimental controls and/or improper randomization (Marks, 1986, 121; Hyman, 1994, 19). Currently, there exists no scientifically credible evidence that demonstrates a psi mechanism (Krauss, 1998, 51).

In contrast, many parapsychologists attribute the discrepancy in extrasensory performance not to methodological issues, but to differences in "test conditions." Test conditions are hypothesized to influence the outcome of parapsychological studies (Bem and Honorton, 1994, 14–15; Schmeidler, 1966, 387). Bem and Honorton (1994) suggest that "psi performances should covary with experimental and subject variables in psychologically sensible ways" (15). For example, "good rapport" and a confident attitude in the testing environment should facilitate extrasensory

perception (ESP), while "negativism" and "hostility" in the testing environment should result in psi-missing (Schmeidler, 1966, 396).

In support of the test conditions hypothesis, parapsychologists have identified variables believed to influence psi performance:

1. Participants with a belief in ESP (sheep) score above chance while skeptical participants (goats) score below chance (Broughton, 1991, 109; Schmeidler, 1943, 212; 1966, 389).
2. Subjects who interact with a "positive" (e.g., friendly and supportive) experimenter show ESP while subjects who interact with a "negative" (e.g., abrupt and unfriendly) experimenter show psi-missing (Honorton, Ramsey, and Cabibbo, 1975, 137–8).
3. Experimenter attitude towards psi is believed to alter performance (Schmeidler, 1997, 83). For example, a psi-positive researcher is more likely to index ESP while a skeptical researcher increases the chances of psi-missing (Rhine, 1952, 108).
4. A reduction in sensory input facilitates ESP (Bem and Honorton, 1994, 5–6) while distractions in the testing environment have been associated with psi-missing (Sharp and Clark, 1937, 136).

5. Implementing scientific controls or subjecting psi phenomena to observation is hypothesized to sometimes cause "stage fright" that results in psi-missing (Rhine, 1952, 108).

6. Marks (1986, 120) reports that some parapsychologists have theorized that the readership of the journal (if skeptical) can alter psi performance through backward causality. Therefore, a psi-positive readership should increase the chances of ESP while a skeptical readership should increase the chances of psi-missing.

While this literature is consistent with the theory that test conditions alter psi performance in predictable ways, support for the test conditions hypothesis is often speculative, can be questioned on methodological grounds, and has not met the scientific standard of independent verification.

Note that the mentioned literature implies that skeptics are not the appropriate experimenters to test for above chance claims of psi (e.g., ESP). One reviewer of Bem and Honorton (1994, 14) worried that this emphasis upon test conditions provides "an escape clause." In other words, if a skeptic were to replicate a parapsychological study and find no variation from chance, results could be dismissed due to inappropriate test conditions. While this literature implies that skeptics are not the ideal researchers to test for ESP, it also suggests that skeptics are appropriate to elicit psi-missing. Thus, one way for skeptics to empirically evaluate the test conditions hypothesis is for skeptics to test for psi-missing.

The purpose of this paper is to evaluate if test conditions can elicit a reliable reduction from chance (i.e., psi-missing) on a card-guessing task. The test conditions implemented in this study incorporate the above parapsychological literature. If test conditions do alter psi-results in predictable ways (and a psi mecha-

nism exists), a psi-hostile testing environment should elicit psi-missing. If psi-missing can be reliably demonstrated with proper research controls (i.e., double blind) and randomization by skeptics, this would strengthen the test conditions hypothesis and help to explain the consistent failure of skeptics to replicate above chance psi findings. In contrast, results consistent with chance would question the validity of the research used to support the test conditions hypothesis.

Methods

Experiment 1 Participants

Our subject pool of 100 females (Mean 21.4 years; Standard Deviation 6.87) and 52 males (M 21.5 years; SD 4.21) met the a priori criteria to participate (i.e., goats) in this study from introductory psychology courses at Adams State College (Alamosa, Colorado). An additional 45 students participated, but were excluded because they believed they possessed ESP.

Procedures. Prior to the experiment, a brand new set of regular playing cards was purchased. The cards were divided into five piles of 10 cards each with 5 red and 5 black cards in each pile. The five piles each were shuffled thoroughly by an independent "goat" blind to the study, and subsequently placed into five opaque envelopes.

Also prior to the experiment, participants were asked (on a handout) if they believed they personally possessed any psychic ability. Participants circled "yes" or "no." Only those who indicated no (i.e., the goats) were included in any subsequent data analysis. Participants were instructed they would be required to carry out two simultaneous tasks to evaluate ESP ability. First, participants would perform a mental counting task (i.e., an environmental distraction). Second, participants would guess the color of the card (red or black) selected by the experimenter from a pile of 10 cards (5 red and 5 black cards). The card was selected as the experimenter simultaneously read numbers at a slow and steady pace and shuffled cards. As the experimenter read the last number, the top card was placed face down and the experimenter stated "Please guess the correct card and total the numbers." Participants were told this process would be repeated 5 times.

The numbers used for the mental arithmetic tasks were randomly generated in length from four to ten total numbers. The numbers ranged from 1 to 10 (randomly determined). Random generation was implemented so participants could not accurately anticipate when the mental arithmetic task would end. A practice example ($8 + 1 + 6 + 3 + 9 + 1$ "Please guess the correct card and total the numbers") was given. No card was drawn for the practice trial.

No attempt was made to create a "warm" experimental environment and the experimenter behaved in a cold, formal, and impersonal manner. The experimenter also did not believe in psi. The following statements were read by the experimenter immediately before testing:

1. After tens of thousands of experiments, no one has been able to convincingly demonstrate Extra Sensory Perception (ESP). Thus, the majority of psychologists agree that ESP does not exist.
2. The Central Intelligence Agency (CIA) has recently abandoned their psychic spy program after spending millions of dollars and classifying the project as "useless."
3. Currently, a 1.1 million dollar reward exists on the internet (www.randi.org) for anyone who can demonstrate genuine ESP or any other psychic ability. While

many people claiming Extra Sensory abilities have been tested, nobody has yet claimed the reward.

The experiment began immediately after these statements were read. The process of reading numbers, shuffling cards, and selecting a card for each trial was repeated five times during the experiment. Only five seconds were given between each trial. During the experiment, at no time did either the experimenter or the participants know the color of the card selected (i.e., a double-blind format). To ensure that no inadvertent cues were transmitted to the participants, the experimenter shuffled and selected the cards behind a podium. The use of new cards and the practice of simultaneously reading the numbers for the counting tasks ensured that the experimenter was also "blind." After the five trials were completed, answer sheets were collected and the experimenter recorded the correct answers for the five trials.

Data Analysis. In order to ensure that participants were attending to the counting task, it was determined in advance that only those trials in which participants had accurately totaled the counting tasks would be included for statistical analysis. The data sheets were "blindly" tallied and loaded into a spreadsheet. The statistical analysis was limited to one a priori test in order to control for statistical errors (Riniolo and Schmidt, in press).

Results. In response to the counting task, participants scored correctly an average of 4.08 (out of five). The criteria indicating psi-missing defined a statistically significant reduction from 2.04 correct identifications (50% of 4.08). A one sample t-test (one-tailed) was performed using a 95% confidence interval. Group results indicated that participants (N=152) identified the card color correctly an average of 2.16 times. Results did not statistically differ from what was expected by chance

(95% confidence a chance result would fall between 2.0128 and 2.3162).

Experiment 2 Participants

Our subject pool consisted of 124 females (M 21.2 years; SD 1.59) and 32 males (M 21.5 years; SD 1.98) from a large introductory psychology course at McMaster University, Ontario, Canada. Of these, 76 were excluded from data analysis because of a belief they personally possess psychic abilities.

Procedures. For the replication study, two minor modifications were made. First, Dr. Schmidt implemented the replication, whereas Dr. Riniolo implemented the initial study. Second, the mental counting task was eased by reducing the length to randomly vary from 4 to 7 numbers.

Results. Participants scored correctly an average of 4.70 (out of five) on the counting task. The criterion to indicate psi-missing for the group average is a statistically significant reduction from 2.35 correct identifications (50% of 4.70). A one sample t-test (one-tailed) was performed using a 95 confidence interval. Group results indicated that participants (N=155) identified the card color correctly an average of 2.32. Results did not statistically differ from what was expected by chance (CI95, 2.1792, 2.4531).

Discussion

The purpose of this paper was to empirically evaluate if psi-hostile test conditions could elicit psi-missing. Results were consistent with chance expectation despite implementing multiple variables previously identified by parapsychologists as increasing the chances of psi-missing. Several interpretations of the results

deserve attention. First, our results are consistent with the non-existence of a psi-mechanism. Simply put, test conditions cannot alter a phenomenon that does not exist when proper experimental controls and randomization procedures are implemented. However, because it is impossible to disprove a negative, other interpretations are possible.

Specifically, perhaps the test conditions were not sufficiently hostile to elicit psi-missing, or our experiments lacked adequate statistical power. This is unlikely as parapsychologists have reported psi-missing using much less "psi-hostile" conditions (e.g., Honorton, Ramsey and Cabibbo, 1975, 136–7) and with much less statistical power (e.g., Sharp and Clark, 1937, 136) than implemented here. For example, we analyzed the data provided by Sharp and Clark (1937, 136, Table VI) using the same statistical approach above. Results indicated statistical evidence of psi-missing and ESP (depending on test conditions) with only four and 11 participants, respectively. This inconsistency raises the possibility that inadequate methodology or random error was responsible for previous findings of psi-missing.

In addition, others may argue that the presence of skeptics (i.e., the authors) would not facilitate psi-missing, but rather would inhibit any demonstration of psi performance (both above and below chance). This belief that some researchers are psi-conducive (can find reliable variations from chance) and others are psi-inhibitory (repeatedly find chance results) is an endless cycle that makes psi "untestable" (Blackmore, 1985, 429). After-the-fact explanations to find a psi-inhibitory link responsible for chance results can be invoked endlessly. More important, the scientific standard of independent verification of results is impossible. As psi-research has a long history of fraud (Hansen, 1990, 25) and methodological error (Marks, 1986, 120–1), reliance upon a few "psi-conducive" individuals to establish an extraordinary claim (i.e., a psi-mechanism exists) is unacceptable. Perhaps the only consistent finding in parapsychological research the last 100 plus years is that irrespective of test conditions, when proper methods and randomization procedures are used (by both believers and nonbelievers), participants score at chance expectation over repeated evaluations. Being "psi-inhibitory" may simply reflect the experimenter's ability to prevent bias from influencing testing results.

Our results are inconsistent with the hypothesis that test conditions can alter psi-performance in predictable ways. We are unconvinced of the validity of the test conditions hypothesis that is often used post-hoc to dismiss results inconsistent with a psi-mechanism. Unfortunately, there is a long and continuing history of after-the-fact rationalizations for failures to scientifically demonstrate paranormal phenomena. For example, Kurtz (1985, 180–1) reports that when the Fox sisters could not produce "rappings" during an empirical evaluation in 1851, they claimed the presence of skeptics caused the spirits to retire. Recently, therapeutic touch practitioners attempted to rationalize their failure by questioning the test conditions despite agreeing in advance that the experimental paradigm was fair (Rosa, Rosa, Sarner, and Barrett, 1998, 1008). To our knowledge, there currently exist as many scientifically credible studies supporting the test conditions hypothesis as there are for other psi phenomena—zero.

References:

Bem, D. J., and C. Honorton. 1994. "Does Psi Exist? Replicable Evidence for an Anomalous Process of Information Transfer." *Psychological Bulletin*, 115, 4–18.

Blackmore, S. 1985. "The Adventures of a Psi-inhibitory Experimenter." In P. Kurtz (Ed.), *A Skeptic's Handbook of Parapsychology* (425–448). Buffalo, NY: Prometheus Books.

Broughton, R. S. 1991. *Parapsychology: The Controversial Science.* New York: Ballantine Books.

Hansen, G. P. 1990. "Deception by Subjects in Psi Research." *The Journal of the American Society for Psychical Research*, 84, 25–80.

Honorton, C., M. Ramsey, and C. Cabibbo. 1975. "Experimenter Effects in Extrasensory Perception." *The Journal of the American Society for Psychical Research*, 69, 135–149.

Hyman, R. 1994. "Anomaly or Artifact? Comments on Bem and Honorton." *Psychological Bulletin*, 115, 19–24.

Krauss, L. M. 1998. "May the Force Be with You." *Skeptical Inquirer*, 22, 49–53.

Kurtz, P. 1985a. "Spiritualists, Mediums, and Psychics: Some Evidence of Fraud." In P. Kurtz (Ed.), *A Skeptic's Handbook of Parapsychology* (177–223). Buffalo, NY: Prometheus Books.

——. 1985b. "Is Parapsychology a Science?" In P. Kurtz (Ed.), *A Skeptic's Handbook of Parapsychology* (503–518). Buffalo, NY: Prometheus Books.

Marks, D. F. 1986. "Investigating the Paranormal." *Nature*, 320, 119–124.

Rhine, J. B. 1952. "The Problem of Psi-missing." *The Journal of Parapsychology*, 16, 90–129.

Riniolo, T. C., and L. A. Schmidt. (In press). "Searching for Reliable Relationships with Statistics Packages: An Empirical Example of the Potential Problems." *The Journal of Psychology*.

Rosa, L., E. Rosa, L. Sarner, and S. Barrett. 1998. "A Close Look at Therapeutic Touch." *Journal of the American Medical Association*, 279, 1005–1010.

Schmeidler, G. R. 1943. "Predicting Good and Bad Scores in a Clairvoyance Experiment: A Final Report." *The Journal of the American Society for Psychical Research*, 37, 210–227.

——. 1966. "The Influence of Attitude on ESP Scores." *International Journal of Neuropsychiatry*, 2, 387–397.

——. 1997. "Psi-conducive Experimenters and Psi-permissive Ones." *European Journal of Parapsychology*, 13, 83–94.

Sharp, V., and C. C. Clark. 1937. "Group Tests for Extrasensory Perception." *The Journal of Parapsychology*, 1, 123–142.

Recovered Memory Therapy and False Memory Syndrome

A Father's Perspective as a Test Case

MARK PENDERGRAST

"I can't believe that!," said Alice.

"Can't you?" the Queen said in a pitying tone. "Try again: draw a long breath, and shut your eyes."

Alice laughed. "there's no use trying," she said. "One can't believe impossible things."

"I daresay you haven't had much practice," said the Queen. "When I was your age, I always did it for half-an-hour a day. Why, sometimes I've believed as many as six impossible things before breakfast."

—Lewis Carroll,
Through the Looking-Glass

A few decades ago some bright agronomist imported a nifty Japanese vine called "kudzu" to my native Georgia, hoping to halt erosion and provide cheap cow fodder. The insidious kudzu, with its broad, shiny green leaves, now covers entire forests, swallowing trees whole. While cows may indeed eat the stuff, I suspect a few of them have been enveloped, too, along the way. I have come to regard the initial incest suspicion that fuels the repressed memory movement as being a kind of mental kudzu seed—perhaps a perverse analogue to Jesus' parable of the sower and the seed.

Repressed memories seem to grow in the same way. It does not take much—just a small seed, planted in your fertile brain by a television program, a book, a friend, or a therapist. Maybe, just maybe, all of your problems stem from childhood incest. Maybe you have forgotten it. Maybe that is why you are uncomfortable at family reunions. Maybe. No, no, that's insane! Forget it, not Dad, not Mom! You try to dismiss the idea. But it won't go away. It takes root, sends out creepers, and grows. Soon the mental kudzu is twining out of your ears, sending roots down to your gut, taking over your life. It's true! Your worst fears were justified!

Given that our memories can fool us sometimes, it is still hard to understand why or how people would want to believe that their parents committed such awful acts upon them. Numerous types of "evidence" are used to provoke and "prove" the reality of repressed memories. These include hypnotic regression, sodium Amytal, dreams, visualizations, bodily pangs or marks, panic attacks, or just general unhappiness. Once the seed is planted, once the idea takes hold, it does not matter what method is employed. The results are almost foreordained. I should know. I am a victim of the "recovered memory" movement. I am an accused parent.

Lost Daughters

"Stacey" and "Christina" (my daughters have changed their surnames, and I have changed their first names to protect their identities) are exceptionally attractive, intelligent, creative, caring young women. Both have graduated with high marks from fine Ivy League schools. And both, through therapy, have recently retrieved "memories" of sexual abuse which they think I inflicted on them. I do not know exactly what I am supposed to have done, because they will not tell me. In fact, they do not communicate with me at all, and I am forbidden to call or write.

It all started five years ago, when Christina, my youngest daughter, was in college and went to a counselor. In therapy, she uncovered a repressed memory of being molested by my housemate when she was nine years old. Within the next year, without accusing me, she nonetheless cut off all contact. Then, in the fall of 1992, she apparently "remembered" something terrible I did to her, though she has never directly confronted me. She told Stacey, who in turn entered therapy and wrote me a letter, which began: "I'm sorry if you aren't ready for this letter, but it must be written. I have recently recalled some memories I have of you . . ."

The letter was filled with what I now recognize as recovered memory jargon. I had violated her "boundaries" and made her and Christina my "surrogate wives." I was "abusive" and "manipulative," and had probably been sexually abused myself as a child. "I know what you did to my sister," she wrote. "You have to recall what happened and deal with this on your own." She ended the letter by forbidding me to contact her.

I have not heard from my children in over two years now. It breaks my heart, and I am deeply concerned for them, especially after conducting the research for my book *Victims of Memory*. Though accused parents certainly suffer terribly, I have become convinced that the real victims of memory are the children, who have been sucked into a destructive belief system that strips them of their identities, pasts, and families.

In the rest of this article I will detail a few of the methods used to create such a belief system.

Hypnosis: Memory Prod or Production?

After Stacey wrote me that awful letter, I thought that maybe I really had done something horrible to my children and had repressed the memory myself. So I went to a hypnotist. Like most people, I thought that when you sank into a deep hypnotic trance, you could magically tap into your dormant subconscious, unlocking long-forgotten memories. Fortunately, I went to an ethical hypnotist who did not lead me into believing I had committed incest on my children. She failed, however, to tell me how questionable memories are when "uncovered" in hypnosis. I discovered that fact during my research.

From its inception, hypnosis has caused considerable controversy and spawned innumerable myths. One thing that experts agree on, however, is that memories retrieved under hypnosis are often contaminated mixtures of fantasy and truth. In many cases, outright "confabulations"—the psychologists' term for illusory memories—result.

The reason that memories retrieved under hypnosis are suspect goes to the very definition of the process, which invariably includes the concept of suggestion. Clark Hull and A. M. Weilzenhoffer defined hypnosis simply as "a state of enhanced suggestibility." When a subject agrees to be hypnotized, he or she tacitly agrees to abide by the suggestions of the hypnotist. This state of heightened suggestibility can work quite well if the goal is to stop smoking, lose weight, enhance self-esteem, reduce perceived pain, or improve one's sex life. But it is not an appropriate method for retrieving supposedly repressed memories, as psychiatrist Martin Orne and psychologist Elizabeth Loftus have repeatedly stressed in courtroom settings.

The hypnotized subject is not the only one who is deluded. The hypnotist who believes that he or she is delving for hidden memories takes an active part in the shared belief system. Both hypnotist and subject are engaged in a tacitly accepted mini-drama in which they act out prescribed roles.

I am not trying to imply that "hypnosis," whether a real state or not, does not have a profound effect. The human imagination is capable of incredible feats, and herein lies the potential problem. Similarly, the "guided imagery" exercises that trauma therapists employ to gain access to buried memories can be enormously convincing, whether we choose to call the process hypnosis or not. When someone is relaxed, willing to suspend critical judgment, engage in fantasy, and place ultimate faith in an authority figure using ritualistic methods, deceptive scenes from the past can easily be induced.

Hypnotism entails a powerful social mythology. Just as those "possessed" by demons believed in the process of exorcism, most modern Americans believe that in a hypnotic state, they are granted magical access to the subconscious, where repressed memories lie ready to spring forward at the proper command. Holly-wood movies have reinforced this mythology, beginning with a spate of amnesia-retrieval dramas, such as Hitchcock's *Spellbound*, in the 1940s. A good hypnotic subject therefore responds to what psychologists call "social demand characteristics." As psychologist Robert Baker puts it, there is a "strong desire of the subject to supply the information demanded of him by the hypnotist." Psychiatrist Herbert Spiegel says it more graphically: "A good hypnotic subject will vomit up just what the therapist wants to hear."

The hypnotist is often completely unaware that he is influencing the inductee, but what psychologists term "inadvertent cuing" can easily occur, often through tone of voice. "It is incredible," wrote French psychologist Hippolyte Bernheim in 1888, "with what acumen certain hypnotized subjects detect, as it were, the idea which they ought to carry into execution. One word, one gesture, one intonation puts them on the track." Simply urging the subject to "go on" at a crucial point, or asking, "How does that feel to you?" can cue the desired response. A person who agrees to play the role of the hypnotized subject is obviously motivated to believe in that role and act it properly. This goes double for clients in psychotherapy who are desperately seeking to locate the source of their unhappiness. If the therapist has let them know, either subtly or directly, that they can expect to find scenes of sexual abuse while under hypnosis or through guided imagery, they are likely to do so.

One of the characteristics of well-rehearsed hypnotic confabulations is the over confidence with which they are eventually reported. Such memories tend to become extraordinarily detailed and believable with repetition. "The more frequently the subject reports the event," Martin Orne has written, "the more firmly established the pseudomemory will tend to become." As a final caution, he warns that "psychologists and psychiatrists are not particularly adept at recognizing deception," adding that, as a rule, the average hotel credit manager is a far better detective.

Dream Work

Ever since Joseph saved Egypt by properly interpreting the Pharaoh's dreams—and probably long before that—humans have sought deep meaning from the strange stories they picture in their sleep. In our dreams, anything is possible. We can fly, jump through time, read other people's thoughts. Animals can talk, objects appear and disappear quickly, one thing metamorphoses quickly into something else. Sometimes our dreams are exciting, sexy, or soothing. Often, they are bizarre and frightening. What are we to make of them?

No one really knows, not even the most renowned dream researchers who shake people awake to ask what they're experiencing when their REM (rapid eye movements) indicate that they are in an active dreaming state. Some interpreters, including Freud, have asserted with great authority that dream ingredients symbolize certain objects, emotions, or events. For example, a skyscraper represents a penis. In the second century, Artemidorus used the same kind of logic. For him, a foot meant a slave, while a head indicated a father. The kinky ancient Egyptians apparently dreamed frequently of sexual congress with various animals. One papyrus explained, "If an ass couples with her, she will be punished for a great fault. If a he-goat couples with her, she will die promptly."

Modern trauma therapists also use sexual dreams as a form of interpretation. They tell their clients to be particularly aware of any night visions that could be interpreted as sexual abuse. This is called "dream work." Not too surprisingly, such dreams are often forthcoming. "Oh, my God!" the woman reports in therapy. "It's all true! In my dream last night,

my Dad and uncle were taking turns having sex with me. And I was just a little kid!" Such dreams are taken as recovered memories and are presumed to represent literal truth, even though some events seem unlikely—in one well-publicized case, for instance, a daughter recalled being raped by her mother, who was equipped with a penis.

But if these dreams don't necessarily stem from repressed memories of actual events, where do they come from? From the same place that spawns hypnotically guided fantasies—the fertile and overwhelmed imagination. Here is someone feverishly working on her memory recovery, reading books describing horrible abuse, her life consumed with the possibility that her father did something to her. As Calvin Hall noted in *The Meaning of Dreams*, "It has been fairly well established that some aspects of the dream are usually connected with events of the previous day or immediate past." It is not surprising that someone with an obsession about incest would dream about it. Hall also warned that "dreams should never be read for the purpose of constructing a picture of objective reality," but therapists and patients eager for repressed memories ignore such advice.

The role of expectation in all aspects of memory recovery is crucial. What we expect to see, we see, as Joseph Jastrow observed in his 1935 classic, *Wish and Wisdom*: "Everywhere, once committed by whatever route, the prepossessed mind finds what it looks for." Elizabeth Loftus tells the true story of two bear hunters at dusk, walking along a trail in the woods. Tired and frustrated, they had seen no bear. As they rounded a bend in the trail, they spotted a large object about 25 yards away, shaking and grunting. Simultaneously, they raised their rifles and fired. But the "bear" turned out to be a yellow tent with a man and woman making love inside. The woman was killed. As psychologist Irving Kirsch notes, "response expectancy theory" explains how "when we expect to feel anxious, relaxed, joyful, or depressed, our expectations tend to produce those feelings." At its extreme, such a mindset can even lead to self-induced death, as has been well-documented among tribes in which those under a powerful curse fulfill it by wasting away and dying, unless some way to reverse the curse can be found.

Similarly, when we expect to have a particular type of dream, we tend to perform accordingly. As Jerome Frank notes in *Persuasion and Healing*, patients routinely give their therapists the dreams they want. "The dream the therapist hears is, of course, not necessarily the one the patient dreamed," Frank explains, "since considerable time has usually elapsed between the dream and its report. One study compared dreams reported immediately upon awakening with the versions unfolded before a psychiatrist in a subsequent interview. Any material the patient anticipated would not be approved was not recalled." In his classic 1957 text, *Battle for the Mind*, psychiatrist William Sargant described an acquaintance who had entered first Freudian, then Jungian therapy. "His contemporary notes show that dreams he had under Freudian treatment varied greatly from those he had under Jungian treatment; and he denies having experienced the same dreams before or since." Sargant concluded: "The increased suggestibility of the patient may help the therapist not only to change his conscious thinking, but even to direct his dream life."

Therapist Renee Fredrickson certainly believes in such directives. "You can also prime your dream pump, so to speak," she writes in *Repressed Memories*. "Before you go to sleep at night, visualize yourself as a little child. Then suggest that your inner child show you in a dream what you need to know about the abuse." Nor does the dream abuse have to be obvious. Fredrickson describes how Diane reported a dream in which "she was on her hands and knees in a kitchen, washing the floor. Floating in the air were green U-shaped neon objects. Her father was standing next to a large mirror over the sink, watching her." Eventually, Diane interpreted her dream as follows:

> My father raped me in the evenings when I was cleaning the kitchen. He would make me crawl around naked while he watched in the mirror. I also believe the green neon things are about a time he put a cucumber in me.

Sleep Paralysis

Another fascinating form of semi-dream, which typically occurs in the twilight state between waking and sleeping, accounts for many "repressed memories." The psychological term is either a "hypnogogic" or "hypnopompic" state, respectively referring to the time just before sleep or prior to waking, but more commonly it is just called "sleep paralysis." During this curious in-between semiconscious state, people often report chilling visions.

Robert Baker describes the phenomenon: "First, the hallucinations always occur just before or after falling asleep. Second, the hallucinator is paralyzed or has difficulty moving. . . . Third, the hallucination is usually bizarre. . . . Finally, the hallucinator is unalterably convinced of the reality of the entire event." The vision's content is often related to the dreamer's current concerns. In one study, as many as 67% of a normal sample population reported at least one experience of sleep paralysis, with its attendant hallucinations. Many people experience sleep paralysis during the day, particularly if they take afternoon naps. Those with narcolepsy—a relatively common disorder characterized by brief involuntary periods of sleep during the day, with difficulties resting at night—are particularly prone to these frightening hallucinations. The word "nightmare" actually stems from sleep paralysis. A "mare," or demon, was supposed to terrorize people—mostly women—by sitting on their breasts, making it difficult to breathe. Often, the mare was a Satanic incubus or succubus who also forced the frightened sleeper into sexual intercourse. The following is a 1763 description of the phenomenon:

> The nightmare generally seizes people sleeping on their backs, and often begins with frightful dreams, which are soon succeeded by a difficult respiration, a violent oppression on the breast, and a total privation of voluntary motion. In this agony they sigh, groan, utter indistinct sounds [until] they escape out of that dreadful torpid state. As soon as they shake off that vast oppression, and are able to move the body, they are affected by strong palpitation, great anxiety, languor, and uneasiness.

David Hufford has written an entire book about sleep paralysis, *The Terror That Comes in the Night*. His 1973 interview with Caroline, a young graduate student, sounds quite similar to the reports of many "incest survivors." When Caroline woke up one day, she reports, "I felt like there was a man next to me with his arm underneath my back, and holding my left arm." His smell was quite distinct, "all sweaty and kind of dusty." When she tried to move, he gripped her arm tighter. "Now if I move again, he's going to rape me," she thought. She tried to scream, but she could make no sound. "Then he was on top of me, and I tried to look up to see who it was or something—I could just see this—it looked like a white mask, like a big white mask." After several minutes of this horrible experience, Caroline "felt sort of released, you know. And I—I could sit up, and I got the feeling there was nobody there." In the 1990s, such experiences are frequently interpreted as "flashbacks" or "body memories," and women are encouraged to visualize a face to fill in the blank mask. Other "evi-

dence" of repressed memories also relates to sleep—or its lack. In *The Courage to Heal*, Ellen Bass and Laura Davis quote one typical woman's experience as she obsessed over possible repressed memories: "I just lost it completely. I wasn't eating. I wasn't sleeping." Sleep deprivation is a well-established technique used in brain-washing. As sleep expert Alexander Borbely writes, chronic lack of sleep blurs the borderline between sleeping and waking, "so that the kind of hallucinations that often occur at the moment of falling asleep now begin to invade the waking state as well . . . the floor appears to be covered with spider webs, faces appear and disappear. Auditory illusions also occur." In addition, "when sleep deprivation experiments last more than four days, delusions can manifest themselves, in addition to the disturbances of perception. The participants grow increasingly suspicious and begin to believe that things are going on behind their backs."

Body Memories and Panic Attacks

People who are trying to recover repressed memories are often told that "the body remembers what the mind forgets," particularly in cases of abuse suffered as a pre-verbal infant. These "body memories" can take the form of virtually any form of physical ailment, from stomach aches to stiff joints. Psychosomatic complaints such as these have always been common in Western culture and almost invariably accompany general unhappiness and anxiety. Add to this the "expectancy effect," and it isn't surprising that during the "abreaction" or reliving of an event, a woman might feel terrible pelvic pain, or a man might experience a burning anus.

Those in search of memories often submit to massages by experienced "body workers," who can trigger feelings either by light touch or

RECOVERED MEMORY THERAPY: A FATHER'S PERSPECTIVE | 603

deeper muscle manipulation. "An area of your body may get hot or feel numb," Renee Fredrickson assures readers in *Repressed Memories*. "Powerful emotions may sweep over you, causing you to weep or even cry out." It is certainly true that people can experience profound, inexplicable emotions while they are being massaged, particularly if they are tense and unhappy in general. When they let down their guards and relax, allowing intimate touch by a stranger, they often do weep. Given the admonition to be on the look-out for any stray sensation, many subjects have no difficulty locating and interpreting various body memories. Fredrickson gives two examples: "She [Sarah] was undergoing a passive form of body work involving laying on of hands when she had a slowly burgeoning sense of rage at her father for abusing her." Later on, Sarah discovered that the "exquisite sensitivity" of her toes was caused by her grandfather having shoved a wood chip under her toenail.

Some "body memories" take the form of rashes or welts that fit particular memory scenarios. The mind can apparently produce remarkable and sometimes quite specific effects on the body. It has been demonstrated that hypnotic suggestion can actually remove warts, while some people can consciously control their pulse rates, respiration, or blood flow. In *Michelle Remembers*, Michelle Smith evidently possessed similar powers, producing a red rash on her neck that her psychiatrist interpreted as a welt left by the devil's tail.

Nothing so dramatic need account for most "body memories," however. One of the most common was recounted by A. G. Britton in her article, "The Terrible Truth." She experienced a choking sensation and interpreted that as evidence that her father had forced his penis into her mouth when she was a baby. It turns out, though, that a constricted throat is one nearly universal human reaction to fear and anxiety. In fact, the word "anxious" derives from the Latin word meaning "to strangle."

This classic symptom—an inability to swallow and the feeling of being choked—is now one of the diagnostic symptoms for panic disorders. For hundreds of years it was called, among other things, *globus hystericus*, because it felt as though a ball were rising from the abdomen and lodging in the throat.

Many people who fear that they may have been abused suffer repeated panic attacks at unexpected moments and, with their therapists' encouragement, interpret them as repressed memories surging forth from the subconscious. Yet these little-understood episodes are extremely common. As psychologist David Barlow points out in his comprehensive text, *Anxiety and Its Disorders*, "Anxiety disorders represent the single largest mental health problem in the country, far outstripping depression." In Western cultures, reports of this affliction are much more common among women than among men, although that is not so in Eastern countries. Recent surveys indicate that 35% of Americans report having experienced panic attacks. Unfortunately, those seeking help for severe anxiety disorders are frequently misdiagnosed, seeing an average of 10 doctors or therapists before receiving appropriate help. As listed in the third revised edition of the *Diagnostic and Statistical Manual of Mental Disorders*, familiarly known as DSM-III-R, the symptoms experienced during panic attacks (four or more being sufficient by the official definition) sound like a check-list for what trauma therapists interpret as body memories:

(1) shortness of breath (dyspnea) or smothering sensations; (2) dizziness, unsteady feelings, or faintness; (3) palpitations or accelerated heart rate (tachycardia); (4) trembling and shaking; (5) sweating; (6) choking; (7) nausea or abdominal distress; (8) depersonalization or derealization (the feeling that you don't really exist or that nothing is real); (9) numbness or tingling sensations (paresthesias); (10) flushes (hot flashes) or chills; (11) chest pain or dis-

comfort; (12) fear of dying; (13) fear of going crazy or of doing something uncontrolled.

Surprisingly, Barlow reports that "the overwhelming evidence is that many phobias and the majority of fears are not learned through a traumatic experience." Instead, panic attacks appear to stem from contemporarily stressful life situations and a fearful mindset—though biological factors and early childhood trauma may contribute to a predisposition to anxiety disorders. Psychologists Aaron Beck and Gary Emery give an example of a typical episode involving a 40-year-old man who, while on the ski slopes, began to feel shortness of breath, profuse perspiration, and faintness. He thought he was having a heart attack. In the midst of this, he had a vivid image of himself lying in a hospital bed with an oxygen mask. It transpired that this man's brother had just died of a heart attack, and he feared the same might happen to him.

Similarly, people who think they may have repressed memories fear that they may be like others they know (or have read about or seen on television). They, too, may be unknowing incest victims who will have flashbacks. For such people, panic attacks are often triggered when they become over-tired or over-stressed and spontaneously envision images of their worst fears, which, in turn, provoke even more anxiety. "Once the fear reaction has started," Beck and Emery write, "it tends to build on itself." These "autonomous" images then persist "without the patient's being able to stop them," and they seem utterly real, "as though the traumatic episode were actually occurring in the present."

After the first attack of this inexplicable fear, a vicious cycle can commence in which the very fear of another episode provokes it. This would be particularly likely for a woman who is extremely stressed by the idea that she might have been sexually abused and is minutely aware of every bodily and emotional twinge. As David Barlow notes, "self-focused attention greatly increases sensitivity to bodily sensations and other aspects of internal experience. Furthermore, this sensitivity . . . quickly spreads to other aspects of the self, such as self-evaluative concerns." Barlow calls this process a "negative feedback cycle" which leads to a chronic feeling of helplessness, dependence, and self-absorption. As Ann Seagrave and Faison Covington—two women who have overcome their panic attacks—write in *Free from Fears*, "We can become frightened to such a degree that we learn to monitor every twitch, every ache, and it is in that way that we often scare ourselves needlessly."

One final point related to panic attacks seems quite puzzling. Attacks are often triggered by deep relaxation exercises such as those which induce hypnosis or guided imagery sessions. In one study, 67% of a group of panic-disorder patients experienced three or more symptoms while listening to a relaxation tape. As David Barlow notes, "relaxation is surely the strangest of panic provocation procedures." He hypothesizes that it may be caused by a fear of losing control. Whatever the reason, this finding certainly relates to therapy clients who are led to a "safe place" during deep relaxation exercises. It contributes to our understanding of why they might experience panic attacks during the process.

The Contexts of Insanity

In conclusion, a vicious cycle of social influence, combined with a widespread belief in massive repression of sexual abuse memories, has produced an epidemic of Survivors. In the current situation, it is sometimes difficult to ascertain who is fulfilling whose expectations. A woman enters therapy, already afraid that her problems may stem from repressed memories. Her therapist plays into those fears, and between the two of them, they find "evidence" in the form of dreams, flashbacks, or body memories. They see dysfunction everywhere, and when the client sinks into a hypnotic trance, she pictures horrifying events from her childhood.

In 1993, a CNN reporter took a hidden camera into a counseling session with a therapist known to have convinced at least six other women that they were Survivors. The reporter said that she had been "kind of depressed" for a few months, and that her marital sex life had worsened. At the end of the first session, the therapist suggested that she might have been sexually abused as a child. When the reporter said she had no such memories, the therapist stated that many women completely forget incest. "They have no idea, in fact. I mean, what you've presented to me, Lee-Anne, is so classic that I'm just sitting here blown away, actually." Once a therapist labels someone an Incest Survivor, everything the client says is perceived as evidence to validate the diagnosis. And the client, having accepted the possibility that the label might be accurate, quickly falls into the trap of seeing the same life problems as symptoms of a childhood full of sexual abuse. Once that belief system is in place, "memories" are not far behind.

Recovered Memory Therapy and False Memory Syndrome

A Patient's Perspective as a Test Case

LAURA PASLEY

With the exception of my former counselor, the names in my story are real. My attorney's name and firm have been used with his permission.

It was Monday, November 18, 1991. My appointment was for 4:00 P.M. I arrived early as I always do. Simpson & Dowd is a law firm in Dallas, Texas, specializing in mental health issues. I was to meet with Skip Simpson, Attorney at Law, along with a couple of other families who had been polluted by a perverse group of therapists. Here I was, meeting a family that I had heard for years were Satanists. Imagine my shock when I read their story in a popular magazine—false accusations, devastation, hurt, pain, humiliation, the separation from their only daughter, a daughter they professed much love for, a daughter I knew well. She was a woman in the same sort of circumstances I was in, needing a reason why she felt so "abnormal." She was a daughter that I watched accuse these people before the rest of the group, to her therapists, to anyone who would listen, just as I had done. Now here I was with her parents in the office of an attorney, attempting to sort out the mess and to help put an end to this senseless destruction of the family system.

As I look back, I wonder how it got this far. How could a relationship with a therapist become the sole focus of my life for four long years? How could I have sold my soul to a mere human being?—a man who, it turns out, has untouched problems in his own life; a man so sick he needed me and other women to stay "sick" in order for him to excel. I trusted this man with my innermost soul. I shared my dreams with him, confessed my sins to him. "Steve" was my mother, my father, my brother, my sister, my best friend, my husband, boyfriend, decision maker, choice maker, teacher and pastor. He had become everything to me. If Steve said it, it was so. My life became so enmeshed and intertwined with his life, my ability to think for myself disappeared. I thought what he wanted me to think. I believed what he wanted me to believe. I became what he wanted me to become. Skeptics might call this a "therapy cult." By any other name it was destructive. How in the world did I allow therapy to become the most important function in my life?

My ordeal began on Friday, December 20, 1985. Steve was supposed to be a specialist in treating eating disorders and I had one in a big way. Since I was ten years old I would eat and then force myself to throw up. By the time I got to Steve I was nearly 32 years of age. For 22 years I had been forcing myself to vomit. When I began therapy, I was binging and purging sometimes 15 to 20 times a day! I would gain weight, lose weight, then gain weight again. I abused laxatives, diuretics and diet pills. I could not deal with feelings of any kind. *Any* emotion would trigger a binge, then a purge. Food was my best friend and my worst enemy. My parents did not know I had bulimia. I did not even know it had a name until 1981. I read an article in the paper and it said this disorder was coming out of the closet and was a widespread problem. At first I was relieved because I had felt so alone and different from other people. Then I became frustrated because there seemed to be no one out there who knew how to treat it.

Then I heard about Steve. He was supposed to be the expert. I was told, "Steve will save your life." "Steve is your answer." "Go to him, trust him, do whatever he says and you will get well." God knows how badly I wanted to be well, how badly I wanted to feel "normal."

I began my journey with Steve by sitting on the couch in his office and spending the next hour with him staring at me. He was overweight and balding but seemed very confident and sure of himself. He seemed to be looking right into my soul. I was very uncomfortable. What few things I was able to tell him did not even seem to faze him. He seemed cold and uncaring and unfeeling. I told him I did not like him staring at me and he asked, "Why is that?"

I snapped back at him, "Hell, I don't know, I just don't like it." After that he only seemed to stare harder. I left my session feeling confused but I was so desperate and determined to end this terrible disorder that had plagued my life since childhood that I was ready to do anything to get my life in order. "Trust him, believe him, he is your answer." So, I put all my energy, all my money, everything into this

therapy. Although much of the time Steve was staring, he also did something else. He was listening.

I was so hungry for someone to listen to me, just listen. To hear what I had to say, no matter what it was. Nobody had ever done that. If I felt something when expressing my feelings I was used to hearing such answers as "You don't really feel that way." "That's not the 'right' way to feel." "You don't really think that." "If you think about those kinds of things, you're gonna make God mad." "He's ashamed of you, I'm ashamed of you, you should be ashamed of you."

Now I had met a man, a parental figure, an authoritative figure who would listen to anything I had to say and not once did he say, "You should be ashamed." With this strategy he won my trust. I began seeing him every week, then twice a week. Steve would have me close my eyes. He would make me keep them closed throughout most of the session. Before long I was saying anything and everything that came into my mind. There were thoughts, ideas, images, and feelings that I had never shared with anyone until now. I never believed I was worth listening to. My heart was so empty and lonely, and for so many years the only comfort I had found was in binging and purging and then binging and purging some more. But now it appeared that someone who could help me cared.

In the beginning of my therapy, I brought with me some very real hurts and disappointments. I had spent five years of my life with a man, loved him deeply, had his child and then he was gone. Not only gone, but he discounted what we had shared for five years. The loss of this relationship alone had put me into a deep depression for several years. Add to that recurring female problems, financial difficulties, raising a child as a single parent and many other things that had my life out of control. Steve was not concerned with those things. In four years of therapy, we never dealt with issues that had occurred in my adult life. Steve was not concerned with those and discounted their importance when I brought them up. He said the pain was "deeper," and that it had been buried, or "repressed." According to Steve, my bulimia was "slow suicide." To have such a "death wish" to the magnitude I had, Steve explained, I had to have repressed something so horrible and so traumatic that only a lengthy therapy, hypnosis, and hard work were going to make me better.

By this time, Steve controlled me. He had bought my loyalty and dependence by giving me the one thing that I was starving for—attention. It was attention with absolutely no boundaries, but plenty of control. I called him anytime I wanted to, day or night, and we talked as long as I needed it, unless he got mad at something I said and hung up in my face. If I showed any concern for my family, he got mad. He said I was hurting myself to protect them. If I was at home when I called him and I was upset or crying, he would have me take a broom and beat the hell out of my bed while he listened on the phone. At times, I would voice concern that my six-year-old daughter was in the house and it might frighten her. He told me I was "showing her how to exhibit anger in a healthy way." I found out years later that this behavior terrified her.

Week after week, session after session, through hypnosis and going deep within myself, strange images began to appear. At first they were images of this tiny blond with the biggest and saddest eyes I have ever seen. Steve said it was my "little girl"—the child within. It was as if I were sitting on a chair as high as the ceiling watching her. Steve wanted me to reveal to him each and every image or movement the "little girl" made.

My first "flashback" came while I was home vacuuming the floor. I had been to therapy earlier in the day. All of a sudden, I broke out into a sweat and I could not breathe. I was in a total panic. It was like a nightmare, only I was awake. I had images of a young boy holding a pillow over the face of an infant. It was a terrifying experience. I called Steve and he "walked" me through the "flashback." After I was calmed down, he literally put me to sleep on the phone. I went to see Steve the next day and my session was very uncomfortable. Steve kept drilling me, "When are you going to accept the fact that your brother tried to kill you?" I argued with him that this was not my brother, it could not have happened in my family. Over and over he said, "You'll have to accept the fact that your brother tried to kill you."

This flashback got Steve's attention, as did all the others. The images in my head got more and more bizarre. I began going to therapy more. I was going to the group room to write, a place where Steve said I would be "safe." Every flashback I had was judged to be actual, factual data from my past. Every dream, no matter how bizarre, was what had actually happened to me. The images grew. The scenes became more and more horrific. Had all of this junk really been hidden in my mind? Were these horrible scenes things that really took place in my family? Was this reality? What was reality? I got caught up in a full circle of flashbacks. They would reach out and snatch me up and engulf me in them at almost any moment. I cannot say where my logical mind was at this point. The flashbacks took control.

Steve told me to ask my doctor for a drug called Xanax, a sedative. I did. I began taking them, as Steve put it, "to take the edge off." I was swallowing them left and right. Soon I needed two, then three, then more. I was playing Russian roulette with my life. I would take a few too many pills and end up in the emergency room and guess who I called? Steve.

What was Steve giving me? The worse the flashback, the more self-destructive I was, the more attention I was getting from the main source for all things in my life. Steve kept telling me, "You have to get worse before you get better." Well, I was definitely getting worse. I was overmedicating myself, vomiting more and more, my weight was climbing. I got no exercise, and my life seemed more out of control than ever before.

In addition, no matter how many times I overmedicated myself or ended up in an emergency room, my doctor kept prescribing Xanax to me. Not only Xanax, but numerous other pills. There were pills to help me sleep, pills to relieve depression, pills to "mellow out my rage." If I had it there was a pill for it, and I took them all. My therapist would goad me, make me angry and push me over the edge and then the doctor would step in and medicate me so I would not be in such a rage. The therapy group in the hospital (I was hospitalized twice in a psychiatric hospital for 30 days each time) would get on a subject and harass me until I was livid and then the nurse would come get me and put me in a little room because I was angry. The nurses at the hospital said they had to take the "control" away from me; yet when I did what they said, I was tagged with being "over compliant." My mind was apparently gone, although at the time I was convinced this was the only way I would ever get well.

I lost control on so many occasions and Steve was the only one who could calm me down, make me "think right" again. I wanted more than anything in the world to be well, to be "normal." In spite of the still small skeptical voice inside of me, doubting, questioning, and wondering, I trusted this man to know the truth. That voice would soon fade over time. I believed in him so deeply I began telling other people, "Trust him, believe in him, he will make you whole." I trusted him so completely, in fact, that in 1986 I spent five months coordinating a retreat for women suffering from bulimia. In that period, I spoke or corresponded with over 350 people suffering from this disorder. I wanted them all to know about Steve. The retreat was held in a beautiful wooded retreat campground in East Texas. There were 77 women and one man in attendance. They came to hear the "truth." I wanted the world to come and hear Steve speak. If he said it I believed it.

It was not long until the "repressed memories" of child abuse began to come up. The visions in my head were of severe physical and sexual abuse. The images were so incredibly bizarre, yet they seemed so real. My picture of my family became distorted. Was it the drugs the doctors had me on, was it television shows or traumatic events I had witnessed over the years, or was it actual memories? I did not know, but Steve said they were fact and to deny them meant that I did not want to get well. He said I was in denial, I was running, I was "protecting" my family, I was staying sick to "cover up" for my family. He always had an answer. He was always right.

I was put into a group therapy situation. This is where my therapy team grew to include Steve's partner, Dave. I did not want to go but Steve said I was just transferring the fear of my family onto the group. He said I must go. At first we all just talked and I found a common ground with the other women. Then, slowly, right before my very eyes, the group emerged into a room full of "victims." We began as Eating Disorders (EDs), then on to Sexual Abuse Victims (SA), then on to Incest Victims (where family members became the perpetrators), then there was Satanic Ritual Abuse Victims (SRAs), and then on to Multiple Personality Disorders (MPD). It was a veritable "disease-of-the-month" laundry list. All of the women systematically had similar flashbacks, uncovered repressed memories and severe abuse. It was eerie at times. Each week we sat in a group and the stories were enough to make a strong stomach sick. One woman might have a flashback one week about her parents or someone else in the family and then the next week another one would have a similar memory come up. My mind became so confused and tormented. It was not long before my own flashbacks got even more bizarre. There was "group sexual abuse," a dead man hanging from a rope, killed by my grandfather, being sexually abused by animals, and much more.

Most of the time, members of the group were advised to stay away from their families and/or anyone who challenged their therapy. There was much anger aimed at all of the parents. If someone had some doubt that a flashback or memory was reality, Steve and Dave would goad them, then the whole group would join in, "You're in denial," "You want to stay sick for your family," "You don't want to get well." This type of input from people we trusted so very much and were so very dependent on kept us enmeshed in their treatment program.

There were many times when a group member was instructed to write her parents (the perpetrators) very hostile and mean letters, divorcing them, accusing them of terrible acts they believed they had done to them. These letters were coached by the group and group leaders. They were always read out loud to the group to get support. In many cases, such as mine, Steve said it would be too dangerous to send my mom a letter with accusations. Some were encouraged to send them and cut off all ties with their families. In my case, because I lived so close to my parents and refused to move, Steve and Dave felt I was in more danger than some of the others.

Once Steve instructed me to write my mother and list every mean thing she had done to me (that is, what I believed she had done at the time). Then, he stood beside me reading every horrible word in the most hateful, hostile tone imaginable. I was standing there with balls of clay, throwing them against the wall. The louder and meaner he read, the harder I threw those balls. It was a very intense session. This was supposed to release my repressed anger. After each session such as this

one I was exhausted. I believe if you constantly fill your head with vile images, it will spit out vile images. Being placed in that situation had my mind being filled with a constant flow of it. Drinking blood, killing babies, sexual abuse of everything imaginable—incest, torture, murder, you name it.

Out of the women in my particular Monday night group, nearly all of them have since realized their "flashbacks" were not reality. Most will not speak out. I am not sure if it is loyalty to Steve and Dave or maybe lack of courage, or an inability to stand up for something that is right. Whatever the reason, it makes me angry because if they would come forward and be outspoken, more people would come out of this delusional state much more quickly.

One woman who was one of my very favorites accused her family of being Satanist. She "divorced" her parents, and her in-laws helped her through the toughest parts of her therapy. She had some horrible flashbacks, including of a baby, supposedly her twin, being hung in a tree and one of herself severely abused by most of her family members. She did question Steve and Dave about the fact that her birth certificate had "single birth" on it. Steve said that the coven had people who took care of all of those things to cover up reality. Later on in her therapy when she seemed to be doing well, she said she wanted to drive to the nearby state her parents lived in and talk to them about all of her "memories." Steve was livid in group and kept trying to talk her out of going. "What about the coven?" he said. He was furious and yelled at her that her life was in danger. This beautiful, petite woman said, "I don't care, I've got to find out." She went home to her parents, talked everything out and made peace with them. Shortly afterward, her mom died of a heart attack. I talked with her just recently and she told me when she went home that time there was absolutely nothing to substantiate her claims of Satanic Ritual Abuse. She said to me, "You know, I live with guilt each and every day of my life about what I did to mom."

My relationship with my family became extremely troubled. My sister would not allow my nephew to spend the night in my home. I looked at my parents with suspicion. Steve had me believing my mother had been trying to kill me for years. Not in an obvious attempt, but in the things she would do for me. I was bulimic. If Mama bought us groceries and any of them were easily ingested "binge foods," Steve said it was to kill me. At one point, I took some badly needed groceries back to her, threw the bag and asked if she was trying to kill me because there were some cookies and chips in the bag. I looked at her with disgust. I suspected her every move, her every motive. I questioned every remark. I missed many family functions and at the ones that I did attend, I was cold and suspicious of everyone there.

For years, I was consumed with suspicion, anger, fear, confusion. Could anyone in the world be trusted? Even my pastor, who was also my dear friend, became suspect when he began "doubting" my therapy. I called him when I was admitted into the hospital in 1988 and he was really upset. He said, "Pasley, you don't belong in a nut house and I will not support this therapy any longer." After that, Steve began telling me that he was using me and wanted to keep me sick. I was losing everyone and everything who meant anything to me.

Police officers who were friends of mine that I worked with (I am an employee of a large police department in Texas) would tell me I was turning into a "pill head." One officer took my purse one night and dumped all of the pills out into the trash. I became so enraged, I jerked the phone out of the wall in the jail and threw it at him. I screamed, "I have to get worse before I get better. This therapy is going to save my life." He told me they were quacks and after my money. Other officers told me I was not acting normally, I was not myself any longer, and that they missed the person I used to be. Steve and Dave would tell me, "The group is your 'new family.' Move away from your family of origin, divorce them, they are dangerous, you will never get well living near them." They even wanted me to quit my job with the police department because they said I was trying to shut my "little girl" up with the violence.

Desperate to be normal, feeling so abnormal, I was in a constant rage for years. I was furious with every single thing that had ever happened to me, or that did not happen to me. My family members had become my enemies— people placed on this earth to destroy me. I could not distinguish memory from reality. Nothing seemed real anymore.

To be sure, my parents made mistakes— plenty of them. But, let's be real. Is there any human being, parent or child, who has not made mistakes? I make them every day with my daughter. I believe the key is to acknowledge them, ask for forgiveness, and move forward. I also believe it is important for our children to see us as human, not to continually profess perfection. The question here in my case is, were my parents intentionally trying to destroy me? Of course not. But this is precisely what my therapy team, my group family made me believe.

My family's response to accusations I made would not have mattered. If they said nothing, it was because they were guilty. If they cried innocence, they were trying to hide something. If they did not remember something the way I remembered it, they were in denial. There was always an answer. This was ingrained into every conversation and thought I had. I was told to read books about evil, sexual abuse, dysfunctional families, co-dependency, etc. Some of the required reading was *People of the Lie, Courage to Heal, Healing the Shame That Binds You, On Becoming a Person*, and *The Child Within*. I "lived" therapy seven days a week, 24 hours a day, 365 days a year. When I was not at therapy, I was calling my therapist.

When I was not talking to my therapist, I was thinking about my therapy. The entire ordeal consumed every ounce of energy I had and every penny I could get my hands on. All of this was "necessary" for me to "get well." Steve repeatedly told me, "You have to get worse before you get better." I continued to get worse believing this was progress.

One lesson from this experience is that we can never underestimate what a desperate person will do. Any person, no matter how bright or intelligent, if they are desperate enough, can fall into the same pit I fell into. I had worked in a jail for a large city in Texas since I was 19 years old. I knew the correct name for every charge in the Texas Penal Code, the Penal Code number and the penalty class. I could tell you what kind of time you could get for nearly every crime listed in our penal code. I could catch an error on an arrest report with a simple glance, book a drunk in 30 seconds, and usually determine the elements of arrest if I chose to read the report. I mastered county and city computers. I could research a criminal history and "find" just about anyone. I know literally hundreds of police officers, most of their badge numbers, and most of them would do nearly anything for me. Before entering this therapy situation, I had many commendations and was nominated by my sergeant for Non-Sworn Employee of the Year. After getting into therapy, I was still good at what I did, but my work, the officers, my daughter, everything took a back seat. By the time I left therapy, I had expended all of my sick time, my vacation time and came close to being fired over one of my stays in the hospital. I was also on the verge of losing my home. Was this progress?

I believe the worst part of this type of therapy is living through the flashbacks. It was frightening and left me empty and drained. I would literally "feel" pain of the things I was seeing in my head. My mother became my sexual abuser, then my brother and grandfather and a neighbor. The sexual abuse was vivid and seemed so real. Ordinary objects terrified me because they were sexual abuse tools in my flashbacks. It started out with simple fondling or molestation; it ended with torture, torment and indescribable pain.

I would emerge from one of these flashbacks and feel such rage. At times, I believe I was homicidal. My nostrils would flare and I would throw things, rant and rave, chain smoke, sometimes two cigarettes at one time, lock myself in the bedroom and pace back and forth. I used to scream and pray to God, "Why did you let these things happen to me?" "What did I ever do to anyone to merit this kind of pain?" Confusion at this point was a way of life for me.

My anger was constant. My therapy also included "rage reduction." It consisted of throwing things like clay, bean bags, etc. I was ripping phone books, beating with bataaka bats and screaming into pillows. I personally got more relief from breaking glass. I would drive down the street and throw coke bottles into the ground. When they would shatter, it was like a sedative, temporarily. These things were supposed to decrease my "repressed anger." In essence, the more anger I expressed, the madder I got. I was in a constant state of rage. After a flashback, Steve would have me direct that rage at Mama. He literally hated my mother. He would insult her, distorting everything that she said or did. Once, she wrote a check for my therapy because I simply did not have the money and he tore it up in my face. "I don't want her money," he said. (He then added it to my bill.) My mother knew better than to speak against Steve. I would not tolerate that. He was going to save me.

I spent four years with this therapy team. After four years, I wanted to do more. I wanted to be more. I was at the point of feeling like I would never get well. There was no hope for me, I was too far gone. I wanted to make the best of my life. I called Steve on December 20,

1989, exactly four years after I had walked into his office. I said I wanted to write a book about my experiences in the jail. I had contacted an author of a book about police and felt sure he would help me get started. Steve was quiet. I asked him if he thought I could do this. I waited, listening like a child waiting for approval from a parent. The words that followed tore into me, stinging me to the core of my being. "You are not through with flashbacks."

Disenchanted. Angry. Frustrated. I terminated my therapy. I grieved so much for them I had to enter therapy with another counselor to get through it. I went to her, telling her the same stories I had come to believe in therapy about my family. I spent the next 22 months still convinced these things had happened to me.

In October, 1991, I picked up an article on a family who had been accused of horrible abuse by their daughter in therapy. I was at Kroger and never left the parking lot until I had read every single word. The daughter was in therapy with me. I had listened to her pain and suffering. Now, I was getting another side to this picture. Steve and Dave insisted these people were Satanists—the cruelest, meanest people in the world. They had committed indescribable acts on their children. What really interested me was that some of the "stories" I had heard from Steve and Dave were presented differently than those in the article. Could Steve and Dave maybe have lied to me? Lied to us all? I was glued to the article. Then, after I read it, I drove home and read it again. I wanted to know these people. I wanted to meet them and see for myself that they were not really what I had heard. In meeting them and seeing the severe contrast to what I had heard, I was able to begin to discern my reality. They had lied to me—the con job of all con jobs.

This therapy has snatched something from me that I can never get back. I lost years of my life where I was emotionally distant from my family and my daughter. There was pain, despair, humiliation, fear, and frustration. It caused me to be paranoid. I have had trouble trusting anyone. Professionals had me scared to death, even ones there to help me. My daughter and I had no financial security and nearly lost our home. I did not have a car that ran. All my energy, all my money, everything I had went to them. When I woke up, my daughter was 12 years old and I missed it. I missed some of her most precious years while searching endlessly for the next "memory."

With the help of Skip Simpson, his law firm, my faith in God and the support of family and friends, I have held these two men accountable for what they did to me and my daughter. They were responsible for unethical, unprofessional treatment of me and my child. They injured us and it will take a long time to undo the damage. On December 19, 1991, Skip filed a lawsuit on behalf of myself and my daughter, Jennifer. We sued them, in part, for creating false memories, for giving me substandard care, for therapeutic negligence, and for fraud. It was extremely hard to trust anyone, especially an attorney. It was quite a while before I felt I could trust Skip but through his being trustworthy, I am learning to trust again. Now, however, I do it with my thinking cap on. I have learned through all of this that no one, not one single person in this world, has all of the answers. One of the quickest ways to turn me off is for someone to tell me "This is the only answer, the only way." I am now into critical thinking and proper skepticism. I look back now and see so many things that were just not logical. I will never again allow another person to control my mind or my life.

On June 25, 1993, Skip Simpson called me at work. He told me they were having a meeting to possibly settle my case and for me to stay by the phone. When the call came, I went to his office. We talked and he gave me two options for a settlement. We decided which would be the best one for my particular situation and that of my daughter. He went downstairs and moments later came back up. He said, "It's over." Tears were streaming down my face. We hugged. I looked at this man who had taken my case before he knew it was a national problem, believed in me before I could believe in myself, and I said, "You helped me get my power back from those who took it from me. I have my mind back and for this, I cannot thank you enough." (As a condition of my settlement I cannot disclose the settlement amount, the location where I was treated, or the names of my counselors.)

My life has changed so drastically this past year. Since my case broke on the news I have been talking with people all over the country who have lost children to this therapy, and adults who have absolutely had their lives destroyed and lost everything by being in it. I was speaking in Illinois and we got picketed. The signs read, "We believe the children." I would like to ask at what point do they believe the children? Is it when they are insisting nothing happened, or, after they place them with a social worker, or therapist with an agenda, who spends hours, days, weeks and months trying to get them to say what they want them to say?

What happened to me is not about sexual abuse or child abuse by a parent. It is about therapeutic negligence and fraud. We must begin to think critically about this situation. If we do not do something to stop this, the family structure as we know it will be gone. Families have been shattered and homes destroyed because troubled, hurting, vulnerable people

sought out help and those who have taken an oath to do no harm abused the trust placed in them and did, in fact, harm. They not only hurt the patient, they destroy the patient's parents, siblings, their own children, and virtually anyone else who has been in their lives.

My life now is only getting better because I am not into the blame game any longer. I am no longer searching out "memories." After only one year with a good competent counselor, and two years working with an attorney who refuses to treat me like a "mental patient," I have begun to rebuild my life. Skip Simpson had faith in me and recognized my strength before I could see it. I responded to him because he treated me like I had a brain. He expected me to use it. The pain of what I went through is still there; however, I now take responsibility for my own life, for changing it the way I want it to be. I could sit forever and worry about the past and what this one or that one did or did not do, but the ultimate choice for my life is mine to make. I now take that challenge.

If you have been affected by this type of therapy, or are interested in further information on the subject, please contact the False Memory Syndrome Foundation, 3401 Market, Suite 130, Philadelphia, PA 19104. 800/568-8882.

To obtain a copy of *True Stories of False Memories* by Eleanor Goldstein and Kevin Farmer, in which Laura Pasley's story appears, contact the SIRS Publishing Company: 800/232-7477.

Recovered Memory Therapy and False Memory Syndrome

A Psychiatrist's Perspective as a Test Case

JOHN HOCHMAN

Thousands of patients (mostly women) in the United States have undergone or are undergoing attempted treatment by psychotherapists for a non-existent memory disorder. As a result, these same therapists have unwittingly promoted the development of a real memory disorder: False Memory Syndrome. To make sense of this unfortunate situation, I need to offer a few definitions.

Some psychotherapists believe that childhood sexual abuse is the specific cause of numerous physical and mental ills later in life. Some term this Incest Survivor Syndrome (ISS). There is no firm evidence that this is the case, since even where there has been documented sexual abuse during childhood, there are numerous other factors that can explain physical or emotional complaints that appear years later in an adult.

These therapists believe that the children immediately repress all memory of sexual abuse shortly after it occurs, causing it to vanish from recollection without a trace. The price for having repressed memories is said to be the eventual development of ISS.

Therapists attempt to "cure" ISS by engaging patients in recovered memory therapy (RMT), a hodge-podge of techniques varying with each therapist. The purpose of RMT is to enable the patient to recover into consciousness not only wholly accurate recollections of ancient sexual traumas, but also repressed body memories (such as physical pains) that occurred at the time of the traumas.

In actuality, RMT produces disturbing fantasies which are misperceived by the patient and misinterpreted by the therapist as memories. Mislabeled by the therapist and patient as recovered memories, they are actually false memories.

The vast majority of false memory cases developing from RMT are in women, which is why this article assumes patients to be female.

Initiation of Patients into RMT

A woman consults a psychotherapist for relief of various emotional complaints. The therapist informs her that she may have been molested as a child and does not know it, and this could explain her symptoms. Some patients think this idea is absurd and go to another therapist; others accept the therapist's suggestions and stay on. More than a few women have heard about repressed memories from talk shows or tabloids even prior to coming to the therapist's office, and may even make the appointment believing they too could be "victims."

Though the patient has no memories of abuse, she becomes motivated for "memory recovery" since she is told this will cure her symptoms. The therapist will offer encouragement that "memories" will return. Suggestive dreams or new pains are interpreted by the therapist as proof that repressed memories are lurking.

The therapist may refer the patient to a "survivor recovery group." There she will meet women who further encourage her to keep trying to remember. Attendance at these support groups, as well as assigned reading in self-help books, surrounds the patient with validation for the therapist's theories.

The vast majority of women with FMS are white, middle class, and above average in education. This corresponds to the profile of a typical woman who enters long term psychotherapy, and who perceives such activity as an important way to solve life's problems.

Generating False Memories

Unlike courts of law which obtain objective evidence where allegations of evil-doing are made, RMT solely directs the patient to attend toward her inner world for "proof" she was sexually abused. Such RMT techniques may include:

– Meditation on fantasy production, such as pictures drawn in "art therapy," dreams, or stream of consciousness journal writing.

– Hearing or reading about the "recovered memories" of other women which can serve as inspirations.
– Amytal interviews ("truth serum") and/or hypnosis (including "age regression" where the patient is told she is temporarily being transformed into the way she was when she was five years old).
– Telling the patient to review family albums; if she looks sad in some of her childhood photos, she is told this is further confirmation that abuse occurred.

The Dark Side of "Recovery"

Patients start out RMT with the hope that things will be better once they recover their repressed memories. But usually life becomes far more complicated.

The FMS patient will often become estranged from the "perpetrator" (most often her father). If the patient has small children, they will be off limits to "perpetrators" as well. Relationships with other family members become contingent on their not challenging the patient's beliefs.

Therapists may urge parents to come for a "family conference" in order to allow the patient to surprise the "perpetrator" with a rehearsed confrontation. Family members are usually too shocked and disorganized to coherently respond to accusations. The rationale for this scenario is that since "survivors" feel powerless, they need "empowerment."

FMS patients may file belated crime reports with local law enforcement agencies and may go on to sue "perpetrators." Such lawsuits demand compensation for bills from psychotherapists and possibly other doctors who treated adult medical problems that therapists somehow link to childhood traumas. Of course, there may be demands for "punitive damages." Spouses of "perpetrators" (usually the patient's mother) may be sued as well for being negligent, thus making householder's insurance into a courtroom piggy bank. Since FMS patients sincerely believe they have been victimized, more than a few juries have given verdicts sympathetic to them.

Preoccupied with the continuing chores of "memory recovery," the FMS patient may come to ignore more pressing problems with her marriage, family, schooling, or career. Often the time demands and expense of the therapy itself become a major life disruption.

Some patients during the course of RMT develop "multiple personality disorder" (MPD). RMT therapists have claimed that they need to not only recover repressed memories, but also to uncover repressed personality fragments; some women come to believe they are repositories of dozens of hidden personalities ("alters"). "Alters" have their own names and characteristics, and may identify themselves as men or even animals. An increasing number of psychiatrists and psychologists are coming to view MPD as a product of environmental suggestion and reinforcement, since the diagnosis was hardly made prior to ten years ago. One area where there is no controversy: once MPD is diagnosed, therapy bills become astronomical.

Some FMS patients become convinced that their abuse was actually "satanic ritual abuse" (SRA), due to participation by relatives in a secret satanic cult. Some therapists believe SRA is the work of a vast underground cult network in these United States. No evidence beyond "recovered memories" has ever been offered as proof that satanic cults exist at this claimed level of frequency. Therapists who lecture on the topic have explained away the lack of evidence that such cults exist by claiming that no defectors speak out due to iron-clad secrecy via brainwashing and terror.

The Care and Maintenance of False Memories

FMS involves a combination of mistaken perceptions and false beliefs. The fledgling FMS patient is encouraged to "connect" with an environment that will reinforce the FMS state, and is encouraged to "disconnect" from people or information that might lead her to question the results of RMT.

The FMS subculture is victim-oriented. Even though they have not undergone anti-cancer chemotherapy or walked away from airplane crashes, FMS patients are told they too are "survivors." This becomes a kind of new identity, giving FMS patients the feeling of a strong bond with other "survivors" of abuse. Patients will often start attending "survivor" support groups, subscribe to "survivor" newsletters, or even attend "survivor" conventions (sometimes with their therapists).

They will read books found in "recovery" sections of bookstores. The best known book, *The Courage to Heal*, is weighty, literate, and thus appears authoritative. Authors Laura Davis and Ellen Bass have no formal training in psychology, psychiatry, or memory. This paperback, modestly priced at $20, has sold over 700,000 copies.

Patients are told to shy away from dialogue with skeptical friends or relatives, since this will hinder their "recovery." "Perpetrators" who proclaim their innocence cannot be taken seriously since they are "in denial" and incapable of telling the truth.

Aside from these social influences, people by nature often resist seeing themselves as being in error. It can be terribly painful to acknowledge having made a big mistake, particularly when harmful consequences have resulted.

RMT exploits the tendency within each of us to blame others for our problems, and to latch onto simple answers for life's complicated problems. RMT therapists suggest that aside from entirely ruining childhoods, childhood sexual abuse can explain anything and everything that goes wrong during adulthood. RMT becomes the ultimate crybaby therapy.

How Memory Really Works

In Freud's theory of "repression" the mind automatically banishes traumatic events from memory to prevent overwhelming anxiety. Freud further theorized that repressed memories cause "neurosis," which could be cured if the memories were made conscious. While all this is taught in introductory psychology courses and has been taken by novelists and screenwriters to be a truism, Freud's repression theory has never been verified by rigorous scientific proof.

Freud, were he alive today, would be traumatized to see how RMT has redefined his pet concept. While Freud talked of the repression of single traumatic episodes, today's therapists maintain that dozens of similar traumatic episodes occurring over years are repressed with 100% efficiency.

The well known syndrome of Post Traumatic Stress Disorder shows us that verifiable traumatic events, rather than disappearing from memory, leave trauma victims haunted by intrusive memories in which the victim relives the trauma. For those who were in Nazi concentration camps or underwent torture as POWs in Vietnam, this can become a serious lifelong problem.

People forget most of what occurs to them, including some events that were pleasant or significant to them at the time. If an event is lost from memory, there is no scientific way to prove whether it was "repressed" or simply forgotten. And there is no reason that memories of sexual abuse should be handled any differently than childhood memories of physical abuse or of emergency surgery.

Events that have slipped away from memory cannot be recalled with the accuracy of a videotape. Individuals forget not only insignificant events in their entirety, but also significant events. Some events (traumatic or not) are recalled, but with significant details altered.

A study of children whose school was attacked by a sniper showed that some who were not on the school grounds later insisted they had personal recollections of being in school during the attack. These false memories apparently were inspired by exposure to the stories of those who truly experienced the trauma.

Memories can be deliberately distorted in adults by presenting a display of visual information, and later exposing subjects to verbal disinformation about what they saw. This disinformation often becomes incorporated into memory, contaminating the ultimate memories that are recalled.

To be sure, some who enter therapy were abused as children, but they have always remembered this abuse. They do not need special help in "memory recovery" to tell the therapist what happened to them.

Why Recovered Memory Therapy Is Bad Therapy

RMT purportedly is undertaken to help patients recover from the effects of sexual abuse from childhood; however, at the onset of RMT there is no evidence that such abuse ever occurred. Thus, instead of a therapist having some evidence for a diagnosis and then adopting a proper treatment plan, RMT therapists use the "treatment" to produce their diagnosis.

Some RMT therapists over-attribute common psychological complaints as signs of forgotten childhood sexual abuse. In their zeal to find memories, these therapists overlook any and all alternative explanations for the patient's complaints.

RMT therapists ignore basic psychological principles that all individuals are suggestible, and that patients in distress seeking psychotherapy are particularly likely to adopt beliefs and biases of their therapist.

Many RMT therapists have studied neither basic sciences related to memory nor the diagnosis of actual diseases of memory. Their knowledge is often based on a single weekend seminar, as opposed to years of formal training in any graduate program they attended to get their licenses.

Hypnosis and sodium amytal administration ("truth serum") are unacceptable procedures for memory recovery. Courts reject hypnosis as a memory aid. Subjects receiving hypnosis or amytal as general memory aids (even in instances where there is no question of sexual abuse) will often generate false memories. Upon returning to their normal state of consciousness, subjects assume all their refreshed "memories" are equally true.

RMT therapists generally make no attempt to verify "recovered memories" by interviewing third parties, or obtaining pediatric or school records. Some have explained that they do not verify the serious allegations that arise from RMT because their job is simply to help the patient feel "safe" and "recover."

Many patients who have known all their lives that they were mistreated or neglected by their parents decide as adults to be friends with the offending parents. By contrast, RMT therapists encourage their patients, on the basis of "recovered memories," to break off relationships with the alleged "perpetrators" as well as other relatives who disagree with the patient's views. This is completely at odds with the traditional goals of therapists: to allow competent patients to make their own important decisions, and to improve their patient's relationships with others.

Patients undergoing RMT often undergo an increase of symptoms as their treatment progresses, with corresponding disruption in their personal lives. Few therapists will seek consultation in order to clarify the problem, assuming instead that it is due to sexual abuse having been worse than anyone might have imagined.

Other Kinds of FMS

Some individuals come to believe that they lived "past lives" as a result of having undergone "past life therapy." This phenomenon generally develops in participants who are grounded in the New Age zeitgeist and already open to "discovering" their past lives. They enroll in seminars which can run up to an entire weekend and will involve some measure of group hypnotic induction and guided meditations. This sort of FMS also involves continuing group reinforcement. In contrast to horrific images of sexual abuse, recollections of "past lives" are generally pleasant and interesting. Few participants will recall spending prior lives in lunatic asylums or dungeons. The whole experience is assumed to be therapeutic by helping participants better understand the situation of their present lives.

A small number of individuals develop "recovered memories" of being abducted by aliens from outer space. Almost always these individuals had some curiosity about this area and were hardly skeptics before they fell into an alien abduction FMS.

In contrast to women who are plagued with concerns that they were sexually abused, these varieties of FMS are of a much more benign nature and do not disrupt personal functioning or family life. While some of these individuals suffer the ignominy of being perceived as "kooks," they may receive compensating group support from those who share their beliefs.

A Word about the Future

Increasing numbers of women who claimed to have recovered memories of sexual abuse have retracted their claims and now see themselves as having had FMS. This may spontaneously occur when women relocate to another locale and lose contact with their prior therapists and support group. Without the "positive reinforcement" from others to encourage false memory development and maintenance, some women begin to doubt the veracity of what they had believed was true. While some remain suspended in a twilight of doubt, others have fully recanted.

These retractors may have a profound influence on getting women with an active FMS to re-evaluate their situation. While FMS patients learn from the FMS culture to dismiss critics as either "perpetrators" or their apologists, the voice of a woman who says she is recovering from FMS is more easily heard.

Although most influential among family counselors and social workers, RMT affected the practices of some licensed psychologists and psychiatrists, some of whom were practicing in special "dissociative disorders units" in psychiatric hospitals. These activities have gone on with little challenge, until recently.

The number of women with FMS who have become retractors is increasing. Some have sued their former therapists for malpractice (see Laura Pasley's story in the previous entry), and others are weighing the possibilities of doing so. One malpractice insurance carrier for clinical psychologists in California recently tripled its rates without explanation; this has led to speculation that the carrier is anticipating increasing numbers of lawsuits alleging that psychologists caused FMS.

The False Memory Syndrome Foundation, formed in 1991, has been contacted by over 7,000 families in the U.S. and Canada who believe their grown children have FMS, and these families let their views be known to state licensing boards and professional organizations. Managed care administrators are starting to question megabills submitted by RMT therapists, some of whom see their patients through lengthy psychiatric hospitalizations. Understandably, all of this has gained the attention of the American Psychiatric Association and American Psychological Association, who are setting up task forces to try to examine the whole phenomenon.

Meanwhile, there is a large FMS subculture consisting of women convinced that their "recovered memories" are accurate, therapists keeping busy doing RMT, and of authors on the "recovery" lecture and talk show circuits. In addition, there are some vocal fringes of the feminist movement that cherish RMT since it is "proof" that men are dangerous and rotten, unless proven otherwise. Skeptical challenges to RMT are met by emotional rejoinders that critics are front groups for perpetrators, and make the ridiculous analogy that "some people even say the Holocaust did not happen."

RMT will eventually disappear, but it will take time.

4

SCIENCE AND PSEUDOSCIENCE—
FOR AND AGAINST

Evolutionary Psychology as Good Science

FRANK MIELE

Is "the fault, dear Brutus, not in our stars but in ourselves?" In our genes? Or in our jeans? Why do some "bestride the narrow world like a Colossus" while other "petty men [most of us] peep about to find ourselves dishonorable graves"? Are not men, as Shakespeare suggested in *Julius Caesar*, at least sometimes "masters of their fates"? Or, as Jack Nicholson's "average horny little devil" asks about the differences between men and women, in the film version of Updike's *The Witches of Eastwick*:

> Do you think God knew what he was doing ... or do you think it was just another of his minor mistakes—like tidal waves, earthquakes, floods. . . . When we make mistakes, they call it evil; God makes mistakes, they call it nature.

A mistake? Or did he do it on purpose? Because if it's a mistake, maybe we can do something about it—find a cure; invent a vaccine; build up our immune system.

Throughout most of human history, the answers to these questions have come from myth or literature. Starting with the Enlightenment, however, the answers have usually been couched in the allegedly "objective findings" of either history or science. Since the end of World War II, the "standard model of social science," as summarized by Robert Wright in his very readable introduction to evolutionary psychology, skeptically (if not cynically) titled *The Moral Animal*, has held that "the uniquely malleable human mind, together with the unique force of culture, has severed our behavior from its evolutionary roots; . . . [and] there is no inherent human nature driving events . . . our essential nature is to be driven" (1994, 5).

For example, Emile Durkheim, the patriarch of modern sociology, referred to human nature as "merely the indeterminate material that the social factor molds and transforms." He argued that even such deeply felt emotions as sexual jealousy, a father's love of his child, or the child's love of the father are "far from being inherent in human nature." Robert Lowie, a founding father of American cultural anthropology, argued that "the principles of psychology are as incapable of accounting for the phenomena of culture as is gravitation to account for architectural styles." Ruth Benedict, one of the founding mothers of American anthropology, and a crusader against the theory of racial differences (which was the norm in pre–World War II days), wrote that "we must accept all the implications of our human inheritance, one of the most important of which is the small scope of biologically transmitted behavior, and the enormous role of the cultural process of transmission of tradition." (All quotes from Wright, 1994.) B. F. Skinner founded the school of behavioral psychology, dominant in American psychology in the 1950s and 1960s, on the bedrock assumption that human and animal behavior could be accounted for in terms of rewards and punishments.

To all of this, evolutionary psychologists reply with the gusto of a Wayne and Garth "NOT!" Human nature is real, it is important, and it isn't going to go away. Here is a sampling of the sorts of questions evolutionary psychologists ask and attempt to answer:

- Are we all naturally the same or naturally different?
- Is our mind all of one piece or is it composed of modules?
- Are we naturally moral and good and only become evil through circumstance, or are we naturally evil and only made good through enforced circumstance?
- Why are men and women so different?
- Do men naturally want young and beautiful women—and as many as they can get?
- Do women naturally want rich and powerful men—and a bonded, monogamous, caring relationship?
- Are men naturally turned on (maybe too turned on) by the sight of a woman—or even a silhouette or cartoon of one?
- Do men like sex more than women do? If so, why?
- Just how much does a man's or woman's looks tell a member of the opposite sex about them and their value as a potential mate?
- Why do men get turned on by "lips like rubies, eyes like limpid pools, and skin like silk"? And why do women spend so much time and money trying to achieve and reinforce that appearance?
- Why do human males have such large penises relative to our nearest primate relatives the great apes?
- Do some human groups, on average, have larger (and therefore less ape-like) penises than other groups? If so, why?

- Why do human females have such large breasts relative to our nearest primate relatives the great apes?
- Do dominant Alpha Males have all the fun and leave the most descendants, or do "Sneaky Fuckers" beat them at their own game?
- Why do women have orgasms?
- Why do cute, lovable children so quickly transmogrify into wild, ungrateful teenagers?
- Why, as we grow old, do we feel, in the words of retiring Supreme Court Justice Thurgood Marshall, that we're "just fallin' apart"?
- Do men naturally form power pyramids and hierarchies while women naturally form cliques?
- Do we naturally partition the world into US v. THEM?
- Does maternal instinct explain why moms usually act like moms, while dads all too often act like cads?
- Do we naturally prefer those who physically resemble us and find them to be more like us in other ways as well?

Are such questions even scientifically meaningful or do they more properly fall in the realm of religion, literature, or politics? They are certainly great openers to liven up even the dullest party. But the new and emerging field of evolutionary psychology, building on work from Charles Darwin's *Descent of Man* and *The Expression of Emotion in Man and Animals,* tells us that the answers to these age-old questions, dear Brutus, are in our evolutionary history and our genes. And they claim they've got the "bloody daggers" to prove it!

This introduction cannot examine the evolutionary argument on each of these points. Instead, it merely outlines the case and describes the type of evidence and the nature of the arguments to be placed before you, the skeptical jury. The references in the bibliography provide a more complete "transcript." The article that follows presents a case against evolutionary explanations of human behavior.

From Survival of the Fittest to Inclusive Fitness

The fundamental theorem upon which evolutionary psychology is based is that behavior (just like anatomy and physiology) is in large part inherited and that every organism acts (consciously or not) to enhance its inclusive fitness—to increase the frequency and distribution of its selfish genes in future generations. And those genes exist not only in the individual but in his or her identical twin (100%), siblings (on average, 50%), cousins (on average, 25%) and so on down the kinship line. Thus, aid to and feelings for relatives make evolutionary sense.

This revision and extension of Darwinian evolution, from "survival of the fittest" to inclusive fitness, was worked out primarily by George Williams (in the US) and by William Hamilton and John Maynard Smith (in the UK) in the 1960s, with some clever twists added by Robert Trivers (in the US) in the 1970s. How efficiently can the Darwinian mill grind? they asked. It largely depends on the type of grain fed in. Darwinian selection operates most effectively if the units on which it is working:

1. are more, rather than less, variable;
2. have shorter, rather than longer, lifetimes;
3. are more heritable, rather than environmental.

Richard Alexander (1979) has argued convincingly that "genes are the most persistent of all living units, hence on all counts the most likely units of selection. One may say that genes evolved to survive by reproducing, and they have evolved to reproduce by creating and guiding the conduct and fate of all the units above them" (38).

Implicit in this reasoning is the conclusion that species and populations (races) are very unlikely units of selection. Hence, all talk of individuals doing things, especially dying, for the good of the species or the race appears improbable if not downright impossible. But if that is the case, then how could any sort of cooperative behavior, of which there are as many examples all around us as there are of competitive behavior, have ever evolved?

Well, humans, like most complex species, don't pass on their genes by simply dividing and producing exact replicas of themselves the way amoebas do. It takes at least two, not only to tango, but to reproduce. While you need not share any genes with your mate, you must share some, but not necessarily all of them with your relatives (except in the interesting case of an identical twin, who shares all your genes). Work out the arithmetic and it produces some interesting consequences in terms of whom you should help and when, as summarized in Figure 1 (adapted from Alexander, 1979). Rather than anything so simple as either "every man for himself" or "all for one and one for all," Figure 1 shows that, like it or not, you're stuck in a complex, time-directed matrix of cooperation, competition, trust, and deception with all your blood relatives and even those you might think are blood relatives.

Appropriately enough, you watch out for Number 1 first; your parents, children, and full siblings next; and so on in order of decreasing genetic similarity. But given that time's arrow flies in one direction only, you have a better chance of passing on your genes by helping your children than by helping your aging parents.

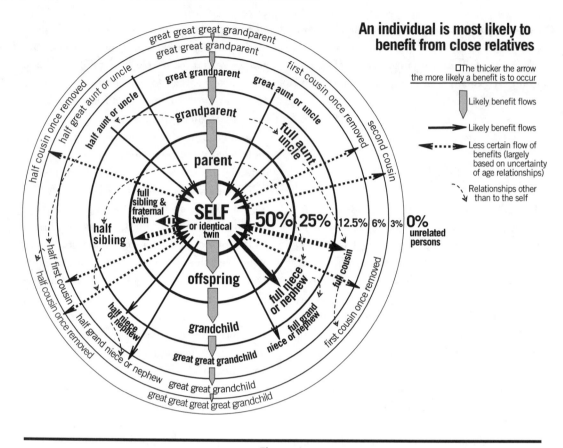

Figure 1

Symons Says

What does evolutionary theory predict you should expect from your mates? The answer is even more disconcerting. A corollary to the fundamental theorem is that the differences between males and females in humans, just as in most mammalian species, are readily explainable in terms of differential parental investment. That is, the male contributions to the reproductive process—lots of sperm and a few minutes of light work—are plentiful and cheap, short and pleasurable; while the female contributions—eggs and months of pregnancy—are rare and expensive, long, dangerous, and often painful. Given that, the best way for a male to maximize his inclusive fitness is to . . . well, diversify his genetic portfolio; while the

best way for a female to insure the survival of the baby she has invested so much time and effort in is to try and get that guy to meet his monthly payments.

In *The Evolution of Human Sexuality* (27, 1979), anthropologist Donald Symons provides evolutionary psychology's point-by-point reply to "the horny little devil's" soliloquy on men and women:

1. Intrasexual competition generally is much more intense among males than among females, and in preliterate societies competition over women probably is the single most important cause of violence.

2. Men incline to polygyny, whereas women are more malleable in this respect and,

depending on the circumstances, may be equally satisfied in polygynous [one male–multiple females], monogamous, or polyandrous [one female–multiple males] marriages.

3. Almost universally, men experience sexual jealousy of their mates. Women are more malleable in this respect, but in certain circumstances, women's experience of sexual jealousy may be characteristically as intense as men's.

4. Men are much more likely to be sexually aroused by the sight of women and the female genitals than women are by the sight of men and the male genitals. Such arousal must be distinguished from arousal produced by the sight of, or the description of, an actual sexual encounter, since male-female differences in the latter may be minimal.

5. Physical characteristics, especially those that correlate with youth, are by far the most important determinants of women's sexual attractiveness. Physical characteristics are somewhat less important determinants of men's sexual attractiveness; political and economic prowess are more important; and youth is relatively unimportant.

6. Much more than women, men are predisposed to desire a variety of sex partners for the sake of variety.

7. Among all peoples, copulation is considered to be essentially a service or favor that women render to men, and not vice versa, regardless of which sex derives or is thought to derive greater pleasure from sexual intercourse.

To many, this sets a new standard in arguing for the inherent and therefore inescapable nature of the double standard. What evidence is there to support the argument that male-female differences are so deeply rooted in our nature? Anthropologists Lionel Tiger and

Robin Fox argued in 1971 in *The Imperial Animal* that if "we look at enough primates to see what we all have in common, we'll get some idea of what it was we evolved from. If we see what we had to change from to get to be what we are now, it might help to explain what we in fact are."

Of Belles and Balls

Figures 2 and 3 are adapted from Jared Diamond's *The Third Chimpanzee* (73–74). They compare the relevant male and female anatomy for humans and our nearest living relatives, the great apes.

First look at the amount of sexual dimorphism in the four species. As Diamond notes, "chimps of both sexes weigh about the same; men are slightly larger than women, but male orangutans and gorillas are much bigger than females" (73). These are interesting facts from comparative anatomy, but what do they have to do with behavior? Throughout the animal kingdom, polygynous species (i.e., those in which each dominant male breeds with multiple females) are sexually dimorphic. This makes sense from an evolutionary point of view. The only way a male can pass on his genes is to breed with a female, and to better the odds, the more the merrier. But since there are only so many females to go around, from day one males are in competition with other males for those females. An arms race begins in which males are selected for their ability to win out against other males for access to the females. And since nothing escalates like an arms race, you end up with male gorillas and orangs that are not only twice the size of the females, but armed with huge canines, and loaded with secondary sexual characteristics like crested heads and silver backs that are easily recognizable at a distance and help to attract mates.

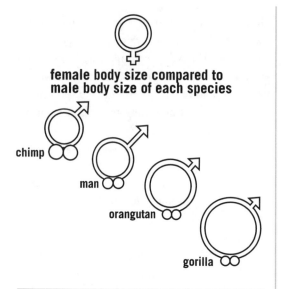

female body size compared to male body size of each species

chimp

man

orangutan

gorilla

Figure 2

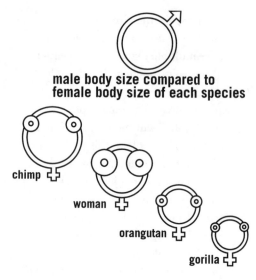

male body size compared to female body size of each species

chimp

woman

orangutan

gorilla

Figure 3

Chimps, on the other hand, show little sexual dimorphism, less even than humans. The gibbon (an ape, but not a great one) shows the least sexual dimorphism. Males and females look identical at a distance and the gibbons' strict adherence to monogamy should win an award from the Moral Majority (though that would mean acknowledging man's common primate ancestry and therefore ditching creationism). Going simply by the dope sheet of sexual dimorphism, an evolutionary handicapper would bet the rent that *Homo sapiens* would, by nature, be mildly polygynous. And he'd walk away from the pay window a big winner. A cross-cultural analysis of 853 societies revealed that 83% of them are polygynous. Polygyny occurs frequently, even when legally prohibited. There are an estimated 25,000 to 35,000 polygynous marriages in the US; a study of 437 financially successful American men found that some maintained two separate families, each unknown to the other (Buss, 177–178). Polyandry (one female with multiple males), on the other hand, is "virtually absent" among hunter/gatherers and confined to "agriculturalists and pastoralists living

under very difficult economic conditions" and disappears quickly "when more usual conditions are present" (Symons, 225).

To move on from gross anatomy to gross discourse, if the male gorilla is so big and tough, how come he has such small balls? How does evolutionary theory account for those differences in testicle, penis, and breast size? It may be a tough climb to the top of the male gorilla dominance pyramid, but once there, things become quieter. Until dethroned, you have virtually uncontested access to all the females, so sex is no big thing. In fact, the dominant male with a harem of females "experiences sex as a rare treat: if he is lucky, a few times a year" (Diamond, 73). So just a little bit of sperm goes a long way to insuring the male gorilla's inclusive fitness.

For the minimally sexually dimorphic chimp, things get a little dicier. Chimps do have power pyramids. Compared to the gorilla and the orang, their hierarchies are so complex that Frans de Waal entitled his study of them *Chimpanzee Politics*. Getting to the top and staying there calls more for the skills of a Machiavelli than of a Mike Tyson. Dominant males have frequent though not exclusive access to the females. Rather than simply their bodies, it is their sperm that must compete against those of their fellow dominants, as well as those of the occasional "sneaky fucker." And all of this follows directly from one of the triumphs of evolutionary biology—the Theory of Testicle Size. To wit, "species that copulate more often need bigger testes; and promiscuous species in which several males routinely copulate in quick sequence with one female need especially big testes (because the male that injects the most semen has the best chance of being the one to fertilize the egg). When fertilization is a competitive lottery, large testes enable a male to enter more sperm in the lottery" (Diamond, 72).

Humans, according to evolutionary theory, should therefore be intermediate between chimps and gorillas both in polygyny and in promiscuity—and the data fit the prediction. I leave it to the reader to speculate as to what the evolutionary result would be if groups of religious cultists (in which the leader tries to monopolize the females) and outlaw biker gangs (who after all gave us the term "gang bang") were to each pursue their own evolutionary path, separate from the rest of human society.

Diamond provides more hard anatomical data (75):

> The length of the erect penis averages 1 1/4 inches in a gorilla, 1 1/2 inches in an orangutan, 3 inches in a chimp, and 5 inches in a man. Visual conspicuousness varies in the same sequence: a gorilla's penis is inconspicuous even when erect because of its black color, while the chimp's pink erect penis stands out against the bare white skin behind it. The flaccid penis is not even visible in apes.

To date, however, there is no adequate evolutionary explanation of the between-species differences in penis size. J. P. Rushton has offered a very controversial explanation of the mean differences in penis size between various racial groups within the human species. His letter to *Skeptic* (Vol. 3, No. 4, 22–25), with an accompanying table, summarizes his argument that there is a "tradeoff" between cognitive assets (brain size and IQ score) and reproductive assets (penis size and gamete production). Both neurons and gametes are expensive and Rushton's data are replicable, but most evolutionary biologists and psychologists do not accept his interpretation.

Rushton's work highlights two important differences among evolutionary explanations of behavior. Evolutionary explanations of genetic differences between individuals, and especially between groups of individuals, have an air of an earlier Social Darwinism which many today find downright offensive. Which is not to say that they are, for that reason, factually wrong. But most of today's evolutionary psychologists are concerned with the universals of human nature, not the differences. They argue that "genetic differences among individuals surely play a role, but perhaps a larger role is played by genetic commonalities: by a generic, species-wide developmental program that absorbs information from the social environment and adjusts the maturing mind accordingly." They therefore believe that "future progress in grasping the importance of environment will probably come from thinking about genes" (Wright, 9).

And whereas Rushton and others, located on the pro side of *The Bell Curve* controversy, argue for a unitary view of the mind (usually manifested in a single trait variously referred to as intelligence, IQ, cognitive ability, or psychometric g) on which all individuals (and even groups) can be measured and ranked from top to bottom ("alphabetically by height" as legendary New York Yankee manager Casey Stengel once put it), most of today's evolutionary psychologists argue that evolution would rather select for distinct mental modules. In their view, evolution can give males a "love of offspring" module, and make that module sensitive to the likelihood that the offspring in question is indeed the man's. But the adaptation cannot be foolproof. Natural selection can give women an "attracted to muscles" module, or an "attracted to status" module, and . . . it can make the strength of those attractions depend on all kinds of germane factors. . . . As Tooby and Cosmides say, human beings aren't general purpose "fitness maximizers." They are "adaptation executors." The adaptations may or may not bring good results in any given case, and success is especially spotty in environments other than a small hunter-gatherer village (Wright, 106–107).

In the view of most evolutionary psychologists, the modules may differ in effectiveness from one individual to another, but given the number of different modules, their effect is to "average out" individual differences to the point where any attempt to "line everyone up" on a single dimension is as nebulous as Casey's syntax.

Now let's look at the females. "Human females are unique in their breasts, which are considerably larger than those of apes even before the first pregnancy" (Diamond, 74). Since the female gorilla and her baby are comparable in size to their human counterparts, the bulk of the huge (by primate standards) human female breast consists of fat, not milk glands, and breast size varies greatly among human females without affecting their ability to nurse young. Thus, the explanation cannot be based on the need to nurse infants. Rather, human female breasts are secondary sexual characteristics that evolved to attract mates. According to Desmond Morris (1967), this took place along with the switch from front-to-rear to front-to-front mating, the pendulous shape and cleavage of the breasts mimicking the pre-existing attractiveness of the female buttocks. This also, according to the theory, explains why men find other pendulous shapes

(like ear lobes) and other cleavages (like toes in low-vamped shoes) such a turn-on.

And while we're on the subject, what other female attributes turn men on? Gentlemen prefer young, nubile women, with lips like rubies, eyes like limpid pools, skin like silk, breasts like a milch cow, and legs like a race horse. According to evolutionary theory, this is not the result of either Hollywood or Madison Avenue, but because all of these features have served as cues to a female's health, reproductive potential and sexual availability over the course of human evolutionary history. Evolution has built into every red-blooded male a desire to find "Pornotopia"—the fantasy land where "sex is sheer lust and physical gratification, devoid of more tender feelings and encumbering relationships, in which women are always aroused, or at least easily arousable, and ultimately are always willing" (Symons, 171). The entire cosmetics, fashion, and pornography industries are attempts to create Pornotopia here on Earth.

Figure 4, adapted from Daly and Wilson (1988), depicts human female reproductive value, calculated in terms of expected live births among hunter/gatherers, as a function of female age. This curve parallels the curve for men's preferences in females as determined in cross-cultural studies (Buss, 49–60; Symons, 187–200).

Men naturally prefer young women because

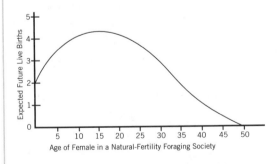

Figure 4

they provide the most reproductive potential for passing on the male's genes. If anything, males are biased toward selecting females before reproductive age in order to insure that no other male has beaten them to the finish line. From an evolutionary perspective, the least wise thing a male can do is to divert his hard-earned resources to rearing another man's child. Indeed, evolutionary psychologists would argue that this is why cuckolds are universally held in such low regard.

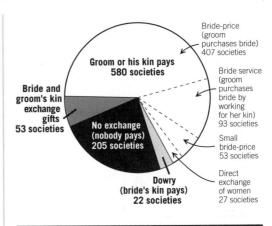

Figure 5

Murder 1, Incest 0

According to evolutionary theory, sex is a service women provide to men in return for resources. Evolutionary psychologists Martin Daly and Margo Wilson note that (188, emphasis theirs):

> marriage is a contract not between husband and wife, but between *men,* a formalized transfer of a woman as a commodity. And indeed when one examines the material and labor exchanges that surround marriage, it does begin to look like a trafficking in women. In our society, as in many, a father *gives* his daughter in marriage. Men purchase wives in the majority of human societies, and they often demand a refund if the bargain proves disappointing. Although the relatively rare practice of dowry might be construed to mean that who pays whom is arbitrary and reversible, dowry and bride-price are not in fact opposites: A bride-price is given as compensation to the bride's kin, whereas a dowry typically remains with the newlyweds.

Figure 5 (adapted from Daly and Wilson, 189) summarizes the exchange considerations at marriage in a cross-cultural comparison of 860 societies and emphasizes the universality

of compensation for rights to female reproductive capacity.

Even worse from the point of view of the male and his family than failure by the female to live up to her part of the contract is the thought that the male's investment in resources may be going into a competitor's product. Figures 6 and 7 (adapted from *Homicide* by Daly and Wilson) show that child abuse and even murder are much more common for adoptive parents than for natural parents.

While evolutionary theory predicts a certain level of parent-child and sibling rivalry, its predictions are contrary to another mainstay of social science—the Freudian Oedipus Complex. Under evolutionary theory, fathers have a strong vested interest in their son's well-being; provided, of course, it is their son. As sons mature, they may in fact compete with their fathers for status and for females (as daughters may compete with their mothers for males), but not for their *own* mother (or father). Many evolutionists argue that, given the decreased viability of children born out of incest, selection has created an incest taboo, especially against mother-son incest. The comparative ethnographic data support the existence of the incest taboo, not the Oedipus complex (Alexander, 165; Wright, 315–316).

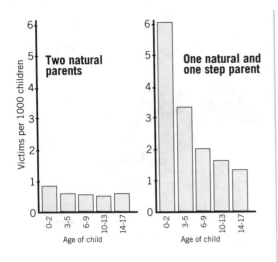

Figure 6

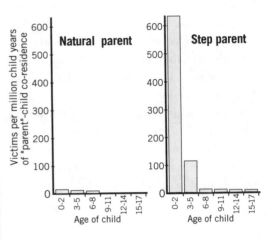

Figure 7

They Say That Breaking up Is Hard to Do: Fisher's Divorce Law Says It Isn't

Evolutionary psychology provides explanations not only of why we pair up, but why we split up. Conservative social critics have decried the alarming increase in divorce in the US since the 1960s, and variously attribute it to removing Bible reading from the public schools, rock 'n' roll, TV and movies, liberal social welfare programs, decriminalization of abortion, women's lib, and even the teaching of evolution. The evolutionary perspective, on the other hand, leads one to see lifetime monogamy as the exceptional result of an increased level of social pressure rather than as the rule for humans.

Anthropologist Helen Fisher has gathered divorce data from 62 societies around the world (Figures 8 and 9). She finds that "human beings in a variety of societies tend to divorce between the second and fourth years of marriage, with a divorce peak during the fourth year" (360). She also finds that the divorce statistics for the US in 1986, well past the sexual revolution of the 1960s, fit the same pattern, with most divorces taking place between the second and third year of marriage (362).

Fisher's evolutionary explanation attributes the universality of the divorce statistics to the "remarkable correlation between the length of human infancy in traditional societies, about four years, and the length of many marriages, about four years. Among the traditional !Kung, mothers hold their infants near their skin, breast-feed regularly through the day and night, nurse on demand, and offer their breasts as pacifiers. As a result of this constant body contact and nipple stimulation, as well as high levels of exercise and a low-fat diet, ovulation is suppressed and the ability to become pregnant is postponed for about three years" (153). She therefore concludes (154):

> The modern divorce peak—about four years—conforms to the traditional period between human successive births—four year . . . . Like pair-bonding in foxes, robins, and many other species that mate only through a breeding season, human pair-bonds originally evolved to last only long enough to raise a single dependent child through infancy, the first four years, unless a second child was conceived.

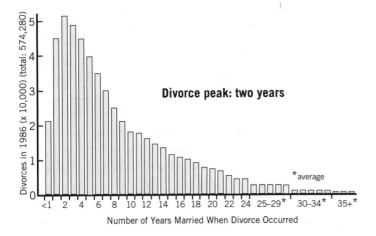

Figure 8

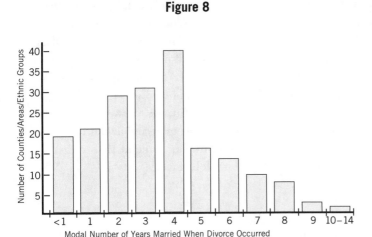

Figure 9

Human, All Too Human

It may seem that either evolutionary psychology or the examples selected for this quick and dirty summary are more suited to tabloid TV than to *Skeptic* magazine. Are we trying to increase circulation by slumming to the lowest common denominator of human behavior? Well, evolutionary psychology has an answer for that one too. It is precisely because of our evolutionary history and the importance of maximizing inclusive fitness that humans in all cultures, throughout history, have found such lurid tales so irresistible. Some may prefer

them told with British accents on *Masterpiece Theatre*, rather than in the dialect of Rap or the twang of Country & Western, but the archetypal themes are the same and evolutionary psychology tells us that they will never go away.

But just how scientific are these attempts to explain human behavior in evolutionary terms? To what extent do the questions we ask automatically set up the answers we get? After all, as Cassius taunted Brutus, we are sometimes masters of our own fate! To what extent are human nature and individual and group differences scientifically meaningful concepts, rather than the social constructions of learning and experience, political and economic conditions? Is there any scientific there there?

In *Skeptic*, vol. 4, no. 1, Harry Schlinger, a psychologist at Western New England College, critically analyzes evolutionary theories and argues that human behavior can be more scientifically and parsimoniously explained in terms of the verifiable laws of learning, without recourse to evolutionary or genetic arguments. Harmon Holcomb, a philosopher of science at the University of Kentucky, skeptically examines the theories of evolutionary psychology and finds that for the most part, at this point, they are neither pseudoscience nor hard science, but protoscience, that is, science in the making. To graduate to the status of true science evolutionary psychology must put forth hypotheses that are capable of being critically disproven, rather than just reinforced or reconfirmed. He is a fair skeptic. Edward O. Wilson wrote on the cover of Holcomb's book *Sociobiology, Sex, and Science*, "Holcomb is now clearly the leading authority on sociobiology among philosophers of science" and (the book) "can and should be the standard reference on the subject." Reviewing the papers presented at the 1996 meeting of the Human Behavior and Evolution Society, he shows which research has reached the level of real science. Frank Salter of the Max Planck Institute supplies a biological counterattack. He critically examines sociology by taking us on a skeptical browse through *The Oxford Dictionary of Sociology*, and finds that its studied avoidance of basic human nature amounts to little more than modern alchemy.

Also in that issue of *Skeptic*, we matched pairs of interviews and book reviews. Lionel Tiger and Robin Fox, two of the grand old men of evolutionary theories of behavior, look back on what's taken place in the field in the 25 years since they published their groundbreaking and controversial book *The Imperial Animal*. *Skeptic* advisory board member Stephen Jay Gould, a longtime critic of excessive appeals to evolution and genetics in the explanation of human behavior, offers his thoughts on evolution, his own revision of Darwinism, the problems with ultra-Darwinism, and the politics of science. Philosopher of science Michael Ruse, an expert on the nexus between philosophy and biology, reviews one of the most controversial new books in this field—Daniel Dennett's *Darwin's Dangerous Idea*—which is very critical of those who would revise basic Darwinian explanations, such as Gould with his theory of punctuated equilibrium. *Skeptic* publisher Michael Shermer also reviews Dennett's book, though from a different perspective than Ruse, in his analysis of "Gould's Dangerous Idea"—contingency, necessity, and the nature of history. And lest we be accused of presenting only the evolutionary side of the argument, we conclude with some

comic relief as anthropologist and long-time creationist observer, Tom McIver, takes us on "A Walk through Earth History: All Eight Thousand Years" in his skeptical tour of the Institute for Creation Research's museum.

So here then, ladies and gentlemen of the jury, is the issue at hand: Should we accept as a default hypothesis that human behavior, and the similarities and differences in behavior between individuals and groups, are the result of a complex interaction of the genes that reflect our evolutionary history as well as the environment in which we find ourselves? Or should we opt for the statistically null hypothesis that any invocation of genes and evolution to explain human behavior must be proved beyond a reasonable doubt? If nothing else, I think you will be forced to conclude, in the words of Nobel Prize Winner and co-discoverer of DNA James Watson, that "Charles Darwin will eventually be seen as a far more influential figure in the history of human thought than either Jesus Christ or Mohammed."

References:

Alexander, Richard. 1979. *Darwinism and Human Affairs*. Seattle, WA: University of Washington Press.

Buss, David. 1994. *The Evolution of Desire*. New York: Basic Books.

Daly, Martin, and Wilson, Margo. 1988. *Homicide*. New York: Aldine.

de Waal, Frans. 1982. *Chimpanzee Politics: Power and Sex among the Apes*. Baltimore: Johns Hopkins.

Diamond, Jared. 1992. *The Third Chimpanzee*. New York: Harper.

Fisher, Helen. 1992. *The Anatomy of Love: The Natural History of Monogamy, Adultery, and Divorce*. New York: Norton.

Morris, Desmond. 1967. *The Naked Ape*. New York: McGraw Hill.

Rushton, J. P. 1995. *Race, Evolution, and Behavior*. New Brunswick, NJ: Transaction.

Symons, Donald. 1979. *The Evolution of Human Sexuality.* New York: Oxford University Press.

Tooby, John, and Cosmides, Leda. "The Psychological Foundations of Culture" in Barkow, Jerome; Cosmides, Leda; and Tooby, John. 1992. *The Adapted Mind: Evolutionary Psychology and the Generation of Culture.* New York: Oxford.

Wright, Robert. 1994. *The Moral Animal: The New Science of Evolutionary Psychology.* New York.: Vintage.

Evolutionary Psychology as Pseudoscience

HENRY SCHLINGER JR.

In 1902 Rudyard Kipling published a children's book of stories and poems with the curious title *Just So Stories*. They included such natural curiosities as "How the Elephant Got Its Trunk," "How the Rhinoceros Got Its Skin," and "How the Leopard Got Its Spots." The stories, of course, are pure fantasy, and "just so stories" has become a critical cliche for similarly fanciful tales that attempt to explain nature. The new field of evolutionary psychology, while different in many respects from its predecessor sociobiology, is still subject to the accusation of telling just so stories.

As a sampling from this new science, the following are headlines from recent articles or reviews of various books appealing to evolutionary explanations of human behavior:

Cheating Husband: Blame It on His Genes?
Is There a Gene for Compassion?
Is Prejudice Hereditary?
A Scientist Weighs Evidence That the
    X Chromosome May Carry a Gene for
    Gayness.
IQ: Is It Destiny?

Headlines such as these are meant to capture the attention and imagination of readers, and they usually do. They suggest that the books to which they refer are going to offer serious scientific evidence for their claims of an evolutionary explanation of much human social and intellectual behavior. Do these claims reflect the results of serious science or just more "pop sociobiology," as Kitcher (1985) calls it?

Most books on sociobiology appeared in the decade between about 1975 and 1985. Barash's 1977 *Sociobiology and Human Behavior*, Lumsden and Wilson's 1983 *Promethean Fire*, and especially E. O. Wilson's two great works, *Sociobiology: The New Synthesis* (1975) and *On Human Nature* (1978), created a new field of study of human behavior that forcefully challenged the hegemony of behavioral psychology that had reigned so long. Despite the existence of serious critical analyses of sociobiology (e.g., Bock, 1980; Futuyma, 1979; Gould, 1981; Kitcher, 1985; Sahlins, 1976), in the past few years, there has been an explosion of books offering evolutionary explanations for a variety of human behaviors, including intelligence, morality, mating, sexual preference, aggression, xenophobia, prejudice, and even our tendency to seek out various forms of nature, such as trips to zoos and visits to national parks. These books may be classified according to two distinct but related arguments about the evolution of human behavior: (a) individuals and groups that differ behaviorally in some way (e.g., IQ) do so because of underlying genetic differences; and (b) invariant, universal human traits (e.g., morality, aggression) represent fixed expressions of the human genome (Futuyma, 1979).

Recent books that argue for genetic differences between groups of humans with respect to such characteristics as intelligence include *The Bell Curve: Intelligence and Class Structure in American Life* (1994) by Herrnstein and Murray, *Race, Evolution, and Behavior* (1995) by Rushton, and *The Decline of Intelligence in America: A Strategy for National Renewal* (1994) by Itzkoff. Books that make the case that there are distinctly human behaviors—collectively called human nature—that reflect a uniquely human evolutionary history, include *Homicide* (1988) by Daly and Wilson *The Biophilia Hypothesis* (1993) edited by Kellert and Wilson, *The Moral Animal* (1994) by Wright, *The Evolution of Desire* (1994) by Buss, *Why We Get Sick: The New Science of Darwinian Medicine* (1994) by Nesse and Williams, *Eve's Rib: The Biological Roots of Sex Differences* (1994) by Poole, *The Science of Desire: The Search for the Gay Gene and the Biology of Behavior* (1994) by Hamer and Copeland, and *The Adapted Mind* (1992) by Barkow, Cosmides, and Tooby.

Both arguments on the evolution of human behavior rely to varying degrees on a combination of three types of supporting evidence:

1. Evolutionary logic supported by casual observations or statistical data.
2. Behavioral analogies and comparisons with animals.
3. Statistical analyses of data generated by non-experimental research methods.

Each of these types of evidence, while sometimes compelling and frequently interesting, is often flawed scientifically. This does not mean that the explanations themselves are wrong, only that the supporting evidence is insufficient. In many instances, an alternative and much more plausible approach to understanding human behavior is that rather than selecting for specialized behavioral traits, human evolutionary history has selected for behavioral plasticity, or learning capacity (Futuyma, 1979). Experimental evidence from the litera-

ture on learning shows overwhelmingly the powerful influence of the environment in shaping human behavioral similarities and differences.

In the present essay I describe the three types of evidence with supporting examples from both evolutionary positions on human behavior and then critique them according to certain methodological criteria. I argue that, in most cases, a much more cautious and scientifically defensible position on the origin of many human behaviors is that they are a function of individual environmental, and not evolutionary, history.

Evolutionary Logic

One of the hallmarks of the scientific method is the interpretation of phenomena that have not been subjected to experimental analysis. Scientific interpretation is the use of already established principles of science to explain novel instances of the subject matter. Hence, the logical or mathematical use of Darwinian principles of selection to interpret human behavior could have a sound basis in science. The main questions are (a) whether the data presented for interpretation are both valid and reliable, and (b) whether the interpretations of human behavior as presented in recent books and articles represent an appropriate extension of Darwinian theory.

Theorists from both positions on the evolution of human behavior cite examples of evolutionary logic and supporting data that are problematic. Theorists who emphasize genetic differences between groups of humans (races) have employed evolutionary logic to explain differences in intelligence (Herrnstein and Murray, 1994; Itzkoff, 1994; Rushton, 1995a), brain and head size and aggressiveness (Rushton, 1995a), among other traits. Evolutionary psychologists have used evolutionary logic to explain, among other things, why people kill one another (Daly and Wilson, 1988), why mothers who have just given birth seem to mention their neonate's resemblance to the father more than to themselves (Daly and Wilson, 1982), why social rejection may produce feelings of insecurity (Wright, 1995), and why people seek out zoos and parks and easily develop phobias to natural objects, like spiders (Wilson, 1993). The data cited by these theorists consist of casual observation, personal reflection, and anecdote, as well as statistics derived from non-experimental studies. To illustrate, consider an example of the use of evolutionary logic from each of the two positions on the evolution of human behavior.

Rushton (1995a) uses evolutionary logic to support his claim that human racial groups evolved under conditions where different environmental pressures selected for differences in a wide range of physical and intellectual characteristics. Rushton suggests that an r-K reproductive strategy analysis combined with information on human evolution can be used to understand important behavioral differences between Mongoloids, Caucasoids, and Negroids, as he calls them. The r-strategies are those with high reproductive rates, and the K-strategies are those with high levels of parental investment in offspring. According to Rushton (1995a), "Mongoloid people are more K-selected than Caucasoids, who, in turn, are more K-selected than Negroids" (xiii). In other words, Mongoloids invest relatively more in the care of their offspring than Caucasoids who invest relatively more in the care of their offspring than Negroids. Rushton appeals to evolutionary logic to explain the presence of these different r-K strategies in different human racial groups. Specifically, Rushton claims that the selection pressures in the hot African savanna, where Negroids evolved, were far different in terms of the required relationship between parental investment and high reproductive rates than selection pres-

sures in the cold Arctic environment where Mongoloids evolved. Presumably, higher reproductive rates and lower rates of parental investment are more favorable in hotter climates, whereas the opposite is true in colder climates. According to Rushton, this is the evolutionary basis for the differences in r-K reproductive strategies supposedly observed in humans.

The first problem with Rushton's analysis concerns the reliability of the data offered to support his evolutionary logic. For example, he provides a table of the relative ranking of races on diverse variables such as physical maturation rate, including age of first sexual intercourse and pregnancy; reproductive effort, including relative frequency of two-egg twinning and of intercourse; personality, including aggressiveness and impulsivity; brain size; and intelligence (Rushton, 1995a, 1995b). The data for these rankings were generated by non-experimental research methods where average differences between groups were often very small. Moreover, there is no scientific evidence, other than correlations, to support many of Rushton's assumptions, including his assumption that brain size is functionally related to cognitive ability.

Rushton often relies on statistical analyses of aggregated data to bolster his claim that small differences between groups are significant. Even if we assume that the data cited by Rushton were derived from well-designed and well-controlled studies—a questionable assumption—his evolutionary interpretation of the data has several attendant problems. First, there is no way to test and thereby falsify his claim that these characteristics represent evolutionary adaptations. Rushton's evolutionary logic is not too dissimilar from that used by his sociobiological predecessors, as summarized by Futuyma (1979). He has simply imagined that higher reproductive rates and lower rates of parental investment must have conferred differential fitness in different climates, compared the predicted outcome with observations from correlational studies, and then concluded that these characteristics represent adaptive genetic traits. A second problem with Rushton's hypothesis is that his extension of the r-K reproductive strategy analysis (usually used to compare large differences between different species) to the small variations between groups within the human species represents a "fatal scientific error" by assuming that behavioral differences between groups within one species can be accounted for by genetic differences (Tavris, 1995). It is not even clear that behavioral differences between individuals reflect genetic differences or, if they do, to what extent (Futuyma, 1979). A third problem is that Rushton's concept of race, which reflects that of Western culture—based on a few physical features such as skin color, hair form, and the epicanthal fold—is subjective (Futuyma, 1979). And finally, any reliable differences in Rushton's data are just as likely to be due to environmental variables as genetic ones. Still, Rushton (1995a) boldly contends that his book will offer "new truths about racial group differences."

Consider, now, an example of how evolutionary logic might be used to interpret some human characteristic from the perspective of evolutionary psychology. Robert Wright, a science journalist, writing in *The New Yorker* (March, 1995), illustrates how evolutionary psychologists would approach the explanation of some presumably universal human behavioral trait. Suppose, Wright asks, that social rejection early in a person's life results in an enduring insecurity. According to Wright, we should ask whether this pattern "might have had a genetic payoff during evolution" (71). Presumably, our ancestors who faced such rejection were less likely to reproduce unless they became more socially vigilant about nourishing their social ties as a result of the insecurity. Insecurity as a response to social rejection, then, may have been reproductively

advantageous for humans. The assumptions inherent in Wright's argument can be stated as follows: (a) human evolutionary history has selected a genetic "program" that is somehow sensitive to environmental input called "social rejection," (b) this genetic program is especially sensitive to input early in an individual's life, and (c) the behavioral response called insecurity is essentially the same for all people to this input.

There are several obvious problems with this example that are relevant to many such examples cited by evolutionary psychologists. The first problem is with the validity of the behavioral data. Wright simply assumes that insecurity, which is not objectively defined, is a general human response to early social rejection, which is also not objectively defined. Wright offers no evidence that his evolutionary model is based on precise behavioral observations. Rather, his analysis is based on common sense assumptions about human nature which have no scientific basis. A second problem deals with Wright's evolutionary interpretation of the data. Even if such a reaction could be precisely measured and were observed in most humans as a result of a precisely defined set of environmental inputs, an evolutionary interpretation that it was adaptive is untestable because there is no crucial test that can falsify the hypothesis (Futuyma, 1979). Finally, an evolutionary explanation of the pattern of behavior in Wright's example may not be the most parsimonious one. For example, it might be that the reaction to rejection that we refer to as "feelings of insecurity" might be a more general physiological response to the withholding or withdrawal of reinforcement following some behavior. The effect of such environmental operations is to simultaneously produce physiological responses and to alter the stimuli that define the situation such that they suppress the behavior under similar circumstances. These are the scientific principles of operant extinction and punishment. The "feeling of insecurity" may be a by-product of the withholding or withdrawal of reinforcement with no special selective advantage of its own.

Cross-Species Comparisons

A second type of evidence frequently used to support evolutionary explanations of human similarities and differences consists of analogies or comparisons between nonhuman and human behavior. It is common linguistic practice among humans, including scientists, to give names to things. When two or more forms of behavior are given the same name, it may see reasonable to assume that they are alike functionally as well. Kitcher (1985) points out that because we have such a rich vocabulary for describing human behavior, it is easy to use this vocabulary to describe nonhuman behavior that resembles it. Once described in similar ways, it becomes easier to then move freely from the nonhuman instance back to the superficially similar human instance and to assume that both result from similar processes. According to Kitcher (1985), "vulgar anthropomorphism" is the original sin of pop sociobiologists, in that they neglect "to investigate the kinship of forms of behavior that are superficially similar" (185). Even if scientists discovered a genetic basis for a behavior in an animal, which is rare, this does not mean that the human behavior that appears to be similar also has a genetic basis. As evolutionary biologists know, phenotypic similarity does not necessarily imply genotypic similarity.

Social theorists, like Rushton, who emphasize genetic differences between groups of humans typically point to between-species differences that are more than likely a function of differences in genes to make the case that within-species differences in humans are also a function of differences in genes. Rushton

(1995a) employs an interesting kind of cross-species analogy to make a case for the genetic basis of human racial differences. First, he points out that significant differences in learning ability between species are due to genetic differences. Thus, mammals with larger brains, such as chimpanzees, rhesus monkeys, and spider monkeys, learn faster than mammals with smaller brains, such as marmosets, cats, gerbils, rats, and squirrels. Rushton then uses these comparisons to argue that within-species differences in human brain or head size are related to differences in intelligence, at least as measured by standardized IQ tests, and are likewise related to genetic differences. Rushton's ultimate point is that blacks have statistically smaller heads (and brains) than whites and that this correlates positively with differences in intelligence between the two groups, at least as measured by standardized tests. It is interesting to note that of the 32 studies summarized by Rushton on head size and intelligence in humans, most found low correlations.

Rushton takes a reasonable between-species example and extends it to an insupportable within-species difference. Even if the measurements of brain size and intelligence can be defended as reliable, Rushton's explanation of the behavioral differences is not the most parsimonious one, especially when one considers the myriad differences in environments on average between black and white children. Before genetic explanations of differences in learning ability between individuals or groups are proffered, environmental factors, such as nutrition, prenatal care, learning, and educational opportunities, should be investigated if for no other reason than the variables are easier to test.

Another example of questionable cross-species analogizing by Rushton (1995a) concerns the r-K reproductive strategies described previously. According to Rushton, the great apes exemplify the extreme end of the K-strategy because they produce one infant every five or six years and provide much parental care. At the other extreme are oysters who exemplify the r-strategy, producing 500 million eggs a year but providing no parental care. Although this scale is generally used to compare the life histories of widely disparate species, Rushton (1995a) applies it to the much smaller variations within the human species. Although Rushton believes that all humans are K-selected relative to other species, he also believes that some humans may be more so than others. He cites data showing that, compared to white women, black women average a shorter period of ovulation and produce more eggs per ovulation which is evidenced by their comparatively higher rate of two-egg twinning. His data also show that black women have comparatively lower intelligence than white women as measured by standardized tests. Rushton claims that the correlation between IQ and biological variables related to reproduction supports his view that the within-species variations in humans can be accounted for in the same way that between-species variations can. Even if the correlation can be proven to be valid, there are serious problems with Rushton's cross-species comparison. First, there is no biological justification for extending an analysis of between-species differences to within-species differences. Second, Rushton provides no evidence other than correlations that differences in IQ and certain biological variables between women represent adaptations resulting from natural selection. Third, simply demonstrating a correlation between two or more variables in no way clarifies causal relations.

Evolutionary psychologists, like their sociobiological predecessors, frequently employ cross-species analogies and comparisons to argue their case for the existence of universal human characteristics. For example, Daly and Wilson (1988) use an analogy with female ground squirrels to show how the concept of inclusive fitness may be used to understand sibling rivalry in humans. They argue that genetic relationship should be important to solidarity and social conflict. In other words, the closer the family relationship between two individuals, the more solidarity and the less conflict should exist between them. Daly and Wilson point out that such a theory has been tested in female ground squirrels who discriminate between their full sisters and half sisters when occupying adjacent territories as adults. Full sisters will apparently help each other whereas half sisters will exhibit more territorial aggression. They then suggest that the same prediction can be made with regard to human siblings; namely, that the intensity of sibling rivalry should reflect the likelihood of common paternity. In other words, full siblings should show less competition than half siblings. In their own words, "we might have evolved specialized psychological mechanisms whose function is to assess the likelihood of common paternity and to adjust the intensity of sibling competition accordingly," and some "psychologist should check it out" (1988, 11).

Cross-species analogies, such as the one offered by Daly and Wilson (1988), are intriguing, suggesting as they do that certain human characteristics that we seem to have in common with other species may be understood as part of our deeper human nature. There are serious problems with such analogies, however. The first problem is that the similarity between human and nonhuman behaviors is subjective and is only suggested after it is believed that there may be a common genetic basis for both. In other words, behavioral similarity is often in the eyes of the beholder. Who is to say that territorial aggression among ground squirrels is anything but superficially similar to disagreements or fights among human half-siblings? The causes of these similar behaviors could be completely different. A second problem is that even if the behavior of human siblings could be compared to female ground squirrels, there is no independent evidence for the existence of an evolved "psychological mechanism" or any suggestion as to how it would work to "assess the likelihood of common paternity and to adjust the intensity of sibling competition accordingly." In the absence of such a suggestion, based on some kind of objective scientific evidence rather than inferences, Daly and Wilson's explanation is simply hypothetical.

Futuyma (1979) has pointed out several other problems with cross-species analogies. For example, even if behavioral generalizations could be supported by reliable observations, we are still left with the nagging question of whether behaviors between species that are superficially similar are functionally similar; that is, whether the same processes are responsible for both. If we discover the genetic bases of territorial aggression in female ground squirrels, does this mean that behaviors we refer to as "human sibling rivalry" also have a genetic basis? A simpler approach would be to consider first whether other factors, such as environmental ones, could produce the human behaviors of interest. Such an approach might lead us to ask, for example, whether there is as much sibling rivalry between half-siblings who are raised together from birth or infancy and who are not aware of their genetic relationship to each other as there is between siblings who know they are half-siblings. Other than the interesting evolutionary theorizing that superficially similar behaviors in different species may be functionally similar, evolutionary psychologists offer no direct scientific evidence that they are.

Correlative Analysis

It should be noted that social evolutionary theorists typically do not conduct experiments, nor do they, in most instances, cite experimental data. Rather, they rely almost exclusively on a combination of anecdotal and statistical evidence to make their case that there are species-specific behaviors in humans. Moreover, in almost no case is direct genetic evidence used to support evolutionary theories of human behavior (see below). Since genes are identified as playing a causal role in important similarities and differences between humans, a true experimental test of the hypothesis would necessarily involve direct manipulation of genes as independent variables. Such manipulations are only carried out by geneticists and, for obvious reasons, they have been constrained in such endeavors to working with relatively simple organisms, such as fruit flies with extremely short gestation periods, where the focus is more on structural than behavioral characteristics. Those who write about the genetic bases of human behaviors are typically not geneticists, however. And because they cannot make their genetic case experimentally, these evolutionary theorists must rely on data generated by non-experimental, usually correlational, research methods. There are several problems with the ways in which some evolutionary theorists use correlative analysis.

Validity and Reliability of the Data. The first problem is, the validity and reliability of the methods used to generate the actual data are often questionable. E. O. Wilson (1993) states that one mode of testing an evolutionary hypothesis "is the correlative analysis of knowledge and attitudes of peoples in diverse cultures" (34). Knowledge and attitudes, poorly defined as they are, must be obtained from surveys and questionnaires. Methodological problems with such devices are well known among researchers. For instance, there are numerous ways in which researcher bias may affect the outcome, such as the sampling procedure used and the way in which questions on surveys and questionnaires are worded. Even when safeguards are included, inferences to larger populations (the ultimate goal of surveys or questionnaires) are questionable. Also, as most good researchers know, the reliability of verbal self reports is notoriously poor.

In addition to surveys and questionnaires, evolutionary theorists may use psychological tests to assess more general and presumably universal characteristics of populations. Rushton (1995a) provides an example of the use of such a test. His thesis of racial differences is based on the assumption that there is "a core of human nature" or character traits "around which individuals and groups consistently" differ. To wit, he cites a study conducted in the 1920s by Hartshorne and May called the "Character Education Enquiry" in which 11,000 elementary and high school students were given a battery of 33 different tests of altruism, self-control, and honesty in various contexts (home, school, church, etc.). Children's reputations with teachers and classmates were also obtained and then correlated with the scores on the battery of tests. Notwithstanding the problems with questionnaires, the only behavior measured by such tests is that of answering questions on the test. The actual behaviors called "altruistic" or "honest" are not measured in the context wherein one would normally call them altruistic or honest. This is not to say that we cannot discern something of value with such tests, but only that the test may correlate poorly with the behaviors of interest, and only a direct experimental approach can potentially yield a scientific understanding of the behaviors.

Of course, the most notorious type of test cited in the literature on evolutionary theories of human behavior is the IQ test. Volumes have been written on problems with intelligence tests, and I will not repeat them here. Suffice it to say that one problem with such tests is what they purport to measure. Rather than measuring some qualitatively distinct structure or process as defenders of such tests would have us believe, intelligence tests literally measure only the correctness of a variety of learned behaviors—answers to questions on

the test—in a contrived context—the test taking situation (Schlinger, 1992). Alfred Binet knew this when he developed the first modern intelligence test (although he eschewed the use of the term "intelligence" in favor of the more descriptive and neutral "intellectual level"). The challenge for serious scientists is to ask about the variables that affect the broad range of behaviors we describe as intelligent; and only an experimental analysis can answer such questions.

The Use of Statistics. A second problem with the use of correlative analyses by evolutionary theorists concerns the complex statistical tests employed to "make sense" of the data generated by surveys, questionnaires, psychological tests, and the like. The importance of correlative analyses in making the argument for genetic explanations of human behavior is underscored in the following quotation by Sir Francis Galton, which Rushton twice cited (1995a, b):

> General impressions are never to be trusted. Unfortunately when they are of long standing they become fixed rules of life, and assume a prescriptive right not to be questioned. Consequently, those who are not accustomed to original inquiry entertain a hatred and a horror of statistics. They cannot endure the idea of submitting their sacred impressions to cold-blooded verification. But it is the triumph of scientific men to rise superior to such superstitions, to devise tests by which the value of beliefs may be ascertained, and to feel sufficiently masters of themselves to discard contemptuously whatever may be found untrue.

The most obvious problem with this quote and the approach to the study of individual differences that it fostered is the equation of statistics, in the absence of experimentation, with scientific practice. Although we may debate the role of inferential statistics in the natural sciences, it is true that Galton's quote predated the application of the experimental method to the behavior of organisms by psychologists (e.g., Skinner, 1938). Rushton (1995a) and Herrnstein and Murray (1994), however, consider Galton to be the intellectual and scientific father of their genetic theories of racial differences. Rushton calls Galton "the originator of scientific research on individual differences" (1995a, 10). Herrnstein and Murray, who refer to the Galtonian tradition of intelligence testing as "the classic tradition," claim: "By accepted standards of what constitutes scientific evidence and scientific proof, that classic tradition has in our view given the world a treasure of information . . ." (1994, 19). This is especially interesting coming from a scientist such as Herrnstein whose own scientific output consists almost exclusively of the use of within-subject experimental designs.

Authors such as Herrnstein, Murray, and Rushton point out that while individual scores on behavioral or psychological tests, for instance IQ tests, correlate poorly, the correlations become much higher when scores are aggregated. The principle of aggregation, according to Herrnstein and Murray (1994), is where the classic (Galtonian) tradition has the most to offer. The rationale for aggregating data is that "randomness in any one measure (error and specificity variance) is averaged out . . . leaving a clearer view of what a person's true behavior is like" (Rushton, 1995a, 19). Also, relationships between individual tests or between scores on tests are more likely to emerge. Thus, aggregating data is supposed to correct for any errors in the actual measurement of the variable(s) in question. The contradiction in this line of reasoning is that the further away one gets from the behavior of the individual, the less can be said about the individual. Herrnstein and Murray acknowledge that the practice of aggregating data does not necessarily permit the prediction, much less the understanding, of individual behavior. More importantly, aggregating data from dif-

ferent tests, or, worse, from different studies, is fraught with so many methodological problems as to render the results meaningless. For example, aggregating data masks differences in methodology (e.g., time, place, populations, sampling procedures, control procedures, measurement tools, etc.). Aggregating data, especially from different studies, can only mean that the results of any individual study were so equivocal that no conclusions could be drawn. Pooling data from different studies is only valid if the studies are methodologically interchangeable which, as I have implied, is a questionable assumption in the present case. Nevertheless, Rushton (1995a) describes instances where low correlations between individual tests were raised by aggregating data from many different tests as if this were sound scientific practice.

In criticizing formalized methods of research and statistics, B. F. Skinner (1972) advocated the use of the experimental method in the study of human behavior. Each approach leads to a different strategy for dealing with measurement error. In contrast to the strategy of aggregating scores from many individuals to increase the statistical reliability of the measurement device (e.g., IQ test) or the sensitivity of the statistical method (e.g., t-Test), Skinner (1972) argued for refining direct experimental control over the behavior of individual subjects. In this way, the reliability of the independent variables is enhanced and sources of variability are eliminated *before* measurements are made rather than after, as is the case when researchers aggregate data. As Skinner (1972) wrote tongue-in-cheek, "No one goes to the circus to see the average dog jump through a hoop significantly oftener than untrained dogs raised under the same circumstances . . ." (114).

Interpreting the Data. A third problem with the use of correlative analyses involves the interpretation of the data. Demonstrating that a correlation exists between two or more variables does not in any way clarify causal relations, although it may hint at possible ones. There is an oft-cited dictum among researchers: "Correlation does not imply causation" (Neale and Liebert, 1973). A correlation between two or more variables is often due to an unspecified process, or "third variable." Those who argue for an evolutionary explanation of human behavior appeal to a third variable—the human genome. Although it is theoretically possible that some human social and intellectual behaviors represent fixed expressions of the human genome, a better explanation for the behaviors in question is one in which a different third variable is implicated—the environmental histories of individuals. In many of the examples cited by social evolutionary theorists, any one or more of the multitudinous environmental variables found in the individual histories of the subjects studied may produce the reported correlations. Just as behavioral similarities between individuals may reflect genotypical similarity, they may just as easily reflect environmental similarity. The correlational evidence offered by evolutionary theorists is simply insufficient to distinguish the biological from the environmental position. The challenge for scientists is to tease apart these possible determinants of behavior, and this cannot be accomplished using correlational methods. Only an experimental analysis can potentially reveal the variables of which human behavior is a function. Galton got it wrong. The "triumph of scientific men" occurs not when human behavior can be subjected to statistical correlation, but rather when it can be subjected to direct experimentation.

Whether one conducts experimental or correlational research in the first place reflects fundamental differences in the types of questions asked. And the types of questions asked reveal differences in the motivations of the researchers. Many authors who either conduct and/or cite correlational research on the relation between behavioral and genetic differ-

ences and similarities between groups of humans do so to show what they already believe—that genetics plays a significant role in such characteristics as intelligence, aggression, and reproductive behavior. Hubbard and Wald (1994) have noted that "scientists only look for genetic components in behaviors which their society considers important and probably hereditary" (93). For instance, they point out that even though European peoples read from left to right, whereas Semitic peoples read from right to left, no one has suggested that these are inherent racial differences. As Futuyma said (473):

> The history of scientists' pronouncements on human genetics and behavior is, to a distressing extent, a history of the conventional societal attitudes on these subjects; science has served more as a defense of the status quo than as a force for change.

Genes

I have referred to the social theorizing discussed in this paper as evolutionary; and such a conception implicitly recognizes that what has evolved due to natural selection is a particular genotype that is different from other possible genotypes. In short, evolutionary theories are genetic theories and, as such, we should expect some supporting genetic evidence. According to Kitcher (1985), physical characteristics most susceptible to rigorous genetic analysis are not those that social evolutionary theorists find most interesting. For example, it was recently reported that scientists at the University of Basel in Switzerland have discovered the master control gene responsible for eye development in fruit flies. The scientists have been able to manipulate the gene directly so as to produce eyes in unusual places, like on the legs and thorax. Human geneticists, by comparison, are relegated to studying genetic variation that produces deleterious effects, such as metabolic disorders and defects in color vision. In other words, human geneticists are unable to manipulate the actual genes and must wait for natural genetic variation to produce outcomes that they can then investigate. The genetic evidence most often cited by social evolutionary theorists comes from the field of behavior genetics. Contrary to their name, behavior geneticists do not directly study genes. Rather, they are constrained to examining correlations between poorly defined variables such as scores on intelligence or other psychological tests and family relationships. The reliability of the observations and measurements reported by behavior geneticists is questionable because of the many methodological problems inherent in such research. For example, several authors have pointed out problems with subject selection in research on separated identical twins (e.g., Horgan, 1993; Hubbard and Wald, 1993; Kamin, 1974; Lewontin, Rose, and Kamin, 1984). Moreover, the fact that conclusions about the differences in genes must be based on family resemblance introduces a well-known confound: Family members resemble each other not only because they share genes but also because they share environments. Despite the perception that behavior geneticists have made impressive gains in demonstrating the genetic bases for a wide range of human conditions, such as aggression, homosexuality, intelligence, schizophrenia, and alcoholism, there have been an equal number of serious methodological critiques which, at the very least, temper the claims by behavior geneticists (e.g., Byne, 1994; Horgan, 1993; Kamin, 1974; Hubbard and Wald, 1993; Lewontin, Rose, and Kamin, 1984).

Some social evolutionary theorists argue their case based on a flawed interpretation of evolutionary and genetic logic. For example, Itzkoff (1985), who is neither an evolutionary biologist nor a geneticist, presents a case for the evolution of human intelligence as a function of the natural selection of the human brain. Itzkoff reasons that because so many biochemical combinations are involved in the growth and patterns of brain structure, slight variations can exist between close relatives and large variations between relatively isolated groups of humans. He concludes: "The brain evolved along a wide diversity of lines" producing differences in both "the quantity and quality of intelligence" (23). He presents this rationale to support his claim that different groups of humans (blacks and whites) come into the world with different genetic potentials for intelligence. There are serious flaws in Itzkoff's reasoning, the most fatal of which is that there is simply insufficient evidence to support his conclusions that normal variation in intelligence has a genetic basis. Moreover, his argument is based on the assumption that there exists genetic variation within populations of humans, and that selection has operated differently in different human groups even though "there is insufficient evidence to conclude that normal variation in human behavioral traits has a genetic basis" (Futuyma, 1979). Finally, there is a broader principle of genetics that is often not fully appreciated by many social evolutionary theorists, as Futuyma notes (476):

> One cannot say that a universal trait . . . is either genetic or environmental, for it is the expression of genes in a series of environments. Genetics provides no means of investigating the inheritance of an invariant trait. Thus to postulate that it is genetic is to pose an untestable and meaningless hypothesis. The only question one can legitimately ask is, Is the trait highly canalized, or does it vary greatly under different environmental conditions, compared to other traits?

If certain behavioral traits, such as aggression, sibling rivalry, sex-role behavior, or intelligence, were highly canalized, then, according to Futuyma, we would not expect them to be modifiable by environmental factors.

Environment

Contrary to most traditional conceptions of the environment, scientists who study the functional relationship between the behavior of organisms and environmental variables—behavior analysts—define environment functionally as all of the stimuli that enter into functional relationships with an organism's behavior at any one time (Schlinger, 1995). Behavior analysts view the environment as consisting of energy changes (stimuli) of various sorts that not only affect the sensory receptors of organisms but, more importantly, affect their behavior. Thus, the environment is not defined necessarily by its structure prior to the study of behavior, but rather after functional relations have been established by experimentation. In other words, behavior analysts define environment by how it functions to control behavior. The environmental history of an individual represents one category of ultimate behavioral causation; the other being the evolutionary history of the species to which the individual belongs.

Over the last 50 years, scientists who study learning have amassed volumes of testable, repeatable, experimental data demonstrating the powerful influence of environmental manipulations on a wide range of behaviors. Several scientific journals are devoted almost exclusively to direct experimentation on the effects of the environment. The *Journal of the Experimental Analysis of Behavior*, for example, has produced almost 40 years of data, including direct and systematic replication experiments. In none of these instances are data aggregated in order to achieve criteria of significance. In fact, in many experiments, little, if any, statistical

analysis is needed to verify the reliability of the results. Internal validity is demonstrated time and time again by direct within-experiment refinement and control of objective independent variables. External validity of these findings has been consistently shown over the same 40-year period by successfully applying the scientific principles discovered in the experimental laboratory to problem human behavior. For example, the *Journal of Applied Behavior Analysis* has produced almost 30 years of experimental research on human behavioral problems, including compliance, crying, social interaction, cooperation, aggression, walking, reading and writing. Perhaps more convincing, numerous experiments have shown that behaviors previously thought to be impervious to environmental manipulation could be dramatically altered via operant conditioning, including psychotic behavior (Ayllon, 1963) mutism (Isaacs, Thomas, and Goldiamond, 1960), coma (Boyle and Greer, 1983; Fuller, 1949), and a wide range of physiological functions, such as diastolic and systolic blood pressure, Galvanic skin response, cardiac function, and asthma (Shapiro and Surwit, 1976), to mention a few. Moreover, the neurophysiological bases of basic learning processes have recently been uncovered, thus strengthening their status as scientific laws. For example, experimental evidence now shows that individual neurons can be operantly conditioned (Stein and Belluzzi, 1988; Stein, Xue, and Belluzzi, 1994). Such experiments demonstrate that the laws of operant conditioning discovered at the level of behavior-environment have their basis in neurophysiology.

Although volumes could be written summarizing the findings of the experimental science of behavior, suffice it to say that this is the only "cold-blooded verification" of theory that one should accept. Although not every human behavior that we find interesting can be subjected to experimental verification, a large corpus of experimental findings on basic learning processes is valuable in part because scientists can extrapolate from that foundation to novel behaviors. This is the essence of scientific interpretation (Palmer, 1991; Schlinger, 1995).

Some psychologists who espouse evolutionary theories of human behavior, however, cite non-experimental, and even non-quantitative, approaches to the understanding of certain human behaviors as evidence against a behavior analytic interpretation. For example, Cosmides and Tooby (1987 and 1992) cite Chomsky extensively to make their argument that behaviorist approaches to language have been falsified and, therefore, cannot account for the acquisition of human language. Their conclusion is that evolutionarily adapted cognitive learning mechanisms constitute the only adequate explanation of human language acquisition. It is interesting that these citations consist solely of rationalist argument and not scientific experimentation and yet they are presented as if they are scientifically conclusive. Behavior analysts, in contrast, have not only provided substantive rebukes of Chomsky's critique of behaviorist interpretations of language (MacCorquodale, 1970), but they have also argued persuasively that Chomsky's own evolutionary account of language is untenable when held to Darwinian standards (Palmer, 1986; Dennett, 1995).

The susceptibility of human language to operant conditioning is no longer a debatable issue. During the past 50 years the operant control of verbal behavior has been demonstrated numerous times, including experiments on the operant conditioning of infant vocalizations (Poulson, 1983; Whitehurst, 1972), the content of conversation (Azrin, Holz, Ulrich, and Goldiamond, 1961), fluent requests (Rosenfeld and Baer, 1970), and grammatical forms, such as prepositional phrases (Lee, 1981) and plural morphemes (Guess, 1969). Experiments have also verified Skinner's (1957) hypothesized functional verbal operants (see Oah and Dickinson, 1989, for a review). Moreover, be-

havior analytic principles have been used fruitfully to interpret a diverse group of studies on language development in infancy (Schlinger, 1995). The critical question regarding human language, or any complex human behavior for that matter, is whether plausible mechanisms or processes have been postulated. Operant learning principles constitute a plausible process both for verbal and nonverbal behavior, if for no other reason than they have already been shown experimentally to affect a wide range of human behaviors. Cognitive learning mechanisms, however, are not plausible in part because they are almost wholly inferred from the very behavior they are invoked to explain. Cognitive theorists cannot tell us what cognitive mechanisms look like or how they actually affect behavior.

Nature-Nurture

Perhaps it would be appropriate to conclude with a word about nature-nurture, the phrase first coined by Galton. The issue of the nature or nurture of behavior is not as meaningless as some might suppose, as Dobzhansky asked (1964, 55): "To what extent are differences observed among people conditioned by the differences of their genotypes and by the differences between the environments in which people were born, grew and were brought up?"

The question about the genesis of a given behavior is an empirical question. The only truly scientific approach is to conduct experiments in an attempt to uncover functional relations between behavior and its determinants. The amount of data demonstrating the overwhelming effects of environment on behavior establishes the plausibility of environmental interpretations not only of behavioral similarities but also of behavioral differences between humans. Evolution has obviously played an important part in human behavior. But rather than selecting for behavioral rigidity, it has selected for behavioral plasticity (Dobzhansky, Ayala, Stebbins, and Valentine, 1977). As Futuyma concluded (491):

> On balance, the evidence for the modifiability of human behavior is so great that genetic constraints on our behavior hardly seem to exist. The dominant factor in recent human evolution has been the evolution of behavioral flexibility, the ability to learn and transmit culture.

Conclusion

The problem with evolutionary explanations of behavior is that the evidence proffered to support them is so fraught with methodological problems that it is simply insufficient to warrant any conclusions about the role of genes and, thus, evolution. In contrast, there is already a wealth of experimental evidence establishing the plausibility of an environmental/learning account of much human behavior. This is not to say that genes play no role in human behavioral differences or similarities, only that the jury is still out on the verdict regarding the extent and nature of that role. The only way to truly make a case for genetic influence on behavior is to control for environmental variables and manipulate genetic variables, which, at present, are simply not possible with humans. Finally, from a practical point of view, environmental explanations are more valuable than evolutionary ones because they suggest immediate ways in which behavior can be changed.

Evolutionary theorists certainly succeed in making an interesting and often compelling case that perhaps there is some deeper core of human nature that ties us all together and around which we as individuals, and maybe even as groups, differ. It is a case that appeals to many people, including the media, all of whom are hungry for some evidence that sheds light on our nature. Unfortunately, the case is replete with evidential problems, and will have to be retried if and when more substantial evidence can be obtained. Until then, we should rely on what we know scientifically about human behavior.

References:

Ayllon, T. 1963. "Intensive Treatment of Psychotic Behaviour by Stimulus Satiation and Food Reinforcement." *Behaviour Research and Therapy.* 1:53–61.

Azrin, N. H., W. Holz, R. Ulrich, & I. Goldiamond. 1961. "The Control of the Content of Conversation through Reinforcement." *Journal of the Experimental Analysis of Behavior.* 4:25–30.

Barash, D. 1977. *Sociobiology and Human Behavior.* New York: Elsevier.

Barkow, J. H., L. Cosmides, and J. Tooby. 1992. *The Adapted Mind: Evolutionary Psychology and the Generation of Culture.* New York: Oxford University Press.

Bock, K. 1980. *Human Nature and History.* New York: Columbia University Press.

Boyle, M. E., & R. D. Greer. 1983. "Operant Procedures and the Comatose Patient." *J. of Applied Behavior Analysis.* 16:3–12.

Buss, D. M. 1994. *The Evolution of Desire: Strategies of Human Mating.* New York: Basic Books.

Byne, W. 1994. "The Biological Evidence Challenged." *Scientific American.* 270:50–55.

Cosmides, L., & J. Tooby. 1987. "From Evolution to Behavior: Evolutionary Psychology as the Missing Link." In J. Dupre (Ed.), *The Latest on the Best Essays on Evolution and Optimality.* Cambridge, MA: MIT Press.

Daly, M., & M. Wilson. 1982. "Whom are Newborn Babies Said to Resemble?" *Ethology and Sociobiology.* 3:69–78.

——. 1988. *Homicide.* New York: Aldine de Gruyter.

Dennett, D. C. 1995. *Darwin's Dangerous Idea: Evolution and the Meanings of Life.* New York: Simon & Schuster.

Dobzhansky, T. 1964. *Heredity and the Nature of Man.* New York: Harcourt, Brace & World.

Dobzhansky, T., F. J. Ayala, G. L. Stebbins, & J. W. Valentine. 1977. *Evolution*. San Francisco: Freeman.

Freedman, D. G. 1979. *Human Sociobiology*. New York: The Free Press.

Fuller, P. F. 1949. "Operant Conditioning of a Vegetative Human Organism." *American Journal of Psychology*. 69:587–590.

Futuyma, D. J. 1979. *Evolutionary Biology*. Sunderland, MA: Sinauer.

Gould, S. J. 1981. *The Mismeasure of Man*. New York: Norton.

Guess, D. 1969. "A Functional Analysis of Receptive Language and Productive Speech: Acquisition of the Plural Morpheme." *J. of Applied Behavior Analysis*. 2:55–64.

Hamer, D., & P. Copeland. 1994. *The Science of Desire: The Search for the Gay Gene and the Biology of Behavior*. New York: Simon & Schuster.

Herrnstein, R. J., & C. Murray. 1994. *The Bell Curve: Intelligence and Class Structure in American Life*. New York: The Free Press.

Horgan, J. 1993. "Eugenics Revisited." *Scientific American*. 268:123–131.

Hubbard, R., & E. Wald. 1993. *Exploding the Gene Myth*. Boston: Beacon Press.

Isaacs, W., J. Thomas, & I. Goldiamond. 1960. "Application of Operant Conditioning to Reinstate Verbal Behavior in Psychotics." *J. of Speech and Hearing Disorders*. 25:8–12.

Itzkoff, S. W. 1985. *Triumph of the Intelligent: The Creation of Homo Sapiens Sapiens*. Ashfield, MA: Paideia.

———. 1994. "The Decline of Intelligence in America: A Strategy for National Renewal." Westport, CT: Praeger.

Kamin, L. 1974. *The Science and Politics of IQ*. Potomac, MD: Erlbaum.

Kellert, S. R., & E. O. Wilson. 1993. *The Biophilia Hypothesis*. Washington, DC: Island Press.

Kitcher, P. 1985. *Vaulting Ambition: Sociobiology and the Quest for Human Nature*. Cambridge, MA: The MIT Press.

Lee, V. L. 1981. "Prepositional Phrases Spoken and Heard." *J. of the Experimental Analysis of Behavior*. 35:227–242.

Lewontin, R. C., S. Rose, L. J. Kamin. 1984. *Not in Our Genes*. New York: Pantheon Books.

Lumsden, C., & E. O. Wilson. 1983. *Promethean Fire*. Cambridge, MA: Harvard University Press.

MacCorquodale, K. 1970. "On Chomsky's Review of Skinner's Verbal Behavior." *J. of the Experimental Analysis of Behavior*. 13:83–89.

Neale, J. M., & R. M. Liebert. 1973. *Science and Behavior: An Introduction to Methods of Research*. Englewood Cliffs, NJ: Prentice-Hall.

Nesse, R. M., & G. C. Williams. 1994. *Why We Get Sick: The New Science of Darwinian Medicine*. New York: Times Books.

Oah, S., & A. M. Dickinson. 1989. "A Review of Empirical Studies of Verbal Behavior." *The Analysis of Verbal Behavior*. 7:53–68.

Palmer, D. C. 1986. "Chomsky's *Nativism*: A Critical Review." In L. J. Hayes & P. N. Chase (Eds.), *Dialogues on Verbal Behavior*. Springfield, IL: Thomas.

———. 1991. "A Behavioral Interpretation of Memory." In L. J. Hayes and P. N. Chase (Eds.), *Dialogues on Verbal Behavior*. Reno, NV: Context Press.

Poole, R. 1994. *Eve's Rib: The Biological Roots of Sex Differences*. New York: Crown.

Poulson, C. L. 1983. "Differential Reinforcement of Other-Than-Vocalization as a Control Procedure in the Conditioning of Infant Vocalization Rate." *J. of Experimental Child Psychology*. 36: 471–489.

Rosenfeld, H. M., & D. M. Baer. 1970. "Unbiased and Unnoticed Verbal Conditioning: The Double Agent Robot Procedure." *J. of the Experimental Analysis of Behavior*. 14:99–107.

Rushton, J. P. 1995a. *Race, Evolution, and Behavior: A Life History Perspective*. New Brunswick: Transaction Publishers.

———. 1995b. "J. Philippe Rushton Responds." *Skeptic*. 3:22–25.

Sahlins, M. 1976. *The Use and Abuse of Biology*. Ann Arbor: University of Michigan Press.

Schlinger, H. D. 1992. "Intelligence: Real or Artificial?" *The Analysis of Verbal Behavior*. 10:125–133.

———. 1995. *A Behavior Analytic View of Child Development*. New York: Plenum.

Shapiro, D., & R. S. Surwit. 1976. "Learned Control of Physiological Function and Disease." In H. Leitenberg (Ed.), *Handbook of Behavior Modifi-*

cation and Behavior Therapy. Englewood Cliffs, NJ: Prentice-Hall.

Skinner, B. F. 1938. *The Behavior of Organisms.* Englewood Cliffs, NJ: Prentice-Hall.

——. 1972. "A Case History in Scientific Method." In *Cumulative Record* (3rd ed.). New York: Meredith.

Stein, L., & J. D. Belluzzi 1988. "Operant Conditioning of Individual Neurons." In M. L. Commons, R. M. Church, J. R. Stellar, & A. R. Wagner (Eds.), *Quantitative Analysis of Behavior: Vol. 7.* Hillsdale, NJ: Erlbaum.

Stein, L., B. G. Xue, & J. D. Belluzzi. 1994. "In Vitro Reinforcement of Hippocampal Bursting: A Search for Skinner's Atoms of Behavior." *J. of the Experimental Analysis of Behavior.* 61:155–168.

Symons, D. 1992. "On the Use and Misuse of Darwinism in the Study of Human Behavior." In J. Barkow, L. Cosmides, & J. Tooby (Eds.), *The Adapted Mind.* New York: Oxford University Press.

Tavris, C. 1995. "A Place in the Sun." *Skeptic.* 3:62–63.

Tooby, J., & L. Cosmides. 1989. "Evolutionary Psychology and the Generation of Culture, Part II." *Ethology and Sociobiology.* 10:51–97.

——. 1992. "The Psychological Foundations of Culture." In J. Barkow, L. Cosmides, & J. Tooby (Eds.), *The Adapted Mind.* New York: Oxford University Press.

Whitehurst, G. J. 1972. "Production of Novel and Grammatical Utterances by Young Children." *J. of Experimental Child Psychology.* 13:502–515.

Wilson, E. O. 1975. *Sociobiology: The New Synthesis.* Cambridge, MA: Harvard University Press.

——. 1978. *On Human Nature.* Cambridge, MA: Harvard University Press.

——. 1993. "Biophilia and the Conservation Ethic." In Kellert & Wilson (Eds.), *The Biophilia Hypothesis.* Washington, DC: Island Press.

Wright, R. 1994. *The Moral Animal: The New Science of Evolutionary Psychology.* New York: Pantheon.

——. 1995. "The Biology of Violence." *The New Yorker,* March, 69–77.

Memes as Good Science

SUSAN J. BLACKMORE

Without the theory of evolution by natural selection nothing in the world of biology makes much sense. Without Darwin and neo-Darwinism, you cannot answer questions like Why do bats have wings? Why do cats have five claws? or Why do our optic fibres cross in front of our retinas? You can only fall back on appeals to an imaginary creator.

I am going to make a bold claim. Without the theory of evolution by memetic selection nothing in the world of the mind makes much sense. Without memetics you cannot answer questions like Why can't I get that thought out of my mind? Why did I decide to write this article and not another one? Who am I? Without memetics you can only fall back on appeals to an imaginary conscious agent.

In this article I want to lay the groundwork for a theory of memetics and see how far we can get. I shall outline the history and origins of the idea, explore how it has been used, abused, and ignored, and how it has provided new insight into the power of religions and cults. I shall then take on a meme's-eye view of the world and use this to answer five previously unanswered questions about human nature. Why can't we stop thinking? Why do we talk so much? Why are we so nice to each other? Why are our brains so big? And, finally, what is a self?

A History of the Meme Meme

In 1976 Dawkins published his best-selling *The Selfish Gene*. This book popularised the growing view in biology that natural selection proceeds not in the interest of the species or of the group, nor even of the individual, but in the interest of the genes. Although selection takes place largely at the individual level, the genes are the true replicators and it is their competition that drives the evolution of biological design. Dawkins, clear and daring as always, suggested that all life everywhere in the universe must evolve by the differential survival of slightly inaccurate self-replicating entities, which he called replicators.

Furthermore, these replicators automatically band together in groups to create systems, or machines, that carry them around and work to favour their continued replication. These survival machines, or vehicles, are our familiar bodies—and those of cats, E-coli, and cabbages—created to carry around and protect the genes inside them. At the end of the book Dawkins suggested that Darwinism is too big a theory to be confined to the narrow context of the gene. So he asked an obvious, if provocative, question. Are there any other replicators on our planet? Yes, he concluded. Staring us in the face, though still drifting clumsily about in its primeval soup of culture, is another replicator—a unit of imitation. He gave it the name *meme*, to rhyme with dream or seem. As examples he suggested—tunes, ideas, catch-phrases, clothes fashions, ways of making pots or of building arches—memes are stored in human brains and passed on by imitation.

In just a few pages Dawkins laid the foundation for understanding the evolution of memes. He discussed their propagation by jumping from brain to brain, likened them to parasites infecting a host, treated them as physically realised living structures, and showed how mutually assisting memes will group together just as genes do. He argued that once a new replicator arises it will tend to take over and begin a new kind of evolution. Above all he treated memes as replicators in their own right, chastising those of his colleagues who tended always to go back to biological advantage to answer questions about human behaviour. Yes, he agreed, we got our brains for biological (evolutionary and genetic) reasons but now we have a new replicator that has been unleashed and it need not be subservient to the old. In other words, memetic evolution can now proceed without regard to its effects on the genes.

A few years later Douglas Hofstadter wrote about viral sentences and self-replicating structures in his *Scientific American* column "Metamagical Themas." Readers replied, with examples of text using bait and hooks to ensure their own replication. They suggested viral sentences from the simplest instruction, such as "copy me!", through those with added threats ("I put a curse on you") or promises ("grant you three wishes"), to examples of virulent chain letters (Hofstadter, 1985). One reader suggested the term *memetics* for the discipline of studying memes.

Yet memetics did not really take off. Why not? The basic idea is very simple. If Dawkins is right then everything you have learned by imitation from someone else is a meme. This includes all the words in your vocabulary, the stories you know, the skills and habits you have picked up from others and the games you like to play. It includes the songs you sing and the rules you obey. So, for example, whenever you drive on the right (or on the left in my case here in England), eat a hamburger or a pizza, whistle Happy Birthday to You or Mama I Love You, or even shake hands, you are dealing in memes. Memetics is the study of why some memes spread and others do not.

The greatest proponent of memetics since Dawkins has been the philosopher Dan Dennett. In his books *Consciousness Explained* (1991) and *Darwin's Dangerous Idea* (1995) Dennett expands on the idea of the meme as replicator. In *On the Origin of Species*, Darwin (1859) explained how natural selection must happen if certain conditions are met. If there is heredity from parent to offspring, variation among the offspring, and not all the offspring can survive—then selection must take place. Individuals who have some useful relative advantage "have the best chance of being preserved in the struggle for life" (Darwin, 1859, 127) and will then pass on this advantage to their offspring. Darwin clearly saw how obvious the process of natural selection is once you have grasped it. Dennett describes evolution as a simple algorithm—a mindless procedure that when carried out must produce a result. You need three things—heredity, variation and selection—to make evolution inevitable. Evolution need not produce us, of course, or anything remotely like us; for evolution has no plans and no foresight. Nevertheless, you must get something more complex than what you started with. The evolutionary algorithm is "a scheme for creating Design out of Chaos without the aid of Mind" (Dennett, 1995, 50). This, says Dennett, is *Darwin's Dangerous Idea*. No wonder people have been terrified of it, and fought so hard against it. It is outrageously simple and terrifyingly powerful.

If evolution is an algorithm then it should

be able to run on different substrates. We tend to think of evolution as depending on genes because that is the way biology works on this planet, but the algorithm is neutral about this and will run wherever there is heredity, variation and selection; or as Dawkins puts it, a replicator. It doesn't matter which replicator. If memes are replicators then evolution will occur. So are memes replicators? There is enormous variety in the behaviors human beings emit; these behaviors are copied, more or less accurately, by other human beings, and not all the copies survive. The meme therefore perfectly satisfies the conditions of heredity, variation and selection. Just think of jokes.

Millions of variants are told by millions of people. Only a few get passed on and repeated and even fewer make it into the big time or the collections of classics. Scientific papers proliferate but only a few get long listings in the citation indexes. Only a few of the disgusting concoctions made in woks actually make it onto the TV shows that tell you how to wok things and only a few of my brilliant ideas have ever been appreciated by anyone! In other words, competition to get copied is fierce.

Of course memes are not like genes in many ways and we must be very careful in applying terms from genetics to memetics. The copying of memes is done by a kind of "reverse engineering" by one person copying another's behaviour, rather than by chemical transcription. Also we do not know just how memes are stored in human brains and whether they will turn out to be digitally stored, like genes, or not. However, the important point is that if memes are true replicators, memetic evolution must occur. Dennett is convinced they are and he explores how memes compete to get into as many minds as possible. This competition is the selective force of the memosphere and the successful memes create human minds as they go, restructuring our brains to make them ever better havens for more memes. Human con-

sciousness, claims Dennett, is itself a huge meme-complex, and a person is best understood as a certain sort of ape infested with memes. If he is right then we cannot hope to understand the origins of the human mind without memetics.

This makes it all the more fascinating that most people interested in the human mind have ignored memetics or simply failed to understand it. Mary Midgley (1994) calls memes "mythical entities" that cannot have interests of their own; "an empty and misleading metaphor." In a 1996 radio debate, Stephen Jay Gould called the idea of memes a "meaningless metaphor" (though I am not sure one can actually have a meaningless metaphor!). He wishes "that the term cultural evolution would drop from use" (1996, 219–220).

The word *meme* does not even appear in the index of many important books about human origins and language (e.g., Donald, 1991; Dunbar, 1996; Mithen, 1996; Pinker, 1994; Tudge, 1995; Wills, 1993); nor is it in an excellent collection on evolutionary psychology (Barkow, Cosmides and Tooby, 1992); nor in books about evolutionary ethics (Ridley, 1996; Wright, 1994). Although there are many theories of the evolution of culture, almost all make culture entirely subservient to genetic fitness, as in E. O. Wilson's (1978) metaphor of genes holding culture on a leash, or Lumsden and Wilson's claim that "the link between genes and culture cannot be severed" (1981, 344). Cavalli-Sforza and Feldman (1981) treat "cultural activity as an extension of Darwinian fitness" (362), and even Durham (1991)—the only one to use the word *meme*—sticks to examples of cultural features with obvious relevance to genetic fitness such as color naming, dietary habits and marriage customs.

Perhaps Boyd and Richerson (1990) come closest to treating the cultural unit as a true replicator. However, they still view "genetic and cultural evolution as a tightly coupled co-evolutionary process in humans" (Richerson and Boyd, 1992, 80). As far as I can understand them, no one except Cloak (1975) and Dawkins treats their unit of cultural exchange as a true replicator. If there is a continuum from Gould's outright rejection at one end, to Dawkins and Cloak at the other, then most scholars lie in between. They accept cultural evolution but not the idea of a second replicator. When they say adaptive or maladaptive they mean for the genes. When it comes to the crunch they always fall back on appeals to biological advantage, just as Dawkins complained his colleagues did 20 years ago.

Dawkins is clear on this issue when he says "there is no reason why success in a meme should have any connection whatever with genetic success." I agree. I am going to propose a theory of memetics that lies at the far end of this continuum. I suggest that once genetic evolution had created creatures that were capable of imitating each other, a second replicator was born. Since then our brains and minds have been the product of two replicators, not one. Today many of the selection pressures on memes are still of genetic origin (such as whom we find sexy and what food tastes good), but as memetic evolution proceeds faster and faster, our minds are increasingly the product of memes, not genes. If memetics is true then the memes have created human minds and culture just as surely as the genes have created human bodies.

Religions as Meme-Complexes

Dawkins (1976) introduced the term *co-adapted meme-complex*. By this he meant a group of memes that thrive in each other's company. Just as genes group together for mutual protection, leading ultimately to the creation of organisms, so we might expect memes to group together. As Dawkins (1993, 20) puts it, "there will be a ganging up of ideas that flourish in one another's presence." Meme-complexes include all those groups of memes that tend to be passed on together, such as political ideologies, religious beliefs, scientific theories and paradigms, artistic movements, and languages. The most successful of these are not just loose agglomerations of compatible ideas, but well-structured groups with different memes specializing as hooks, bait, threats, and immune systems. (Memetic jargon is still evolving and these terms may change but see Grant's "memetic lexicon," 1990.)

When I was about 10 years old I received a postcard and a letter that contained a list of six names that instructed me to send a postcard to the first name on the list. I was to put my own name and address at the bottom and send the new list to six more people. It promised me I would receive lots of postcards. This was a fairly innocuous chain letter as these things go, consisting just of a bait (the promised postcards) and a hook (send it to six more people). Threats are also common (send this on or the evil eye will get you) and many have far worse consequences than a waste of stamps. What they have in common is the instruction to "duplicate me" (the hook) along with co-memes for coercion. These simple little groups can spread quite well.

With the advent of computers, viral meme-groups have much more space to play in and can leap from disk to disk among "unhygienic" computer users. Dawkins (1993) discusses how computer viruses and worms use tricks to get themselves spread. Some bury themselves in memory only to pop up as a time bomb; some infect only a small proportion of those they reach, and some are triggered probabilistically. Like biological viruses they must not kill their host too soon or they will die out. Their final effect may be quite funny, such as one that makes the Macintosh computer's loudspeaker say "Don't Panic!," but some have clogged up entire networks and destroyed whole doctoral theses. My students have recently encountered a virus in WORD 6 that lives in a formatting section called "Thesis"—tempting you to get infected just when your year's work is almost finished. No wonder we now have a proliferation of anti-virus software—the equivalent of medicine for the infosphere.

Internet viruses are a relatively new arrival. Last week I received a very kind warning from someone I've never met. "Do not download any message entitled Penpal Greetings" it said—and went on to warn me that if I read this terrible message I would have let in a Trojan Horse virus that would destroy everything on my hard drive and then send itself on to every e-mail address in my mail box. To protect all my friends, and the world-wide computer network, I had to act fast and send the warning on to them.

Have you spotted the trick? The virus described does not make sense; in fact, it does not exist. The real virus is the warning. This is a very clever little meme-complex that uses both threats and appeals to altruism to get you—the silly, caring victim—to pass it on. It is not the first—Good Times and Deeyenda Maddick used a similar trick—and it probably won't be the last. However, as more people learn to ignore the warnings, these viruses will start to fail and perhaps that will let in worse viruses, as people start to ignore warnings they ought to heed. So, Watch Out!

What does this have to do with religions? According to Dawkins, a great deal. The most controversial application of memetics is undoubtedly his treatment of religions as co-adapted meme-complexes (Dawkins, 1976, 1993; Miele, 1995). Dawkins unashamedly describes religions as "viruses of the mind" and sets about analysing how they work. They work, he says, because human brains are just what info-viruses need; brains can soak up information, replicate it reasonably accurately, and obey the instructions it embodies. Dawkins uses the example of Roman Catholi-

cism, a gang of mutually compatible memes that is stable enough to deserve a name. The heart of Catholicism is its major beliefs: a powerful and forgiving God, Jesus his son who was born of a virgin and rose again from the dead, the holy spirit, and so on. If these aren't implausible enough you can add belief in miracles or the literal transubstantiation of wine into blood.

Why should anyone believe these things? Threats of hell fire and damnation are an effective and nasty technique of persuasion. From an early age children are brought up by their Catholic parents to believe that if they break certain rules they will burn in hell forever after death. The children cannot easily test this since neither hell nor God can be seen, although He can see everything they do. So they must simply live in life-long fear until death, when they will find out for sure, or not. The idea of hell is thus a self-perpetuating meme.

Did I say test the idea? Some religious beliefs could be tested, such as whether wine really turns into blood, or whether prayer actually helps; hence the need for the anti-testing meme of faith. In Catholicism, doubt must be resisted, while faith is nurtured and respected. If your knowledge of biology leads you to doubt the virgin birth—or if war, cruelty and starvation seem to challenge the goodness of God—then you must have faith. The biblical story of Doubting Thomas is a cautionary tale against seeking evidence. As Dawkins puts it, "Nothing is more lethal for certain kinds of meme than a tendency to look for evidence" and religions, unlike science, make sure they discourage it (Dawkins, 1976, 198). Also unlike science, religions often include memes that make their carriers violently intolerant of new and unfamiliar ideas, thus protecting themselves against being ousted in favour of a different religion—or none at all.

Finally the meme-complex needs mechanisms to ensure its own spread. A kill the infidel meme will dispose of the opposition. Go forth and multiply will produce more children to pass itself on to. So will forbidding masturbation, birth control, or interfaith marriages. If fear of going blind doesn't work, there are prizes in heaven for missionaries and those who convert unbelievers (Dawkins, 1993; Lynch, 1996). Catholicism generally spreads from parent to child but celibate priests play a role too. This is particularly interesting since celibacy means a dead end for the genes, but not for the memes. A priest who has no wife and children to care for has more time to spread his memes, including that for celibacy. Celibacy is another partner in this vast complex of mutually assisting religious memes.

Dawkins (1993) gives other examples from Judaism, such as the pointlessness of rabbis testing for the kosher-purity of food, or the horrors of Jim Jones leading his flock to mass suicide in the Guyana jungle. Today he might add Heaven's Gate to the catalogue. "Obviously a meme that causes individuals bearing it to kill themselves has a grave disadvantage, but not necessarily a fatal one . . . a suicidal meme can spread, as when a dramatic and well-publicised martyrdom inspires others to die for a deeply loved cause, and this in turn inspires others to die, and so on" (Dawkins, 1982, 111).

Dawkins might equally have chosen Islam, a faith that includes the concept of the jihad (holy war), and has particularly nasty punishments for people who desert the faith. Even today the author and heretic Salman Rushdie lives in fear of his life because many Muslims consider it their holy duty to kill him. Once you have been infected with powerful memes like these you must pay a high price to get rid of them.

Lynch (1996) explores in depth some techniques used by religions and cults. "Honour thy father and mother" is an excellent commandment, increasing the chance that children will take on beliefs from their parents, including the commandment itself. As a secular meme it might not succeed very well, since kids would surely reject it if they thought it came straight from the parents. However, presented as an idea from God (who is all powerful, all-seeing and punishes disobedience) it has a much better chance—a good example of memes ganging up. Dietary laws may thrive because they protect against disease, but may also keep people in the faith by making it harder for them to adapt to other diets outside. Moral codes may enhance effective cooperation and survival but may also be ways of punishing lapses of faith. Observing "holy days" ensures lots of time for spreading the memes, and public prayers and grace at meals ensure that lots of people are exposed to them. Learning sacred texts by heart and setting them to inspiring or memorable music ensure their longevity.

In the long history of religions, most of them have spread vertically—that is, from parent to child. Even today the best predictor of your religion is your parent's religion—even if you think you rationally chose the best or truest one! Today, however, more and more new religions and cults spread horizontally—from any person to any other person. The two types use different meme tricks for their replication. As an example of the first type Lynch (1996) cites the Hutterites. They average more than 10 children per couple, a fantastic rate that is possibly helped by the way they distribute parental responsibility, making each extra child only a slightly greater burden for its natural parents. Other religions put more effort into conversion, like the evangelical faiths which thrive on instant rewards and spiritual joy on conversion.

In case I seem to be implying that people have deliberately manufactured religions this way, that is not the case. Imagine in the long, long history of human religious endeavour, all the millions and millions of different statements, ideas, and commandments that must have been uttered at some time or another. Which would you expect to have made it to the present? The answer is, of course, the ones that just happened to have included clever tricks or come together with other ideas they could gang up with. The countless millions of other ideas have simply been lost. This is memetic evolution, and extinction.

Taking the Meme's Eye View

We are now ready to take the meme's eye view. Imagine a world full of hosts for memes (e.g., brains) and far more memes than can possibly find homes. Which memes are more likely to find a safe home and get passed on again? It's that simple.

In doing this I try to follow some simple rules. First, remember that memes (like genes) do not have foresight! Second, consider only the interests of the memes, not of the genes or the organism. Memes do not care about genes or people—all they do is reproduce themselves. Shorthand statements like memes want x or memes try to do y must always be translatable back into the longer version, such as memes that have the effect of producing x are more likely to survive than those that do not. Third, memes, by definition, are passed on by imitation. So learning by trial and error or by feedback is not memetic, nor are all forms of communication. Only when an idea, behaviour, or skill is passed on by imitation does it count as a meme. Now, remembering these rules, we can ask the question and see where it leads.

Imagine a world full of brains, and far more memes than can possibly find homes. Which memes are more likely to find a safe home and get passed on again? Some of the consequences are startlingly obvious—once you see them. And some are frighteningly powerful. I shall start with two simple ones, partly as exercises in thinking memetically.

1. *Why Can't We Stop Thinking?* Can you stop thinking? If you have ever meditated you will know just how hard this is—the mind just seems to keep blithering on. If we were thinking useful thoughts, practising mental skills, or solving relevant problems there might be some point, but mostly we don't seem to be. So why can't we just sit down and not think? From a genetic point of view all this extra thinking seems extremely wasteful—and animals that waste energy don't survive. Memetics provides a simple answer. *Imagine a world full of brains, and far more memes than can possibly find homes. Which memes are more likely to find a safe home and get passed on again?* Imagine a meme that encourages its host to keep on mentally rehearsing it, or a tune that is so easy to hum that it goes round and round in your head, or a thought that just compels you to keep thinking it. Imagine in contrast a meme that buries itself quietly in your memory and is never rehearsed, or a tune that is too unmemorable to go round in your head, or a thought that is too boring to think again. Which will do better? Other things being equal, the first lot will. Rehearsal aids memory, and you are likely to express (or even sing) the ideas and tunes that fill your waking hours. What is the consequence? The memosphere fills up with catchy tunes, and thinkable thoughts. We all come across them and so we think an awful lot. The principle here is familiar from biology. In a forest, any tree that grows tall gets more light. So genes for growing tall become more common in the gene pool and the forest ends up being as high as the trees can make it.

2. *Why Do We Talk So Much?* Imagine a world full of brains, and far more memes than can possibly find homes. Which memes are more likely to find a safe home and get passed on again? Imagine any meme that encourages talking. It might be an idea like talking makes people like you or it's friendly to chat. It might be an urgent thought that you feel compelled to share, a funny joke, good news that every-

body wants to hear, or any meme that thrives inside a talkative person. Imagine in contrast any meme that discourages talking, such as the thought talking is a waste of time. It might be something you dare not voice aloud, something very difficult to say, or any meme that thrives inside a shy and retiring person. Which will do better? Put this way the answer is obvious. The first lot will be heard by more people and, other things being equal, simply must stand a better chance of being propagated. What is the consequence of this? The memosphere will fill up with memes that encourage talking and we will all talk an awful lot. And we do!

A simpler way of putting it is this: people who talk more will, on average, spread more memes. So any memes which thrive in chatterboxes are likely to spread. This makes me see conversation in a new light. Is all that talking really founded on biological advantage? Talking takes a lot of energy and we talk about some daft and pointless things. Do these trivial and stupid thoughts and conversations have some hidden biological advantage? I think not. In fact, in this case memes seem to be working against genes. This sets the stage for a more audacious suggestion.

3. *Why Are We So Nice to Each Other?* Of course we aren't always nice to each other, but human cooperation and altruism are something of a mystery—despite tremendous advances made in understanding kin selection and inclusive fitness, reciprocal altruism and evolutionarily stable strategies (Wright, 1994; Ridley, 1996; *Skeptic*, Vol. 4, Nos. 1 and 2). Human societies exhibit much more cooperation than is typical of vertebrate societies, and we cooperate with non-relatives on a massive scale (Richerson and Boyd, 1992). As Cronin puts it, human morality "presents an obvious challenge to Darwinian theory" (1991, 325). Everyone can probably think up their own favorite example. Dawkins (1989, 230) calls blood doning "a genuine case of pure, disin-

terested altruism." I am more impressed by charitable giving to people in faraway countries who probably share as few of our genes as anyone on Earth and whom we are unlikely ever to meet. And why do we turn in wallets found in the street, rescue injured wildlife, support eco-friendly companies, or recycle our bottles? Why do so many people want to be poorly paid nurses and counselors, social workers and psych techs, when they could live in bigger houses, attract richer mates, and afford more children if they were bankers, stock brokers, or lawyers?

Many people believe all this must ultimately be explained in terms of biological advantage. Perhaps it will, but I offer an alternative for consideration: a memetic theory of altruism. We can use our, by now, familiar tactic. *Imagine a world full of brains, and far more memes than can possibly find homes. Which memes are more likely to find a safe home and get passed on again?* Imagine the sort of meme that encourages its host to be friendly and kind. It might be a meme for throwing good parties, for being generous with the homemade marmalade, or just being prepared to spend time listening to a friend's woes. Now compare this with memes for being unfriendly and mean—never cooking people dinners or buying drinks, and refusing to give your time to others. Which will spread more quickly? The first type, of course. People like to be with nice people. So those who harbor lots of friendliness memes will spend more time with others and have more chances to spread their memes. In consequence many of us will end up harboring lots of memes for being nice to others. A simpler way of putting it is this: people who are altruistic will, on average, spread more memes. So any memes which thrive in altruistic people are likely to spread—including the memes for being altruistic.

Is this hypothesis testable? Well, research in social psychology reveals that people are more likely to adopt ideas from people they like

(Eagly and Chaiken, 1984). Whether this is a cause or a consequence of the above argument is debatable. This memetic explanation predicts that people should act in ways that benefit the spread of their memes even at some cost to themselves. We are familiar with buying useful information, and with advertisers buying their way into people's minds for the purposes of selling products, but this theory predicts that people will pay (or work) simply to spread the memes they hold—because the memes force them to. Missionaries, Mormons, and Jehovah's Witnesses come to mind.

Many aspects of persuasion and conversion to causes may turn out to involve meme-driven altruism. Altruism is yet another of the meme tricks that religions have purloined. Almost all of them thrive on making their members work for them and believe they are doing good. Of course, being generous is expensive. There will always be pressure against it, and if memes can find alternative strategies for spreading they will. For example, powerful people may be able to spread memes without being altruistic at all! However, that does not change the basic argument that altruism spreads memes.

You may have noticed that the underlying theme in all these arguments is that the memes may act in opposition to the interest of the genes. Thinking all the time may not use much energy but it must cost something. Talking is certainly expensive, as anyone who has been utterly exhausted or seriously ill will attest. And, of course, any altruistic act is, by definition, costly to the actor. I would say that this is just what we should expect if memes are true replicators. They do not care about the genes or the creatures the genes created. Their only interest is self-propagation. So if they can propagate by stealing resources from the genes, they will do so.

4. *Why Are Our Brains So Big?* Yes, I know there are lots of good answers to this old chest-nut, but are they good enough? Let us not forget how mysterious this issue really is. Brains are notoriously expensive both to build and to run. They take up about 2% of the body's weight but use about 20% of its energy. Our brains are three times the size of the brains of apes of equivalent body size. Compared to other mammals our encephalisation quotient (the ratio of actual brain size to brain expected for the average animal of that body size) is even higher, up to about 25 (Jerison, 1973; Leakey, 1994; Wills, 1993). On many measures of brain capacity and behavioral complexity humans stand out alone. The fact that such intelligence has arisen in an animal that stands upright may or may not be a coincidence but it certainly adds to the problem. Our pelvises are not ideally suited for giving birth to huge brains and so childbirth is a risky process for human beings—yet we do it. Why? The mystery was deepened for me by thinking about the size of the biological advantage required for survival. In a study concerned with the fate of the Neanderthals, Zubrow (Leakey, 1994) used computer simulations to determine the effect of a slight competitive edge. He concluded that a 2% advantage could eliminate a competing population in less than a millennium. If we needed only such a tiny advantage why do we have such a huge one? Several answers have recently been proposed. For example, Dunbar (1996) argues that we need large brains in order to gossip, and gossip acts as a kind of verbal grooming to keep very large bands of people together. Christopher Wills (1993) argues that the runaway evolution of the human brain resulted from an increasingly swift gene-environment feedback loop. Miller (1993) proposes that our vast brains have been created by sexual selection; and Richerson and Boyd (1992) claim they are needed for individual and social learning, favored under increasing rates of environmental variation.

What these authors all have in common is

that their ultimate appeal is to the genes. Like Dawkins' bewailed colleagues, they always wish to go back to biological advantage. I propose an alternative based on memetic advantage. Imagine early hominids who, for good biological reasons, gained the ability to imitate each other and to develop simple language. Once this step occurred memes could begin to spread, and the second replicator was born.

Remember—once this happened the genes would no longer be able to stop the spread! Presumably the earliest memes would be useful ones, such as ways of making pots or knives, or ways of catching or dismembering prey. Let us assume that some people would have slightly larger brains and that larger brains are better copiers. As more and more people began to pick up these early memes, the environment would change so that it became more and more necessary to have the new skills in order to survive. A person who could quickly learn to make a good pot or tell a popular story would more easily find a mate, and so sexual selection would add to the pressure for big brains. In the new environment larger-brained people would have an advantage and the importance of the advantage would increase as the memes spread. It seems to me that this fundamental change in selection pressures, spreading at the rate of meme propagation, provides for the first time a plausible reason why our brains are totally out of line with all other brains on the planet. They have been meme-driven. One replicator has forced the moves of another.

5. *Who Am I?* We can now see the human mind as the creation of two replicators, one using for its replication the machinery created by the other. As Dennett pointed out, people are animals infested with memes. Our personalities, abilities, and unique qualities derive from the complex interplay of these replicators. What then of our innermost selves—the real me, the person who experiences my life?

I would like to suggest that selves are co-adapted meme complexes—though only one of many supported by any given brain (Blackmore, 1996). Like religions, political belief systems, and cults, they are sets of memes that thrive in each other's company. Like religions, political belief systems, and cults, they are safe havens for all sorts of travelling memes and they are protected from destruction by various meme tricks. They do not have to be true. In fact we know that selves are a myth. Look inside the brain and you find only neurons. You do not find the little person pulling the strings or the homunculus watching the show on an inner screen (Dennett, 1991). You do not find the place where my conscious decisions are made. You do not find the thing that lovingly holds all those beliefs and opinions. Most of us still persist in thinking about ourselves that way. But there is no one in there!

We now have a radically new answer to the question Who am I?, and a rather terrifying one at that. I am one of the many co-adapted meme-complexes living within this brain. This scary idea may explain why memetics is not more popular. Memetics deals a terrible blow to the supremacy of self.

The Future of Memes

The memes are out! For most of human history memes have evolved alongside genes. They were passed on largely vertically—from parent to child—and therefore evolved at much the same rate as genes. This is no longer true. Memes can leap from brain to brain in seconds—even when the brains are half a planet apart. While some memes hang around in brains for weeks, months, or years before being passed on, many now spread in multiple copies at the speed of light. The invention of the telephone, fax machine, and e-mail all increase the speed of meme propagation. As high speed, accurate, horizontal copying of memes increases we can expect some dramatic developments in the memosphere.

First, the faster memes spread, the weaker is the hold of natural (genetic) selection. This relative decoupling of genes and memes may mean that more than ever before memes will spread that are detrimental to their carriers. We may be seeing this already with some of the dangerous cults, fads, political systems, copy-cat crimes, and false beliefs that can now spread so quickly. Second, we may expect memes to build themselves ever better vehicles for their own propagation. Genes have built organisms to carry themselves. What is the memic equivalent? Artifacts such as books, paintings, tools, and aeroplanes might count (Dennett, 1995), but they are feeble compared with computers or the internet. Even these recent inventions are still largely dependent on humans for their functioning, and on the genes those humans are carrying—after all, sex is the most popular topic on the internet.

Can the second replicator ever really break free of the first? It might if ever we construct robots that directly imitate each other. Fortunately this is such a difficult task that it will not be achieved very soon and perhaps by then we will have a better understanding of memetics and be in a better position to cope with our new neighbors.

Conclusion

I have shown how a theory of memetics provides new answers to some important questions about human nature. If I am right, then we humans are the product of two replicators, not one. In the past century we have successfully thrown off the illusion that a God is needed to understand the design of our bodies. Perhaps in the next century we can throw off the illusion that conscious agents are needed to understand the design of our minds.

References:

Barkow, J. H., Cosmides, L., and Tooby, J. (Eds.). 1992. *The Adapted Mind: Evolutionary Psychology and the Generation of Culture.* New York: Oxford University Press.

Blackmore, S. J. 1996. "Waking from the Meme Dream." The Psychology of Awakening: An International Conference on Buddhism, Science and Psychotherapy, Dartington, Nov. 9.

Boyd, R., and Richerson, P. J. 1990. "Group Selection among Alternative Evolutionarily Stable Strategies." *Journal of Theoretical Biology,* 145: 331–342.

Cavalli-Sforza, L. L., and Feldman, M. W. 1981. *Cultural Transmission and Evolution: A Quantitative Approach.* Princeton: Princeton University Press.

Cloak, F. R. 1975. "Is a Cultural Ethology Possible?" *Human Ecology,* 3: 161–182.

Cronin, H. 1991. *The Ant and the Peacock.* New York: Cambridge University Press.

Darwin, C. 1859. *On the Origin of Species by Means of Natural Selection.* London: Murray.

Dawkins, R. 1989 (1976). *The Selfish Gene.* Oxford University Press.

——. 1982. *The Extended Phenotype.* Oxford University Press.

——. 1993. "Viruses of the Mind." In B. Dahlbohm (Ed.), *Dennett and His Critics: Demystifying Mind.* Oxford: Blackwell, 13–27.

Dennett, D. 1991. *Consciousness Explained.* Boston: Little, Brown.

——. 1995. *Darwin's Dangerous Idea.* London: Penguin.

Donald, M. 1991. *Origins of the Modern Mind: Three Stages in the Evolution of Culture and Cognition.* Cambridge: Harvard University Press.

Dunbar, R. 1996. *Grooming, Gossip and the Evolution of Language.* London: Faber & Faber.

Durham, W. H. 1991. *Coevolution: Genes, Culture and Human Diversity.* Stanford: Stanford University Press.

Eagly, A. H., and Chaiken, S. 1984. "Cognitive Theories of Persuasion." In L. Berkowitz (Ed.), *Ad-*

vances in Experimental Social Psychology, 17: 267–359. New York: Academic Press.

Gould, S. J. 1996. *Full House*. New York: Harmony Books.

Grant, G. 1990. Memetic lexicon: http://pespmc1. vub.ac.be/*memes.html

Hofstadter, D. 1985. *Metamagical Themas: Questing for the Essence of Mind and Pattern*. New York: Basic Books.

Jerison, H. J. 1973. *Evolution of the Brain and Intelligence*. New York: Academic Press.

Leakey, R. 1994. *The Origin of Humankind*. London: Weidenfeld and Nicolson.

Lumsden, C. J., and Wilson, E. O. 1981. *Genes, Mind and Culture*. Cambridge: Harvard University Press.

Lynch, A. 1996. *Thought Contagion: How Belief Spreads through Society*. New York: Basic Books.

Midgley, M. 1994. "Letter to the Editor." *New Scientist*, Feb. 12: 50.

Miele, F. 1995. "Darwin's Dangerous Disciple: An Interview with Richard Dawkins." *Skeptic*, 3: 4, 80–85.

Miller, G. 1993. *Evolution of the Human Brain through Runaway Sexual Selection*. Ph.D. Thesis, Stanford University Psychology Department.

Mithen, S. 1996. *The Prehistory of the Mind*. London: Thames and Hudson.

Pinker, S. 1994. *The Language Instinct*. New York: Morrow.

Richerson, P. J., and Boyd, R. 1992. "Cultural Inheritance and Evolutionary Ecology." In E. A. Smith and B. Winterhalder (Eds.), *Evolutionary Ecology and Human Behaviour*, 61–92. New York: Aldine de Gruyter.

Ridley, M. 1996. *The Origins of Virtue*. London: Viking.

Skeptic. 1996. Special Theme Issue: "Are We Slaves to Our Evolutionary Past?" Volume 4, #1.

——. 1996. Special Theme Issue: "Where Does Morality Come From? Did Ethics Evolve?" Volume 4, #2.

Tudge, C. 1995. *The Day before Yesterday: Five Million Years of Human History*. London: Jonathan Cape.

Wills, C. 1993. *The Runaway Brain: The Evolution of Human Uniqueness*. New York: Basic Books.

Wilson, E. O. 1978. *On Human Nature*. Cambridge: Harvard University Press.

Wright, R. 1994. *The Moral Animal*. New York: Pantheon Books.

Memes as Pseudoscience

JAMES W. POLICHAK

In his 1976 book *The Selfish Gene*, Richard Dawkins introduced the term "meme" to refer to a hypothetical unit of imitation or information that is transmitted from person to person. In Dawkins' and later memetic analyses of information processing, cultural information is treated as being analogous to genetic information—it exists in discrete self-replicating units that are subject to environmental selective forces. These forces result in differential survival of memes, much as environmental forces result in differential survival of genes. In short, memetic theorists argue that cultural evolution is analogous to, but partially independent from, biological evolution.

Proponents of memetics have made a number of extremely bold claims about the power of memetic analysis and the insights to be gained by applying such an analysis to culture and the transfer of information. The memetic approach has been called a new and revolutionary way of looking at culture and information, and even a "paradigm shift" (Brodie, 1996; Lynch, 1996). Memetics is viewed as the "missing link" that will allow researchers (specifically memeticists) to unify the social sciences (Lynch, 1996). Finally, it has been argued that "without the theory of evolution by memetic selection, nothing in the world of the mind makes much sense" (Blackmore, 1997, 43). Such a powerful approach should surely be appreciated, yet even such a strong proponent as Susan Blackmore noted that "the very

idea of the meme seems to strike fear into even the most hardened evolutionist" (1996, 1). She shows (1997, and in the previous entry), in fact, that few books on evolution and culture even mention the word "meme," much less delve into analyses based on memes.

In this article I will endeavor to explain why most scientists dismiss the meme and theories based on it. In short, it is because memetic analyses are very shallow and imprecise compared to more traditional approaches, and because proponents of such analyses are all too willing to offer untested, unsupported, or incorrect assertions as proof of the value of their approach. I suggest that hardened evolutionists and social scientists are not fearful of memes. Rather, they are far more likely to be dismayed at the overzealous promotion of memes, the lack of supporting data or strong logical arguments, and the circularity of the "answers" memeticists offer to challenging questions concerning the origins and nature of culture, the human mind, and information. It is likely that these are the reasons that the memetic approach has been largely dismissed or ignored for the past 20 years. The problem can be enumerated as follows:

1. Memeticists have not done an adequate job of defining the meme, nor have they offered any examples of what a meme might be that withstand scrutiny.
2. Memeticists have failed to show that memes are necessary to understanding

culture. As a consequence they are unable to show that models based on biological selection are inadequate.

3. By largely ignoring the principles and data concerning information processing from the social sciences, especially psychology, memeticists have argued for a highly inaccurate model of information transfer, and a highly limited model of the activity of the human brain.

4. Memeticists have offered inaccurate and circular claims about what kind of explanatory power is obtained by assuming the existence of memes.

What Is a Meme?

The first major problem with meme-based approaches to understanding information processing and culture is that no one seems to be quite sure what a meme is. There is no direct evidence for the existence of any meme (i.e., no single meme has been isolated in the way that single genes have), nor does anyone know what memes might be made of (i.e., there have been no discoveries of meme-units analogous to the four base pairs of DNA). This lack of direct evidence does not doom memetic analyses to failure, however. Darwin (1859) produced his theory of evolution by natural selection and Mendel performed a number of seminal experiments on genetic transmission long before anyone knew what a gene was or what it might be made of. Indeed, it was the rediscovery of Mendel's experiments that changed the then current scientific belief that hereditary information was carried in the bloodstream, and demonstrated that there were somewhat discrete units of hereditary information.

Given the lack of direct evidence for memes, we are left with a wide assortment of analogies. Memes were originally conceived of by Dawkins (1976/1989) as a self-replicating en-

tity consisting of information in some form. According to Dawkins, the meme is "a unit of cultural transmission, or a unit of imitation" (192), much like a gene is the unit of biological or hereditary transmission. This definition is, of course, quite imprecise, and Dawkins recognized this. The extent to which memes are analogous to genes is not clear. For this analogy to be effective, memes must be self-replicating and they must be so with the chance for error, and certain memes must be more successful than others. While memes are interested only in ensuring their transmission, there also must be some memes that offer an advantage to their hosts that is not reducible to a biological reproductive advantage, possibly an advantage that is actually reproductively detrimental but memetically advantageous. In other words, possessing a particular meme may lead one to engage in activities that lessen the chance of transmitting one's genes to future generations while increasing the chances that one will spread one's memes.

The analogy between genes and memes has been filled out or modified in various ways, so much so that proponents of meme theory have directly contradicted each other. For example, while Blackmore writes that "memes are not like genes" (1996, 3), the Meme FAQ (frequently asked questions) at Meme Central states that "memes are the basic building blocks of our minds and culture, in the same way that genes are the basic building blocks of biological life" (Brodie, 1997, 2).

Other memeticists have seemingly tried to avoid deciding how exactly memes are or are not like genes by instead trying to develop the analogy to viral transmission (which seems to be simply making the analogy less direct, given that viruses are composed mostly of genetic material). The *Memetic Lexicon* defines a meme as "a contagious information pattern that replicates by symbiotically infecting human minds and altering their behavior, causing them to propagate the pattern" (Grant,

Sandberg, and McFadzean, 1995, 2). Lynch (1996) does not offer much discussion of the meme-gene analogy, instead focusing on the various ways to spread "thought contagions," while Dawkins (1993) and Brodie (1996) look at memes as "viruses of the mind." The more precise treatments of the analogy (e.g., Dawkins, 1993) focus on computer viruses, but again suffer from the same problem as the meme-gene analogy. How exactly are memes like or not like viruses, computer or biological? One way that memes and viruses are apparently not alike is that not all memes are detrimental to their hosts. Regardless of whether or not this is an accurate conception of viruses, developers of this analogy (Brodie, 1996; Dawkins, 1993; Grant et al., 1995; Lynch, 1996) have been forced to take special pains to make the point that memes are often beneficial to their hosts. This, however, leaves us in the unsatisfactory state of saying that some memes are like viruses, including being bad for you, and others are like viruses except for not being bad for you.

At least one memeticist has tried to avoid using analogies by defining a meme as "a single unit of thought" (Nehring Bliss, 1997, 1). This definition, however, loses the benefits of the analogies to genes and viruses. It does not include the concept of self-replication with error that is necessary for meme theory to have any force. Additionally, it is far from clear what "thought" is and what one unit of it might be. Does any brain activity count as "thought," or must "thought" be conscious, whatever that is? Memeticists have largely failed to offer a precise, useful definition of the meme. Nor have they managed to fully develop either the analogy with genes or with viruses in a manner that states which parts of the analogy hold and which do not. This is an admittedly difficult task. A systematic series of controlled experiments will be necessary to fully establish whether memes are genuine self-replicating entities and how they are similar to the other known self-replicator (the gene).

Unfortunately, the attempt to get at what a meme is by looking at the examples offered also fails. Dawkins gives a number of examples of memes: "tunes, ideas, catch-phrases, clothes fashions, ways of making pots or of building arches" (1976/1989, 192). Most have followed Dawkins' lead to the extent of quoting or paraphrasing his examples (e.g., Blackmore, 1997; Grant et al., 1995; Speel, 1997). Here, to better describe a poorly defined concept, we are given a series of poorly defined terms. I doubt that Dawkins or any of those who have followed his lead have an adequate definition of "idea" or even of a "clothes fashion." Dawkins recognized this problem to some extent in his original chapter, writing, "I have said that a tune is one meme, but what about a symphony? Is each movement one meme . . . ?" (1976/1989, 195). It is still not clear what exactly a "tune" is, though. Dawkins further suggests that "if a single phrase of Beethoven's Ninth Symphony is sufficiently distinct and memorable to be abstracted from the context of the whole symphony . . . then to that extent it deserves to be called one meme" (195). While this example seems more precise, it introduces another difficulty. A chunk of information is a meme to the extent that it is distinct and memorable. This would seem to suggest that, for the time being at least, we can only offer probabilistic examples of what a meme is, and that probabilistic example rests on quite shaky ground, especially when one wants to provide evidence for a discrete entity. A chunk of information must be sufficiently distinct and memorable, but to whom? Dawkins suggests that use as a call-sign of "European broadcasting station" might be sufficient to determine if a chunk of information is a single meme (195). But if memes are defined in this manner, then what may be a meme to me or to a radio station manager may not be a meme to you. If I notice an idea in a book that you do not, is that detail then a meme or not a meme or both? I don't think Dawkins or anyone else wants to define memes in a manner that seems to be largely based on individual differences in attention or memory, but his analysis suggests just that. How many people, or which people, would have to notice and remember a chunk of information for it to be sufficiently distinct and memorable to be a meme? Perhaps for now memes can be like pornography—we may not know exactly what memes are, but we know them when we see them.

Another important issue that remains unclear from the examples in the memetics literature is whether a chunk of information has to be in a human brain or not to be considered a meme. While using terms like "idea" and "thought" seems to imply a residence in the human brain, this is not necessarily the case. The *Memetic Lexicon* defines a meme as "dormant" when it is currently without human hosts, seemingly indicating that printed or televised (and so on) information counts as memetic, but that information in one of these forms is not as good in an important way (Grant et al., 1995). Brodie (1996) and Lynch (1996) also, at the very least, imply that the human brain is the preferred meme habitat. It is not clear why, if memes are concerned only with replicating themselves as much as possible, being transmitted from computer to computer is not as good as being transmitted from brain to brain. If memes are not concerned with whether their human hosts live or die, as long as they are replicated (as the analyses suggest), why would the human brain necessarily be the best place to be? Others recognize this issue and suggest that memes do not necessarily need human hosts. For example, Blackmore (in quite a flight of science fiction) suggests that one day robots may directly imitate each other, and thus transmit memes, and

furthermore that our knowledge of memetics might help us better understand our new neighbors (1997, 49). Dawkins seems to suggest that computer viruses are not quite memes yet (since they do not "strictly evolve") but may become memes in the future (1993, 18). Vajk, however, has gone so far as to state that "hula hoops, pet rocks, and Frisbees" are memes (1989, 7). Perhaps Vajk meant to refer metonymically to the idea of the Frisbee but this is not very clear from his writing. Similar questions arise about some of Dawkins's famous examples. Does "ways of making pots" refer to the ideas about making pots or the actions that people perform in order to make pots (given the unlikely assumption that one can distinguish among these in such a case)? Imprecision appears to be one of the hallmarks of memetic theory.

Memetics and the Social Sciences

While considering the inadequate definition of terms and poorly thought out analogies and examples found in the memetic literature, one must keep in mind that this is a new field, and that precision and clarity may come in the future. We may wish to examine alternate ways of justifying and supporting the memetic enterprise. As noted above, memeticists have made strong claims about the utility of memetic analyses. Recall Blackmore's assertion that "nothing in the world of the mind makes much sense" without memetic theory. This assertion implies two claims, as does meme theory in general. First, that more widely accepted approaches to the study of culture and information processing have in some important ways shown themselves incapable of reasonably accounting for what is actually happening in the world. Second, that memetics can supply the theoretical framework to account for what is actually happening in the world. Note that the two claims are logically distinct: If it were demonstrated that other approaches to the study of culture and information processing were indeed lacking, it would in no way necessarily imply that memes exist and that meme theory is adequate to explain what these other models cannot.

Scientific investigation of culture and information processing by humans is still in its infancy. Numerous attempts to examine and model how genes interact with the environment and influence cultural development have been made (e.g., Barkow, Cosmides, and Tooby, 1992; Cavalli-Sforza and Feldman, 1981; Richerson and Boyd, 1992). These works, as their authors or editors acknowledge, are only beginnings and are necessarily incomplete. We clearly do not yet understand the full extent to which genes and environment can account for human culture and human brain activity. As such is the case, it might seem premature to many to postulate an entirely new class of replicating entities to account for the as-yet-unknown inadequacies of the more widely accepted approaches to the development of the human brain and culture. Yet this has been the method of memeticists from the very start. Dawkins writes, "we do not have to look for conventional biological survival values of traits like religion, music, and ritual dancing, though these may also be present. Once the genes have provided their survival machines with brains that are capable of rapid imitation, the memes will automatically take over" (1976/1989, 200). Dawkins postulates the existence of a new class of entity, then assumes its existence and decides that we can therefore ignore the effects of genes and biological evolution, whatever they may be. It seems that we should look for conventional survival values for religion, for example, before we decide that it makes any sense to look for non-conventional survival values. Dawkins and his later followers have failed to present any strong evidence that

conventional approaches are inadequate. They have instead asserted this as if it were a fact and used this assertion to then assume the existence of memes.

Memeticists have also largely focused their attention, when describing conventional approaches to studying culture and information transfer, on evolutionary biology. Examining the bibliography in a long work on memetics, for example Lynch's (1996) *Thought Contagion*, will turn up book after book on the applications of evolutionary theory to culture. Blackmore's (1997) list of references shows a similar strong bias toward books on biological evolution and culture. There are, however, a number of other fields concerned with human culture and human information processing. They are generally known collectively as the social sciences, and any research that has been done in these areas over the past hundred years to elucidate and describe information processing and culture has been largely ignored by memeticists. This has, among other things, led memeticists to argue for a highly inaccurate model of information processing.

Lynch (1996) contains the chapter "A Missing Link: Memetics and the Social Sciences" on how a memetic approach might fit in with the established social sciences. However, Lynch's review of the social sciences is far from complete and even somewhat disturbing. Lynch offers a few pages of superficial analysis about, for example, economics and memetics, or sociobiology and memetics, and so on. These fields and nearly all that Lynch discusses are interesting areas of inquiry, with well-developed methodologies and well-accepted findings. The exception is psychohistory. Some readers may be unfamiliar with psychohistory, and with good reason. Psychohistory is not a social science. Psychohistory is an idea from Isaac Asimov's (1974) highly acclaimed *Foundation* science fiction series. The basic premise is that in the far distant future humans will know enough about social change and history to predict, on a rather coarse scale, future events, similar to the way we can currently predict the weather. While Asimov's books and the idea of psychohistory are interesting and appealing, such an idea certainly does not belong on an equal footing with economics or sociobiology. More disturbingly, Lynch writes that psychohistory and memetics have "surprising similarities" (38) in their concerns and scope, though Lynch sees psychohistory as a more wide-ranging theory. I will leave it to readers to consider further the implications of this failure to distinguish fact from fantasy.

What is notably absent from Lynch's review and from the analyses of most memeticists is any mention of the research that has been done in two fields that are directly concerned with human information processing and the behaviors that result from the intake of information—cognitive and social psychology. Researchers in these fields have been systematically investigating how humans receive, process, and transfer information (Hunt, 1993). A cursory examination of some of the basic findings in these fields will show that, rather than unifying the study of the human brain and culture, memetic theory is based on an inaccurate model of information processing, is incapable of accounting for much of the activity of the human brain, and can only consider human thought in an extremely limited way.

Meme theory is concerned with the way information is transferred. To examine these issues, memeticists have chosen to focus on the information itself, treating humans as hosts who may be active to a greater or lesser extent in transmitting the information. It is the lack of emphasis on the actual activity of the human being with the information that dooms memetics to failure. Memeticists have adopted the view that information is independent of either its source or of its receiver, and can be effectively examined with little regard for either.

The idea that one can examine the transfer of information without regard for the systems sending and receiving it has been challenged on a number of levels. Shuy (1993) argues, based on his linguistic training and experience as an expert linguistic witness at a number of trials, that such a position is a common misunderstanding jurors have about the way language works. Using examples from real criminal trials, Shuy demonstrates that people have the mistaken belief that they can examine verbal testimony in the absence of context because all of the necessary information is contained in the words spoken. This belief, Shuy argues, has led to wrongful convictions a number of times. Reddy (1979) argues that this inaccurate belief is based on the way the English language has developed, and refers to the mistaken idea that information is sent and received unaltered by the acts of sending and receiving as the conduit metaphor.

This model of information transfer has been shown false most powerfully by experimental psychologists studying human memory. Cognitive psychologists developed and rejected as inadequate models of memory that focused on the properties of information and ignored the activities of the receiver and the context in which the information was received. They have also rejected as inadequate to explain the experimental data models that focus solely on the properties of the information and the processing it is given at the time of reception (Craik and Lockhart, 1972; Morris, Bransford, and Franks, 1977). Kolers and Roediger (1984), after examining numerous controlled studies on human memory, conclude that it makes little sense to consider information to be remembered without considering the conditions and processes involved in receiving it and the conditions and processes involved in its retrieval (which must be considered if information is to be transmitted—information that can't be remembered can't be passed on to others). Memory researchers have shown in hundreds of studies that the match between the conditions in which a person receives information and the conditions in which that person attempts to retrieve the information has powerful effects on the amounts and kinds of information remembered. This is known as the principle of transfer appropriate processing (Morris et al., 1977). The factors that affect memory include such seemingly non-memetic influences like whether the receiving and remembering occurred under the same drug influence or not, whether they occurred in the same room or with the same experimenter, and so on (Tulving, 1983). Memetic approaches ignore the extent to which environmental factors influence human memory and determine what information will be remembered. They also ignore the important consequences of the processing that the human brain performs on information, which demonstrates the inadequacy of claiming that we can separate information from its processing.

Examining the research on false memories will effectively demonstrate the difficulties of separating information from information processing. Roediger and McDermott (1995) presented participants with study lists of words that were associates of one nonpresented word. For example, one list contained the words "bed," "rest," "awake," and nine other sleep-associated words, but the word "sleep" was never presented. During later free recall tests, participants recalled the nonpresented words (e.g., "sleep") 40% and 55% of the time, in Experiments 1 and 2, respectively. Similar results were found using word recognition tests, and participants were highly confident that the words they had recalled were on the study lists. This finding of false memories using word lists has been replicated and extended by a number of researchers. (In fact, Roediger and McDermott's study was a replication of Deese, 1959; for review, see Payne, Neuschatz, Lampinen, and Lynn, 1997.) Similar false memory data have been obtained us-

ing memory for sentences (Bransford and Franks, 1971), eyewitness testimony (Lindsay, 1990), and childhood events (for review, see Loftus, 1997). Experimental research on human memory has shown that people "remember" information that they never saw and events that never happened under a wide number of conditions and with a variety of testing methods. Payne et al. (1997) summarize their theoretical position on human memory: "the act of remembering involves the reperception of internal representations that are created from experiences with the world . . . these internal representations frequently are not separate and distinct from the sensory and perceptual processes that give rise to them" (59).

This description of human memory, while echoing that of Kolers and Roediger (1984), is clearly inconsistent with memetic ideas about information processing. People do not receive information and transmit it to others without processing and altering it in a way that is both highly sensitive to the environmental conditions at both the time the information is received and the time it is remembered, and highly dependent on the perceptual, attentional, and cognitive capabilities of those involved at both times. Given the memory research it is far from clear to what extent we can meaningfully discuss information independently of the activities of the people involved in the process of transmitting it. Memeticists must demonstrate that they can account for the sensitivity of memory to the factors identified by experimental psychologists. They must also adequately deal with the numerous false memory phenomena, which are a powerful challenge to meme theory. Presumably the word "sleep" fits the vague criterion for meme-hood, given that, in this experimental paradigm, words are presented to participants one at a time, and participants are expected to recall and rate their confidence in each individual word. Yet this word, recalled by about half of all people, was never seen. It does not seem that we can reasonably view this information as having been transmitted—who could have done so? In these and the other cases, it is better to view the memory as having been created. It is up to memeticists to challenge the dominant theory in experimental psychology—that all memories are created in a similar manner to the false memories through active reconstruction of past experiences that are heavily dependent on environmental, perceptual, and cognitive factors whose impact varies at different times. Cognitive psychologists have developed powerful models of human memory that challenge memetic theory; it is up to memeticists to show that the experimental data have been misinterpreted.

It is clear that accurate transmission of information is difficult and highly sensitive to a number of environmental and mental factors that have not been considered by memeticists. Unfortunately, in addition to ignoring decades of memory research, memeticists have also ignored the best source concerning how people learn and act with information they are exposed to on a more coarse-scaled behavioral level. Lynch (1996) uses epidemiology as a model for the way information is transferred from person to person on a relatively coarse scale (i.e., he is not concerned with perceptual, attentional, or the cognitive factors discussed above), extending the virus-meme analogy to methodology. Brodie (1996) and Dawkins (1993) pursue similar courses. It is not clear why they do this. For the past 50 years, social psychologists have studied specifically how people form and change attitudes and beliefs. Hundreds of carefully controlled experiments have been performed examining the factors that affect whether a person will be persuaded by information (or "infected" to use memetic terminology), how lasting that persuasion might be, and whether the person will actually act in response to the information to which they have been exposed (Eagly and Chaiken,

1993). One would think that this large body of research would form a much stronger starting point for memetic analyses than would an analogy to epidemiology. Yet, aside from a brief mention by Blackmore (1997), this work has been ignored by memeticists. Memeticists have neglected to consider virtually all of the experimental data, from both social and cognitive psychology, concerning information processing, and the behaviors based on this information processing, in favor of an inaccurate model of information transmission (the conduit metaphor) and an untested and underdeveloped analogy with the distantly related field of epidemiology. The emphasis on these flawed analogies has also led memeticists to adopt an extremely limited and incomplete view of human mental activity, as examination of the research will show.

Cognitive psychologists regularly hypothesize and find evidence for thought processes that are largely or entirely unavailable to conscious introspection. For example, Allbritton and Gerrig (1991) hypothesized that when people read stories with unfavorable outcomes (e.g., a bomb exploding) they are mentally generating alternate outcomes that affect their ability to recognize the actual outcome. These alternate outcomes are not generated in any way of which readers are necessarily aware. These counterfactual alternatives express themselves as a difference in reaction time to recognize the actual outcome between items that had favorable or unfavorable outcomes. This methodology is far from unusual in cognitive psychology. With regard to memetics, one can then ask: Does subconscious mental activity (which comprises most of the activity of the brain; Baars, 1988) count as memetic in any way? It does not seem to. The *Memetic Lexicon* states that "an idea or information pattern is not a meme until it causes someone else to replicate it, to repeat it to someone else. All transmitted information is memetic" (Grant et al., 1995, 2). Ignoring the inconsistency of this quotation (certainly information can be transmitted without causing someone to repeat it; most information falls into this class), it implies that the mental alternatives generated are not memes, and similarly that most of the mental activity that occurs in the human brain is not memetic. However, difficulties with this position arise when we consider that the consequences of these counterfactual thoughts were demonstrated by Allbritton and Gerrig, suggesting that they were then transmitted. Can these thoughts be called into existence as memes by the processes of measurement used by Allbritton and Gerrig, even though no individual thought has actually been transmitted? Cognitive psychology is based on methodologies of this kind, and has demonstrated the existence of many kinds of thought processes through the measurement of behaviors in a manner that seems to be inconsistent with memetics.

A brief excursion into introspection will make it clear just how limited the memetic approach to information processing is. (I am aware of the general inadequacy of this method, but I believe it will do here. See Hunt, 1993, for discussion of the role of introspection in psychology.) While you are reading this article, an incredible number of conscious and unconscious thoughts are occurring, and most of these thoughts are entirely dependent on your individual circumstances. While you read, your attention wanders, and you consider getting up for something to eat. While you read, you are inspired to think about the text in a unique way, supplementing or modifying your knowledge and experience of the text based on your prior experience and knowledge (e.g., Bartlett, 1932/1977). For example, the earlier mention of Asimov's (1974) work may have spurred you to remember your childhood love of science fiction, or the word "foundation" may have caused you to remember that your house is sinking and needs its foundation repaired. Few to none of these

thoughts will be transmitted in any way, yet they comprise much of our brain activity (excluding the vast amount of brain function devoted to various autonomic and regulatory activities). They are ephemeral, existing for a moment and disappearing, only to be replaced by others. They are not memetic; nor is there any obvious way that some biological survival value can be applied to them. (Though there may be. Unlike some theorists, I am unwilling to say that the absence of intuitive biological survival value implies that there is none.) However, these thoughts do have important consequences on behavior and cognition as has been demonstrated by psychologists.

Memetic theory, even when fully developed, will not be able to account for these thoughts, and this is a problem. Given the strong evidence that the reading of a text is supplemented and modified by prior experiences in accordance with the reconstructive nature of memory, it seems that memeticists will not be able to describe how a reader obtains information from reading a book (similar concerns exist for films, conversation, observational learning, and so on). Memetic theory will not prove able to unify the social sciences when many of the concerns of social scientists about information processing and transfer cannot be addressed by memetic analyses.

With regard to how information is transmitted with potential mutation and is subject to selective forces leading to differential survival, the writings of memeticists are about as vague as their attempts to define the meme. It is also not clear to what extent we can meaningfully discuss transmission of information (as opposed to reconstruction of information). Memeticists have also not done enough to differentiate memetic transmission of information from non-memetic transmission. It is known that humans can transmit information to each other that could not reasonably be considered memetic. For example Russell, Switz, and Thompson (1980) showed that human menstrual cycles become synchronized through olfactory cues. Presumably there is some variance in the degree to which people's menstrual cycles become synchronized, but we would probably not want to say that this variability is evidence for mutation and differential survival of any particular menstrual cycle. It is up to memeticists to demonstrate that the information that they deal with is different, and this will prove difficult. Cognitive psychologists have demonstrated that learning and remembering are sensitive to environmental and perceptual factors, which are not considered in memetic analyses, and that most human thought is not likely to be memetic. They have also shown evidence for the recall of information never transmitted. Memeticists must show that, after accounting for these pieces of evidence and the psychological theories based on them, there is some form of discrete information left over that is subject to mutation (not merely variability) and differential selection (not based on perception, attention, or mental reconstruction of experience). In other words, they must demonstrate that, contrary to current psychological models, all forms of information in the human brain are not like the information discussed above before they can develop meaningful predictions and models of memetic transmission.

What Is Memetics Used For?

Memeticists have mostly focused their efforts at explaining how large-scale behavioral patterns and complex beliefs are transmitted in an attempt to demonstrate the power of memetic approaches to information transmission. These examples show that memetic analyses of information transmission are as simplistic and flawed as their attempts to define memes and their beliefs about the nature of information processing.

Lynch (1996), for example, suggests that a meme can be transmitted by giving its hosts reproductive advantages. In particular, Lynch writes that: "the 'baby doll for girls' meme replicates partly by training females to play the domestic role that leads to more children. Parents who give baby dolls to their daughters thus have their memes imparted to more grandchildren" (56). This is quite an interesting and controversial claim and Lynch unfortunately offers no evidence of the supposed greater reproductive of women who were given dolls as children and those who were not.

One wonders why, if dolls make women have more children, they would not do the same for men? Wouldn't memes get spread more effectively (in particular a more general "give baby dolls to your kids" meme) if boys were encouraged to have dolls and thus be more interested in domestic affairs? Wouldn't this shared set of interests in childrearing encourage husbands and wives to interact more and thus exchange more memes with each other? (Lynch also gives a similarly superficial analysis of "hero dolls for boys." What I hope is clear from my discussion is that these analyses amount to no more than memetic just-so stories, and are, if anything, less believable than their oft-maligned gene-based equivalents.) A second concern with this analysis is the fact that the people who give their children the most and nicest dolls—that is, the wealthiest segments of the population—have the lowest birthrates. Birthrate is generally negatively correlated with wealth across cultures, as the poorer peoples of the world tend to have the most children and also (presumably) the fewest baby dolls (cf. Dasgupta, 1995; Wattenberg, 1997). The final concern is that Lynch is content to reduce a complex pattern of behavior to a simple phrase and to act as if he has explained things. Buying dolls for one's children involves interacting with the child to determine if the child wants a doll and which one, traveling to a store in some manner, selecting and purchasing the doll, and so on. The difficulty of performing these activities is highly variable, as are the particular circumstances of each doll-buyer. It seems likely that the environment and a person's past experiences will determine whether, when, and how a person buys a doll. Memeticists may challenge this by arguing that regardless of the complexity of the overt behaviors, a person is really buying the doll because they have the meme. Given the absence of evidence for memes this objection cannot be taken very seriously. Furthermore, even if memes exist, it seems unlikely that the knowledge required for a person to buy a doll is reducible to a single meme.

Blackmore (1997) makes a series of even more controversial and sweeping claims than the above claim by Lynch (1996), designed to show how powerful "thinking memetically" is. Blackmore asserts that the memetic approach can be used "to answer five previously unanswered questions about human nature" (1997, 43). She first seeks to learn "why can't we stop thinking?" It seems to her that much of the time spent thinking is wasteful. Little of it seems to have any benefit for survival and is thus a waste of energy. Such thinking is maladaptive, Blackmore believes, writing that "animals that waste energy do not survive" (47). Blackmore's answer to this quandary is to suggest that it is memes that lead to this excessive thinking, that when we are doing (genetically) needless thinking we are actually rehearsing our memes, and that this rehearsal will result in an increased likelihood of transmission. Our excess thought is for the benefit of our memes.

There are a number of problems with this analysis. The first is that we simply do not yet know which thought processes are adaptive and which are not. We cannot yet label most mental activities as biologically adaptive or maladaptive, nor can we decide that any mental activity is beneficial to the survival of the

as-yet-undocumented meme. Second, meme theory, with its emphasis on the transmission of information, cannot account for the vast amount of human thought that is unconscious and untransmittable, and these thoughts are whirring through our brains all of the time. If memetics cannot account for these thoughts, or at least explain the relationship between them and memes, it cannot offer an answer to Blackmore's question. Finally, even if we accept Blackmore's assertion that animals which waste energy do not survive, we still cannot accept Blackmore's answer. Calling the energy waste "meme rehearsal" does nothing to solve this problem. These meme-infested animals should just be rehearsing their memes and themselves to death. The only way an organism can avoid this dire fate is if the memes it possesses at least compensate for the loss of energy due to their rehearsal—in other words the activities used in rehearsing memes (i.e., thinking) must contribute to biological survival. If this is the case—that all our thinking actually does have survival value whether it is memetic or not—it seems unnecessary to refer to memes in the first place to explain the value of thinking.

Blackmore then turns to examine the issue: "why do we talk so much?" Again her answer is memes. We talk so much so that we can spread our memes. Again, Blackmore is assuming such behavior is biologically maladaptive, and, again, this assumption is not justified nor will labeling the wasteful activity "meme transmission" provide an answer. There have been numerous attempts to relate the emergence of language to biological factors. Blackmore herself cites one such attempt. Dunbar (1993, 1996) has argued that language evolved as a way to reinforce social relationships when the band size of our ancestors became too large for the earlier grooming techniques to function effectively. While Dunbar's analysis is far from achieving general scientific consensus (see the commentary following

Dunbar, 1993), it seems at least more plausible than Blackmore's assertion that it is memes that make us talk. Blackmore offers nothing to challenge Dunbar's analysis. This is unfortunate because Dunbar challenges the major point Blackmore bases her argument on. Blackmore writes that "we talk about some pretty daft and pointless things" (47) that to her mind cannot possibly have any survival value. However, in Dunbar's analysis, such talk, the gossip and so on, is used to reinforce our social bonds, discouraging aggression, and promoting food sharing and mating. Perhaps these are the "hidden biological advantages" (47) Blackmore is missing?

Blackmore's (1997) analysis of why we talk so much also conflicts, like so much in memetics, with psychological theory and research. Blackmore presents an extremely competitive model of the development of human language and its current use—we don't seem to care much what anyone else has to say because we're just waiting for our turn so that we can transmit our memes. There is a growing body of experimental evidence in psychology for a collaborative theory of language use (e.g., Clark, 1992). Numerous experiments have examined the ways that speakers work together to decide what to call ambiguous objects. Parallels to figuring out where to go to dinner, how to put together a bicycle, and so on, should be obvious. According to Clark's collaborative theory, language is used by people so that they can attain a reasonable degree of mutual understanding of their environments and intentions in order to interact effectively. Like Dunbar's (1993, 1996) analysis of language development, Clark's theory is based on the idea that language is an important way to coordinate activity among people and to effectively describe and manipulate each other and the environment. Blackmore's ideas about language use and development seem far more limited and far less likely.

Blackmore (1997) offers three similar analyses for why we are so nice to each other, why our brains are so big, and why we think we have a self. In each case, of course, the answer is memes. Throughout her analyses, Blackmore asks the reader to continually "imagine a world full of brains, and far more memes than can possibly find homes." This pattern of thought, imagining all those memes struggling to survive in the limited human brain, she suggests, will allow us to answer the difficult questions. Blackmore does not, however, offer any evidence for why and how memes might actually be the cause of our thoughts, big brains, niceness, and so on. We are asked to take our excessively big brains as evidence for the existence of memes and are expected to accept memes as a reason for our big brains existing. Blackmore, and other memeticists, are essentially asserting that memes are out there, without evidence or even an adequate example, and without regard for the conflict with psychological models. They then expect us to assume the existence of memes and insert that term as an answer to life's mysteries.

I hope that the above critique has shown that memeticists have grossly overstated the power of a memetic approach to understanding information processing and culture. They have much work to do to convince the skeptical scientist of the value of the meme, much less its existence. Memeticists should start by looking at the data from the social sciences and the models developed from them. They need to show that they can account for the objections put forth in this paper based on those psychological models and on logical grounds. Memeticists need to more clearly define the kinds of information they are going to deal with, and show that existing models are flawed when it comes to understanding this kind of information. Then they must demonstrate that the memetic approach can succeed where biological or psychological approaches have failed. Nothing presented in the memetics literature thus far suggests that memeticists will be able to accomplish this. Ill-considered examples, ignorance of relevant experimental research, and exaggerated claims of explanatory power do not make for a convincing scientific theory.

References:

Allbritton, D. W., & Gerrig, R. J. 1991. "Participatory Responses in Text Understanding." *Journal of Memory and Language,* 30, 603–626.

Asimov, I. 1974. *The Foundation Trilogy: Three Classics of Science Fiction.* New York: Avon.

Baars, B. J. 1988. *A Cognitive Theory of Consciousness.* New York: Cambridge University Press.

Barkow, J. H., Cosmides, L., & Tooby, J. 1992. *The Adapted Mind: Evolutionary Psychology and the Generation of Culture.* New York: Oxford University Press.

Bartlett, F. 1932/1977. *Remembering: A Study in Experimental and Social Psychology.* Cambridge: Cambridge University Press.

Blackmore, S. 1996. *Memes, Minds and Selves:* http://www.memes.org.uk/lectures/mms.html

Blackmore, S. 1997. "The Power of the Meme Meme." *Skeptic,* 5, 43–49.

Boyd, R., & Richerson, P. J. 1985. *Culture and the Evolutionary Process.* Chicago: University of Chicago Press.

Bransford, J. D., & Franks, J. J. 1971. "The Abstraction of Linguistic Ideas." *Cognitive Psychology,* 2, 331–350.

Brodie, R. 1996. *Viruses of the Mind: The New Science of the Meme.* New York: Integral Press.

Brodie, R. 1997. *Meme Central:* http://www.brodietech.com/rbrodie/meme.htm

Cavalli-Sforza, L. L., & Feldman, M. W. 1981. *Cultural Transmission and Evolution.* Princeton: Princeton University Press.

Clark, H. H. 1992. *Arenas of Language Use.* New York: Cambridge University Press.

Craik, F. I. M., & Lockhart, R. S. 1972. "Levels of Processing: A Framework for Memory Research." *Journal of Verbal Learning and Verbal Behavior,* 11, 671–684.

Darwin, C. 1859/1947. *On the Origin of Species by Means of Natural Selection.* New York: Oxford University Press.

Dasgupta, P. S. 1995. "Population, Poverty, and the Local Environment." *Scientific American,* 272, 41–46.

Dawkins, R. 1976/1989. *The Selfish Gene* (new edition). New York: Oxford University Press.

Dawkins, R. 1993. "Viruses of the Mind." In B. Dahlbom (Ed.), *Dennett and His Critics: Demystifying Mind.* Cambridge, MA: Blackwell, 13–27.

Dunbar, R. I. M. 1993. "Coevolution of Neocortical Size, Group Size and Language in Humans." *Behavioral & Brain Sciences,* 16, 681–735; commentaries and response follow.

Dunbar, R. I. M. 1996. *Grooming, Gossip, and the Evolution of Language.* London: Faber & Faber.

Eagly, A. H., & Chaiken, S. 1993. *The Psychology of Attitudes.* Fort Worth, TX: Harcourt Brace Jovanovich College Publishers.

Grant, G., Sandberg, A., & McFadzean, D. 1995. *Memetic Lexicon:* http://maxwell.lucifer.com/virus/memlex.html

Hunt, M. 1993. *The Story of Psychology.* New York: Doubleday.

Kolers, P. A., & Roediger, H. L. 1984. "Procedures of Mind." *Journal of Verbal Learning and Verbal Behavior,* 23, 425–449.

Lindsay, D. S. 1990. "Misleading Suggestions Can Impair Eyewitness' Ability to Recall Event Details." *Journal of Experimental Psychology: Learning, Memory, and Cognition,* 16, 1077–1083.

Loftus, E. F. 1997. "Memory for a Past That Never Was." *Current Directions in Psychological Science,* 6, 60–65.

Lynch, A. 1996. *Thought Contagion: How Belief Spreads through Society.* New York: Basic Books.

Morris, C. D., Bransford, J. D., & Franks, J. J. 1977. "Levels of Processing versus Transfer Appropriate Processing." *Journal of Verbal Learning and Verbal Behavior,* 16, 519–533.

Nehring Bliss, C. 1997. *Dawn of the info-age:* http://www.ice.net/%7Enehring/info1.htm

Payne, D. G., Neuschatz, J. S., Lampinen, J. M., & Lynn, S. J. 1997. "Compelling Memory Illusions: The Qualitative Characteristics of False Memories." *Current Directions in Psychological Science,* 6, 56–60.

Reddy, M. J. 1979. "The Conduit Metaphor: A Case of Frame Conflict in Our Language about Language." In A. Ortony (Ed.), *Metaphor and Thought*. New York: Cambridge University Press, 164–201.

Roediger, H. L., & McDermott, K. B. 1995. "Creating False Memories: Remembering Words Not Presented in Lists." *Journal of Experimental Psychology*. Learning, Memory, and Cognition, 21, 803–814.

Russell, Switz, & Thompson 1980. "Olfactory Influences on the Human Menstrual Cycle." *Pharmacology, Biochemistry, and Behavior*, 13, 737–738.

Shuy, R. W. 1993. *Language Crimes: The Use and Abuse of Language Evidence in the Courtroom*. Cambridge, MA: Blackwell.

Speel, H. C. 1997. *Memetics: On a Conceptual Frame Work for Cultural Evolution:* http://www. sepa. tudelft. nl/webstaf/hansseinst. htm

Tulving, E. 1983. *Elements of Episodic Memory*. New York: Oxford University Press.

Vajk, J. P. 1989. *Memetics: The Nascent Science of Ideas and Their Transmission:* http://www. geocities.com/Athens/2424/memetics.html

Wattenberg, B. J. 1997. "The Population Explosion Is Over." *The New Times Magazine*, November 23.

Race and I.Q. as Good Science

VINCE SARICH

*T*he *Bell Curve* and the many commentaries on it have brought several issues into an often uncomfortably sharp focus. Though race is by no means the most important of these, the historical baggage the term carries and the reality it symbolizes require us to get past it before we are able to deal with more substantive matters. Yet that same baggage and those same realities often raise emotional barriers so powerful that they defy facts, reason, and logic.

Many commentators would have us believe that *The Bell Curve* is obsessed with race, and thereby provide a prime exemplar of pots, kettles, and blackness, evidenced in the following quote from the sociologist Alan Wolfe: "Murray and Herrnstein may not be racists, but they are obsessed by race. They see the world in group terms and must have data on group membership." This is an interesting charge, says Charles Krauthammer (1994), "given the fact that for the last two decades it is the very liberals who so vehemently denounce Murray who have been obsessed by race, insisting that every institution—universities, fire departments, Alaskan canneries—must have data on group membership."

It is the liberals who have oppressively insisted that we measure ethnic "over-" and "underrepresentation" in every possible field of human endeavor. Here is a liberal establishment forcing racial testing for every conceivable activity, and when a study comes along which does exactly that for SATs and IQ, the authors are pilloried for being obsessed by race.

No one who has actually read *The Bell Curve* could honestly document any such obsession. But, by the same token, no one even moderately conversant with the American society of the last 20 to 30 years could deny the accuracy of Krauthammer's assertion that "it is the very liberals who so vehemently denounce Murray who have been obsessed by race."

Further, it is these "very liberals" who deny that there is any significant genetic, biological, and evolutionary substance to race, and argue that it is, in effect, nothing more than a social and cultural construct. This view is epitomized in a recent story in *Time* (January 16, 1995) that carries the subtitle: "A landmark global study flattens *The Bell Curve*, proving that racial differences are only skin deep." The reference is to *The History and Geography of Human Genes*, a recent, massive compilation and analysis of human gene frequency data (Cavalli-Sforza et al., 1994). The story is an honest summation of that work—given that the genetic distances among human races are minimal, and that sections 1.5 and 1.6 of the book are entitled "Classical Attempts to Distinguish Human 'Races'" and "Scientific Failure of the Concept of Human Races." One looks in vain, however, in both the *Time* piece and the book on which it is based for any definition of the term "race." This omission is typical of race-debunking efforts. They never bother to define what it is that they are debunking. So let's start there.

The Reality of Human Races

We can begin this trip out of political correctness by noting that there is a substantial amount of agreement on both a working definition of the term "race" and on the existence of races in species other than our own. Races are populations, or groups of populations, within a species, that are separated geographically from other such populations or groups of populations, and distinguishable from them on the basis of heritable features.

We can agree that we are all members of a single species—*Homo sapiens*—and that each of us is also a unique individual. The most basic evidence that races exist is the fact that we can look at individuals and place them, with some appreciable degree of accuracy, into the areas from which they or their recent ancestors derive. The process involved is illustrated by a thought experiment where one imagines a random assortment of 50 modern humans and 50 chimpanzees. No one, chimp or human, would have any difficulty in reconstituting the original 50 member sets by simple inspection. But the same would be true within our species with, say, 50 humans from Japan, 50 from Malawi, and 50 from Norway. Again, by simple inspection, we would achieve the same 100% sorting accuracy. Granted, in the second experiment fewer sorting characteristics were available, but not nearly so few as to produce

any doubt as to the placement of any individual. Extending this look-see experiment to the whole of the human species would obviously give us a substantial number of such geographical groupings. The addition of direct genetic evidence—from blood groups to DNA sequences—would provide further resolving power. But there is a real problem here that goes well beyond ideology and political correctness.

The Nature of Categories

One might clarify the problem of defining groups by reference to the issue of color categorization. We know that speakers of various languages that have a term for "red" (and who also have a comparable number of basic color terms) will also show a remarkable degree of agreement as to the range of the spectrum to which the term applies, and as to which hues are better reds than others (Berlin and Kay, 1969). We look at a rainbow and we tend to see not continuity, but rather a small number of specific colors that we have no trouble naming. This example tells us that whatever may be going on with respect to cognitive processing of the visible light spectrum, we have no operational difficulties in at least this realm with the notion that categories do not have to be discrete. Red does shade imperceptibly into orange, and orange into yellow, but we have no difficulty in agreeing as to where red becomes orange, and orange, yellow. Thus, human cognition can handle categories that are not discrete. The flip side of that is that categories can be real without necessarily being enumerable—and that is the critical matter for this article.

In other words, we can easily forget that categories do not have to be discrete. If this were not so, then why should the notion of "fuzzy sets" have been seen as so revolutionarily productive? Races are fuzzy sets.

How Many Races Are There?

One of the most commonly asked questions about race is: "How many races are there?" I contend that this is the wrong question. "How many" requires a precise integer as an answer—3, 7, 15, whatever. But the nature of the category "race" is such as to make such an answer impossible, depending as it necessarily does on the degree of sorting accuracy required in a context where the categories involved are not discrete. Races, after all, are not species, since all humans are fully interfertile. Therefore, races must necessarily grade into one another. But they do not do so evenly. Even today, for example, to drive along the road north from Aswan to Luxor (a hundred miles or so) is to cross a portion of ancient boundary between, to use old anthropological terms, Caucasians and Negroes. These two large groupings have been separated for millennia by the Sahara Desert. The Sahara has caused the populations north and south of it to evolve in substantial genetic independence from one another. And that is all one needs for race formation—geographical separation plus time.

The race quantity answer depends on the degree of sorting accuracy with respect to individuals. If it is something close to 100%, then the areas involved could become smaller and more distant from one another, with at least 20 races easily recognized, or larger and less separated, in which case one would see the few "major" races that everyone has tended to see. If, however, the criterion were something more like the 75% which has often sufficed for the recognition of races in other species, then obviously the number would be very large. In either case, if we use a straightforward definition of race, such as a population within a species that can be readily distinguished from other such populations using only heritable features, then there can be no doubt of the existence of a substantial number of human races. But, I hear you ask, don't the races all blend into one another? Yes, they are supposed to blend into one another. That's what races do. Nature's categories need not be discrete. It is not for us to impose our cognitive limitations upon Nature.

The Cause of Racial Separation

If all that is needed for racial differentiation is geographic separation and time, then why have humans remained a single species? The answer almost certainly lies in the fact of glacial cycles throughout the existence of our genus. These have necessitated major movements of human populations at fairly frequent, if irregular, intervals throughout the million years or so that *Homo* has existed outside of sub-Saharan Africa and therefore been susceptible to differentiation into races. Thus, there would have been periods of relative glacial stability (such as the last 10,000 years or so) during which racial differentiation would have become more marked, and periods of glacial movement, such as the retreat which began about 18,000 years ago, during which gene flow would have pretty much obliterated the previously developed racial boundaries. This logic also leads to the conclusion that most existing racial variation must have developed since that last period of large-scale, world-wide gene flow; that is, over the last 15,000 or so years. There is extensive evidence at a number of disciplines—anatomy, linguistics, biochemistry, archeology—which is consistent with such a scenario. The most straightforward is the fact that *Homo sapiens* fossil skulls found in areas currently populated by "Caucasians" and ranging in age from about 15,000 to 30,000 years are not more similar to those of modern "Caucasians" than they are to those of other major racial groupings.

The question of the antiquity of human racial lineages remains one of the most controversial areas of human evolution. Basically two quite opposed views predominate, neither of which takes the fact of glacial cycles into account. (1) Regional Continuity or Multiregional Evolution. *Homo erectus* populations in different areas of the world are seen as having appreciable direct genetic continuity with modern populations in those same areas. This theory sees significant aspects of modern racial variability as having separate histories for the high hundreds of thousands of years. (2) Out of Africa or African Eve. *Homo sapiens* have a single, relatively recent (something around 100,000 years ago) origin in some limited area and are characterized by some novel adaptation which enabled them to expand out of that homeland, replacing the more primitive humans they found along the way. Racial differentiation then followed. Most people in the field have tended to see #1 as implying much more significant racial differences because they would have had longer to develop. This has also been a major factor contributing to its relative lack of support.

But, as the late Glynn Isaac (perhaps the most influential archeologist involved in studies of early *Homo*) pointed out to me in a Berkeley seminar many years ago, it is the Out of Africa model, not that of regional continuity, which makes racial differences more functionally significant. It does so because the amount of time involved in the raciation process is much smaller, while, obviously, the degree of racial differentiation is the same—large. The shorter the period of time required to produce a given amount of morphological difference, the more selectively important the differences become. The Out of Africa model in its earlier formulations envisioned perhaps 40,000 years for raciation of anatomically modern *Homo sapiens*. The current formulations would nearly triple that figure, and, thus reduce the implied significance of racial differences. Obviously the model I outlined above would do the opposite, increasing that signifi-

cance well beyond anything contemplated in recent years. But that might not be all. During the last 10,000 years human cultures have differentiated to a much greater extent with respect to achievement than was the case previously. Thus, not only might the time involved for raciation have been brief, but the selective demands on human cognitive capacities might have differed regionally to a substantially greater extent than could have been the case previously (see Sarich, 1995, for an extended discussion of these matters).

How Large Are Actual Racial Differences?

Current textbooks on human biology and human evolution go out of their way to deny either the reality, the significance, or both of race in our species. Their efforts would appear to be based in the hope that if we can make races disappear, racism will follow. For example:

> *Race:* In terms of biological variation, a group of populations sharing certain traits that make them different from other groups of populations. In practice, the concept of race is very difficult to apply to patterns of human variation.

The first sentence is fine. But the second implies that most human variation is not racially patterned. Which is certainly true. Most of the variation in our species, and in all other species, is found within and among individuals. But truth here has nothing to do with relevance. No one argues that race is the only dimension along which humans vary genetically. But, by the same token, there is more than enough heritable variation to produce human groupings which conform to any generally accepted definition of the term "race." This fact tells us that a substantial amount of human variation is clearly racially distributed, and leads to the question of how different from one another human races are.

The answer is, it depends on what you are looking at. At the level of morphology human races are more strongly differentiated from one another than are any other mammalian species. I first became aware of this fact when considering the arguments in the anthropological literature as to the place of the Neandertals. There one would often see statements to the effect that "Neandertals are too different from us to be part of our evolutionary history," but "too different" was never quantified. Quantifying it by using a standard set of measurements, correcting for size and calculating an average percent difference per measurement, gave some substance to the claim. Neandertals are, in fact, about twice as distant, on the average, from various extant human populations as the latter are from one another. But that exercise also demonstrated that (1) the anatomical distances among some modern races, for example, East Africans and Central Siberians, were much larger than those between Neandertals and the modern human populations most similar to them, and (2) racial morphological distances within our species are, on the average, about equal to the distances among species within other genera of mammals, as, for example, between pygmy and common chimpanzees. I am not aware of another mammalian species where the constituent races are as strongly marked as they are in ours.

The genetic distances are, in contrast, very small, and the no-races-in-our-species protagonists (such as Cavalli-Sforza) have seized on this fact to buttress their position. However, one needs to put the data into an evolutionary context to see what they really mean. The problem here lies in the fact that morphological evolution in our species has been extremely rapid, and this is not some sort of anthropocentric judgment. It can be demonstrated through two simple observations. We

and our two closest living relatives—gorillas and chimpanzees—are about equidistant from one another at the DNA level with about 1.7% sequence difference seen in each of the three comparisons. Yet, morphologically chimps and gorillas are far more similar to one another than either is to us. This must mean that there has been much more morphological change along our lineage than along those leading to the African apes since the three genera last shared a common ancestor some 4.5 million years ago (the amounts of sequence change at the DNA level are the same). The current racial situation in our species is then entirely consistent with the history of our lineage: much morphological variation and change, little genetic variation and change.

Racial Differences in Athletic Ability

Another tack has been to acknowledge racial differences, but then argue that they are generally small with respect to differences among individuals within races, and, in any case, likely to be functionally irrelevant for any features of particular importance for the species. Consider the following example from sports. Every year perhaps 75 young men newly make NBA (National Basketball Association) teams. Of these, about 60 will be Black, and 15 White. (I am here using four years as the average length of an NBA career, and the current racial composition of the league as a source for these figures. "Black" means, in this country, that the individual has a substantial amount of obvious recent sub-Saharan African ancestry. "White" means no obvious ancestry other than European.) These numbers mean that the chance for a Black to play in the NBA is about one in 4,500; the corresponding figure for a White is about one in 90,000. We can then ask from how far out on their respective bell curves these 75 are drawn. Recourse to a z-score table tells us that 1 in 4,500 takes us about 3.4 SD (standard deviations) from the mean; 1 in 90,000 is about 4.3 SD from the mean. I submit that this almost one SD difference between populations in this suite of abilities based on a fundamental human trait is pretty substantial. In other words, it is simply not true that "bipedalism is such a critical aspect of the human adaptation that one would not expect to see great differences from either the individual to individual level, or between populations." Bipedalism is certainly a "critical aspect of the human adaptation," but it does not follow that therefore individual and group variation in what might be termed the quality of the bipedal adaptation would have been reduced. Indeed, it seems to me that, if anything, we might expect quite the opposite result. It took me a long time to figure this out, and thus it might prove useful to others to recount some of that process. The context is the relationship, if any, between brain size and cognitive performance.

Racial Differences in Brain Size

Discussing racial differences in athletic ability can get you into trouble, as some sportscasters have discovered. Discussing racial differences in brain size can be literally life threatening, as some psychologists have discovered. This issue ultimately divided Charles Darwin from Alfred Russel Wallace. Darwin was entirely comfortable with the notion that the human mind had evolved through natural selection, just as did the human body. Wallace, on the other hand, to the end of his much longer life, insisted that while our body had evolved, our mind must have been created. (See Michael Shermer's book, *In Darwin's Shadow: The Life and Science of Alfred Russel Wallace*.) A century later the very influential book *The Mismeasure of Man* by Stephen Jay Gould also, in effect, de-

nied that our brains had evolved. Gould spends the first two chapters telling us that brain size and intellectual performance have nothing to do with one another, without once bothering to remind us that our brains have not always been the size they are today. Nor is that awkward fact mentioned anywhere else in the book. You could never learn from it that in our evolutionary lineage brain size had increased from around 400cc to 1300–1400cc over the last four million years. Why this omission?

I think the answer is quite straightforward. That part of Gould's psyche concerned with basic evolutionary biology knew that those large brains of ours could not have evolved unless having large brains increased fitness through minds that could do more. In other words, individuals with larger brains must have been, on the average and in the long run, slightly better off than those with smaller brains. How advantaged? Dare one say it? By being smarter. What else? If variation in brain size mattered in the past, as it must have, then it almost certainly still matters. And if you are going to argue that it does not, then you are going to have to explain why it does not. I do not think you can do this while maintaining your intellectual integrity. Thus Gould just ignored the demands of the evolutionary perspective by denying, implicitly, that our brains had evolved. I find it of some interest that no one has really challenged him on this point.

The evolutionary perspective demands that there be a relationship—in the form of a positive correlation—between brain size and intelligence. That proposition, I would argue, is not something that need derive from contemporary data (although, as we will see, those data do give it strong support). It is what we would expect given our particular evolutionary history; that is, it is the evolutionary null hypothesis, and, thus, something to be disproven. It seems to me that a demonstration of no correlation between brain size and cognitive performance would be about the best possible refutation of the fact of human evolution. It took me a long time to figure out what really ought to have been obvious: descent with modification by means of natural selection has been, and continues to be, the reality. It should be incumbent on those who would deny our evolutionary history to show that our biology is not involved. Otherwise there is an implicit creationism present in those who persist in ignoring the evolutionary perspective when they try to explain some aspect of our behavior (all too common in the social sciences). Brain size is an effective proxy for behavior, and it reminds us that evolutionary processes and evolutionary lineages are rather good data.

In other words, natural selection requires genetically based phenotypic variation to work on; thus throughout the period of change in brain size, there must have been present a substantial amount of genetic variation for brain size, and, likely, the greater the advantage of larger brains, the greater the underlying genetic variation for brain size. I had long been frustrated by the canalization argument (the more important the characteristic, the less variation) with respect to human intelligence, my teaching experiences telling me that cognitive performance was one of our most variable features. Yet at the same time I was unable to refute the logic of the argument. This lasted until 1983 when I remembered Fisher's Fundamental Theorem of Natural Selection: "The rate of increase in the fitness of any organism at any time is equal to its genetic variance in fitness at that time."

This says it all. An earlier statement of the general argument was made by the late Bernard Davis in 1976:

> Let me further emphasize that, even if no one had ever devised a test for measuring IQ, we could still be confident, on grounds of evolutionary theory, that our species contains wide genetic variance in intelligence. The reason is

that natural selection cannot proceed unless it has genetic diversity, within a species, to act on; and when our species is compared with its nearest primate relatives, it is obvious that our main selection pressure has been for an increase in intelligence. Indeed, this change proceeded at an unprecedented rate (on an evolutionary time scale): in the past three million years the brain size of the hominid line increased threefold. Such rapid selection for increased intelligence could not have occurred unless the selection pressure had a large substrate of genetic variation to act on.

Brain Size and Cognitive Performance: Data Validate Theory

Any suggestion on one's part that people with bigger brains are, on the average, smarter by virtue of those bigger brains leads the listener to doubt one's intelligence, if not one's sanity. The general belief is that this inherently sexist and racist notion died an ignoble death sometime in the last century. Its recent resurrection began with a 1974 article by Leigh Van Valen. In it he reviewed the literature and concluded that the published correlations between brain size and intelligence (as measured by standardized tests) were unrealistically low because they did not allow for the fact that external measurements of head size were an imperfect indicator of brain size. Correcting for this attenuation indicated that the actual value was probably about 0.3. (*The Mismeasure of Man* does not even mention Van Valen's work.) A subsequent large-scale study of Belgian army recruits, which also used a much wider variety of tests of cognitive function, gave figures consistent with Van Valen's analyses (Susanne, 1979). Since 1987, there have been several studies on this subject in which the brain size of living individuals was measured directly and accurately using magnetic resonance imaging (e.g., Willerman et al., 1991; Andreasen, et al., 1993; Wickett et al., 1994). These suggest that Van Valen's estimate was, if anything, conservative—the consensus being in the area of 0.4 or a bit more. Although, as argued above, a positive relationship was to be expected on the basis of simple evolutionary considerations, the actual correlations found are higher than just about anyone would have predicted prior to Van Valen's pioneering effort.

A correlation of 0.4 means that of the average of 17 IQ points separating two randomly chosen individuals (within sex and population), about 7 IQ points would derive from the differences in the sizes of their brains. The same would hold for populations, and existing human populations can differ in their means by as much as 2 SD in brain size. Thus, this variable alone could lead to close to a 1 SD difference in mean intellectual performance among them. With respect to the difference between American Whites and Blacks, the one good brain size study we have (Ho et al., 1980) indicates a difference between them of about 0.8 SD; this could correspond to a difference of about 5 IQ points; that is, about one-third of the observed differential.

It should also be noted that these data strongly suggest that IQ tests are, in fact, measuring something that has been significant in human evolution, given that performance on them correlates so nicely with brain size. And what of the common accusation of circularity that intelligence is what the tests test? As Daniel Seligman notes, in *A Question of Intelligence* (1992, 15):

> [Herrnstein] said it was not at all intended as a put-down of IQ tests, certainly not as a complaint about circularity. It represented, rather, the perspective of a psychologist who believed (a) that "intelligence" needed to be anchored to some unambiguous operational definition

and (b) that the cluster of abilities measured by IQ tests constituted a reasonable anchor. Fast analogy: You could define length . . . as "a distance or dimension expressed in units of linear measure." You could also define it as the thing that tape measures measure.

Individuals and Groups

So far I have tended to go from group to individual and back again without addressing the fact that any number of commentators on *The Bell Curve* have argued that: (1) individual variation within groups is generally greater than variation between groups, and (2) the existence of functionally significant genetic differences among individuals (with which most of them apparently feel comfortable) does not necessarily imply such among populations (with which they, along with most people, definitely do not). But the obvious truth of these two assertions in no sense justifies the object lesson we are supposed to draw from them—that therefore group variation is not something that need particularly concern us. First, the fact is group differences can be much greater than individual differences within them; for example, hair form in Kenya and Japan, or body shape for the Nuer and Inuit. And even when the first assertion is correct, as it is for most human characteristics, the differences between groups can, as already noted, be quite consequential. There is a much weaker case to be made for the relevance of the second assertion. While a qualification such as "does not necessarily" makes it technically correct, the statement as a whole implies that we should expect a connection between individual and group variation to be the exception, rather than the rule.

The evolutionary perspective begs to disagree. Consider again the example of brain size. Within sex and population, the coefficient of variation (standard deviation/mean × 100) is about 10%, a value typical for mass or volume characters. Two randomly chosen same-sex individuals within a population would then differ by about 12%, or about 150cc. But so can two populations. And this should not surprise us. Remember that our brain has increased in size some 1000cc in the last 3 million years. This is often termed "an explosive rate of growth," yet it works out to only 1/4 drop per generation. It could have gone faster, given what we know of individual variation and heritability for the character. That it did not implies that the huge advantages conferred by having more brain to work with must have been offset by (almost) equally large disadvantages. In other words, the adaptation here is best seen as a very slow moving compromise involving small relative differences between large forces. We should then have no expectation that those advantages and disadvantages would have balanced out in the same way in different populations at differing times and in differing ecological and cultural circumstances. But this same argument will apply to most aspects of individual variation. Given the number of characteristics in which functional variation is present, the ways in which they will balance out in two populations evolving more or less independently of one another are almost guaranteed to be different in the two. The balancing will take place at the level of individual phenotypes, and thus there is, in general, going to be a direct, inescapable connection between individual and group variation whenever evolutionary change is taking place.

Harmful Truths or Useful Lies?

Of all the thousands of words in print about *The Bell Curve*, about its data and arguments, perhaps none cut so close to the bone as those of Nathan Glazer in the October 31, 1994, issue of the *New Republic* (15–16):

> The authors project a possible utopia in which individuals accept their places in an intellectual pecking order that affects their income, their quality of life, their happiness. It may be true that we do not commonly envy the intellectual capacities of others—we allow Albert Einstein and Bobby Fischer their eminence—though I think even at this level the authors underplay the role of envy and rancor in human affairs. But how can a group accept an inferior place in society, even if good reasons for it are put forth? It cannot.
>
> Richard Wollheim and Isaiah Berlin have written: "If I have a cake, and there are ten persons among whom I wish to divide it, then if I give exactly one-tenth to each, this will not . . . call for justification; whereas if I depart from this principle of equal division I am expected to produce a special reason." Herrnstein and Murray have a very good special reason: smarter people get more and properly deserve more, and if there are more of them in one group than another, so be it. Our society, our polity, our elites, according to Herrnstein and Murray, live with an untruth: that there is no good reason for this inequality, and therefore our society is at fault and we must try harder. I ask myself whether the untruth is not better for American society than the truth.

And Bill Clinton, in a press conference of similar vintage, said:

> I haven't read it. But as I understand the argument of it, I have to say I disagree with the proposition that there are inherent, racially based differences in the capacity of the American people to reach their full potential. I just don't agree with that. It goes against our entire history and our whole tradition.

Are All Men Created Equal?

The issue here is not so much about "inherent, racially based differences in the capacity of the American people to reach their full potential." It is about inherent, racially based differences in the potentials themselves. The "entire history and our whole tradition" is, of course, encapsulated in our Declaration of Independence, where Thomas Jefferson wrote:

> We hold these truths to be self-evident, that all men are created equal, that they are endowed by their creator with certain unalienable rights, that among these are life, liberty, and the pursuit of happiness. That to secure these rights, governments are instituted among men, deriving their just powers from the consent of the governed. . . .

Which takes us back to Glazer, and the real need to ask "whether the untruth is not better for American society than the truth." The untruth in Jefferson is his first truth: "that all men are created equal." We know Jefferson did not believe that to be literally true, or perhaps more fairly, that he could not have believed it true unless one word were added to his sacred text: ". . . all men are created equal, in that they are endowed by their creator with certain unalienable rights. . . ." This addition in no way detracts from the power of the text (and only slightly from its rhythm), but does provide the advantage of literal truth—understanding, of course, that, ever since 1859, "creator" has had to be read as "the evolutionary process." Reading it that way also has the virtue of ultimately leading us to an understanding of why "the evolutionary process has made all men equal" is no better than the original text. Also note that last right—it is not "happiness" but "the pursuit of happiness"—an opportunity, not a result.

There have, in fact, been attempts to provide a justification based in evolutionary biology for a literal reading of "all men are created equal." Gould, for example, entitled one of his essays "Human Equality Is a Contingent Fact of History," and summarized his argument as such (1985, 198):

> *Homo sapiens* is a young species, its division into races even more recent. This historical context has not provided enough time for the evolution of substantial differences. But many species are millions of years old, and their geographic divisions are often marked and deep. *H. sapiens* might have evolved along such a scale of time and produced races of great age and large accumulated differences—but we didn't. Human equality is a contingent fact of history.

The problems with this line of argument are many. First, it is strange to have one of the inventors of the theory of "punctuated equilibrium" argue that human races cannot be very different from one another because they are too young. Second, nowhere in the article does Gould give us an example of a species in which races are as strongly marked as ours. The reason very likely is, as I have already noted, that there isn't any such species. Third, there are substantial racial differences present today—however they may have come about. I have already discussed two of these: athletic performance and brain size. Thus, Gould has it backwards. It is from the present that we obtain most of our knowledge of the past, and not, as most paleontologists would have it, the other way around. Finally, at least for our purposes, there is a strong tendency just about everywhere to extend the "there are no significant racial differences" argument to one which says "there are no significant gene-based differences between individuals." And as more and more groups are seen as needing some sort of official recognition, this extension becomes more and more inevitable as society becomes more sensitive to various groups.

Nature, Nurture, and the Individual

The above extension is, and for a long time has been, the prevailing point of view in the social sciences and humanities. If one takes a course at U.C. Berkeley in, say, Anthropology 3 (Introduction to Social and Cultural Anthropology), or Sociology 1 (Introduction to Sociology), one will hear an enormous amount about individuals as constituents of groups, and precious little about individuals as individuals. There will be little discussion of genes, evolution, or biology. It then goes almost without saying that you are not going to hear anything about free will or personal responsibility. The willful development of this situation in this country is very nicely documented in Carl Degler (1991). His Preface begins (and I quote directly and at length because the statement is so representative):

Like most white Americans of my sex and class (the son of a fireman) and my generation (born in 1921) I came into a world that soon made me a racist and a sexist. And then, like most well-educated people of that generation, as I grew up I repudiated both race and sex as explanations for differences in the behavior of human beings. Indeed, I spent a good deal of my youth and adulthood arguing by voice and in print against biology as a source of human behavior, not only in regard to race and sex, but in other respects as well. How and why that sea change occurred in my thinking concerned me only peripherally. I knew there had been a time when biology was thought to be an important way of explaining why social groups differed, why some people were considered better than others. But that was another time. In my new outlook it was a given that the repudiation of biology had resulted from a penetrating, perhaps even lengthy scientific investigation of biology's inadequacy in accounting for the ways in which human groups differed. In ruling out biology as a

cause for human differences, I thought of myself as defending a truth as solidly established as the heliocentric universe. Human nature, I believed, was constructed over time, not inherited from time. I had no trouble accepting Karl Marx's famous remark that man made his own history, not entirely as he pleased, meaning that history may limit us at times, but biology has little to say about our social behavior.

Today, in the thinking of citizens and social scientists alike the deeply held assumption is that culture has severed for good the link between human behavior and biology. The conviction is that human beings in their social behavior, alone among animals, have succeeded in escaping biology. The irony is heavy here. For that belief is accompanied by another deeply held conviction: that human beings, like all other living things, are the products of the evolution that Charles Darwin explained with his theory of natural selection. The irony is almost palpable as Darwin entertained no doubt that behavior was as integral a part of human evolution as bodily shape. And that is where Book III enters. It seeks to tell the story of how biological explanations have begun to return to social science.... It is important to recognize that this "return of biology" is not simply a revival of repudiated ideas, like racism, sexism, or eugenics.

The problem here is that a "return of biology" means a return to the idea that sex and race will have consequences, and if you recognize this publicly, then you become, for many, a racist or a sexist. But the fact is, the evolutionary process cannot and does not produce equality either among individuals or groups.

Much of the furor surrounding *The Bell Curve* thus derives from a very real problem. Herrnstein and Murray are officially agnostic on the degree of genetic involvement in racial differences in intellectual performance, give gender differences one small paragraph on page 275, and mention the implications of our evolutionary history not at all—but all that does not really help. The fact is that deep down all too many of us are aware of the reality of group differences, and of the virtual certainty that genes are somehow involved in producing some of those differences. But, as Ernst Mayr pointed out in 1963: "Equality in the face of evident nonidentity is a somewhat sophisticated concept and requires a moral stature of which many individuals seem incapable."

Consider the treatment of E. O. Wilson after the publication of his masterful *Sociobiology* in 1975. Or, a more recent example, the June, 1993 issue of *Scientific American* features a lengthy essay by John Horgan, one of their staff writers, entitled "Eugenics Revisited," and teased on the cover as "The dubious link between genes and behavior." This one was so egregious—especially given the venue—that I was moved to send a long letter to the editor, publisher, and other officials of the magazine. I had no illusions that it would be publicly acknowledged by them (and it wasn't, though I did get a letter from the editor Jonathan Piel). *Scientific American* continued in this vein in its January and February, 1995 issues. In the first, Tim Beardsley, one of their staff writers, authored a piece entitled "For Whom the Bell Curve Really Tolls," and subtitled: "A tendentious tome abuses science to promote far-right policies." My thought is that you have to be pretty far left to see any of Herrnstein and Murray's "messages" as "far right." And Beardsley apparently has no compunction about penning flat-out lies, such as: ". . . numerous studies have demonstrated that early childhood surroundings have a large role in molding IQ scores—while very few studies have indicated a significant role for heredity." Anyone who could write those last 10 words presumably would also describe our national debt as composed of very few dollars. The February issue then contains a review of *The Bell Curve* by Leon Kamin, one of the authors of the 1984 book *Not in Our Genes*. His position

can be inferred from the title, and from the fact that he and his coauthors were willing to state: "For all we know, the heritability (of IQ) may be zero. . . ." And, in its final paragraph:

> We should recall that the title of the article by A. R. Jensen . . . was "How Much Can We Boost IQ and Scholastic Achievement?" The answer, from cross-racial and cross-class adoption studies, seems unambiguous. As much as social organization will allow. It is not biology that stands in our way.

I submit that someone who could seriously entertain the notions that the heritability for any human performance measure could really be zero, and that our biology places no limits on a human performance, has thereby removed himself from serious consideration as a scholar of anything.

The Decline of Racism in Society

From an evolutionary perspective freedom can only mean freedom of opportunity, which, in the context of this article, necessarily leads to the question of how we are to recognize it among races and groups when we are living in a world where functionally significant, gene-based, racial and other group differences may well be the rule rather than the exception. It is here I think *The Bell Curve* makes its most meaningful single contribution (323–4). There we find the income data for young (average age = 29) year-round workers of three racial/ethnic groups: White, Black, Latino—with Latinos earning 86% and Blacks 77% as much as Whites. But when IQ is held constant (average = 100 for all three groups), both the Latino and Black figures climb to 98% of that for Whites. This result (which could be seen as remarkable only if one accepts the "this is a racist society" mantra) tells us about the degree of equality of opportunity in recent American society, and yet only one commentator of the more than 100 I have read or heard (including Murray and Herrnstein themselves) seems to have found it worthy of comment. This was Daniel Seligman, himself the author of the highly readable and most informative 1992 volume, *A Question of Intelligence*, who titled his brief column in the December 12, 1994, issue of *Fortune*, "News Nobody Noticed":

> Your servant has now read scores of reviews of *The Bell Curve*. Most have fiercely criticized the book's thesis, which emphasizes the centrality of IQ in lives and careers, and most have dwelt insistently on race and the 15-point black-white IQ gap. But, oddly, we have yet to read a review noticing the racial news built into a table on page 324. In a rational world, the news would be on the front pages. . . . The news is about racial discrimination in America. As we all keep reading, blacks earn a lot less than whites, even when you compare workers of similar ages and educational backgrounds. This table confirms this finding. But it points to something else one has never before read: that when you control for age and IQ, the black-white earnings gap just about disappears. . . .
>
> Obvious implication: At least so far as younger workers are concerned, employers no longer engage in irrational discrimination based on race. They discriminate based on IQ—which is rational, given the avalanche of data linking IQ to performance in many different job markets. Fascinating question: How can it be, in a world where racial discrimination is (properly) an object of enormous concern, that we are ignoring powerful evidence of its decline?

I would add that Seligman's comment that employers "discriminate based on IQ" has to be taken metaphorically. What they are doing

is rewarding performance (as any rational employer would). The connection with IQ, as Herrnstein and Murray point out (80–81), is that it is the best single predictor of performance—better than biographical data, reference checks, education, interview, or college grades. And as to his final question? The cynic in me cannot help commenting "So what else is new?" One does not really expect our media to report anything positive about this society, does one?

The Rise of Racism on College Campuses

No society has an unstained history. The treatment of individuals of sub-Saharan African ancestry is without doubt our largest and deepest stain, and that history, as are all histories, is beyond change. Given those truths, the worst thing we could do is to repeat that past in the name of producing an equality of results, by again allowing the treatment of an individual to be influenced by that individual's race (or sex, or ethnicity, or any other grouping). Yet, increasingly over the past 30 years we have been doing just that.

My own direct experiences with such race-norming, quota-driven treatment of individuals has been at U.C. Berkeley, where, for the last 10 years or so, a substantial percentage of freshman admissions (up to about 40%) has been reserved for "underrepresented minorities," and where race, ethnicity, and sex have become major factors in the hiring of new faculty. For students, what this has done is to produce two populations separated by race/ethnicity and performance who wind up, in the main, in different courses and pursue different majors. That is only to be expected when the SAT difference between the White and Asian students on the one hand, and Black and Latino students on the other, is about 270 points (1270 v. 1000; about 1 SD difference).

This is equivalent to about three to four years of academic achievement, and U.C. Berkeley is no place to play catch-up. And, as far as anyone knows (there are no published studies on the matter), no catching-up in fact takes place. I wrote of this situation in 1990:

> The Berkeley administration has, in its admissions policies, especially over the past five years or so, ignored certain unpalatable realities, and given us an even more unpalatable set of results. They have given us a situation where the association between race/ethnicity and performance is real, obvious, and of ever-increasing strength. What we are getting at Berkeley is two communities, separable on racial/ethnic grounds, and increasingly divergent from one another academically, socially, and in ethos—a result desired, presumably, by no rational soul. It is, frankly, difficult to imagine policies more deliberately crafted or better calculated to exacerbate racial and ethnic tensions, discourage individual performance among all groups, and contribute to the decay of a magnificent educational institution.

The fact is that any group-based policies are bound to have effects of this sort. As I have already noted, the evolutionary necessity of individual variation is almost always going to lead to group variation, and statistical realities require that group differences get exaggerated as one goes toward the ends of the bell curves involved. Thus, when you look at group representations with respect to the high-visibility pluses (e.g., high-paying jobs) and minuses (e.g., criminality) in any society, one can virtually guarantee that they are not going to be equal—and that the differences will not be trivial. The problem is in recognizing and adapting to those realities, and not, as has so often been the case with responses to *The Bell Curve*, denying them. I noted this in a letter to a Berkeley Faculty Senate committee on "diversity":

This current focus on "diversity," if continued and "successful," can only have the effect of rewarding individuals for making their primary allegiances to certain defined groups, and, thus, of tribalizing our society. It would require a mind completely closed to current realities, never mind historical ones, to remain ignorant of the disastrous effects of tribalization. One therefore has to suspect that anyone supporting policies that tribalize is either ignorant, or simply playing the very effective political game of "divide and conquer." The number of different roles to be played in a society increases as the complexity of a society increases. Ours is a very complex society that will only become more complex in the future. The number of different roles to be played will thus increase, requiring a larger number of allegiances for individuals within the society, and selecting against those whose primary allegiance is to a particular group—be it one based on biology (race, sex, age) or culture (ethnicity, religion). If one of your roles is chemist, then one set of your allegiances is to the community of chemists and chemistry. You are then a chemist, period—and not a female, or White, or Catholic, or old. To the extent that you do not look at it that way; that is, to the extent that you see yourself as some sort of hyphenated chemist, you will necessarily reduce the effectiveness of your chemistry. And this is going to be true for each of the other roles you will come to play. To the extent that you see yourself as a hyphenated anything, your achievement in that "anything" will tend to be reduced. And to the extent that a society encourages and rewards individuals for looking at themselves in such a fashion, it necessarily reduces its total level of accomplishment.

There are certain harsh realities in life. One of these is that groups, whether age, sex, race, ethnic, or whatever, are groups, and groups of anything are very likely going to differ from one another. If they didn't, then they wouldn't be groups, would they? I can then confidently guarantee that when we measure performance by groups, we are going to find group differences in performance. Some part of those differences will be nature-based, some part will be nurture-based, some will be will-based. No society has, or can have, the power to even things up. Societies are not omnipotent. They can provide opportunity; they cannot mandate individuals or groups making equal use of those opportunities, and, therefore, they cannot make either individuals or groups come out even. Individual and group variation are realities that they cannot will out of existence. They can try, and what happens then is, unfortunately, no secret: a temporary leveling-down bought at enormous cost. They can in no sense make groups equal. They cannot level up—only down—and thus any such leveling is necessarily at the expense of individual freedom and, ultimately, that society's total level of accomplishment.

Ending Racism without Ending Race

There would appear to be a substantial consensus among some of the more "conservative" commentators on *The Bell Curve* as to its policy implications, and, for better or worse, I find myself in total agreement with them. Seligman, for example, closes his *A Question of Intelligence* with: "One major message of the IQ data is that groups are different. A major policy implication of the data, I would argue, is that people should not be treated as members of groups but as individuals." Herrnstein and Murray give us the same message, but at much greater length, in their Conclusion (549–552).

I opened with a quote from Charles Krauthammer. His conclusion says it better than I can:

I distrust all multiculturalism, liberal or conservative. The Balkans amply demonstrate the perils of balkanization. My answer is simpler: Stop counting by race. Stop allocating by race. Stop measuring by race. Let's return to measuring individuals.

It seems hopelessly naive to propose this today. But it was not naive when first proposed by Martin Luther King and accepted by a white society that was finally converted to his vision of color blindness. Instead, through guilt and intimidation, a liberal establishment has since mandated that every study of achievement be broken down by race. "The Bell Curve" takes that mandate to its logical conclusion.

Enough. As both Murray and Thomas Sowell explicitly state, knowing the group score tells you nothing about the individual. Well, we have seen the group score. Let's go back to counting individuals. How many of Murray's critics will agree to that?

Amen. Let's go back to counting individuals. And how do we encourage such behavior? Simple. Just remove all reference to group identity from both statutory and administrative law. Period.

References:

Andreasen, N. C., M. Flaum, V. Swayze, D. S. O'Leary, R. Alliger, G. Cohen, J. Erhardt, and W. T. C. Yuh. 1993. "Intelligence and Brain Structure in Normal Individuals." *American Journal of Psychiatry* 150:130–134.

Beardsley, T. 1995. "For Whom the Bell Curve Really Tolls." *Scientific American* 272:1:14–17 (January).

Berlin, B., and P. Kay. 1969. *Basic Color Terms: Their Universality and Evolution.* Berkeley: University of California Press.

Cavalli-Sforza, L. L., P. Menozzi, and A. Piazza. 1994. *The History and Geography of Human Genes.* Princeton, N.J.: Princeton University Press.

Davis, B. 1976. "Evolution, Human Diversity, and Society." In *Zygon* 11:2:80–95.

Degler, C. N. 1991. *In Search of Human Nature.* New York: Oxford University Press.

Gould, S. J. 1981. *The Mismeasure of Man.* New York: Norton.

——. 1985. "Human Equality Is a Contingent Fact of Evolution." In *The Flamingo's Smile.* New York: Norton.

Hardin, G. 1959. *Nature and Man's Fate.* New York: Holt, Rinehart, and Winston.

Ho, K.-C., U. Roessmann, J. V. Straumfjord, and G. Monroe. 1980. "Analysis of Brain Weight." *Archives of Pathology and Laboratory Medicine* 104:635–645.

Horgan, J. 1993. "Eugenics Revisited." *Scientific American* 270:6:122–131 (June).

Kamin, L. 1995. "Behind the Curve." *Scientific American* 272:2:99–103 (February).

Krauthammer, C. 1994. "Liberals, Obsessed by Race, Can Hardly Complain." *The News & Observer* (Raleigh, N.C.) 23 October 1994.

Mayr, E. 1963. *Animal Species and Evolution.* Cambridge: Harvard University Press.

Sarich, V. M. 1995. *Race and Language in Prehistory.* In press. For copies write: 555 Pierce, Unit 730, Albany, CA 94706.

Seligman, D. 1992. *A Question of Intelligence: The IQ Debate in America.* New York: Birch Lane Press.

——. 1994. "News Nobody Noticed." *Fortune* 12 December:255.

Smith, C. L., and K. L. Beals. 1990. "Cultural Correlates with Cranial Capacity." *American Anthropologist* 92:193–200.

Subramanian, S. 1995. "The Story in Our Genes." *Time* 145:2:54–55 (16 Jan 1995).

Susanne, C. 1979. "On the Relationship between Psychometric and Anthropometric Traits." *American Journal of Physical Anthropology* 51:421–424.

Van Valen, L. 1974. "Brain Size and Intelligence in Man." In *American Journal of Physical Anthropology* 40:417–424.

Wickett, J. C., P. A. Vernon, and D. H. Lee. 1994. "In Vivo Brain Size, Head Perimeter, and Intelligence in a Sample of Healthy Adult Females." *Personality and Individual Differences* 16:831–838.

Willerman, L., R. Schultz, J. N. Rutledge, and E. D. Bigler. 1991. "In Vivo Brain Size and Intelligence." *Intelligence* 15:223–228.

Race and I.Q. as Pseudoscience

DIANE HALPERN

As I read *The Bell Curve* by Richard J. Herrnstein and Charles Murray I was reminded of a cartoon from the popular children's television show *Sesame Street*. As regular viewers of *Sesame Street* already know, every episode is brought to you courtesy of a number and letter. On those days when the star of the show is the letter "I," we are shown a group of hard-working cartoon characters whose job it is to polish a giant letter "I" until it glistens like an expensive jewel in the sunlight. In fact, this small army of letter polishers spend their entire day polishing the letter "I" because it is such an Important and Interesting letter. In a similar manner, Herrnstein and Murray also polish their "I"—Intelligence—and its related measure, IQ, which assume the spotlight as the best predictors of socioeconomic class and a diverse range of variables that cover the rest of the alphabet from Abusive relationships to Xenophobia and Zealotry.

Commenting on *The Bell Curve* is a lot like trying to catch a ball of jello. The arguments are slick and, like most skilled rhetoricians who are attempting to change how people think, the authors provide a veneer of fairness to cover the flaws and biases in their message. In this case, the veneer is thin—so thin that it allows their hypocrisy and social agenda to peek through. In making their points, the authors present, discredit, and then dismiss all opposing points of view. Contradictory evidence is criticized as statistically or methodologically flawed. Unfortunately, the stringent criteria that they apply to counterarguments are abandoned when they present the evidence in support of their favored conclusions. The authors shape their arguments like skilled word smiths. A factual statement like "some educational programs have not worked" is gradually morphed into a misleading statement like "educational programs have not worked," and then, "educational programs cannot work," a subtle change in wording that occurs as the authors stray from their data.

Can anyone seriously believe that Murray was shocked and dismayed when he found that he had upset many people with his pronouncements of racial inequality or the way he used IQ data to support an ultra-conservative political agenda? The authors have created the perfect medium for a growing media frenzy with a very long book in which much of the supporting evidence is relegated to a statistical appendix and extreme claims are succinctly summarized. The voracious appetite of the media is whetted by controversies, sound bites, and simple explanations of complex subjects. Even lengthy and thoughtful articles are condensed into a few words for newspaper headlines that are supposed to pique the reader's interest. This is the stuff that sells newspapers, keeps people tuned to the chatty banter that passes as television news, and sustains conversations in countless barber shops, bus stops, and kitchen tables. Despite Murray's protestations to the contrary, this is a book about race, and race is one topic in which we are all self-proclaimed experts. Each of us has an opinion about racial similarities and differences and a story to tell that shows how right our own opinions are. Cognitive psychologists who study stereotypes and prejudice have known for a long time that strongly held beliefs are difficult to change, and that people cling to their beliefs even when confronted with evidence that shows that these beliefs are wrong. We are more likely to change our interpretations of experience and our memory for events so that they fit our existing belief system than we are to abandon our beliefs. Perhaps books like this one should be sold with warning labels in which readers are urged to be alert for misleading statements, missing evidence, and biased interpretations—sort of a surgeon general's warning. The messages in *The Bell Curve* are at least as dangerous as cigarettes and alcohol.

My response to Herrnstein and Murray's thesis is organized around a brief summary of seven main points that they make in their controversial and massive tome, so that my comments and criticisms can be understood in their appropriate context even by readers of this article who have not read their book.

Intelligence Is Important

According to Herrnstein and Murray:

This is a basic underlying assumption of the authors' argument. It is difficult to disagree with the statement that intelligence is important, although I would have to add, "Important for what purpose?" Most of us would agree that it is also important to be a kind and loving person and that empathy and other socially desirable traits are at least equally important for the betterment of society or individual happiness. Although this is not the place to en-

gage in philosophical musings about whether it is more important to be a good person or a smart one, the authors do provide a definitive answer to a similar burning question. They ask if it is better to be born intelligent or rich, which, for most of us, would seem to be a rhetorical question or one in which the answer depends on individual values. According to the authors, however, the correct answer is intelligent, and lots of intelligence is even better than lots of money. But, what is intelligence, and how can we tell who has more or less of it?

Intelligence is one of the most controversial topics in psychology even though the concept has a long history and the term is commonly used in everyday language. If I asked you to list the characteristics of an intelligent person, you would probably include terms like "reasons logically and well," "keeps an open mind," "reads with high comprehension," and "can understand complexities." In addition, most people believe that they are about average or above average in intelligence. It seems that Garrison Keillor's mythical Lake Wobegon is not the only place where the laws of mathematics are suspended so that everyone can be in the top half of the distribution.

Today's most commonly used intelligence tests, the Stanford-Binet and Wechsler Intelligence Tests, are normed so that the average score is 100 and measures of how the scores are spread out (standard deviations) are derived by transforming scores so that they conform to a mathematical formula. IQ scores greater than 100 indicate greater than average intelligence, and scores less than 100 indicate less than average intelligence. Intelligence tests are based on the idea that the more questions you answer correctly, the more intelligent you are. Tests of intelligence are like other sorts of tests, and the scores depend on all of the factors that affect performance on any other test—variables like the nature of the test questions and the test takers' motivation, knowledge of the material, health, and willingness to guess when unsure of an answer. The scores that are obtained on intelligence tests are known as "intelligence quotients" (because they used to involve forming a fraction or quotient) or, more informally, IQ scores. IQ is a number that is obtained on a test that supposedly measures intelligence—it is not a direct measure of intelligence.

Here are some examples that are similar to questions on common intelligence tests:

Verbal Test Items:
1. At what temperature does water freeze?
2. Who wrote *The Republic*?
3. How many inches are in 3 1/2 feet?
4. Explain the meaning of "strange."
5. Explain the meaning of "adumbrate."
6. Repeat a series of digits after the test administrator recites them. For example, repeat the following digits: "8175621."

Performance Test Items:
1. Use wooden cubes painted red and white to duplicate a design shown on cards.
2. Arrange a series of cartoons into a logical sequence.
3. Assemble a jig-saw puzzle.

Most psychologists believe that intelligence is a multidimensional construct, although there is much disagreement over how many different kinds of intelligence there are. One way of dividing intelligence is to consider it as made up of fluid intelligence, the kind of intelligence that you would use when you are dealing with a novel task, like writing your first computer program, and crystallized intelligence, the kind of intelligence you would use when dealing with information that you have already learned, like finding the area of a pyramid when you know the formula. There are many other ways to divide intelligence including verbal intelligence, which involves the use of words and language, and spatial intelligence, which involves the use of spatial displays like maps.

A major controversy among psychologists concerns the existence of a general intelligence factor called "g." The question is whether it makes sense to think about people as being generally "smart" or "dumb," or is it more accurate to think that people can be smart in some ways and not in others? If people can be smart in some areas and not others, then a single score on an intelligence test will not be able to measure how intelligent they are, but if people can be thought of as generally smart or generally dumb, then a single number could assess the extent to which they are intelligent. In order to answer this question, the data from intelligence tests are analyzed with mathematical procedures to determine whether a single factor, "g," emerges or whether the data are described more accurately with multiple factors. Some of the disagreements over the existence of a general factor of intelligence concern the mathematical procedures, and other disagreements concern the way that intelligence is conceptualized. The measurement of intelligence is not separable from the way it is conceptualized because the mathematics that we use influences the way psychologists think about intelligence, and the way we think about intelligence influences the mathematical procedures that we use. Many of the controversies surrounding the measurement of intelligence involve the mathematical analyses that are used in understanding the data. This is one of the reasons why it is difficult to explain to the general public why the experts cannot agree about intelligence.

When Administered Properly, Intelligence Tests Are Fair and Valid Measures of Intelligence

Although the authors have felled many trees to make this point, I do not agree that their conclusion is fair or valid. IQ is a number on a test. The test questions reflect the sort of information that most people know and the intellectual activities that most people can perform. IQ scores seem to predict academic success equally well for all racial and ethnic groups, a point that the authors make in several different places in their book, but this does not mean that they measure intelligence equally well. In addition, IQ scores can only account for a relatively small proportion of the variance in academic or job success. Success depends on many other variables like motivation, persistence, expectations, and education. The influences of variables other than intelligence are quickly dismissed by the authors, a practice that suggests that they are not important when, in fact, they are.

All intelligence tests are culturally dependent, but all people are not equally exposed to the "majority" culture. Suppose we called "intelligence tests" by some other name, such as tests of acculturation to middle-class American life. This could be a descriptive name for these tests because the questions on the tests reflect what most people in the standardization sample knew and did not know at some point in time. For example, we might expect an average American adult in 1995 to know what a disk drive is, but we would not have expected this sort of knowledge from average Americans in 1985.

It is a fact that approximately 50% of African-Americans and other groups of ethnic minority children grow up in poverty. On the average, people who grow up in poverty do not have the same experiences as people who do not grow up in poverty. It is likely that fewer individuals from low income families will know what a disk drive is than individuals from families with higher incomes. Even if the same test predicts academic success equally well for all test-takers, it does not measure intelligence equally well, unless we decide to define intelligence as synonymous with academic success. This sort of definition leads to a type of circular reasoning (intelligence = academic success and academic success = intelligence) that would not be indicative of intelligent thought.

Intelligence Is Mostly Inherited

Of course, the authors prudently claim "we are not so rash as to assert that the environment or culture is wholly irrelevant" (301); however, they definitively conclude that "IQ is substantially heritable" (105). This is an example of the sort of weasel language that I referred to earlier. I do not believe that the data support this sort of blanket conclusion. Intelligence is far too complex to decide that it is mostly any one variable. It is clear to me that intelligence is partly inherited, but it is not meaningful or possible to quantify the size of that part. Also, the role of the environment is not a linear one as we climb the IQ scale. Consider, for example, a profoundly retarded individual—someone who scores below the cut-point designated as "educably retarded." Many such individuals cannot learn to feed themselves, to talk, or to use the bathroom; they need constant custodial care, often with direct feeding through their stomachs. In these rare instances, intelligence is unaffected by environmental variables. By definition, they will not benefit from education. But, as we ascend the intelligence curve, environmental variables become increasingly important. The most brilliant rocket scientist would not be functioning at a high intellectual level if she never attended school or had an opportunity to learn to read or study science. Many of the items on intelligence tests are the sorts of items that are learned in school. How can anyone conclude that formal and informal education doesn't have a massive effect on intelligence (for those who are at least near average and above in intelligence), when we measure intelligence with information that is learned in school?

There are many other problems with the dichotomization of nature and nurture and the attempt to assign a proportional value to each side of the nature-nurture equation. Nature and nurture are not separable components because biological propensities influence the environment that we seek, and through our interactions with the environment our biology changes. We now know that changes in the environment cause changes in brain structures, and altered brain structures change how we interact with the environment. Heredity and environment are like conjoined twins who share a common heart—they cannot be separated. It is impossible to declare a winner in the age-old tug-of-war between nature and nurture.

Low Intelligence Causes a Wide Range of Social Problems Such as Poverty, Injury, Crime, "Illegitimate" Births, and Idleness

My response to this list of social ills is a less-than-intelligent "Huh?" Let's consider the evidence and reasoning that the authors marshal for this conclusion. Take some time to examine the bell curve that is shown in Figure 1.

It is apparent that its name is descriptive of its bell-like shape. The large "hump" in the middle shows that most people are around average in intelligence. The bell curve, which is more formally known as the normal curve, is ubiquitous in the sciences with variables like height, weight, IQ, petal-size in flowers, crop yields, length of pickles, and more—all showing this distribution.

There is a cluster of variables that tend to occur together at the low (left) end of the intelligence curve. They include such "socially undesirable" behaviors and characteristics as child abuse and neglect, poverty, low levels of education, unemployment, "idleness," in-creased injuries, "illegitimate" births, welfare, higher birth rates, and crime. The opposites of these variables cluster with high intelligence and are shown at the upper (right) portion of the curve. The variables that cluster at the low-intelligence end of the distribution are the usual indicators of low socioeconomic status. The authors then conclude that low intelligence is the cause of the other variables in this cluster. They pronounce that: "Socioeconomic status is . . . a result of cognitive ability" (286). How can they know that being unintelligent caused poverty and not the reverse, or, at least, a more reciprocal relationship in which poverty and low intelligence operate jointly and influence each other? Poor people differ from rich people in many ways—they have poorer health, poorer nutrition, and poorer living conditions. Would it not make more sense to reverse the causal arrow and hypothesize that poverty and all of its associates (lack of prenatal care, inadequate heat, ingestion of lead paint, poor diet, etc.) cause low intelligence? The statistical procedures that the authors used to establish which of these related variables was causal cannot be used to establish that low intelligence is the cause of the other variables. The variables are at least interactive or possibly even unidirectional—in the other direction.

Current Social Programs Like Welfare, Affirmative Action, and Head Start Cannot Work

Finally, I understand the reason for this book. Although the data that were used to support their conclusions are from a fairly recent data set, the arguments themselves have been made countless times before. There is nothing new in the Herrnstein and Murray treatise. *The Bell Curve* is a book about money and values

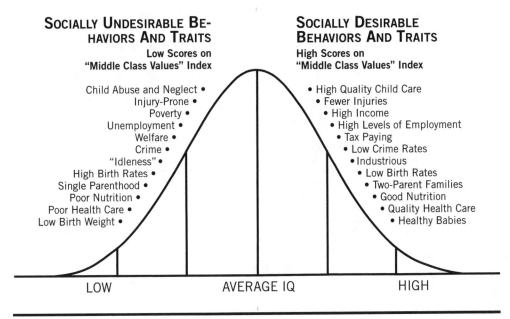

SOCIALLY UNDESIRABLE BE-HAVIORS AND TRAITS
Low Scores on
"Middle Class Values" Index

Child Abuse and Neglect •
Injury-Prone •
Poverty •
Unemployment •
Welfare •
Crime •
"Idleness" •
High Birth Rates •
Single Parenthood •
Poor Nutrition •
Poor Health Care •
Low Birth Weight •

SOCIALLY DESIRABLE BEHAVIORS AND TRAITS
High Scores on
"Middle Class Values" Index

• High Quality Child Care
• Fewer Injuries
• High Income
• High Levels of Employment
• Tax Paying
• Low Crime Rates
• Industrious
• Low Birth Rates
• Two-Parent Families
• Good Nutrition
• Quality Health Care
• Healthy Babies

LOW AVERAGE IQ HIGH

Figure 1

and how we should be spending tax dollars so that they reflect politically conservative values. Social programs like welfare are very expensive, and many, maybe even most, have not worked well. Why? Are the disappointing results because we have made many mistakes in how we set up these programs? Were our expectations too high? Did we set up the wrong contingencies or perhaps use insensitive measures of success? If so, then we should be able to find better ways to provide aid to the poor—ways that help more of them obtain jobs and move out of poverty. But, if social welfare programs cannot work because the recipients are too dumb or too idle or too criminal to benefit, then why spend money on programs that are either doomed to failure or actually increase the number on welfare by paying for out-of-wedlock babies? (Herrnstein and Murray prefer the term "illegitimate," an old-fashioned term that blames the baby for its mother's marital status. Their deliberate use of emotionally laden terms like "illegitimate" makes my skin crawl.)

Although the authors reach an opposite conclusion, it is clear that one kind of social

program that has reaped considerable social benefits is education. Many studies have shown that education does improve thinking abilities, and it is these very abilities that are at the heart of any definition of intelligence. In their usual style, the authors present some of the data that show the beneficial effects of education and then dismiss these data as unreplicated, suspicious, lacking control groups, statistically flawed, etc. It is especially surprising that they arrive at this conclusion because the senior author, Herrnstein, was a contributor to a major program to improve intelligence in Venezuela. The Venezuela program has undergone careful scrutiny by international scientists, including random assignment of subjects to experimental conditions and "blind" scoring so that experimenter expectations cannot influence the outcomes, and it clearly has yielded improvements in thinking skills for those who were involved in the program.

In understanding what is at the heart of the authors' argument, it is important to distinguish between data and the interpretation of data. This relationship is shown in Figure 2.

Yes, poverty, crime, low intelligence, and

Figure 2

Misusing Data as a Shaky Foundation for Public Policy Recommendations

The data presented by Herrnstein and Murray are generally accepted as correct, although these authors slant the way the data are presented (e.g., downplay the importance of environment). Their interpretation of the data is substantially influenced by their beliefs, which reflect their prejudices and stereotypes. Herrnstein and Murray's recommendations for public policies are more dependent on their beliefs and the way they interpret the data than on the data themselves. This figure shows how this is done.

DATA	INTERPRETATION	PRE-EXISTING BELIEFS	PUBLIC POLICY RECOMMENDATIONS
IQ predicts academic success (partially).	Intelligence is a fixed quantity that remains fairly stable throughout life.	Prejudice concerning groups. Stereotypes about groups.	Eliminate Affirmative Action. End welfare for dependent children.
African Americans score, on the average, lower than white Americans on standardized intelligence tests.	Intelligence tests are fair and accurate measures of intelligence.	Poor women have babies as a way of making money from welfare.	Stop social programs that are designed to help poor people achieve.
Poverty, crime, high birth rates, etc. co-occur with low intelligence.	Low intelligence *causes* socially undesirable behaviors.	Social class is determined by intelligence.	Make it easier to convict accused criminals.
Intelligence is, in part, inherited.	Intelligence cannot be raised with education or other experiences.	Need for "breeding" programs that improve general level of intelligence.	End mandatory child support from unmarried fathers.
Some social programs have not raised intelligence or produced desirable outcomes.	Intelligence is a unitary concept ("g") that can be expressed with a single number.	Immigrants reduce the overall level of intelligence in the U.S.	Enact a competency test for immigrants as a criterion for immigration.

---

high birth rates occur together. These are the data, and they are not in question, although the authors often present the data in misleading ways. What is in question is the way these authors interpreted the data and the "cure" or public policy recommendations that arise from their interpretation. Their interpretation or explanation of the data is influenced by their belief system, and their explanations and beliefs intervene between the data and the public policy recommendations that are built on the data. There is good reason to believe that their interpretation of the data is "tainted" or not as pure or data-based as their academic affiliations, thick statistical appendix, and scientific-sounding language make it seem. Consider this quote from *The Bell Curve:* "The median earning of ... workers in 1992 [was] $41,005 for white male graduates with a bachelor's degree

and only $31,001 for black males with a bachelor's degree" (324). Most readers would interpret these data as evidence of persistent discrimination in the labor market. After all, how else could you explain the finding that even when African-Americans and Whites have the same education, and other variables like sex are held constant, African-Americans are paid much less? The authors conclude that this disparity in income shows how important the differences in intelligence really are. The bias in their interpretation of these data is too obvious to deserve additional comment.

Similarly, Herrnstein and Murray cite high drop-out rates for students who are admitted to college as a result of affirmative action programs as evidence that these students lack the intelligence to succeed in college, and therefore affirmative action programs cannot work.

Affirmative action admissions are almost always first-generation students from low income households. Why don't they consider other explanations for the high drop-out rate of students admitted under affirmative action programs, like the fact that these students are more likely to work while they are in college and when they work, they work more hours than their wealthier counterparts? Why don't they even consider the possibility that affirmative action students start college with deficits that are attributable to an inferior secondary education and social pressures that are not compatible with attending college? Wouldn't these facts be expected to increase drop-out rates? Like other interpretations of data in *The Bell Curve*, these conclusions do not ring true.

Follow the Money

This Watergate maxim is a good one to follow here. In deciding whom to believe, it is important to determine if the speaker or writer has an ulterior motive in convincing you that a certain conclusion is valid. For example, if the patent holder on a miracle cream that claims to "melt unsightly fat" told you that it was a wonder product, you would be less likely to believe this claim than if you had heard it from an unbiased scientific source with no potential for financial gain. The authors show a particular bias to cite studies that were funded by the infamous Pioneer Fund, which dispenses about $1 million annually to academics who support the idea that intelligence is genetically determined and that humans should be bred selectively for intelligence. I had a brief run-in with some of the academics whose work they have sponsored. In my book entitled *Sex Differences in Cognitive Abilities* (2nd ed.), I summarized a large body of research on brain size and concluded that although males have, on the average, larger and heavier brains, when these values are adjusted for

body size, there is no sex difference. Following the publication of this book, I received an article from Richard Lynn, an Irish researcher, in which he says that his work shows that I am wrong. At first, I gave this rebuke very little thought because it is not unusual for researchers to come up with different findings and different conclusions, although his results were at odds with those reported by virtually all of the other researchers in this field.

I then received a copy of the Lynn article with a letter from a psychologist whom I know, Philippe Rushton, who is notable for his theory that intelligence is inversely related to penis size. He posits that those males with the largest penises have the lowest intelligence, and furthermore, there are racial differences in both penis size and intelligence. According to Rushton, the racial line-up in descending order of intelligence is Asians, Caucasians, and Africans, with the reverse order for penis size. (No, I don't know how he collected his data, nor do I know how other ethnic groups fare in this linear array.) This sort of theory is reminiscent of the penis-centered theories of Freud which posited a universal stage of development for boys and girls that he named the phallic stage. The word "phallic" means "penis," and Freud saw no reason why this stage should have a different name when it referred to female development. Rushton's penis-centric theory of intelligence suggests that some things never change since he proposes that we can learn about the intelligence of both females and males in an ethnic group by reference to the male anatomy. Much of the contemporary research funded by the Pioneer Fund is both racist and sexist. In fact, the founding fathers of this fund were also anti-Semitic with strong ties to the Nazi movement and its goal to rid the world of Jews. There are 23 separate references to Lynn in the bibliography of *The Bell Curve* and 11 to Rushton. Both of these critics of my work received high praise by Herrnstein and Murray, and, like other frequently cited researchers in *The Bell Curve*, received large amounts of money from the Pioneer Fund.

The parallels between sexist and racist theories became more apparent to me when I received a copy of Rushton's latest research, which was published after *The Bell Curve* went to press. Based on a study of helmet sizes used by the military, he concluded that African-Americans have smaller heads and therefore smaller brains than Caucasians—a result that mirrors the one by Lynn that compared male and female brains. There are many problems with these studies. Most importantly, brain size, weight, and neural structures depend upon life experiences. That is, our brains respond to our environment, so that we cannot know whether larger and heavier brains caused different life experiences or the experiences caused differences in brain size and weight. Many of the correlates of poverty, such as inadequate nutrition, alcohol and other drug use, lack of prenatal and pediatric health care, ingestion of lead-based paint and other toxins, all have negative effects on brain development during the critical prenatal and infancy periods when the brain is most vulnerable. I do not know if the brain weight data are valid, but even if they are, lower brain weight is more likely a consequence of poverty than the reverse. In addition, there is absolutely no evidence that heavy brains are found in smarter people or that skull size is a good measure of brain size. The leaps from the actual data to the conclusions are irresponsible.

Soon after *The Bell Curve* was published, I received a FAX and phone call from Linda Gottfredson, a professor at the University of Delaware, who summarized what she believed was the dominant professional view on intelligence. She asked me to sign her summary statement to indicate my support. She explained that this was important so that the media and the public had a single summary statement on intelligence to guide their understanding of the points raised by Herrnstein and Murray. I found her summary troubling as it essentially agreed with Herrnstein and Murray's conclusions. In fact, I agree with many of the statements made in *The Bell Curve*, but there are many others that I believe are wrong. I did not sign the statement that appeared in *The Wall Street Journal*, although 52 other psychologists did. I later learned that she is also supported by the Pioneer Fund. Although there is nothing morally wrong with being financed by people who share an author's ideological point of view, it is troubling when all of the research that is funded in this manner happens to support the ideology of the funding agency. If you understand the social and political agenda that has financed this work, the next conclusion made by Herrnstein and Murray should not surprise you.

Recent Immigrants Are Less Intelligent Than Immigrants Who Came to the United States Earlier This Century

The reasons in support of this conclusion are so flimsy that I cannot present them in a meaningful way. The authors argue that recent immigrants obtain special entry status because they are related to citizens; whereas immigrants at the turn of the 20th century fled persecution and were more motivated to succeed. Frankly, I cannot understand the logic in this argument. Why should we expect that recent immigrants from war torn and poverty stricken areas of the world would differ in motivation or intelligence from those who fled persecution earlier in the century? The political philosophy that the authors espouse is blatantly anti-immigration, which is as legitimate as any other political philosophy—except that this one is "dressed up" to look like a data-based conclusion, which it is not.

Herrnstein and Murray go on to argue that the recent flood of immigrants, coupled with high birth rates among the low intelligence portions of the population, have lowered the average intelligence of Americans. When the average intelligence of a country is lowered, it is less able to compete in world markets, it is less able to produce and use advanced technologies, and other dire consequences result. While this may seem to be a reasonable argument, they also present data that show that the average IQ scores have risen every decade, an effect known as the Flynn Effect, named for the individual who first hypothesized this rise. I do not know how to interpret these inconsistencies, except to say that they seem to be able to argue that average IQ is both rising and falling, depending on what is more convenient at the time.

How to Make Reasoned Judgments About Controversial Research

1. Read the original research, if possible. Second-hand accounts often distort the facts and make faulty inferences from the original research.
2. Identify the conclusions—What do the authors want you to believe and do?
3. Examine the data and other evidence that are provided to support the conclusions. Were tests of statistical significance used? Was the size of the effect considered (e.g., was the difference between groups large enough to be meaningful)? Was the sample sufficiently large? Was it representative of the population?
4. Is the conclusion a matter of opinion (e.g., euthanasia is wrong) or a matter of fact (e.g., men are taller, on average, than women)?
5. Do the authors have the expertise needed to conduct and interpret the study?
6. Are the authors unbiased or do they have a vested interest in the outcomes of the study?
7. Are appeals to emotion being used to convince readers that the authors' conclusions are correct (e.g., arguments against the person or name calling)?
8. What is missing? Would other explanations fit the data equally well or better?
9. Do the conclusions follow from the data?
10. Are the stated and unstated assumptions acceptable?
11. Are correlational data being used to make causal claims? (Random assignment of subjects to groups is needed to make strong causal claims.)
12. Can you identify fallacies in the reasoning (e.g., false dichotomy)?
13. Are valid and reliable measures being used?
14. Are the results unusual? If so, why? Why is the study controversial?
15. Overall, what is the strength of the support for the conclusions?

There Is Some Good News

Readers may be thinking that *The Bell Curve* forecasts a bleak future unless we stop welfare programs and curtail immigration so that the intelligent portion (or the "over the hill" portion on the right hand side) of the curve will have higher birth rates and the less intelligent portion stops reproducing and entering the country. Well, there is also good news. You and I are not at fault! We are all in the "over the hill" gang, a group repeatedly referred to as the "cognitive elite" because we are intelligent enough to read their massive tome and rich enough to spend $30 to buy it. We can look down on the poor unfortunates who live on the other side of the intelligence hill from us, and like responsible parents we can decide to do the right thing and eliminate social programs. The solutions that the authors offer have a very contemporary sound because they are now heard on Capitol Hill. It is not the politically conservative point of view that I am objecting to in this review—it is the misuse of data and the blatant biases in the way the data are interpreted in support of this point of view that I find objectionable. Yes, we have difficult contemporary problems with welfare and immigration, among others. Responsible social science data are needed to guide public policy on these immensely complex issues, but the authors provide blatantly biased interpretations that are closer to propaganda than responsible research. Social programs may very well be doomed to failure for economic, social, or political reasons, but they are not doomed for the reasons Herrnstein and Murray present.

They also offer other solutions. We can return to simpler times (541) when all people had a "valued place" in society (535). The authors define a "valued place" as "other people would miss you when you were gone" (535). What does this sentimental dribble really mean? Slave masters missed their slaves when they were gone; does this mean that slaves had a "valued place" in society? The call for simpler laws seems like an excellent idea. In fact, I found myself nodding frequently with many of their recommendations until I realized that "simpler" laws really meant fewer rights and safeguards for citizens. The nostalgia for the good old days when the neighborhood cop was your friend were not so good for everyone. African-American children never assumed that the local police officer was their friend, especially if they grew up in the segregated South. Have the authors really thought through their suggestion that fathers who are not married should not be required to pay child support—so-called "deadbeat fathers"? This solution is misogynist, anti-child, and fiscally foolish. How can this proposed policy discourage out-of-wedlock births or save taxpayer dollars? It certainly will not provide males with incentives to use contraception, if they have no financial responsibility for the children they father. How is this policy consistent with the creation of a "valued place" for everyone? What will we gain as a society by getting those deadbeat toddlers off welfare—a move that virtually ensures that many of America's children will be denied access to even the most basic of human needs like adequate nutrition, health care, and heat? I don't know whether to cry for a society that sacrifices its young or rage in anger against the intelligent people who forgot to care about the rest of society. Herrnstein and Murray's proposed solutions drip with hypocrisy and offer simplistic cures for society's most difficult ills. And for these solutions I don't think that even Forrest Gump, the lovable role model for those in the low-intelligence portion of the curve, would offer Herrnstein and Murray a piece of his coveted chocolates.

Race and Sports as Good Science

JON ENTINE

If you can believe that individuals of recent African ancestry are not genetically advantaged over those of European and Asian ancestry in certain athletic endeavors, then you could probably be led to believe just about anything." Or so says biological anthropologist Vincent Sarich. To which professor of sociology Harry Edwards, also of University of California/Berkeley, provides the antithesis: "What really is being said in a kind of underhanded way is that blacks are closer to beasts and animals in terms of their genetic and physical and anatomical make up than they are to the rest of humanity. And that's where the indignity comes in."

For the synthesis, turn to Gideon Ariel, Biomechanist, former U.S. Olympic Committee scientist, former Israeli Olympic athlete: "I know that the American system is very sensitive to statements of black and white. But you cannot defy science. You cannot just say that day is night and night is day. These are facts."

In fact, in running, basketball, football, and soccer—sports in which the social and economic barriers to participation are very low, creating the most level of playing fields—the yawning performance gap between blacks and everyone else is nothing short of astonishing. Yet allegations of racism often quash the overwhelming scientific evidence which convincingly suggests that this growing on-field disparity cannot be explained by culture and environment alone.

Even a casual mention that there exist any meaningful genetic differences between races can ignite a firestorm. In a speech before the British Association for the Advancement of Science in 1995, Roger Bannister, the distinguished neurologist, retired Oxford dean, and the first man to break the four minute barrier in the mile, in 1954, was showered with ridicule for venturing his opinion "as a scientist rather than a sociologist" that all athletes are not created equal. "I am prepared to risk political incorrectness," he said, "by drawing attention to the seemingly obvious but under stressed fact that black sprinters and black athletes in general all seem to have certain natural anatomical advantages."

That's the explosive "N" word—natural. "Nurture" alone cannot explain the remarkable trends. Over the past 30 years, as sports has opened wide to athletes from almost every country, the results have become increasingly segregated. There are only 800 million blacks, or one in eight of the world population, but athletes of African origin hold every major world running record from the 100 meters to the marathon. In the United States, where African Americans make up about 13% of the

705

population, almost 90% of professional basketball players, 70% of the National Football League, and more than a third of professional baseball is black. In Britain, with a black population of less than 2%, one in 5 professional soccer players is black. Blacks have also come to dominate world boxing.

Why do blacks of West African ancestry dominate sports in which the social and economic barriers are lowest?

Fifty years of anthropological and more recent physiological studies have documented clear, if overlapping, biologically based differences between athletes of different populations. Scientists are just beginning to isolate the genetic links to those biologically based differences (though the fact that the biology is grounded in genetics is unequivocal). That's the science. The politics is more precarious. Any suggestion of human differences is publicly and politically seen as divisive or worse in a country which sometimes gives lip service to equal opportunity and where race remains a festering sore.

African Americans understandably are suspicious about where this discussion can lead. "People feel if you say blacks are better athletically, you're saying they're dumber," Frank Deford, the respected author and sports reporter once noted. "But when Jack Nicklaus sinks a 30-foot putt, nobody thinks his IQ goes down."

Athletic achievement has long been a Catch-22 for blacks. When an athlete lost a contest, it encouraged racist notions that blacks were an inferior race, intellectually and physically. But winning reinforced the equally pernicious stereotype that blacks were closer to animals and therefore less evolved than whites or Asians. That is the fate that befell Jesse Owens after he shocked the 1936 Olympics, held in the capital of Hitler's Germany. His four gold medals were subtly devalued as a product of his "natural" athleticism.

The racist stereotype of the "animalistic black" stretches back centuries. Fascination about black physicality and black anger about being caricatured as a lesser human being, closer to a jungle beast, have been part of the dark side of the American dialogue on race, with deep historical roots in hundreds of years of European colonialism. In the 19th century, white Europeans were enraptured by pseudo-sciences such as phrenology. Racial and ethnic groups were ranked by skull size that supposedly proved that white males were intellectually superior. Jews, blacks, and other minorities were targets of the most egregious generalizations, usually associated with physical characteristics and intellectual prowess.

Since World War II, in an understandable reaction to extremist race theories that provided intellectual fuel for Nazism, anthropological orthodoxy has held that the very concept of race is a meaningless social construct. Discussing "race science," as it came to be called, became a taboo subject, publicly and academically. The issue took on incendiary proportions in the early 1970s when it was publicly married to findings of race differences in I.Q.

Growing up in the Sixties, it never occurred to me to judge blacks as less intelligent. And I celebrated with most liberal-thinking Americans when Muhammad Ali redefined boxing and when the raised black fist of the 1968 Mexico City Olympians became a potent symbol of freedom. I entered the shark infested waters of this debate in 1987, when Los Angeles Dodger general manager Al Campanis had been fired after commenting on national television that he believed that blacks didn't have the mental "necessities" to be a manager or general manager. The following January, Jimmy "the Greek" Snyder, a prognosticator with CBS Sports, was fired and publicly ridiculed after making an off-hand comment that slave owners had bred blacks to produce the best physical specimens and that this contributed to black success in sports. At the time,

I was producing for Tom Brokaw at *NBC Nightly News*. After much internal hand-wringing, we decided that maybe we should address the myths and stereotypes of blacks in sports—including the racial taboos. Perhaps dialogue could dissipate some of the noxious poison.

The end product was our 1989 documentary, *Black Athletes: Fact and Fiction*. Before it aired, it provoked intense reaction, dividing journalists, frequently along racial lines. A white columnist at *Newsday* called it "a step forward in the dialogue on race and sports" while a black writer at the same daily wrote that "NBC had scientists answer questions that none but a bigot would conjure up." Yet the public, particularly African Americans, seemed far more receptive to the balanced treatment of a heretofore untouchable subject. Even Harry Edwards, a long-time critic of the suggestion that there are any meaningful racial differences, would comment that "the NBC documentary opened the door to enlightenment on a controversial subject." *Black Athletes* went on to win numerous awards including Best International Sports Film.

Over the next few years, the science of human performance and our knowledge of human genetics barreled forward at breakneck speed. I became even more intrigued by the genetics of human performance. At the urging of my literary agent, I circulated a book proposal that offered to explore the issue in far more depth. The timing, I believed, was opportune. This was a chance to write a cutting edge, popular but scholarly book that discussed genetics and the problematic social history of race. Sports would merely be an access point for a wide-ranging conversation.

As a measure of my commitment, I assembled a "board of advisors"—top biologists, anthropologists, exercise physiologists, and sociologists, black and white, from all over the world, who offered to act as informal scholarly reviewers as the book took shape. They em-braced the proposal as provocative and responsible. Perhaps that's why I was so stunned by the consistently negative response it engendered from publishers, many of whom refused to even read it—on "principle." Again and again, I heard: "This is a racist subject. By even suggesting that blacks may have a genetic edge in sports, you are opening up the Pandora's box of intellectual inferiority."

Finally, after more than a dozen rejections, an independent-minded editor at Macmillan, Rick Wolff, offered a contract for what was to become *Taboo*. The turn of good fortune proved fleeting, however. Soon after, Mr. Wolff moved to Warner Books. Though he wanted to take the book with him, Warner balked. "It was considered too dicey a subject, too controversial," Wolff recalls. "Once the other editors heard it was about racial differences, they wouldn't even let me present it at an editorial meeting."

Unfortunately, Mr. Wolff's eventual replacement as editor, Natalie Chapman, knew nothing about sports and was only vaguely sensitive to the science and politics of race. Nonetheless, I proceeded with an early draft, always staying in close contact with my advisory board and an expanding list of experts, who were sent the evolving manuscript for feedback.

By this time, I had grown quite confident of my findings. Using DNA evidence, scientists were in the process of compiling maps of the waves of human migrations that have led to today's "races." Although the move out of Africa by modern humans to Europe and Asia occurred rather recently in evolutionary time, scientists were nearly unanimous in their belief that even small, chance mutations can trigger a chain reaction with cascading consequences, possibly even the creation of new species, in relatively few generations. Economic ravages, natural disasters, genocidal pogroms, and geographic isolation caused by mountains, oceans, and deserts have deepened these differences.

As a result of evolution, every population group has some unique physical and physiological characteristics, many of which have a genetic basis (Cartmill, 1988; Chakraborty et al., 1993). Most of today's genetic research focuses on finding cures for diseases, more than 3,000 of which are genetically based (Overfield, 1995). For instance, blacks are predisposed to carry genes for sickle cell anemia and susceptibility to colorectal cancer (Weber, 1999). Beta-thalassemia is most prevalent in Mediterranean populations. A form of diabetes has been linked to a gene most commonly found among North American Indians.

So why do we so readily accept that evolution has turned out Ashkenazi Jews with a genetic predisposition to Tay-Sachs, or blonde haired and blue-eyed Scandinavians, yet find it racist to suggest that blacks of West African ancestry have evolved into the world's best sprinters and jumpers?

In fact, highly heritable characteristics such as skeletal structure, the distribution of muscle fiber types, reflex capabilities, lung capacity, and the ability to use energy more efficiently are not evenly distributed across racial groups and cannot be explained by known environment factors (Entine, 2000; Samson and Yerlès, 1988). Consider diving, gymnastics, and ice-skating, sports in which East Asians excel. Asians tend to be small with relatively short extremities, long torsos, and a thicker layer of fat. "Chinese splits," a rare maneuver demanding extraordinary flexibility, has roots in this anthropometric reality (Carter, 1982; Eveleth and Tanner, 1990; Martin and Saller, 1959; Himes, 1988; Behnke, 1974; Hirata and Kaku, 1968; Hirata, 1979).

Eurasian whites are the premier wrestlers and weight lifters in the world. Evolutionary forces have shaped a population with large, muscular upper bodies with relatively short arms and legs and thick torsos. These proportions tend to be an advantage in sports in which strength rather than speed is at a premium. This region also turns out an extraordinary number of top field athletes—javelin throwers, shot-putters, and hammer throwers.

Athletes who trace their ancestry to western African coastal states, including British, Caribbean and American blacks, are the quickest and best leapers in the world. Consequently, they almost completely monopolize the sprints up to 400 meters. No white, Asian, or East African runners have broken 10 seconds in the 100m. The top two hundred times in the 100m—all under 10 seconds—are held by athletes of West African descent. All 32 finalists in the last four Olympic men's 100-meter races were West African. The likelihood of that happening based on population numbers alone is 0.0000000000000000000000000000000001. Yet there are no—not one—premier middle or long distance runners from this region in Africa.

Studies have shown that athletes of West African origin hit a biomechanical wall after about 45 seconds of intense, anaerobic activity, when aerobic skills come into play. East Africans, who have small and slender ectomorphic body types and are therefore hapless in the sprints, dominate distance running (Ama et al., 1990; Saltin, 1973; Levesque, 1995; Simoneau, 1991; Levesque, 1994).

Whereas the West African population evolved in the lowlands and remained relatively isolated, East African runners trace their ancestry to the highlands. This region in Africa is also a genetic stew, with studies indicating a mixture of genes from invading Arabs and Middle Easterners.

Kenya, with 28 million people, is the athletic powerhouse. At the Seoul Olympics in 1988, Kenyan men won the 800, 1,500, and 5,000 meters, along with the 3,000-meter steeplechase. Based on population percentages alone, the likelihood of such a performance is one in 1.6 billion. The Kalenjin people of the Great Rift Valley adjacent to Lake Victoria—who represent 1/2000th of the world population—win

40% of top international distance running honors and three times as many distance medals as athletes from any other nation in the world. One tiny district, the Nandi, with only 500,000 people, swept an unfathomable 20% of major international distance events. By almost any measure, the Nandi region is the greatest concentration of raw athletic talent in the history of sports. It's a potent example of the interacting bio-cultural forces that shape great athletes.

By this time, the draft of *Taboo* was taking shape. I sent it off to Macmillan and waited. And waited. Eight months passed without a word before I received the brush-off in a brusque letter. "Much of the manuscript is smoothly and elegantly written, and most of it is quite enjoyable to read," wrote Chapman. "[But] while I admire the goals of the book, I must regretfully inform you that [it] lacks sufficient persuasiveness . . . to avoid being torn apart by critics, reviewers, and readers."

Years of work were suddenly in mortal danger. My agent embarked on a full court press to find a new publisher, but to no avail. As before, most everyone treated the proposal (and now an early manuscript) as a skunk on the loose. Basic Books, a first-rate independent publisher affiliated with HarperCollins, appeared ready to publish *Taboo* until an African American consultant nixed the book, without reading it, as "potentially racist." One female editor lectured my agent about how insensitive he was even to propose such an idea. Would she please read the book? he responded. "I don't have time for such trash," she retorted.

Such intense personal reaction was all the more dispiriting given the lengths to which I had gone to include, in a non-polemical way, many diverse historical and ideological perspectives. To a man and woman, the board and reviewers were on record that they respected *Taboo* as fair and constructive, with racial healing as one of its messages.

"You will be accused of spouting old fashioned racism for even raising the issue of African American superiority in athletics," wrote Earl Smith, chairman of the department of sociology and ethnic studies at Wake Forest University, a leading black scholar and author of several books on race and sports, and one of my board members. "All this beating around the bush has to stop. This is a good book. I am quite excited with the arguments that are raised."

But Dr. Smith's endorsement, along with reviews and letters of support from the president of the Human Biology Association, the current editor of the *Journal of Human Biology*, a US Olympic Committee scientist, prominent African American anthropologists, and top athletes couldn't crack the political status quo. As I was learning, when it comes to race, "the cortex shuts down." No one would even read the manuscript and give *Taboo* a chance.

Public Affairs, another independent publisher with authors such as international financier George Soros, former Secretary of Defense during the Vietnam war Robert McNamara, and *60-Minutes* commentator Andy Rooney, broke the log jam when an editor read it, loved it, and assumed the rights.

Yet even with a respected publisher behind *Taboo*, the hysteria continues in some quarters. In early January, just before the book was released, *The New York Times Magazine* informed me that it was killing plans to publish an adaptation, calling the book's thesis potentially "dangerous." "Our reluctant decision to drop the project is no reflection of my regard for your work, which remains high," wrote Kyle Crichton, an editor who had championed the article. "In brief, the whole subject worries my editor. . . ."

Taboo is now finally in the hands of the public. Will it be as skittish about the contents as the publishing industry? Apparently not. As of the day I write this, *Taboo* has so far received almost unanimous if sometimes guarded praise in more than three dozen reviews. Most have been raves. The only negative comments have come from those journalists who consider themselves "liberals." For instance, writing in the *Chicago Sun-Times*, columnist Rick Telander, apparently attempting to inject some "balance" into a review that generally praised the book, wrote: "Reviews of *Taboo* have been as uptight as anything, with reviewers figuratively holding the book the way an exterminator might hold a spraying skunk."

To buttress this incendiary conclusion, Telander writes: "'Some Things Are Better Left Unsaid,' is how *USA Today* titled its review." Minor problem: The title of the article was 180 degrees the opposite: "Some Things Not Better Left Unsaid." In fact, *USA Today* columnist Christine Brennan praised the book, writing "the dialogue that [Entine] almost certainly will provoke is not the problem. It's the solution."

Telander's second citation is from a *New York Times* column by Robert Lipsyte. "Entine's research is 'simultaneously silly and dangerous,'" quoted Telander. Oops. Lipsyte wasn't referring to me or my book, but to the issue: "Sports race science can be viewed as silly and dangerous" is the real quote. The *Times* actually praised *Taboo* as "consistently interesting, readable, provocative"—hardly a skunk like renunciation.

Telander's third example—he quoted a *Washington Post* reviewer that *Taboo* "underplays the political and cultural land mines underlying the discussion"—is equally misleading. Paul Ruffins, a former editor of the NAACP's *Crisis* magazine, actually admired the book. "Because it bravely tackles the exhaustive list of ideas that must be considered in any open-minded discussion of this topic, *Taboo* could well be the most intellectually demanding sports book ever written," Ruffins wrote. "*Taboo* is an informed exploration of a fascinating phenomenon. Entine marshals such an impressive array of evidence that we should no longer be content to explain why blacks excel at certain sports by simply resort-

ing to the old cultural argument that athletics have been the only avenues of upward mobility that were truly open to them. He's raised the argument to new heights."

A number of reviewers (every one white and supposedly liberal) apparently felt uncomfortable about being seen as praising a book that suggested that humans are indeed as diverse—culturally and biologically—as multi-culturalists claim. These white writers assumed, incorrectly it turns out, that *Taboo* would provoke widespread anger among blacks.

Claiming that *Taboo* has provoked "racial ire," Stan Hochman, an otherwise thoughtful columnist with the *Philadelphia Daily News*, wrote that "People of many hues say his science is flimsy, his conclusions are racist." He cited Harry Edwards who, he wrote, claimed that "Entine's scientific data is an underhanded way of saying that blacks were 'closer to beast . . . than they are to the rest of humanity.'" These were incendiary claims and grossly inaccurate in regard to both scientists and African Americans.

"*Taboo* is carefully researched and intellectually honest," wrote Jay T. Kearney of the U.S. Olympic Sport Science Committee. Michael Crawford, professor of genetics, former editor of the *Journal of Human Biology* and current president of the Human Biology Association, wrote that "*Taboo* provides a wonderful opportunity to share a message of the importance of human biological and cultural diversity in its myriad forms. Any dialogue between different racial groups should start with the facts."

What about that slashing quote from Edwards? The quote is actually lifted from *Taboo* itself. It is directed not against the book, which had not yet been written, but the misuse of science in the service of racism—the nefarious history that *Taboo* exposes. In fact, Edwards has publicly called my research "enlightening" and had offered to blurb the book.

What has been the reaction from others in

the black community? Intriguingly, the most effusive comments have come from African Americans. Earl Smith ended up writing the introduction. The *Journal of the African American Male* is carrying two chapters in future issues; its editor, Gary Sailes, wrote a blurb for the book in which he calls *Taboo* "Compelling, bold, comprehensive, informative, and enlightening." The black magazine *Emerge*, in its March issue, called the book "thoughtful, thorough, and sensitive.... *Taboo* is a good read for anyone interested in the history of black athletes in the United States and world-wide."

"*Taboo* is both provocative and informed," wrote John C. Walter, professor of history in the American Ethnic Studies Department at the University of Washington, in a review in the *Seattle Times*. "Entine has provided a well-intentioned effort for all to come clean on the possibility that black people might just be superior physically, and that there is no negative connection between that physical superiority and their IQs."

What are we to make of this phenomenon in which some whites, so quick to crow about their own racial sensitivity, recklessly inject racial divisiveness into a debate in which most African Americans see thoughtfulness? It's apparent that many blacks have become irritated to the point of anger by the patronizing censorship and condescension of many journalists and academics. To date no one has yet criticized *Taboo* for racial insensitivity or shoddy science. "I am an editorial columnist," wrote Bill Maxwell of the *St. Petersburg Times* in a personal note to me after his glowing column on *Taboo*. "I reviewed your book because I enjoyed reading it. It cut through all of the bullshit. I am black."

Although the African biological edge is not great, at the level of an elite athlete, even a small advantage can be the difference between a gold medal and finishing out of the money. On-the-field trends create a cultural advantage that forms a biosocial feedback loop, with nature and nurture fueling each other. Nevertheless, it is critical to remember that no individual athlete can succeed without the 'X-factor,' the lucky spin of the roulette wheel of genetics matched with considerable dedication and sport smarts. "It's the brain, not the heart or lungs, that is the critical organ," Sir Roger Bannister told me. "But one would have to be blind not to see a pattern here. I hope we are not at a time and place where we are afraid to talk about remarkable events. I hope not."

Popular thought is now beginning to catch up with scientific knowledge. The genetics revolution has decisively overturned the dated belief that all humans are created with equal potential, a tabula rasa, or blank slate, for experience and culture to write upon. Acknowledging human biodiversity may approach a danger zone, but pretending that there are no slippery questions does not prevent them from being asked, if only under one's breath.

Taboo is not so much a sports book as it is a thought-provoking look at what defines us as human. It debunks facile theories of race that have been used for hundreds of years to justify racism and even genocide. Most important, it shatters stereotypes that blacks or whites or any racial group are innately "superior" or "inferior." This is a book about the rich diversity of life, free of the myths of "ranking" that have plagued Western thought for centuries. That's the message of *Taboo*; for the most part, it is being heard.

"Entine understands the reasons Blacks lash out against the determination theory, knows that whatever White America gives to Black athletes in terms of athletic superiority, it takes from their mental abilities," wrote Carolyn White of *Emerge* magazine. "Great athletes, dumb jocks. And the stereotype, suggests Entine, is probably the single most important reason people have problems debating the issue."

Although it should never be far from anyone's mind that white fascination with black physicality has long framed this issue, it's more than clear that the stereotype that blacks make better athletes than whites is neither wrong nor racist. Censorship and the invocation of a taboo on issues of human diversity, biological and cultural, are not viable options.

"In human biology and clinical studies, as well as in epidemiological research, it is important to understand if age, gender, race, and other population characteristics contribute to the phenotype variation," wrote Claude Bouchard, Laval University geneticist, obesity expert and exercise physiologist, in a recent article in the *American Journal of Human Biology*. "Only by confronting these enormous public health issues head-on, and not by circumventing them in the guise of political correctness, do we stand a chance to evaluate the discriminating agendas and devise appropriate interventions. To disregard monumental public health issues is to be morally bankrupt" (Bouchard, 1988).

"Since the word *race* causes such discomfort, *ethnic groups* is often substituted, but it is inappropriate," adds Theresa Overfield, University of Utah professor of anthropology and expert on the biology of health and illness. "Race is a characteristic used most effectively to describe, rather than explain, health difference. . . . Ignoring the differences between humans is at least shortsighted and can be medically harmful" (Overfield, 1995).

Human beings are different. Limiting the rhetorical use of folk categories such as race, an admirable goal, is not going to make the patterned biological variation on which they are based disappear. The question is no longer whether these inquiries will continue but in what manner and to what end. Science is a skeptical endeavor. It is a method of interrogating reality, a cumulative process of testing new and more refined explanations, not an assertion of dry, unalterable facts. It is a way of asking questions, not of imposing answers. The challenge is in whether we can conduct the debate so that human diversity might be cause

for celebration of our individuality rather than serving as fodder for demagogues.

References:

Ama, Pierre F. M. et al. "Anaerobic Performances in Black and White Subjects," *Medicine and Science in Sports and Exercise* 22, 4 (1990), 508–511.

Behnke, Albert R. *Evaluation and Regulation of Body Build and Composition* (Englewood Cliffs, N.J.: Prentice Hall: 1974), 359–386.

Bouchard, C. A., S. Leon, D. C. Rao, J. S. Skinner, and J. H. Wilmore. "Response," *American Journal of Human Biology* 10, 3 (1998), 279–280.

Carter, E. L. (ed.). *Physical Structure of Olympic Athletes, Part I: The Montreal Olympic Games Anthropological Project* (Basel, Switzerland: S. Karger, 1982).

Cartmill, Matt. "The Status of the Race Concept in Physical Anthropology," *American Anthropologist* 100 (September 1988), 651–660.

Chakraborty, Ranajit, Ranjan Deka, and Robert Ferrell, "Letter to the Editor: Reply to Baer," *American Journal of Human Genetics* 53 (1993), 531.

Entine, Jon. *Taboo: Why Black Athletes Dominate Sports and Why We Are Afraid to Talk about It* (New York: Public Affairs, 2000), 246–271.

Eveleth, P. B. and J. M. Tanner. *Worldwide Variation in Human Growth*, second edition (Cambridge: Cambridge University, 1990).

Himes, John H. "Racial Variation in Physique and Body Composition," *Canadian Journal of Sports Science* 13 (1988), 117–126.

Hirata, K. I. *Selection of Olympic Champions, Vols. I and II* (Toyota, Japan: Chukyo University, 1979).

Hirata, K. I. and K. Kaku. *The Evaluating Method of Physique and Physical Fitness and Its Practical Application* (Gifu City, Japan: Hirata Institute of Health, 1968).

Levesque, M., M. R. Boulay, J. A. Simoneau. "Muscle Fiber Type Characteristics in Black African and White Males before and after 12 Weeks of Sprint Training," *Canadian Journal of Applied Physiology* 19 (1994), Supplement 25P.

Levesque, Martin, M. R. Boulay, G. Thériault, C. Bouchard, J. A. Simoneau. "Training-Induced Changes in Maximal Exercise of Short Duration and Skeletal Muscle Characteristics of Black

African and Caucasian Men," unpublished manuscript, 1995.

Martin, R. and K. Saller. *Lehrbuch der Anthropologie II* (Stuttgart: Fischer, 1959).

Overfield, Theresa. *Biologic Variation in Health and Illness*, second ed. (Boca Raton, Fla.: CRC, 1995), 1–2.

Saltin, Bengt. "Metabolic Fundamentals in Exercise," *Medicine and Science and Sports* 5, 3 (1973), 137–146.

Samson, Jacques and Magdeleine Yerlès. "Racial Differences in Sports Performance," *Canadian Journal of Sports Science* 13 (1988), 110–111.

Simoneau, J. A., C. K. Allah, M. Giroux, M. R. Boulay, P. Lagassé, G. Thériault, C. Bouchard. "Metabolic Plasticity of Skeletal Muscle in Black and White Males Subjected to High-Intensity Intermittent Training," *Medical Science Sports and Exercise* 23 (1991), S149.

Weber, Thomas K. et al. "Novel hMLH1 and hMSH2 Germline Mutations in African Americans with Colorectal Cancer," *Journal of the American Medical Association* 281 (June 23/30, 1999).

Race and Sports as Pseudoscience

MICHAEL SHERMER

In "An Essay on Man," the 19th century English poet and essayist Alexander Pope elucidated the pitfalls of speculating on ultimate causes derived from immediate events:

> *In vain the sage, with retrospective eye,*
> *Would from th' apparent what*
> *   conclude the why,*
> *Infer the motive from the deed, and show*
> *That what we chanced was what we meant*
> *   to do.*

Pope's wise words were in the back of my mind as I began writing this essay on March 5, 2000, a miserably cold and rainy Sunday morning, as I watched the elite runners in the Los Angeles Marathon—just a handful among the 23,000 weekend warriors who braved the elements—cross the finish line. Although I have run the L.A. Marathon, and even once completed a marathon after first swimming 2.4 miles in the open ocean and riding a bike 112 miles in the Hawaiian Ironman triathlon, I would not have given the results a second glance were it not for a book I had just read that called my attention to a characteristic shared by the top five finishers. They were: (1) Benson Mutisya Mbithi, 2:11:55, (2) Mark Yatich, 2:16:43, (3) Peter Ndirangu Nairobi,

2:17:42, (4) Simon Bor, 2:20:12, and (5) Christopher Cheboiboch, 2:20:41.

It was not the times of the top five finishers that stood out in this year's race, since they were well below both world and course records (understandable considering the conditions). What was startling was their country of origin. All were from Kenya. Coincidence? Hardly. Meaningful? To some, yes; to others, no; to science, maybe. That is the subject of the book I had just read, Jon Entine's controversial *Taboo: Why Blacks Dominate Sports and Why We're Afraid to Talk about It.*

I will not dissemble and pretend that I was not aware of the controversy surrounding claims that blacks are better athletes than whites due to heredity and being closer to the origin of humanity in Africa. I've been an athlete and sports fan all my life and recall the vitriolic reaction to Jimmy "the Greek" Snyder's 1988 off-the-cuff remarks at a restaurant about black slaves being bred for superior physicality (on Martin Luther King Day, no less, with a camera crew present): "The black is a better athlete because he's been bred to be that way. During slave trading, the slave owner would breed his big woman so that he would have a big black kid, see. That's where it all started." Blacks, Snyder explained, could "jump higher and run faster" because of their "high thighs and big size."

I even saw live the now-infamous 1987 ABC *Nightline* show (occasioned by a celebration of Jackie Robinson's shattering of the color barrier in baseball) when Ted Koppel asked Los Angeles Dodger baseball executive Al Campanis why there were no blacks in upper management. Campanis said that blacks "may not have some of the necessities" for such positions. "Do you really believe that?" Koppel rejoined. "Well, I don't say all of them," Campanis demurred, "but they certainly are short in some areas. How many quarterbacks do you have, how many pitchers do you have that are black?" After continuing with his folk lesson in sports physiology, Campanis noted why blacks do not compete in elite swimming: "because they don't have buoyancy." Whites are floaters, blacks are sinkers.

Campanis's attempts to explain himself opened the gates into the largely unspoken but pervasive attitudes held by many whites about blacks, even whites who would not consider themselves racist. "I have never said that blacks aren't intelligent, but they may not have the desire to be in the front office," Campanis continued. "I know that they have wanted to manage, and many of them have managed. But they are outstanding athletes, very God-gifted and they're very wonderful people. They are gifted with great musculature and various other things. They are fleet of foot, and this is why there are a number of black ballplayers in the major leagues." Blacks are fast around the bases, slow around the boardroom.

As University of Texas Professor John Hoberman explained in his 1998 book *Darwin's Athletes*, even many blacks embrace part of the thesis (to their cultural detriment, he believes). Dallas Cowboys all-star player Calvin Hill, a Yale graduate, opined: "On the plantation, a strong black man was mated with a strong black woman. [Blacks] were simply bred for physical qualities." San Francisco '49ers wide receiver Bernie Casey explained: "Think of what the African slaves were forced to endure in this country merely to survive. Black athletes are their descendants." Even the liberal champion of cultural determinism, Jesse Jackson, in a 1977 CBS *60 Minutes* segment on his P.U.S.H. program for black school kids, made a case for heredity over environment when he stated (in response to sociologists' environmental explanations for blacks' poorer school performances) that "If we [blacks] can run faster, jump higher, and shoot a basketball straighter [than whites] on those same inadequate diets . . ." then there is no excuse. It is time, Jackson argued, for blacks to start living up to their potentials in the classroom as well as the gym.

With such comments from both blacks and whites it is understandable why some blacks, such as the noted U.C. Berkeley sports sociologist Harry Edwards, respond so strongly, and usually wrongly, going to the opposite extreme of environmental determinism. On a March 8, 2000, radio show I hosted with Entine, Edwards, and Hoberman as guests, Edwards actually made the argument that the only reason blacks dominate NBA basketball, despite more than equal opportunity for whites to make it to the top, was that at this period of time the "black style" of basketball happens to be popular instead of the "white style" prominent in the 1950s, and that neither "style" was in any way superior. My co-host Larry Mantle and I, both enthusiastic L.A. Laker fans, gave each other a knowing glance of acknowledgement that this was, of course, utter nonsense.

Somewhere between Edwards's extreme environmental determinism and the Greek's radical biological determinism lies the truth about the cause and meaning of black-white differences in sports. But the Campanis episode was the most enlightening because these were not the remarks of a rabid bigot spewing racial epithets; rather, Campanis had spent decades in close proximity and in tight friendship with some of the greatest black ballplayers of the 20th century. So his comments were emblematic of the common attitudes shared by many, perhaps most, lay people and sports enthusiasts who know just enough to speculate in a social Darwinian mode about how and why blacks dominate in some fields but not others, and what these differences tell us about the human condition.

What do these differences mean? The answer depends on what it is you want to know. I shall address this subject neither to embrace the theory nor to debunk it; rather, the question itself raises a number of other questions and problems in this field of research that makes reaching grand and sweeping conclusions problematic at best.

From the Particular to the General: Do Black Athletes Dominate Sports?

If you are a basketball, football, or track-and-field fan, the black-white differences are obvious and real. You'd have to be blind not to see the gaping abyss any given day of the week on any one of the numerous 24-hour a day sports channels. Further, there are quantifiable within-race differences in some of these sports. Kenyans dominate marathon running, but you'll likely never see one line up for the 100-meter dash. On the other hand, blacks whose origins can be traced to West Africa own the 100-meter dash but will not likely soon be taking home the $35,000 automobile awarded to the L.A. Marathon winner. And it could be a long while before we see a white man on the winner's platform at either distance. As Entine carefully documents, at the moment "every men's world record at every commonly run track distance belongs to a runner of African descent," and the domination of particular distances are determined, it would seem, by the ancestral origin of the athlete, with West

Africans reigning over distances from 100 meters to 400 meters, and East and North Africans prevailing in races from 800 meters to the marathon.

But my first quibble with the debate is how quickly it shifts from Kenyans winning marathons or West Africans monopolizing the 100-meter dash to, as stated in Entine's subtitle, "why black athletes dominate sports." I understand a publisher's desire to economize cover verbiage and maximize marketability (the actual text of *Taboo* is, appropriately, filled with qualifiers, caveats, and nuances), but the simple fact is that black athletes do not dominate sports. They do not dominate speed skating, figure skating, ice hockey, gymnastics, swimming, diving, archery, downhill skiing, cross-country skiing, biathlons, triathlons, ping pong, tennis, golf, wrestling, rugby, rowing, canoeing, fencing, strong-man competitions, auto racing, motorcycle racing, and on and on.

In my own sport of cycling, in which I competed at elite ultra-marathon distances (200 miles to 3,000 miles) for 10 years, there are almost no blacks to be found in the pack. Where are all those West African sprinters at velodrome track races? Where are all those Kenyans in long-distance road races or ultra-marathon events? They are almost nowhere to be found. In fact, in over a century of professional bicycle racing there has been only one undisputed black champion—Marshall W. "Major" Taylor. And Taylor's reign was a century ago! He started racing in 1896 and within three years he became only the second black athlete to win a world championship in any sport, and this was at a time when bicycle racing was as big as baseball and boxing. Since there were few automobiles and no airplanes, cyclists were the fastest humans on earth and were rewarded accordingly with lucrative winnings and more than 15 minutes of fame. Major Taylor was the first black athlete in any sport to be a member of an integrated team, the first to land a commercial sponsor, and the first to hold world records, including the prestigious mile record. He competed internationally and is still revered in France as one of the greatest sprint cyclists of all time. The fact that outside cycling circles he is completely unknown in America tells us something about the influence of culture on sports.

By the theory proffered by Entine and others, there is no reason blacks should not be prominent in cycling since the physical requirements are so similar to running. The reason they are not, in fact, is almost certainly cultural. Although there are no longer racial barriers (as witnessed by the wide range of colors and nationalities that fill out the pelotons throughout Europe and the Americas), the reason blacks are not in cycling is obvious, says Dr. Ed Burke, a sports physiologist at the University of Colorado in Boulder: "No money, no publicity, no grass roots program. Why would gifted American athletes, with so many lucrative opportunities in other sports, choose cycling?" In Europe working class fathers introduce their sons to the sport at an early age where they can be nursed through junior cycling programs until they turn professional and permanently bootstrap themselves into the middle classes. But there are not that many blacks in Europe, and in America no such social structure exists. Bottom line: in cycling culture trumps biology.

(After Major Taylor, many cite the black sprinter Nelson Vails, since he took the silver medal on the track in the 1984 Olympics. But this is problematic because the East Germans boycotted that Olympics, and they were dominating the sport in those years, having thoroughly trounced both Vails and the 1984 gold medalist, Mark Gorski, in the world championships the year before. After Vails, Scott Berryman was a national sprint champion, and 19-year old Gideon Massie recently won the Jr. Worlds on the track and is an Olympic hopeful for 2004. The few other isolated cases—Shaums March in downhill mountain biking and Josh Weir on the road—only further call our attention to the dearth of blacks in cycling.)

Would blacks dominate cycling ceteris paribus? The problem is that all other things are never equal so it is impossible to say until the natural experiment is actually run. There is no reason why they should not, by the arguments put forth by Entine, since track cycling is much like sprinting, and road cycling is similar to marathon running in terms of the physical demands on the athlete. But we simply do not know and thus it would be unwise to speculate. For that matter, the ceteris paribus assumption never holds true in the messy real world, so this whole question of race and sports is fraught with complications, making it exceptionally difficult to say with much confidence what these differences really mean.

The Hindsight Bias: Did Evolution Shape Black Bodies Best for Running?

Tiger Woods may very well be the greatest golfer of all time. Although he is not "pure" black, he is considered to be black by most people, especially the black community. Thus, he very well could inspire other blacks to go into the sport. What if this were to happen on such a scale that blacks came to dominate golf as they have football and basketball? Would the explanation for this dominance be role modeling coupled to cultural momentum, or would we hear about how blacks are naturally gifted as golfers because of their superior ability to swing a club and judge moving objects at a distance due to the fact that they are closer to the Environment of Evolutionary Adaptation (or EEA, as evolutionary psychologists call the Pleistocene period of human evolution)?

In cognitive psychology there is a fallacy of thought known as the hindsight bias, which states that however things turn out we tend to look back to justify that particular arrangement with a set of causal explanatory variables presumably applicable to all situations. Looking back it is easy to construct plausible scenarios for how matters turned out; rearrange the outcome and we are equally skilled at finding new reasons why that particular arrangement was also inevitable.

Consider professional basketball. At the moment blacks dominate the sport and it is tempting to slip into the adaptationist mode of Darwinian speculation and suggest that the reason is because blacks are naturally superior at running, jumping, twisting, turning, hang time, and all the rest that goes into the modern game. Then it is only a step removed from suggesting, as does Entine and others do, that the reason for their above average natural abilities is that since humans evolved in Africa where they became bipedal, populations that migrated to other areas of the globe traded off those pure abilities through adaptations to other environments—e.g., colder climates led to shorter, stockier torsos (Bergmann's Rule) and smaller arms and legs (Allen's Rule)—thereby compromising the ability to run and jump. African blacks, however, are closer to the EEA and thus their abilities are evolutionarily less modified.

For basketball, however, I would point out the remarkable range of skin tone one sees on the court. Are these black players all equally "black" in this racial sense? I grant that races may exist as fuzzy sets where the boundaries are blurred but the interiors represent a type we might at least provisionally agree represents a group we can label "black" or "white." But when I see a range of "black" skintone on the court—from Manute Bol's dark chocolate to Dennis Johnson's sandy beige—I cannot help but question the validity of allowing a single category to represent so many shades. The fuzzy boundaries of the "black" set are so wide and the overlap with the "white" set so great that it seems scientifically untenable to

draw the same conclusions about basketball that are made for track and field.

I also find it interesting that individuals with a small percentage of "black" genes are always classified in the "black" set, whereas whites are not accorded an equally broad latitude. In other words, if we were to graph the range of skin tones in so-called blacks and whites as two bell curves, the overall width of the black curve would be much greater, and the standard deviation for the black curve would be considerably greater than it would be for the whites. Why is this? The answer is clearly cultural, I suspect, having to do with the eugenics notion of a "pure" white race being contaminated with the blood of other, lesser races. A fuzzy-logic solution to this problem is to have just one set with fractional numbers assigned. For example, just as we might label the early morning sky as .3 blue/.7 orange, the midday sky as .9 blue/.1 orange, and the sunset sky as .2 blue/.8 orange, we could label Manute Bol as .9 black/.1 white and Dennis Johnson as .2 black/.8 white. Better still, we could just not label people by skin color at all.

Finally, the step from racial group differences on a basketball court to racial evolutionary differences in the Paleolithic is a significant one, and it is here where the hindsight bias is especially obvious. Let's go back in time and see how—not to the Paleolithic, but just to the earlier part of the 20th century. It may come as a surprise, especially to younger readers, to hear that at one time Jews dominated basketball. What sorts of arguments were made for their "natural" abilities in this sport? In the 1920s, 1930s, and 1940s basketball was an east coast, inner-city, blue-collar immigrant game largely dominated by the oppressed ethnic group of that age, the Jews. Like blacks decades later, the Jews went into professions and sports open to them. As Entine so wonderfully tracks this history in *Taboo*, according to Harry Sitwack, star player of the South Philadelphia Hebrew Association (SPHA),

"The Jews never got much into football or baseball. They were too crowded [with other players] then. Every Jewish boy was playing basketball. Every phone pole had a peach basket on it. And every one of those Jewish kids dreamed of playing for the SPHA's."

The reason why is obvious, right? Cultural trends and socio-economic opportunities set within an autocatalytic feedback loop (where variables operate on each other to drive the system forward) led more and more Jews to go into the game until they came to dominate it. That is not what the scientific experts of the day said. As Entine shows, according to the wisdom of the time the Jews were just naturally superior basketball players.

Writers opined that Jews were genetically and culturally built to stand up under the strain and stamina of the hoop game. It was suggested that they had an advantage because short men have better balance and more foot speed. They were also thought to have sharper eyes, which of course cut against the other stereotype that they suffered from myopia and had to wear glasses. And it was said they were clever. "The reason, I suspect, that basketball appeals to the hebrew with his Oriental background," wrote Paul Gallico, sports editor of the *New York Daily News* and one of the premier sports writers of the 1930s, "is that the game places a premium on an alert, scheming mind, flashy trickiness, artful dodging and general smart aleckness."

By the late 1940s Jews moved into other professions and sports and, Entine notes, "the torch of urban athleticism was passed on to the newest immigrants, mostly blacks who had migrated north from dying southern plantations. . . . It would not be long before the stereotype of the 'scheming . . . trickiness' of the Jews was replaced by that of the 'natural athleticism' of Negroes." If Jews were dominating basketball today instead of blacks, what explanatory models, in hindsight, would we be constructing? If, in 30 years, Asians come to control the game would we offer some equally plausible "natural" reason for their governance?

Does this mean that blacks are not really better than whites in basketball? No. I would be shocked if it turned out that what we are witnessing is nothing more than a culturally dominant "black style" of play. But because of the hindsight bias I cannot be certain that we are not being fooled and that the reasons for the differences we witness today are far more complex than we understand.

The Confirmation Bias: Why Asians Dominate Ping Pong and Why No One Cares—Sports in Black and White

Why, it seems reasonable to ask, are we so interested in black-white differences in sports? Why not Asian-Caucasian differences? Why has no one written a book entitled *Why Asians Dominate Ping Pong and Why We're Afraid to Talk about It?* The reason is obvious: because no one cares that Asians are the masters at ping pong. This is America, and what Americans care about are black-white differences, especially within high visibility activities. By way of analogy, no first-century Egyptian would have wondered if Cleopatra was black, but 20th-century Americans have debated that very question.

The confirmation bias holds that we have a tendency to seek confirmatory data that support our already-held beliefs, and ignore disconfirmatory evidence that might counter those beliefs. We all do this. Liberals read the paper and see greedy Republicans trying to rig the system so that the rich can become richer. Conservatives read the same paper and see bleeding-heart liberals robbing the rich of their hard-earned dollars to support welfare queens on crack. Context is everything and the confirmation bias makes it very difficult for any of us to take an objective perspective on our own beliefs.

Yes, there are black-white difference in sports, and there may even be good physical reasons for some of these differences. But, as noted above, the vast majority of sports are not dominated by blacks. Why don't we hear about them? Because they don't interest us, or they do not support our preconceived notions about the importance of black-white race questions. Out of the literally hundreds of popular sports played in the world today, blacks dominate only three: basketball, football, and track-and-field. That's it. That's what all the fuss is about. (At 15 percent they don't even dominate baseball.) Why do we focus on those three? Because we live in America where the black-white issue has bedeviled our experiment in democracy from the beginning, and where basketball, football, and track and field are the big sports which pay the big bucks.

I am not arguing that it is scientifically untenable or morally corrupt to focus on these differences, but I am curious why those particular differences are of such interest to some people. Is it nothing more than some people like chocolate pudding and others tapioca? I doubt it. I suspect the confirmation bias directs our attention to differences most likely to support already held beliefs about race differences. This would explain why it is almost always the same people, regardless of the particular trait or characteristic under study, who are interested in looking at racial group differences, and why Americans are interested in black-white differences but not others, and why non-Americans have little or no interest in this difference question.

Let's consider another case of evolutionary adaptation for the ability to run, and of within-species differences in this ability—thoroughbred race horses. Here we find rather disconfirming evidence that the underlying genetic variability of thoroughbreds long ago ran out despite the vigilant efforts of highly motivated

horse breeders with millions of dollars at stake for a horse who could knock off a second or two.

The Kentucky Derby is the most prestigious of all thoroughbred races and has been run since 1875 when, by the way, 13 of the 15 jockeys were blacks. In fact, black jockeys dominated the Derby for the first 30 years, winning half of all races. The first race was 1.5 miles and was won in 2:37. In 1896 the distance was lowered to its present length of 1.25 miles and was won by Ben Brush in a time of 2:07. As evident in the table below (given in five-year increments with variation mostly accounted for by track surfaces being either "fast" or "slow"), since 1950 the horses are just not getting any faster.

1900	Lt. Gibson	2:06
1905	Agile	2:10
1910	Donau	2:06
1915	Regret	2:05
1920	Paul Jones	2:09
1925	Flying Ebony	2:07
1930	Gallant Fox	2:07
1935	Omaha	2:07
1940	Gallahadion	2:05
1945	Hoop Jr.	2:07
1950	Middle Ground	2:01
1955	Swaps	2:01
1960	Ventian Way	2:02
1965	Lucky Debonair	2:01
1970	Dust Commander	2:03
1975	Foolish Pleasure	2:02
1980	Genuine Risk	2:02
1985	Spend a Buck	2:00
1990	Unbridled	2:02
1995	Thunder Gulch	2:02

The greatest thoroughbred race horse of all time, Secretariat, is the only horse to break the two minute barrier at 1:59.2. If million dollar purses and stud fees have not been able to break the bounds of genetic variability, one wonders just how much genetic variability there is or just how much hypothesized adaptations like changes in body build in response to climate change could be achieved.

Blood or Sweat?
The Nature-Nurture Debate in Sports

In the middle of the 1985 3,000-mile nonstop transcontinental bicycle Race Across America I was pedaling my way across Arkansas when the ABC *Wide World of Sports* camera crew pulled up alongside to inquire how I felt about my third place position—way ahead of the main pack but too far behind to catch the leaders. I answered: "I should have picked better parents."

The quote comes from the renowned sports physiologist Per-olof Astrand and was made at a 1967 exercise symposium: "I am convinced that anyone interested in winning Olympic gold medals must select his or her parents very carefully." At the time I regretted repeating it because I meant no disrespect for my always-supportive parents. But it was an accurate self-assessment for I had done everything I could do to win the race, including training over 500 miles a week in the months before, observing a strict diet, employing weight training, utilizing massage therapists and trainers, and more. My body fat was 4.5 percent, and at age 31 I was as strong and fast as I had ever been or would be. Nevertheless it was apparent I was not going to win the race. Why? Because despite maximizing my environmental nurture, the upper ceiling of my physical nature had been reached and was still below that of the two riders ahead of me.

This vignette is symbolic of the larger discussion in sports physiology on the relative roles of heredity and environment. In 1971, the exercise physiologist V. Klissouras, for example, reported that 81–86 percent of the variance in aerobic capacity, as measured by VO^2 uptake, is accounted for by genetics. In 1973 he confirmed his findings in another study that showed that only 20–30 percent of the variance in aerobic capacity can be accounted for by the environment—i.e., training can only improve aerobic capacity by that amount.

Randy Ice, the sports physiologist who has been testing Race Across America cyclists for the past 18 years, estimates that 60–70 percent of the variability between cyclists in aerobic capacity is genetically determined. Others estimate similar percentages for anaerobic threshold, workload capacity, fast twitch/slow twitch muscle fiber ratio, maximum heart rate, and many other physiological parameters that determine athletic performance. In other words, the difference between Pee Wee Herman and Eddy Merckx (the greatest cyclist of all time) is largely due to heredity.

Now, let's be clear that no one—not Jon Entine on one end or, hopefully, Harry Edwards on the other—is arguing that athletic ability is determined entirely by either genetics or environment. Obviously it is a mixture of the two. The controversy arises over what the ratio is, the evidence for that ratio, and the possible evolutionary origins of the difference. What surprised me in reading Entine's book, and other arguments for evolutionary origins of biologically based racial group differences in athletic ability, was the dearth of hard evidence and the need to draw questionable inferences and make sizable leaps of logic.

Although Entine's book is promoted as if it were a polemic for the hereditary position, he confesses that even in his best case examples of the Kenyan marathon runners, we cannot say for certain if they are "great long distance runners because of a genetic advantage or because their high-altitude lifestyle serves as a lifelong training program." It's a chicken-and-egg dilemma, Entine admits: "Did the altitude reconfigure the lungs of Kenyan endurance runners or was a genetic predisposition induced by the altitude? Is that nature or nurture . . . or both?"

It is both. But proving a particular percentage of each is tricky business. "Most theories, including those in genetics, rely on circumstantial evidence tested against common sense, known science, and the course of history," Entine explains. "That scientists may yet not be able to identify the chromosomes that contribute to specific athletic skills does not mean that genes don't play a defining role. . . ." Clearly that is so. But the real debate is not if; it is how, and how much. It is here where the science is weak and our biases strong.

What do we really know, for example, about the genetic coding for running? On the one hand it can be argued that this is a very simple activity compared to, say, a complex gymnastics routine. Even so, running ability depends on a host of variables—fast twitch/slow twitch muscle fiber ratio, VO^2 uptake capacity, lung capacity, maximum heart rate, anaerobic threshold figures (that determine the level one can sustain work output), measures of strength versus endurance, etc. We can estimate that these variables are half or three-quarters determined by genes, but we haven't a clue as to how they are coded, or even how genes and environment interact in the development of the ability under question. Autocatalytic feedback loops are powerful mechanisms in physical, biological, and social systems, and we are discovering them in nature-nurture interactions as well. Some genes are turned on or turned off by environmental stimuli. It may be possible that some human populations with a genetically encoded ability to run fast never have these genes turned on by the proper environment, or during a critical period of development. And perhaps other groups, like the Kenyans, have both the genetic propensity plus the cultural drive, high-altitude training, and so forth. Further, we have no idea if different human groups code for such variables in different ways as they interact with their environment; thus their autocatalytic feedback loops may be different. We just do not know.

Finally, while we can agree that different human characteristics are coded by differing genomic complexes—from simple to complex— we do not know enough genetics to say with any confidence that, for example, the ability to run a 100-meter dash is coded by n genes, the ability to slam dunk in basketball is coded by 2n genes, and that the ability to negotiate a complex gymnastic routine is coded by 8n genes. And this is just for physical abilities. Cognitive skills are another subject entirely, and we have even less knowledge on, say, how spatial reasoning or verbal skills are genetically coded, or autocatalytically determined through gene-cultural co-development.

All of this makes conclusions drawn about racial differences in sports problematic. No doubt some black-white differences in some sports are heavily influenced by genetics and might possibly even have an evolutionary basis of origin. But proving that supposition is another matter entirely. As it is, to be fair, for the extreme environmental position. Harry Edwards, for example, argued on my radio show that Kenyans are tenacious trainers, rising at 5:00 A.M. every morning to run mountains at high altitude. But that's just the hindsight and confirmation biases at work again, where we examine the winner of a race to see what ingredients went into the winning formula. It ignores all the other hard-working jocks who also got up every morning at 5:00 A.M. (oh don't I remember it so painfully well?) but didn't take the gold. Or the other winners who slept in until 8:00 A.M. and went for a leisurely jog on the flats. Training alone won't get you to the finish line first. Neither will genetics. Neither will luck. To be a champion you need all three.

Master of My Fate

We are all products of an evolutionary history of biological descent. Paraphrasing Astrand, our parents have been very carefully chosen for us—by natural selection. Yet as philosopher Michael Ruse notes:

> We are what we are because of our biology in conjunction with the environment. Dogs are friendly; if you beat and starve them, they are vicious. Scotsmen are as tall as Englishmen; if you feed them simply on oats they are runts. As well-known, long-term study has shown . . . thanks to improved nutrition, the height and physique of the Scots has improved dramatically.

The philosopher Karl Schmitz-Moormann also explained that such statistical percentages as those used in describing the relative influence of heredity and environment are descriptive for large populations, not individuals. Even the most complete knowledge of a person will not allow us to predict the precise future of this individual, because the laws for making such predictions are built around populations. Schmitz-Moormann calls this thinking "conditionalism." He writes: "At all levels of the evolving universe statistics might be understood as the description of freely evolving elements within more or less narrowly defined ranges of possibilities created by past evolution. Instead of being determined, the universe appears only to be conditioned on all levels."

The key element here is the range of possibilities. Behavior geneticists call it the genetic reaction range, or the biological parameters within which environmental conditions may take effect. We all have a biological limit, for example, on how fast we can ride a 40k time trial or run a 10k. There is a range from lowest to highest that establishes the parameters of our performance. In the diagram on the left, athlete A has a higher genetic reaction range than athlete B. But there is overlap of the ranges, and this is the key to where such environmental factors as nutrition, training, coaching, and desire take effect. A may be more "gifted" than B, but this does not mean he will always or even ever beat B. If B performs at his best and A is only at 50 percent of his potential, then the genetic advantage is negated. Inheritability of talent does not mean inevitability of success, and vice versa.

Why do some black athletes dominate some sports? For the same reason that some white athletes dominate some other sports, and some Asian athletes dominate still other sports—a combination of biological factors and cultural influences. We do not know for sure how to tease apart these variables, but we've got some reasonably good indications and Entine's book is a good place to start, as is Hoberman's *Darwin's Athletes*. What do the differences really mean? My answer is a consilience of both positions: We are free to select the optimal environmental conditions that will allow us to rise to the height of our biological potentials.

In this sense athletic success is measured not just against others' performances, but against the upper ceiling of our own ability. To succeed is to have done one's absolute best as measured against the high mark of one's personal range of possibilities. To win is not just to have crossed the finish line first, but to cross the finish line in the fastest time possible within the allowable genetic reaction range. The poet William Ernest Henley expressed this concept well in his stirring Invictus:

> *Out of the night that covers me,*
> *Black as the pit from pole to pole,*
> *I thank whatever gods may be*
> *For my unconquerable soul.*
> *It matters not how strait the gate,*
> *How charged with punishments the scroll,*
> *I am the master of my fate:*
> *I am the captain of my soul.*

Science Is at an End

JOHN HORGAN

In 1989, Gustavus Adolphus College in Minnesota held a symposium with the provocative but misleading title "The End of Science?" The meeting's premise was that belief in science—rather than science itself—was coming to an end. As one organizer put it, "There is an increasing feeling that science as a unified, universal, objective endeavor is over" (in Selve, 1992). Most of the speakers were philosophers who had challenged the authority of science in one way or another. The meeting's great irony was that one scientist present, U.C. Berkeley biologist Gunther Stent, had for years promulgated a much more dramatic and persuasive scenario than the one posed by the organizers. Stent had asserted that science itself might be ending, and not because of the skepticism of a few academic sophists. Quite the contrary. Science might be ending because it worked so well.

Stent is hardly a fringe figure. He was a pioneer of molecular biology; he founded the first department dedicated to that field at Berkeley in the 1950s and performed experiments that helped to illuminate the machinery of genetic transmission. Later, after switching from genetics to the study of the brain, he was named chairman of the neurobiology department of the National Academy of Sciences. Stent is also the most astute analyst of the limits of science I have encountered (and by astute I mean of course that he articulates my own inchoate premonitions). In the late 1960s, while Berkeley was wracked with student protests, he wrote an astonishingly prescient book, now long out of print, called *The Coming of the Golden Age: A View of the End of Progress*. Published in 1969, it contended that science—as well as technology, the arts, and all progressive, cumulative enterprises—is coming to an end.

Most people, Stent acknowledged, consider the notion that science might soon cease to be absurd. How can science possibly be nearing an end when it has been advancing so rapidly throughout this century? Stent turned this inductive argument on its head. Initially, he granted, science advances exponentially through a positive feedback effect; knowledge begets more knowledge, and power begets more power. Stent credited the American historian Henry Adams with having foreseen this aspect of science at the turn of the century.

Adams's "law of acceleration," Stent pointed out, has an interesting corollary. If there are any limits to science, any barriers to further progress, then science may well be moving at unprecedented speed just before it crashes into them. When science seems most muscular, triumphant, potent, that may be when it is nearest death. "Indeed, the dizzy rate at which progress is now proceeding," Stent wrote in *Golden Age*, "makes it seem very likely that progress must come to a stop soon, perhaps in our lifetime, perhaps in a generation or two."

Certain fields of science, Stent argued, are limited simply by the boundedness of their subject matter. No one would consider human anatomy or geography, for example, to be infinite endeavors. Chemistry, too, is bounded. "[T]hough the total number of possible chemical reactions is very great and the variety of reactions they can undergo vast, the goal of chemistry of understanding the principles governing the behavior of such molecules is, like the goal of geography, clearly limited." (In fact, many chemists think that goal was achieved in the 1930s when the chemist Linus Pauling showed how all chemical interactions could be understood in terms of quantum mechanics.)

In his own field of biology, Stent asserted, the discovery of DNA's twin-corkscrew structure in 1953 and the subsequent deciphering of the genetic code had solved the profound problem of how genetic information is passed on from one generation to the next. Biologists had only three major questions left to explore: how life began, how a single fertilized cell develops into a multi-cellular organism and how the central nervous system processes information. When those goals are achieved, Stent said, the basic task of biology, pure biology, will be completed.

Stent acknowledged that biologists can in principle continue exploring specific phenomena and applying their knowledge forever. But according to Darwinian theory, science stems not from our desire for truth per se but from our compulsion to control our environment in order to increase the likelihood that our genes will propagate. When a given field of science begins to yield diminishing practical returns, scientists may have less incentive to pursue their research and society may be less inclined to pay for it. Moreover, just because biologists complete their empirical investigations, Stent asserted, does not mean that they will have answered all relevant questions. For example, no purely physiological theory can ever really explain consciousness, since the "processes responsible for this wholly private experience will be seen to degenerate into seemingly quite ordinary, workaday reactions, no more or less fascinating than those that occur in, say, the liver . . ."

Unlike biology, Stent said, the physical sciences seem to be open-ended. Physicists can always attempt to probe more deeply into matter by smashing particles against each other with greater force, and astronomers can always strive to see further into the universe. But in their efforts to gather data from ever-more-remote regimes, Stent contended, physicists will inevitably confront various physical, economic and even cognitive limits.

Over the course of this century, physics has become more and more difficult to comprehend; it has outrun our "Darwinian epistemology," our innate concepts for coping with the world. Stent rejected the old argument that "yesterday's nonsense is today's common sense." Society may be willing to support continued research in physics as long as it has the potential to generate powerful new technologies, such as nuclear weapons and nuclear power. But when physics becomes impractical as well as incomprehensible, Stent predicted, society will surely withdraw its support.

Stent's prognosis for the future was an odd mixture of optimism and pessimism. He predicted that science, before it ends, might help to solve many of civilization's most pressing problems. It would eliminate disease and poverty and provide society with cheap, pollution-free energy, perhaps through the harnessing of fusion reactions. As we gain more dominion over nature, however, we may lose what Nietzsche called our "will to power"; we may become less motivated to pursue further research—especially if such research has little chance of yielding tangible benefits.

As society becomes more affluent and comfortable, fewer young people may choose the increasingly difficult path of science or even of the arts. Many may turn to more hedonistic pursuits, perhaps even abandoning the "real world" for fantasies induced by drugs or electronic devices feeding directly into the brain. Sooner or later, Stent concluded, progress would "stop dead in its tracks," leaving the world in a largely static condition that he called "the new Polynesia." The advent of beatniks and hippies, he surmised, signaled the beginning of the end of progress and the dawn of the new Polynesia. He closed his book with the sardonic comment that "millennia of doing arts and science will finally transform the tragicomedy of life into a happening."

A Trip to Berkeley

In the spring of 1992 I traveled to Berkeley to see how Stent thought his predictions had held up over the years. Stent had moved to the U.S. from Germany as a youth, and his gruff voice and attire still bore traces of his origins. He wore wire-rimmed glasses, a blue, short-sleeved shirt with epaulets, dark slacks and shiny black shoes. Stent had obtained a doctorate in chemistry at the University of Illinois, but upon reading Erwin Schrödinger's book *What Is Life?*, he became entranced by the mystery of genetic transmission. After studying at the California Institute of Technology under Max Delbruck, Stent obtained a professorship at Berkeley in 1952. In these early years of molecular biology, Stent said, "none of us knew what we were doing. Then Watson and Crick found the double helix, and within a few weeks we realized we were doing molecular biology."

Stent began pondering the limits of science in the 1960s partly in reaction to Berkeley's free-speech movement, which had challenged the value of rationalism and technological progress and other aspects of civilization that Stent held dear. The university appointed him to a committee to "deal with this, to calm things down," by talking to students. Stent sought to fulfill this mandate—and to resolve his own inner conflicts over his role as a scientist—by delivering a series of lectures. These lectures became *The Coming of the Golden Age*.

I told Stent that I could not determine, after finishing *Golden Age*, whether he believed the new Polynesia, the era of social and intellectual stasis and universal leisure, would be an improvement over our present situation. "I could never decide this!" he exclaimed, looking genuinely distressed. "People called me a pessimist, but I thought I was an optimist." He certainly did not think such a society would be in any sense utopian. After the horrors wreaked by totalitarian states in this century, he explained, it was no longer possible to take the idea of utopia seriously.

Stent felt his predictions had held up reasonably well. Although hippies had vanished (except for the pitiful relics on Berkeley's streets), American culture had become increasingly materialistic and anti-intellectual; hippies had evolved into yuppies. The cold war had ended, although not through the gradual merging of communist and capitalist states Stent had envisioned. He admitted he did not anticipate the resurgence, in the wake of the cold war, of long-repressed ethnic and even tribal conflicts. "I'm very depressed at what's happening in the Balkans," he said. "I didn't think that would happen." Stent was also surprised by the persistence of poverty and of racial conflict in the U.S., but he thought these problems would eventually diminish in importance. (Aha, I thought. He was an optimist after all.)

Stent was convinced that science was showing signs of the closure he had predicted in *Golden Age*. Particle physicists were having difficulty convincing society to pay for their increasingly expensive experiments, such as the multi-billion-dollar Superconducting Supercollider. As for biologists, they still had much to learn about how, say, a fertilized cell is transformed into a complex, multi-cellular organism, like an elephant, and about the workings of the brain. "But I think the big picture is basically over," he said. Evolutionary biology in particular "was over when Darwin published *The Origin of Species*," Stent said.

Stent was still convinced, in spite of all the advances in neuroscience following the publication of *Golden Age*, that a purely physiological explanation of consciousness would not be as comprehensible or as meaningful as most people would like; nor would it help us to solve moral and ethical questions. In fact, Stent thought the progress of science might give religion a clearer role in the future rather than eliminating it entirely, as many scientists had once hoped. Although it cannot compete with science's far more compelling stories about the physical realm, religion still retains some value in offering moral guidance. "Humans are animals, but we're also moral subjects. The task of religion is more and more in the moral realm."

When I asked about the possibility that computers might become intelligent and create their own science, Stent snorted in derision. He had a dim view of artificial intelligence, and particularly its more visionary enthusiasts. Computers may excel at precisely defined tasks such as mathematics and chess, he pointed out, but they still perform abysmally when confronted with the kind of problems—recognizing a face or a voice or walking down a crowded sidewalk—that humans solve effortlessly. "They're full of it," Stent said of Marvin Minsky and others who have predicted that one day we humans will be able to "download" our personalities into computers. "I wouldn't rule out the possibility that in the 23rd century you might have an artificial brain," he added. "But it would need experience." One could design a computer to become an expert in restaurants, "but this machine would never know what a steak tastes like."

Stent was similarly skeptical of the claims of investigators of chaos and complexity that with computers and sophisticated mathematics they can transcend the science of the past. In *The Coming of the Golden Age*, Stent had discussed the work of one of the pioneers of chaos theory, Benoit Mandelbrot. Beginning in the early 1960s, Mandelbrot had shown that many phenomena are intrinsically "indeterministic"—they exhibit behavior that is unpredictable and apparently random. Scientists can only guess at the causes of individual events, and they cannot predict them with any accuracy.

Proponents of chaos and complexity were attempting to create effective, comprehensible theories of the same phenomena studied by Mandelbrot, Stent said. He had concluded in *Golden Age* that these indeterministic phenomena would resist scientific analysis, and he saw no reason to change that assessment. Quite the contrary. The work emerging from those fields demonstrated his point that science, when pushed too far, always culminates in incoherence. So Stent did not think that chaos and complexity will bring about the rebirth of science? "No," he said with a rakish grin. "It's the end of science."

What Science Has Accomplished

We obviously are nowhere near the new Polynesia that Stent envisioned, in part because applied science has not come nearly as far as Stent had hoped (feared?) when he wrote *The Coming of the Golden Age*. But I have come to the conclusion that Stent's prophecy has, in one very important sense, already come to pass. If one believes in science, one must accept the possibility—even the probability—that science has passed its peak. By science I mean not applied science but science at its purest and grandest, the primordial human quest to understand the universe and our place in it.

Further research may yield no more great revelations or revolutions but only incremental, diminishing returns.

These are trying times for truth-seekers. The scientific enterprise is threatened by technophobes, animal-rights activists, religious fundamentalists, and, most important of all, stingy politicians. Social, political, and economic constraints will surely make it more difficult to practice science, and pure science in particular, in the future. Moreover, science itself, as it advances, keeps imposing limits on its own power. Einstein's theory of special relativity prohibits the transmission of matter or even information at speeds faster than that of light; quantum mechanics dictates that our knowledge of the microrealm will always be uncertain; chaos theory confirms that even without quantum indeterminacy many phenomena would be impossible to predict; Kurt Gödel's incompleteness theorem denies us the possibility of constructing a complete, consistent mathematical description of reality. And evolutionary biology keeps reminding us that we are animals, designed by natural selection not for discovering deep truths of nature, but for breeding.

But by far the greatest barrier to future progress in pure science is its past success. Researchers have already mapped out physical reality, ranging from the microrealm of quarks and electrons to the macrorealm of planets, stars, and galaxies. Physicists have shown that all matter is ruled by a few basic forces: gravity, electromagnetism, and the strong and weak nuclear forces. Scientists have also stitched their knowledge into an impressive, if not terribly detailed, narrative of how we came to be. The universe exploded into existence 15 billion years ago, give or take five billion years (astronomers may never agree on an exact figure), and is still expanding outwards. Some 4.5 billion years ago, the detritus of an exploding star, a supernova, condensed into our solar system. Sometime during the next few hundred million years, for reasons that may never be known, single-celled organisms bearing an ingenious molecule called DNA emerged on the still-hellish earth. These Adamic microbes gave rise, by means of natural selection, to an extraordinary array of more complex creatures, including *Homo sapiens.*

My guess is that this narrative that scientists have woven from their knowledge, this modern myth of creation, will be as viable 100 or even 1,000 years from now as it is today. Why? Because it is true. Moreover, given how far science has already come, and given the physical, social, and cognitive limits constraining further research, science is unlikely to make any significant additions to the knowledge it has already generated. There will be no great revelations in the future comparable to those bestowed upon us by Darwin or Einstein or Watson and Crick.

The Anxiety of Scientific Influence

In trying to understand the mood of modern scientists, I have found that ideas from literary criticism can serve some purpose. In his influential 1973 essay, *The Anxiety of Influence,* the literary critic Harold Bloom of Yale University likened the modern poet to Satan in Milton's *Paradise Lost.* Just as Satan fought to assert his individuality by defying the perfection of God, so must the modern poet engage in an Oedipal struggle to define himself in relation to Shakespeare, Dante, and other masters. The effort is ultimately futile, Bloom said, because no poet can hope to approach, let alone surpass, the perfection of his forebears. Modern poets are all essentially tragic figures, late-comers.

Modern scientists, too, are late-comers, and their burden is much heavier than that of poets. Scientists must endure not merely Shakespeare's *King Lear* but Newton's laws of motion, Darwin's theory of natural selection,

Einstein's theory of relativity. These theories are not merely beautiful; they are also true, empirically true, in a way that no work of art can be. Most researchers simply concede their inability to supersede what Bloom called "the embarrassments of a tradition grown too wealthy to need anything more." They try to solve what the philosopher of science Thomas Kuhn has denigrated as "puzzles," problems whose solutions buttress the prevailing paradigm. They settle for refining and applying the brilliant, pioneering discoveries of their predecessors. They try to measure the mass of quarks more precisely or to determine how a given stretch of DNA guides the growth of the embryonic brain. Others become what Bloom derided as a "mere rebel, a childish inverter of conventional moral categories." The rebels denigrate the dominant theories of science as flimsy social fabrications rather than rigorously tested descriptions of nature.

Bloom's "strong poet" accepts the perfection of his predecessors and yet strives to transcend it through various subterfuges, including a subtle "misreading" of their work; only by so doing can a modern poet break free of the stultifying influence of the past. There are strong scientists, too, those who are seeking to misread and therefore to transcend quantum mechanics or the big bang theory or Darwinian evolution. For the most part strong scientists have only one option: to pursue science in a speculative, post-empirical mode that I call ironic science. Like art, philosophy, literary criticism, theology—the other ironic modes of discourse—ironic science can be neither definitively confirmed nor falsified. It offers not truth in the conventional sense but points of view, opinions which are, at best, "interesting," which provoke further comment. It cannot achieve empirically verifiable "surprises" that force scientists to make substantial revisions in their basic description of reality.

The most common strategy of the strong scientist is to point to all the shortcomings of current scientific knowledge, to all the questions left unanswered. But the questions tend to be ones that may never be definitively answered, given the limits of human science. How, exactly, was the universe created? Could our universe be just one of an infinite number of universes? Could quarks and electrons be composed of still smaller particles, ad infinitum? What does quantum mechanics really mean? (Most questions concerning meaning can only be answered ironically, as literary critics know.) Biology has its own slew of insoluble riddles. How, exactly, did life begin on earth? Just how inevitable was life's origin, and its subsequent history?

Superstring theory, which for more than a decade has been the leading contender for a unified theory of physics, is a particularly striking specimen of ironic science. Often called a "theory of everything," it posits that all the matter and energy in the universe and even space and time stem from infinitesimal, string-like particles wriggling in a hyperspace consisting of 10 (or more) dimensions. Unfortunately, the microrealm that superstrings allegedly inhabit is even less accessible to human experimenters than the quasars haunting the edge of the visible universe. A superstring is as small in comparison to a proton as a proton is in comparison to the solar system. Probing this realm directly would require an accelerator 1,000 light years around. That is why the physicist Sheldon Glashow, a Nobel laureate at Harvard University, once likened superstring theorists to "medieval theologians" (1986, 7).

The practitioner of ironic science enjoys one obvious advantage over the strong poet: the appetite of the reading public for scientific "revolutions." As empirical science ossifies, journalists like myself, who feed society's hunger, will come under more pressure to tout theories that supposedly transcend quantum mechanics or the big bang theory or natural selection. Journalists have, after all, helped superstring theory to win acceptance as a legitimate extension of nuclear physics rather than mathematical smoke and mirrors, as Glashow has put it. Journalists have also created the popular impression that fields such as chaos and complexity represent genuinely "new" sciences superior to the stodgy old reductionist methods of Newton, Einstein, and Darwin.

The *Star Trek* Factor

If my experience is any guide, even people with only a casual interest in science will find it hard to accept that science's days are numbered. It is easy to understand why. We are drenched in progress, real and artificial. Every year we have smaller, faster computers, sleeker cars, more channels on our televisions. Our views of the future are also distorted by what could be called the *Star Trek* factor. How can science be approaching a culmination when we haven't invented spaceships that travel at warp speed yet?

To be sure, applied science will continue for a long time to come. Scientists can keep developing versatile new materials; faster and more sophisticated computers; genetic-engineering techniques that make us healthier, stronger, longer-lived; perhaps even fusion reactors that can provide cheap energy with few environmental side effects (although given the drastic cutbacks in funding, fusion's prospects now seem dimmer than ever). The question is, will these advances in applied science bring about any "surprises," any revolutionary shifts in our basic knowledge? Will they force scientists to revise the map they have drawn of the universe or the narrative they have constructed of the universe's creation and history? Probably not. Applied science in this century has tended to reinforce rather than to challenge the prevailing theoretical paradigms. Lasers and transistors confirm the power of quantum mechanics, just as genetic engineering bolsters belief in the DNA-based model of evolution.

What constitutes a surprise? Einstein's discovery that time and space, the I-beams of reality, are made of rubber was a surprise. So was the observation by astronomers that the universe is expanding, evolving. Quantum mechanics, which unveiled a probabilistic element, a Lucretian swerve, at the bottom of things, was an enormous surprise; God does play dice (Einstein's disapproval notwithstanding). The later finding that protons and neutrons are made of smaller particles called quarks was a much lesser surprise, because it merely extended quantum theory to a deeper domain; the foundations of physics remained intact.

Learning that we humans were created not de novo by God but gradually, by the process of natural selection, was a big surprise. Most other aspects of human evolution—those concerning where, when and how, precisely, *Homo sapiens* evolved—are details. These details may be interesting, but they are not likely to be surprising unless they show that scientists' basic assumptions about evolution were wrong. We may learn, say, that our sudden surge in intelligence was catalyzed by the intervention of alien beings, as in the movie *2001*. That would be a very big surprise. In fact, any proof that life exists—or even once existed—beyond our little planet would constitute a huge surprise. Science, and all human thought, would be reborn. Speculation about the origin of life and its inevitability would be placed on a much more empirical basis.

But how likely is it that we will discover life elsewhere? In retrospect, the space programs of both the U.S. and the U.S.S.R. represented elaborate displays of saber-rattling rather than the opening of a new frontier for human knowledge. The prospects for space exploration on anything more than a trivial level seem increasingly unlikely. We no longer have the will or the money to indulge in technological muscle-flexing for its own sake. Humans, made of flesh and blood, may someday travel to other planets here in our solar system. But unless we find some way to transcend Einstein's prohibition against faster-than-light travel, chances are that we will never even attempt to visit another star, let alone another galaxy. A spaceship that can travel one million miles an hour, an order of magnitude faster than any current technology can attain, would still take almost 3,000 years to reach our nearest stellar neighbor, Alpha Centauri.

That's What They Thought 100 Years Ago

The most common response to the suggestion that science might be ending is the "that's-what-they-thought-at-the-end-of-the-last-century" argument. The argument goes like this: As the 19th century wound down, physicists thought they knew everything. But no sooner had the 20th century begun than Einstein and other physicists discovered—invented?—relativity theory and quantum mechanics. These theories eclipsed Newtonian physics and opened up vast new vistas for modern physics and other branches of science. Moral: Anyone who predicts that science is nearing its end will surely turn out to be as short-sighted as those 19th-century physicists were.

Those who believe science is finite have a standard retort for this argument: The earliest explorers, because they could not find the edge of the earth, might well have concluded that it is infinite, but they would have been wrong. Moreover, it is by no means a matter of historical record that late 19th-century physicists felt they had wrapped things up. The best evidence for a sense of completion is a speech given in 1894 by Albert Michelson, whose experiments on the velocity of light helped to inspire Einstein's theory of special relativity. Michelson stated (*Physics Today*, April 1968, 9):

While it is never safe to say that the future of Physical Science has no marvels even more astonishing than those of the past, it seems probable that most of the grand underlying principles have been firmly established and that further advances are to be sought chiefly in the rigorous application of these principles to all the phenomena which come under our notice. It is here that the science of measurement shows its importance—where quantitative results are more to be desired than qualitative work. An eminent physicist has remarked that the future truths of Physical Science are to be looked for in the sixth place of decimals.

Michelson's remark about "the sixth place of decimals" has been so widely attributed to Lord Kelvin (after whom the Kelvin, a unit of temperature, is named) that some authors simply credit him with the quote. But historians have found no evidence that Kelvin made such a statement. Moreover, at the time of Michelson's remarks physicists were vigorously debating fundamental issues, such as the viability of the atomic theory of matter, according to the historian of science Stephen Brush of the University of Maryland. Michelson was so absorbed in his optics experiments, Brush suggested, that he was "oblivious to the violent controversies raging among theorists at the time." The alleged "Victorian calm in physics," Brush concluded, is a "myth" (1969, 9).

The Apocryphal Patent Official

Other historians, as is their wont, disagree. Questions concerning the "mood" of a given era can never be completely resolved. But the view that scientists in the last century were complacent about the state of their field has clearly been exaggerated. Historians have provided a definitive ruling, moreover, on another anecdote favored by those reluctant to accept that science might be mortal. The story alleges that in the mid-1800s, the head of the U.S. Patent Office quit his job and recommended that the office be shut down because there would soon be nothing left to invent.

In 1995, Daniel Koshland, editor of the prestigious journal *Science*, repeated this story in an introduction to a special section on science's future. In this section, leading scientists offered predictions about what their fields might accomplish over the next 20 years. Koshland, a biologist at the University of California at Berkeley, exulted that his prognosticators "clearly do not agree with that commissioner of patents of yesteryear. Great discoveries with great import for the future of science are in the offing. That we have come so far so fast is not an indication that we have saturated the discovery market, but rather that discoveries will come even faster" (1995).

There were two problems with Koshland's essay. First, the contributors to his special section envisioned not "great discoveries" but, for the most part, rather mundane applications of current knowledge, such as better methods for designing drugs, improved tests for genetic disorders, more discerning brain scans and the like. Some predictions, moreover, were negative in nature. "Anyone who expects any human-like intelligence from a computer in the next 50 years is doomed to disappointment," proclaimed the physicist and Nobel laureate Philip Anderson.

The second problem with Koshland's essay was that his story about the commissioner of patents is apocryphal. In 1940, a scholar named Eber Jeffry examined the patent-commissioner anecdote in an article titled "Nothing Left to Invent," published in the *Journal of the Patent Office Society*. Jeffry traced the story to Congressional testimony delivered in 1843 by Henry Ellsworth, then the Commissioner of Patents. Ellsworth remarked at one point: "The advancement of the arts, from year to

year, taxes our credulity and seems to presage the arrival of that period when human improvement must end."

But Ellsworth, far from recommending that his office be shut down, asked for extra funds to cope with the flood of inventions he expected in agriculture, transportation, and communications. Ellsworth did indeed resign two years later, in 1845, but in his resignation letter he made no reference to closing the patent office; he only expressed pride at having expanded it. Jeffry concluded that Ellsworth's statement about "that period when human improvement must end" represented "a mere rhetorical flourish intended to emphasize the remarkable strides forward in inventions then current and to be expected in the future." But perhaps Jeffry was not giving Ellsworth enough credit. Ellsworth was, after all, anticipating the argument that Gunther Stent would make more than a century later: The faster that science moves, the faster it will reach its ultimate, inevitable limits.

Consider the implications of the alternative position, the one implicitly advanced by Daniel Koshland. He insists that because science has advanced so rapidly over the past century or so, it can and will continue to do so, possibly forever. But this inductive argument is deeply flawed. Science has only existed for a few hundred years, and its most spectacular achievements have occurred within the last century. Viewed from an historical perspective, the modern era of rapid scientific and technological progress appears to be not a permanent feature of reality but an aberration, a fluke, a product of a singular convergence of social, intellectual, and political factors.

The Rise and Fall of Progress

In his 1932 book, *The Idea of Progress*, the historian J. B. Bury stated (italics in the original):

Science has been advancing without interruption during the last three or four hundred years; every new discovery has led to new problems and new methods of solution, and opened up new fields for exploration. Hitherto men of science have not been compelled to halt, they have always found means to advance further. But *what assurance have we that they will not come up against impassable barriers?*

Bury himself had demonstrated through his scholarship that the concept of progress is only a few hundred years old, at most. From the era of the Roman Empire through the Middle Ages, most truth-seekers had a degenerative view of history: the ancient Greeks had achieved the acme of mathematical and scientific knowledge, and civilization had gone downhill from there. Those who followed could only try to recapture some remnant of the wisdom epitomized by Plato and Aristotle. It was such founders of modern, empirical science as Isaac Newton, Francis Bacon, René Descartes, and Gottfried Leibniz who first set forth the idea that humans could systematically acquire and accumulate knowledge through investigations of nature. Most of these Ur-scientists believed that the process would be finite, that we could attain complete knowledge of the world and then construct a perfect society, a utopia, based on that knowledge. (The new Polynesia!)

Only with the advent of Darwin did certain intellectuals become so enamoured with progress that they insisted it might be, or should be, eternal. "In the wake of the publication of Darwin's *On the Origin of Species*," Gunther Stent wrote in his 1978 book *The Paradoxes of Progress*, "the idea of progress was raised to the level of a scientific religion. . . . This optimistic view came to be so widely embraced in the industrialized nations . . . that the claim that progress could presently come to an end is now widely regarded [to be] as outlandish a notion as was in earlier times the claim that the Earth moves around the sun" (27).

It was not surprising that modern nation states became fervent proponents of the science-is-infinite creed. Science spawned such marvels as The Bomb, nuclear power, jets, radar, computers, and missiles. In 1945 the physicist Vannevar Bush (a distant relative of former President George) proclaimed in *Science: The Endless Frontier* that science was "a largely unexplored hinterland" and an "essential key" to U.S. military and economic security. Bush's essay served as a blueprint for the construction of the National Science Foundation and other federal organizations that thereafter supported basic research on an unparalled scale. The Soviet Union was perhaps even more devoted than its capitalist rival to the concept of scientific and technological progress.

Of course, powerful social, political and economic forces now oppose this vision of boundless scientific and technological progress. The cold war, which was a major impetus for basic research in the U.S. and the Soviet Union, is over; the U.S. and the former Soviet republics have much less incentive to build space stations and gigantic accelerators simply to demonstrate their power. Society is also increasingly sensitive to the adverse consequences of science and technology—such as pollution, nuclear contamination, and weapons of mass destruction.

The disillusionment with science was foreseen early in this century by Oswald Spengler, a German schoolteacher who became the first great prophet of the end of science. In his massive tome *The Decline of the West*, published in 1918, Spengler argued that science proceeds in a cyclic fashion, with "romantic" periods of investigation of nature and the invention of new theories giving way to periods of consolidation in which scientific knowledge ossifies. As scientists become more arrogant and less tolerant of other belief systems, notably religious ones, Spengler declared, society will rebel against science and embrace religious fundamentalism and other irrational systems of belief. Spengler predicted that the decline of science and the resurgence of irrationality would begin at the end of this millennium.

Spengler's analysis was, if anything, too optimistic. His view of science as cyclic implied that science may one day be resurrected and undergo a new period of discovery. But science is not cyclic but linear; we can only discover the periodic table and the expansion of the universe and the structure of DNA once. The biggest obstacle to the resurrection of science—human science, the quest for knowledge about who we are and where we came from—is science's past success.

No More Endless Horizons

Scientists are understandably loath to state publicly that they have entered an era of diminishing returns. No one wants to be recalled as the equivalent of those allegedly short-sighted physicists of a century ago. There is always the danger, moreover, that such prophecies will become self-fulfilling. But Gunther Stent is hardly the only prominent scientist to violate the taboo against such prophecies. In 1971, *Science* published an essay entitled "Science: Endless Horizons or Golden Age?," by Bentley Glass, a prominent biologist and the president of *Science*'s publisher, the American Association for the Advancement of Science. Glass weighed the two scenarios for science's future posited by Vannevar Bush and Gunther Stent and reluctantly came down on the side of Stent. Not only was science finite, Glass argued, but the end was in sight. "We are like the explorers of a great continent," Glass proclaimed, "who have penetrated to its margins in most points of the compass and have mapped the

major mountain chains and rivers. There are still innumerable details to fill in, but the endless horizons no longer exist" (23).

According to Glass, a close reading of Bush's *Endless Frontier* essay suggested that he, too, viewed science as a finite enterprise. Nowhere did Bush specifically state that any fields of science could continue generating new discoveries forever. In fact, Bush described scientific knowledge as an "edifice" whose form "is predestined by the laws of logic and the nature of human reasoning. It is almost as though it already existed." Bush's choice of this metaphor, Glass commented, reveals that he considered scientific knowledge to be finite in extent. Glass proposed that the "bold title" of Bush's essay was "never intended to be taken literally, but supposed merely to imply that from our present viewpoint so much yet remains before us to be discovered that the horizons seem virtually endless."

In 1979, in *The Quarterly Review of Biology*, Glass presented evidence to back up his view that science was approaching a culmination. Upon analyzing the rate of discoveries in biology, he found that they had not kept pace with the exponential increase in researchers and funding. "We have been so impressed by the undeniable acceleration in the rate of magnificent achievements that we have scarcely noticed that we are well into an era of diminishing returns," Glass commented. "That is, more and more scientific effort and expenditure of money must be allocated in order to sustain our progress. Sooner or later this will have to stop, because of the insuperable limits to scientific manpower and expenditure. So rapid has been the growth of science in our own century that we have been deluded into thinking that such a rate of progress can be maintained indefinitely."

When I spoke to him in 1994, Glass confessed that many of his colleagues had been dismayed that he had even raised the issue of science's limits, let alone prophesied its demise.

But Glass felt, then and now, that the topic is too important to ignore. Obviously science, as a social enterprise, has some limits, Glass said. If science had continued to grow at the same rate as it had earlier in this century, he pointed out, it would soon have consumed the entire budget of the industrialized world. "I think it's rather evident to everybody," he said, "that there must be brakes put on the amount of funding for science, pure science." This slowdown, he observed, was evident in the decision of the U.S. Congress in 1993 to cuts funds for the Superconducting Supercollider, the gargantuan particle accelerator that physicists hoped would propel them beyond quarks and electrons into a deeper realm of microspace.

Even if society were to devote all its resources to research, Glass added, science would one day still reach the point of diminishing returns. Why? Because science works; it solves its problems. After all, astronomers have already plumbed the farthest reaches of the universe; they cannot see what, if anything, lies beyond its borders. Moreover, most physicists think that the reduction of matter into smaller and smaller particles will eventually end, or may have already ended for all practical purposes. Even if physicists unearth particles buried beneath quarks and electrons, that knowledge will make little or no difference to biologists, who have learned that the most significant biological processes occur at the molecular level and above. "There's a limit to biology there," Glass explained, "that you don't expect to be able to ever break through just because of the nature of the constitution of matter and energy."

Hard Times Ahead for Physics

In 1992, the monthly journal *Physics Today* published an essay entitled "Hard Times," in which Leo Kadanoff, a prominent physicist at the University of Chicago, painted a bleak picture for the future of physics. "Nothing we do is likely to arrest our decline in numbers, support, or social value," Kadanoff declared. "Too much of our base depended on events that are now becoming ancient history: nuclear weapons and radar during World War II, silicon and laser technology thereafter, American optimism and industrial hegemony, socialist belief in rationality as a way of improving the world." Those conditions had largely vanished, Kadanoff contended; both physics and science as a whole are now besieged by environmentalists, animal-rights activists, and other antiscientific movements. "In recent decades, science has had high rewards and has been at the center of social interest and concern. We should not be surprised if this anomaly disappears" (9–11).

Kadanoff, when I spoke to him over the telephone two years later, sounded even gloomier than he had been when he wrote his essay. He laid out his worldview for me with a muffled melancholy, as if he were suffering from an existential head cold. But rather than discussing science's social and political problems, as he had in his essay, he focused on another obstacle to scientific progress: science's past achievements. The great task of modern science, Kadanoff explained, has been to show that the world conforms to certain basic physical laws. "That is an issue which has been explored at least since the Renaissance and maybe a much longer period of time. For me, that's a settled issue. That is, it seems to me that the world is explainable by law."

Of course, scientists still have much to learn about how the fundamental laws generate "the richness of the world as we see it." Kadanoff himself is a leader in the field of condensed-matter physics, which studies the behavior not of individual subatomic particles but of solids or liquids. Kadanoff has also been associated with the field of chaos, which addresses phenomena that unfold in predictably unpredictable ways. Some proponents of chaos—and of the closely related field called complexity—have suggested that with the help of powerful computers and new mathematical methods they will discover truths that surpass those revealed by the "reductionist" science of the past. Kadanoff had his doubts. Studying the consequences of fundamental laws is "in a way less interesting" and "less deep," he said, than showing that the world is lawful. "But now that we know the world is lawful," he added, "we have to go on to other things. And yes, it probably excites the imagination of the average human being less. Maybe with good reason." Is this state of affairs permanent? I asked. Kadanoff was silent for a moment. Then he sighed, as if trying to exhale all his world-weariness. "Once you have proven that the world is lawful," he replied, "to the satisfaction of many human beings, you can't do that again."

Whistling to Keep Our Courage Up

One of the few modern philosophers to devote serious thought to the limits of science is Nicholas Rescher of the University of Pittsburgh. In his 1978 book, *Scientific Progress*, Rescher deplored the fact that Stent, Glass, and other prominent scientists seemed to think that science might be approaching a cul de sac. Rescher intended to provide "an antidote to this currently pervasive tendency of thought" by demonstrating that science was at least potentially infinite. But the scenario he sketched out over the course of his book was hardly optimistic. He argued that science, as a fundamentally empirical, experimental discipline, faces economic constraints. As scientists try to extend their theories into more remote domains—seeing further into the universe, deeper into matter—their costs will inevitably escalate and their returns diminish.

"Scientific innovation is going to become more and more difficult as we push out further and further from our home base toward more remote frontiers. If the present perspective is even partly correct, the half-millennium commencing around 1650 will eventually come to be regarded among the great characteristic developmental transformations of human history, with the age of The Science Explosion as unique in its own historical structure as The Bronze Age or The Industrial Revolution or The Population Explosion."

Rescher tacked what he apparently thought was a happy coda onto his depressing scenario: Science will never end; it will just go slower and slower and slower, like Zeno's tortoise. Nor should scientists ever conclude that their research must degenerate into the mere filling in of details; it is always possible that one of their increasingly expensive experiments will have revolutionary import, comparable to that of quantum mechanics or Darwinian theory.

When I telephoned Rescher, he acknowledged that his analysis had been in most respects a grim one. "We can only investigate nature by interacting with it," he said. "To do that we must push into regions never investigated before, regions of higher density, lower temperature, or higher energy. In all these cases we are pushing fundamental limits, and that requires ever more elaborate and expensive apparatuses. So there is a limit imposed on science by the limits of human resources."

The End of History

In *Golden Age*, Stent suggested that science, before it ends, may at least deliver us from our most pressing social problems, such as poverty and disease and even conflict between states. The future will be peaceful and comfortable, if boring. Most humans will dedicate themselves to the pursuit of pleasure. In 1992, Francis

Fukuyama set forth a rather different vision of the future in *The End of History and the Last Man*. Fukuyama defined history as the human struggle to find the most sensible—or least noxious—political system. By the 20th century liberal democracy, which according to Fukuyama had always been the best choice, had only one serious contender: Marxist socialism. After the collapse of the Soviet Union in the late 1980s, liberal democracy stood alone in the ring, battered but victorious. History was over.

Fukuyama went on to consider the profound questions raised by his thesis. Now that the age of political struggle has ended, what will we do next? What are we here for? What is the point of humanity? Fukuyama did not supply an answer so much as a rhetorical shrug. Freedom and prosperity, he fretted, might not be enough to satisfy our Nietzschean "will to power" and our need for constant "self-overcoming." Without great ideological struggles to occupy us, we humans might manufacture wars simply to give ourselves something to do.

Fukuyama did not overlook the role of science in human history. Far from it. His thesis required that history have a direction, that it be progressive, and science, he argued, provided this direction. Science had been vital to the growth of modern nation states, which saw science as a means to military and economic power. But Fukuyama did not even consider the possibility that science might also provide post-historical humanity with a common purpose, a goal, one that would encourage cooperation rather than conflict.

Hoping to learn the reason for Fukuyama's omission, I called him at the Rand Corporation, where he had obtained a job after *The End of History* became a bestseller. He answered with the wariness of someone accustomed to, and not amused by, kooks. At first, he misunderstood my question; he thought I was asking whether science could help us make moral and political choices in the posthistorical era rather than serving as an end in itself. The lesson of contemporary philosophy, Fukuyama lectured me sternly, is that science is morally neutral, at best. In fact, scientific progress, if unaccompanied by moral progress among societies or individuals, "can leave you worse off than you were without it."

When Fukuyama finally realized what I was suggesting—that science might provide a kind of unifying theme or purpose for civilization—his tone became even more condescending. Yes, a few people had written him letters addressing that theme. "I think they were space-travel buffs," he snickered. "They said, 'Well, you know, if we don't have ideological wars to fight we can always fight nature in a certain sense by pushing back the frontiers of knowledge and conquering the solar system.'"

He emitted another scornful little chuckle. So you don't take these predictions seriously? I asked. "No, not really," he said wearily. Trying to goad something further out of him, I revealed that many prominent scientists and philosophers—not just fans of "Star Trek"—believed that science, the quest for pure knowledge, represented the destiny of mankind. "Hunh," Fukuyama replied, as though he was no longer listening to me but had re-entered that delightful tract by Hegel he had been perusing before I called. I signed off.

Without even giving it much thought, Fukuyama had reached the same conclusion that Stent had in *The Coming of the Golden Age*. From very different perspectives, both saw that science is less a byproduct of our will to know than of our will to power. Fukuyama's bored rejection of a future dedicated to science spoke volumes. The vast majority of humans, including not only the ignorant masses but also highbrow types such as Fukuyama, find scientific knowledge mildly interesting, at best, and certainly not worthy of serving as the goal of all humankind. Whatever the long-term destiny of *Homo sapiens* turns out to be—Fukuyama's eternal warfare or Stent's eternal hedonism, or, more likely, some mixture of the two—it seems unlikely to be the pursuit of scientific knowledge.

Gunther Stent left several loopholes open in his end-of-science scenario. Society might become so wealthy that it will pay for even the most whimsical scientific experiments—particle accelerators that girdle the globe!—without regard for cost. Alternatively, science could achieve some enormous breakthrough, such as a faster-than-light transportation system or intelligence-enhancing genetic engineering techniques that would enable scientists to transcend their physical and cognitive limits. I would add two other possibilites to Stent's list. One is that scientists might discover that life exists elsewhere, creating a glorious new era in comparative biology.

The other possibility—which Stent rejects but a surprising number of other scientists find compelling—is that one day we humans will create intelligent machines that can transcend our physical, economic and cognitive limits and carry on the quest for knowledge without us. In my favorite version of this scenario, machines transform the entire cosmos into a vast, unified, information-processing network. All matter becomes mind. This proposal is not science, of course, but wishful thinking. It nonetheless raises some interesting questions, questions normally left to theologians. What would an all-powerful, cosmic computer do? What would it think about? I can imagine only one possibility. It would try to answer The Question, the one that lurks behind all other questions, like an actor playing all the parts of a play: Why is there something rather than nothing? In its effort to find The Answer to The Question, the universal mind may discover the ultimate limits of knowledge.

References:

Bloom, H. 1973. *The Anxiety of Influence.* New York: Oxford University Press.

Bury, J. 1932. *The Idea of Progress.* New York: Macmillan, New York.

Bush, V. 1945. *Science: The Endless Frontier.* Reissued by the National Science Foundation (1990).

Fukuyama, F. 1992. *The End of History and the Last Man.* New York: The Free Press.

Glashow, S., and P. Ginsparg. 1986. "Desperately Seeking Superstrings?" *Physics Today*, May.

Glass, B. 1971. "Science: Endless Horizons or Golden Age?" *Science*, January 8, pp. 23–29.

——. 1979. "Milestones and Rates of Growth in the Development of Biology." *The Quarterly Review of Biology*, March, pp. 31–53.

Holton, G. 1993. *Science and Anti-Science.* Cambridge: Harvard University Press.

Jeffrey, E. 1940. "Nothing Left to Invent." *Journal of the Patent Office Society*, July, pp. 479–481.

Kadanoff, L. 1992. "Hard Times." *Physics Today*, October, pp. 9–11.

Koshland, D. 1995. "The Crystal Ball and the Trumpet Call." *Science*, March 17.

Rescher, N. 1978. *Scientific Progress.* Oxford: Basil Blackwell.

Selve, R. Q. (ed.). 1992. *The End of Science? Attack and Defense.* Lanham, MD: University Press of America.

Stent, G. S. 1969. *The Coming of the Golden Age: A View of the End of Progress.* Garden City, NY: Natural History Press.

——. 1978. *The Paradoxes of Progress.* San Francisco: W. H. Freeman.

Science Is Just Beginning

JOHN CASTI

Questions about the origin of things—the universe, life, language, human beings—have always held a strong fascination for the intellectually inclined, perhaps because such one-time-only events are difficult to study, thus providing a playpen for unbridled speculation and almost limitless armchair philosophy. Equally fascinating, it seems, are the no-time-only events of how things will end. Recent Cassandras publicly airing their angst over the incipient demise of something beloved range from Steven Weinberg dreaming of a final theory in particle physics (*Dreams of a Final Theory*, Pantheon, New York, 1992) to Francis Fukuyama pondering the end of history (*The End of History and the Last Man*, Free Press, New York, 1992). The latest addition to this cast of doomsayers is journalist John Horgan, who ups the ante by trumpeting to the world the imminent end of all science in a recently published book (*The End of Science*, Addison-Wesley, Reading, MA, 1996). Now what could such a temerarious claim actually mean?

Contrary to many accounts, science is not a noun or adjective by which we carve up the landscape of knowledge, labeling areas like biology and chemistry "science," while denying that label to fields of enquiry such as art, history, and literature. Rather, science is a verb; it is a procedure of a very special type. What distinguishes it from religion, mysticism, poetry, and all the other players in the reality-generation game is the way science gets at the scheme of things. That way is to provide answers to questions about the world around us by invoking a set of rules (read: theory, formula, algorithm, program). But not just any old rule will do. A scientific rule possesses certain properties—public accessibility, clarity, brevity, bias-free—and is generated by following a very definite procedure, the so-called "scientific method." So if science is indeed coming to an end, the only interpretation of this claim that seems to make any sense whatsoever is that either there are no interesting questions left to answer, or that it is flat-out impossible to produce a set of scientific rules by which to answer any question that still piques our curiosity. It stretches the imagination to suppose that anyone would take either alternative seriously.

A few years ago, I published a book (*Paradigms Lost*, Morrow, New York, 1989) in which I looked at six of the major problems facing science today, trying to identify the competing answers, how they were generated, who held to them, and why. These Big Questions are:

1. How did life originate on Earth?
2. Are human social behavioral patterns determined by our genes?
3. How do humans acquire language?
4. Is it possible to build a computing machine that will think, just like you and me?

5. Do there exist intelligent, extraterrestrial life forms in the Milky Way galaxy?

6. Does there exist an objective reality independent of human observers?

I think that even Horgan, who states that science is part of the "primordial human quest to understand the universe and our place in it," would agree that these questions are an integral part of that quest, and that the wellspring of deep and important questions is far from having run dry.

Let me hasten to add that the last time I looked (about a week ago), science was not much closer to offering a knockdown, airtight set of scientific rules for answering any of these questions than it was when my book was first published. But that in no way implies that such a set of rules does not exist. An analogy with similar Big Questions in mathematics is helpful in elucidating this point.

By now it is a well-chronicled story how, in 1931, Kurt Gödel stamped paid to David Hilbert's cherished belief that any mathematical question could be definitively answered. Gödel's result demonstrated the existence of forever unanswerable questions about numbers. So unlike the real worlds of physics, biology, chemistry and all the rest, here we have an area for which we can state unequivocally that there exist questions that can never be answered by following the rules of mathematics. Yet, strangely enough, I cannot ever recall seeing a book or article suggesting that mathematicians are losing any sleep over the end of mathematics. In fact, until recently the undecidable propositions underwritten by Gödel's results were regarded mostly as curiosities by the mathematical community, although occasionally someone might start dreaming in print about one or another famous unsolved problem being one of them. In fact, the celebrated Fermat Conjecture was thought of in just these terms at one time, although we all know now that what it took for the Conjecture to be set-

tled was just a little more genius—and a lot more hard work—on the part of Andrew Wiles in wielding the traditional rules of mathematical argumentation.

Even more philosophically interesting is the 1976 answer offered by Kenneth Appel and Wolfgang Haken to the famed Four-Color Conjecture. In contrast to conventional mathematical proofs, which are at least in principle surveyable by the human mind, the Appel and Haken result affirming that no more than four colors are needed to color any planar map was based upon the computational investigation of nearly 2,000 individual cases. This examination involved many hundreds of hours' worth of supercomputer calculations, and would require thousands of years of work by an army of mathematicians to thoroughly check every step. Many mathematicians rejected this "proof," as it did not play fair by the traditional rules of the mathematician's game. Twenty years later we find that this computational exercise was merely the tip of an iceberg that is now threatening to change the very rules of the games mathematicians play. The same evolution of the rules of the game is just as likely to occur in science as in mathematics. All that is needed is a Big Question requiring new concepts and new methods. Let me briefly outline one.

A large number of the systems constituting the warp and weft of everyday life—a stock market or a road-traffic network, for example—involve a medium-sized number of agents (traders or drivers) interacting on the basis of limited, local information. Moreover, these agents are intelligent and adaptive; their behavior and interactions with one another are determined by rules, just like those governing the behavior of planets or molecules. But unlike these lifeless objects, adaptive agents are ready to change their rules in accordance with new information that comes their way, thus continually adjusting to their environment so as to prolong their own survival. This is about as good a definition as any I know as to what constitutes a complex adaptive system (CAS). At present there exists nothing remotely close to a formalism (that is, a set of scientific rules) for even stating, let alone understanding, the questions surrounding the weird and wondrous ways of such processes.

A few years back, the Santa Fe Institute was formed to serve as a center for the scientific investigation of just these types of complex systems. But the methods of choice for these studies are as different from the methods used in ordinary science as the use of the computer was to resolve the Four-Color Conjecture. Science, Santa Fe style, is based largely on the use of detailed simulations that serve as silicon surrogates for real-world correlates like stock markets or the immune system. The purpose of these surrogates is to provide a laboratory for carrying out controlled, repeatable experiments of the sort that are too expensive, too impractical, too time-consuming, or just plain too dangerous to do on the real-world system itself. I have given a detailed account elsewhere (*Would-Be Worlds*, Wiley, New York, in press) of how this use of the computer-as-a-laboratory promises to change the frontiers of science in the coming century. So let me just say here that there is every reason to believe that computer laboratories will provide the same kind of insight into the workings of CASes that the invention of the microscope gave to cell biologists or the telescope offered to astronomers. And if history is any guide, this tool is going to generate a plethora of as-yet-unstated Big Questions that will in turn serve as the basis for the creation of a bona fide science of complex systems in the decades to come.

Perhaps not surprisingly, one of the principal targets of Horgan's broadsides against the survival of science is exactly this claim. In a recent electronic debate on the World Wide Web with the imaginative theoretical biologist Stuart Kauffman, Horgan argued that the belief of "chaoplexologists" like Kauffman in the emergence of fundamental new laws of complex systems is so much wishful thinking. Reading the transcripts of this debate is eerily reminiscent of an imagined science-fiction dialogue I once ran across between a human and a human-like alien just in from the far corners of Andromeda. In his intellectual ping-ponging with Horgan, Kauffman valiantly upholds (for the most part successfully, in my view) his belief in the endless levels of complexity one sees in the universe around us, complexities that are well-chronicled in his *At Home in the Universe* (Oxford, New York, 1995). Kauffman makes his case by employing standards and styles of argument familiar in the world of scientific discourse. Horgan's response, however, makes one wonder if there might not really be a second Earth out there in Andromeda, where people use terms like "law," "discovery," "fundamental," and even "science," more as they might be employed in a journal of deconstructionist literary criticism or, perhaps, as they would be propounded by certain continental philosophers whose names I shall pass over with the silence of the grave.

Unlike many of today's "endologists," who hint darkly at the end of some field or other from their perspective as active researchers in the area under scrutiny, journalistic members of the "end-of-X" crowd have a predilection for invoking outside authority figures to buttress their woolly-headed claims. For some unaccountable reason, Nobel-prize-winning physicists seem especially popular in this regard. I don't know about you, but I'm not sure that an eminent physicist, actively engaged in promoting his field, is the first person I'd consult if I were seeking a balanced, non-partisan view of the future of physics. Notwithstanding this fairly obvious point, Horgan, for example, cites with benign approval Richard Feynman's remark that, "[This] is the age in which we are discovering the fundamental laws of nature, and that day will never come again."

Let me appeal to the same shameless rhetorical trick in offering an antidote to Feynman's brand of misguided hubris in the words of Lord Kelvin, former President of the Royal Society, and one of the preeminent physicists of the late 19th century. When told of the discovery of X-rays Kelvin solemnly intoned, "X-rays will prove to be a hoax." My friendly neighborhood radiologist will no doubt ponder this point with considerable pleasure on his next trip to the bank. And on his way from the bank to his summer home in the Swiss Alps, perhaps he'll also ponder another of Lord Kelvin's pronouncements: "I can state flatly that heavier-than-air flying machines are impossible." (I wonder if Lord Kelvin ever saw a bird!) All this brings to mind the statement made by science-fiction writer Arthur C. Clarke, an observation so pregnant with relevancy that it's now enshrined in the literature as Clarke's First Law: "When a distinguished but elderly scientist states that something is possible, he is almost certainly right. When he states that something is impossible, he is very probably wrong."

Let me conclude by noting that there is one genuinely interesting point struggling to emerge from the debate between the Kauffmans and the Horgans of the world. And it is not whether science as we know it is coming to an end. I hope that by now you will agree that that question hardly deserves the attention of a disciplined mind. Rather, the issue that merits considerably more attention than it has thus far received is whether the real world may not be just too complex for the human mind to fully comprehend. In other words, are there limits to what we can ever hope to know by using the tools and techniques of what we call "science"? If such limits do indeed exist, I'm sure we'd all like to know about them. But unless these as-yet-unknown limits happen to encompass every Big Question that we can conceive of asking about life, the universe, and everything else, we would still be as far away from the end of science as we were at its beginning.

Just in case you haven't noticed, heavier-than-air flight is alive and well. Unfortunately, so, too, are lighter-than-air frothings about the end of science. After the philosophical smoke-screens, pretentious blatherings, selective quotations, and rhetorical flourishes all fade away, like a trickle of water in the desert, what remains is little more than a shapeless bit of intellectual fluff, pure cotton candy for the mind.

The Science Wars

Deconstructing Science Is Good Science

DR. RICHARD OLSON

"Men of science are now writing a book as fallible and as infallible,
as wise and as foolish, as learned and as greatly mistaken, as are the scriptures . . .
Newton will come to be as old in science as Moses, and, like the last pundit
philosopher, will be smiled at by posterity as a man who saw wonderful things,
but was walking in the thick darkness of the eighteenth century."
—George Dawson, **Sermons on Disputed Points**, 1878

"Nay, it is come to this, that truth meets nowhere with stronger opposition,
than from many of those that raise the loudest cry about it, and would be taken
for no less than the only dispensers of the favors and oracles of heaven.
If any has the firmness to touch the minutest thing that brings them gain or credit,
he's presently pursued with the hue and cry of heresy."
—John Toland, **Christianity Not Mysterious**, 1696

I have been hearing about, reading about, or involved in a series of events during the past two years that have encouraged me to re-visit a set of issues that I had been centrally concerned about during the late 1960s and early 1970s—contemporary relationships between the scientific and technological communities and their critics. During the late 1960s, I was a newly minted Ph.D. in the history of science with an ABD in physics, teaching at U.C. Santa Cruz, one of the national centers of counter-culture (now, "New Age") thinking. I became disturbed at that time by what seemed to me an unwarranted tendency of some of my more radical colleagues to blame many of the ills of contemporary America—including the Vietnam War—on science and technology.

The big problem for me then, as it remains for me now, was that I could see a substantial kernel of legitimacy in the claims that certain notions of rationality and objectivity associated with modern science and technology did undermine important traditional values that I was and am unwilling to abandon. And it did seem that, for reasons I could not yet begin to understand, the destructive and exploitative potentials of new scientific knowledge often seemed far easier to realize than the constructive and liberating ones. At the same time, though I was aware of some of the limitations in the extent of scientific knowledge, I was convinced—as I remain convinced—that most scientists genuinely believe that they are engaged in the pursuit of value-neutral and universal knowledge of a nature which is oblivious to their interests, and that ultimately such knowledge will be more beneficial than harmful to humanity.

The initial occasion for my return to this topic (in one sense, I never left, because I have worked for years on historical attitudes toward science) was a conversation I had almost two years ago with Peter Degan, a historian of 20th century physics with special interests in the interactions between physics and religion. Peter had been asked to review two recent popular works by distinguished contemporary American Nobel Laureate physicists—*The God Particle: If the Universe Is the Answer, What Is the Question?* (1993) by Leon Lederman and *Dreams of a Final Theory* (1992) by Steven Weinberg. Both books seemed to be intended in substantial part to drum up support for the since-cancelled Superconducting Supercollider, and what particularly struck Degan was the authors' open appropriation of theological and spiritual language in defense of their funding appeals. Degan observed (1994): "They portray the high-energy physicist as the last hero of Western Civilization and the divinely inspired bearer of high culture who pursues humanity's search for transcendent truth and beauty. . . . Consequently, the high Spiritual value of this enterprise makes the supercollider an absolute funding priority and justifies whatever amount of money is needed for its construction" [*Isis*, 85 (1994): 738].

Weinberg's argument is particularly intriguing because while it tries to claim a unique epistemic status for *contemporary* attempts to discover unified theories, it adopts the stance which George Dawson predicted in the mid-19th century, explaining that Newtonian mechanics, of course, had to be superseded because it failed to meet the demand for "logical inevitability" which fundamental particle physicists *now* recognize as essential to any truly legitimate comprehensive theory. The capacity to hold simultaneously that scientific theories are fallible and transcendent is quite marvelous. Apparently, as Einstein and Stephen Hawking have argued, physicists really can see into "the Mind of God," giving high energy physics the religious purpose that Jesse Helms insisted upon as a price for his Senatorial support for the Supercollider. At the same time, they only get to see one small and misleading bit at a time, so that complete enlightenment always demands the further investment of the seeker's time and somebody else's money.

The second event to get me riled was a session of the annual History of Science Society held on October 26, 1995. Billed as a panel discussion of the audiences for the History of Science, the conversation got off to an odd and disturbing start when a faculty member from a well known Northeastern institution claimed that Paul Gross and Norman Levitt's *Higher Superstition: The Academic Left and Its Quarrels with Science* (see Jeffrey Shallit's review in *Skeptic*, 3, No. 1, 98–100) received such a favorable reception that the scientists from whom encouragement for a position in Science and Technology Studies (hereafter, STS) was expected had withdrawn their support. Another historian, who had served as a curator in a public museum devoted to science, then reported that he had not been allowed to include clips from the film *Hiroshima, Nagasaki* (which was compiled from footage shot by Japanese cameramen in the aftermath of the two explosions) in exhibits on the atomic bomb because it reflected too negatively on the scientists involved. Finally, another faculty member argued that as historians of science we had to recognize that our primary audience was science students and scientists, and that we should consequently pay less attention to meeting the intellectual demands of our peers and more to keeping our audience happy and supportive, lest our jobs disappear. (I am in complete agreement that science studies types should seek to serve audiences beyond themselves and that in order to do so we need to write in ways that are accessible to others and that are not intended to provoke hostility. What I seemed to hear that disturbed me was an implication that we should go out of our way to be uncritical.)

About a month after this event, I picked up my Winter, 1996, issue of *Science, Technology, and Human Values* (Vol. 21, #1) to read an acrimonious exchange between Ron Gieryn and Paul Gross over the character of the Smithsonian Institution's "Science in American Life" exhibit. Gieryn, representing the Social Studies of Science community on the Advisory Board for the exhibit, became irate that the exhibit did not adequately acknowledge the insights regarding the social construction of scientific knowledge which have been developed within Science Studies in recent years. Gross, on the other hand, was upset because he viewed the exhibit as unbalanced in its extensive emphasis on negative consequences of science and its failure to adequately represent either the unique cognitive content of science or the "unprecedented human adventure of science" (119). Gross cited as his own chemist M. C. Lafollette's complaint about the reason for the character of the exhibit: ". . . the lead curators seemed so fearful of building a 'pro-science' exhibit (which would have antagonized some of their colleagues) that they wound up creating a largely negative one" (118).

Finally, on December 15, 1995, Richard Sclove, whose Loka Institute sponsors FAST-net, an internet newsgroup oriented toward a more democratic politics of science and technology, initiated a fascinating and disturbing exchange of views when he posted a series of questions under the subject heading "Tech Criticism and Emotion." Sclove has for some time given talks and interviews regarding the social effects of particular technologies, and he

notes that those who disagree with him increasingly claim that he is "anti-technology" and react "with great passion, anger, outrage, and/or defensiveness." One of his questions is why so many people react to the criticism of a particular technology or scientific claim by labeling the critic "anti-technology" or "anti-science," since in the parallel case, persons who criticize a particular law are not labeled "anti-law." Second, he wondered about the basis for the intensity of emotion associated with resistance to technology or science criticism. Both questions are of special importance to Sclove for very personal reasons, because, as he writes, "maybe there is little point in pursuing public technology criticism if I'm doing it in ways that are counterproductively pushing a lot of folks' emotional buttons. Perhaps if I understood the 'buttons' better, I could learn to reframe my talks to make them more effective." This posting elicited an outpouring of impassioned responses from scientists and engineers as well as STS scholars and science and technology policy activists, most of which serve better to illustrate the problems that Sclove raises than to provide answers to his questions.

What unifies all of these episodes, it seems to me, is that they are all symptoms of an increasing polarization between scientists, engineers, and the managers of technological enterprises on the one hand, and students and consumers of science and technology on the other. Furthermore, it seems to me that there are at least two major and closely intertwined sets of causes for the current tensions between these two groups.

First is the passing of the "Golden Age" of research and development associated with the Cold War. With a diminished military justification for R&D expenditures, we are seeing a substantial "downsizing" of both governmental and corporate R&D programs in the name of cost cutting. Whether these policies are wise in the long run, even from a purely economic perspective, is debatable. What is absolutely certain is that they have created a real short term threat to the economic health of the science and engineering communities, with physics being hit particularly hard. One symptom of the current hard times in the sciences and engineering is the huge number of applicants for science positions in four year colleges—positions which serious professionally oriented scientists or engineers formerly looked on with disdain. The last two such searches that I know of produced over 1000 and over 800 applicants, respectively, many from senior scientists willing to accept entry level rank and pay.

A second symptom is a tendency on the part of scientists in particular—illustrated by the works of Lederman and Weinberg—to try to justify scientific activities increasingly in non-military and non-economic terms, drawing on longstanding Neo-platonic traditions associated with mystical elements in Christianity and Judaism. (Margaret Wertheim has identified this Neo-platonic or Pythagorean tradition used by Western scientists in an interesting way in her *Pythagoras' Trousers: God, Physics, and the Gender Wars* [New York: Random House, 1995], but she has paid little attention to the social and economic conditions which have recently produced a renewed focus on this line of argument.)

A third symptom is the completely understandable tendency of many contemporary scientists and technologists to respond defensively and violently to any perceived attack on the credibility, authority, or beneficence of the scientific and/or technological enterprises. Any professional elite that perceives itself to be losing status and economic support—whether it be the Anglican clergy in the 17th century in the chaotic aftermath of the English Civil War, or the scientific and technical community in the late 20th century in the chaotic aftermath of the Cold War—is likely to respond defensively and with all of the cultural resources that it can muster to perceived attacks. Indeed,

it would be irrational for its members to do otherwise, according to the notion of rationality prevailing among economists today, for to act rationally is merely to act in ways consistent with one's perceived interests.

The second cause is related to the first. At the same time that scientists and engineers are threatened by social and economic forces that are largely beyond their control, it is certainly true that *some* members of the STS community really are openly and admittedly hostile to science and technology (at least as they are currently practiced or implemented). The STS community provides one of the few identifiable and reachable targets for the anxiety, frustration, and anger which some scientists feel about the very real threats to the status and economic health of their disciplines. If one chooses to define science and/or technology sufficiently narrowly, it is possible to argue legitimately that some of its members really are "anti-science" and/or "anti-technology." In that case it can hardly be surprising that some scientists and engineers are inclined to blame current trends in academic STS for some of their woes and to launch counterattacks against such perceived slight.

None of what I have said so far is intended to trivialize the arguments between certain scientists and certain STS figures, or to suggest that there are not important intellectual issues at stake. Rather, it is intended to suggest why some of these issues have become matters of intense public concern very recently, and why the parties to debates seem to be becoming increasingly strident and uncivil toward one another. When we turn to the content of the conflicts between those who speak on behalf of the scientific/technological community and those who are often taken to be the spokespersons for the STS community, that content seems to hinge on a small number of basic foundational principles, assumptions, and values. Among these, one of the most fundamental seems to be the question of commitment to some form of philosophical realism versus commitment to some form of social constructionism.

Many, perhaps most, scientists believe—with Paul Gross—that scientific knowledge claims refer to some "real" natural world which exists independent of scientists, and that anyone who denies this claim is "anti-science." On the other hand, most students of STS believe that the objects of scientific claims are "representations" whose meanings are always negotiated within a specific social context. The most extreme of these see no way to link such representations to any independent "reality," so they conclude that there is no independent reality to be represented and that scientists who claim otherwise are claiming an authority which does not belong to them. It seems to me that any good skeptic must suspend belief with respect to this issue. While plausibility arguments may be developed on both sides, nothing since the time of David Hume has happened to guarantee that humans have access to any reality underlying their experiences or that experience itself is possible outside the domain of customs and habits which are acquired in social settings. By the same token, we can have no knowledge that warrants the denial of some reality underlying experience, so any insistence upon pure social constructivism seems as unwarranted as an insistence on pure realism. The trans-cultural applicability of many scientific knowledge claims suggests that there may at least be some species-common forms of experience and cognition. Historians and sociologists of science, however, have developed enough case studies that demonstrate the cultural specificity of many explanatory structures to suggest that socio-cultural factors often play a significant role in what representational systems we construct and therefore in what we count as legitimate science at any particular time and place. It would thus seem safest to either admit that both culture-transcendent and culture-dependent factors play a role in the generation of scientific knowledge or to act in ways that are neutral relative to realist/social-constructionist claims.

The realist/social-constructionist dichotomy is related to a second issue connected with the definitions of "science" and "technology." At the heart of this issue is the question of how extensive we believe employment of the terms science and technology should be. Do science and technology include all the motives which underlie the creation of knowledge or artifacts and the uses to which they are put (whether by the creators' designs or otherwise)? Do they include all of the institutions within which knowledge and objects are made and used? Or do they include only the sequences of knowledge claims and artifacts or tools, without regard for whom they were produced, how they were used, and how they have differentially affected the lives of different groups of people?

Until relatively recently (the mid 20th century), most studies of the scientific and technological enterprises were done by scientists and engineers who tended to define science and technology as a special kind of knowledge and as a sequence of inventions, with little regard to any social dimensions or contexts. George Sarton, for example, a physical chemist turned historian of science who founded the History of Science Society, defined science as "systematized positive knowledge, or what has been taken as such at different ages and in different places" (1936, 5). In his famous *A History of Mechanical Inventions*, Albert Payson Usher argued that it was best "to separate the history of the inventions from the discussion of their significance" (1954, ix).

In fact, neither Sarton, Usher nor any of their fellow travellers really thought that science or technology could be completely separated from all human context. Instead, they tended to argue that the communities of scientists and inventor-entrepreneurs are relatively autonomous and that each is self-defined in terms of a set of commitments to unique constitutive values which are aimed at producing objective knowledge or increasing the efficiency of productive processes respectively. For those who define themselves as scientists in this way, the production of objective knowledge—or TRUTH—becomes the ultimate value, with commitment to such subordinate values as honesty, independence of authority, disinterestedness, openness of communications, etc., defining the moral worth of individuals.

With rare exceptions, most scientists and engineers continue to prefer to understand their activities in these narrowly construed ways, with the consequence that they can insulate themselves or deny responsibility for the social consequences of their activities, at least with those that might be considered negative. (They are frequently willing to take credit for the positive ones in a move that is psychologically understandable, but logically suspect.) After all, objective knowledge claims, being value-neutral, are available to all to use, and it is the users who must incur the blame for any misuse.

Modern STS is dominated by persons whose primary interests and commitments are to an understanding of the broad social contexts and consequences of science and technology. These include the social considerations that direct money and effort at certain problems rather than others, as well as the social and economic consequences that follow from the utilization of scientific knowledge or the implementation of technological systems to serve particular interests in society. With rare exceptions most of these persons have a strong commitment to social and economic equity and to participatory democracy, with a concomitant suspicion of expertise. Moreover, they are inclined to think that the search for a good life is a communal rather than an individual enterprise. Such people are, as Gross and Levitt quite rightly point out, largely members of the academic left, although contra Gross and Levitt, that fact does not mean either that they

are wrong or that they are misguided. Above all, in their minds, it does not mean that they are anti-scientific. Many, such as the feminist philosopher Sandra Harding, are inclined to believe that a more egalitarian and inclusive scientific community would be capable of producing a more nearly universal and objective knowledge.

It is a serious mistake, I think, to try to ask which group is more nearly "correct" about the nature of science or technology. How one chooses to define these terms is to a substantial extent an ideological choice which is made largely because of commitments to certain values. That is, in the broadest sense of the word, the choice is made for political or ideological reasons. If it is a set of superstitions or an ideology that guides the leadership of the STS community in its interpretations of the scientific and technological enterprises—and it is—it is no less a set of superstitions or an ideology that guides the scientific community's vision of itself. By the same token, *each* of these sets of value commitments is likely to be equally "rational," in the sense that each is as likely as the other to be consistent with the preferred ends of its advocates.

PLEASE NOTE: I am not suggesting that the definitions of science and technology are arbitrary, any more than the claim that for some purposes light can be considered as exhibiting particle-like characteristics while for other purposes it can be considered to have wave-like characteristics means that the definition of light is arbitrary. What I am suggesting is that different purposes may be served by considering science and technology narrowly as systems of propositions and aggregates of artifacts respectively on the one hand, and as socially and culturally embedded human activities on the other.

What does all of this mean for those of us who seek to make intelligent decisions about issues on which scientists and technologists or members of the STS community have something to say, or who hope to say something worthwhile and not merely inflammatory about contemporary science and technology? One important answer is suggested by the feminist "point of view" theorists. According to the advocates of point of view theory, every party to every argument starts from some set of value orientations that emerge out of the life history of the participant. Moreover, all such sets are probably either equally rational, a-rational, or non-rational. Since to proceed without at least implicitly adopting some set of values is impossible, we might all be better off if we could "own," or become aware of, our own point of view and learn to respect—not necessarily agree with—the points of view taken by others. This stance was articulated in a particularly illuminating way in a "Response to Sclove" posted on FASTnet on January 2, 1996, by Lars Kluver, director of the Danish Board of Technology, which has developed a system of citizen-based "consensus conferences" to assess the potential impact of new technologies. Kluver reports the results of surveys done for the Danish Board of Technology on attitudes toward biotechnologies:

A positive attitude to biotech is seen among people who believe in economic growth, competition, a strong army, and who generally think technology is of the good. A negative or skeptical attitude is found among people who believe in social equality, a healthy environment, and who generally question the benefits of technology. Our general attitudes towards a technology, in other words, do not come from rational thinking, but rather from the values we already have and try to live out—from our value-conservatism. To be short (and of course

ignoring a lot of details) many technology debates [the same is true about science debates] have more to do with ideology (or religion, if you like) than they have with rationality. That may be why your right to open up a debate is not respected. Your opponents simply do not have the strength or ability to question their own values and as a result, they spoil the debate instead.

What can you do about it? I cannot think of any fail safe tactics. In the end we are dealing with psychology here. It is very much up to your skill as a debater to clear away the defenses of your opponent. But respecting the rights of opponents to say what they want to is a prerequisite to getting the same respect back.

There is one final point I would like to make: the reactions you meet can be seen from both sides of the technology debate. Many industrialists meet the same kind of reactions from green-party "believers," when they try to initiate a constructive technology debate (which many industrialists do). One type of reaction from the green people is: "Why should I listen to your arguments—you only want to make money anyway" (the "you-are stupid," or "you are left-wing" kind of argument again). Value-conservatism is a widespread phenomenon.

I am virtually certain that the only real possibility for carrying out constructive discussions about science and technology policies depends upon the growth of abilities among people of all persuasions to question their own values. And of all people who can do this it is, or at least it should be, the skeptics. I believe this ability is precisely what the skeptics should be promoting. What do you think?

The Science Wars

Deconstructing Science Is Pseudoscience

NORM LEVITT

In the process of answering my critics—particularly Richard Olson in his article on the science wars (see previous entry)—I wish to address the difference between knowledge and knowingness. It seems to me transparently obvious that acquiring and extending knowledge about the natural world is the real business of science, and that science has been astonishingly successful in doing this over the past few centuries. Yet even among highly educated people this fact often breeds discontent. Much of this is understandable. A technocratic civilization of global dimensions has been raised on the foundations laid down by science, and not all of its manifestations are admirable or reassuring. What is there to like about toxic waste or multi-megaton warheads? But while moral unease about the fruits of science makes some sense, it has been known to give rise to extravagant philosophical positions.

Specifically there are those who claim to have tamed the monster by declaring that somehow it is all a fake; science isn't "real" knowledge, it's just a "narrative." It's not abstractly preferable to other systems of belief—myth for instance—merely attached to a culture that is, for the moment, more powerful than others. To make this strange doctrine even marginally plausible would seem to require an intellectual engine at least comparably powerful to that deployed by the sciences. How could one hope to reveal the errors of a flawed knowledge-system without having some keener instrument at hand to dissect it?

Quite obviously, no such thing has been invented. What serves in its place, however, is a stubbornly entrenched species of knowingness, an attitude that gives itself permission to avoid the pain and difficulty of actually understanding science simply by declaring in advance that knowledge is futile or illusory.

Knowingness is usually intertwined with cynicism. But cynicism is only palatable when it makes itself one of its own targets. Knowingness has the annoying habit of letting itself off the hook. It functions selectively, casting a nasty shadow only in certain preferred directions. In fact, knowingness can sometimes be allied with the grossest credulity. The UFO buff who will swallow whole the most grotesque tales of alien abduction pulls a very knowing attitude when you try to point out that there is no evidence that a flying saucer crashed in Roswell, New Mexico, in 1947. You can't fool him! He just *knows* that those devious government mandarins will go to incredible lengths to keep the information hidden, just as the militia member knows that the BATF is trying to take away his fully automatic weapons so that the Zionist Occupation Government can impose its New World Order.

It isn't always the case, however, that knowingness is predicated on falsity or delusion. It may well be founded on a truth or a genuine insight. The real problem with knowingness is that it is fundamentally lazy. It looks for a Royal Road to deep understanding, a methodology that excuses one from having to look closely at details or take complexity and fine distinctions into account. Thus, it rapidly becomes formulaic, perfunctory, and extremely closed-minded. Genuine knowledge, suffice it to say, is a very different and vastly more demanding creature.

Let me offer my favorite example of the distinction between knowledge and knowingness—Mozart's great opera *Cosi fan tutte*. The plot is a shallow, brittle piece of fluff that has nothing to recommend it but its superficial knowingness. It regards the perplexities of love with a smirk and a sneer. The idea is that two young soldiers wager on the fidelity of their sweethearts with an embittered friend. They pretend to be called away to the battlefield. Then each dons a disguise and woos the other's mistress. Within a matter of hours the girls' vows of undying faithfuness wilt under a barrage of flattery and hormones. The soldiers then return as themselves to humiliate their lovers. For the sake of theatrical convention, the disenchanted men agree to take back their tarnished goddesses, for all women are the same and these no worse than any others.

Clearly this is a very silly affair. One 19th-century critic called it "too stupid for criticism." And yet, when Mozart's music infuses it, this nasty trifle is transformed into a compelling human story. By some magic no critic can quite account for, the cardboard cutout characters become fully realized human beings and their seemingly absurd plight becomes deeply moving. Not a word or action strays from the conventions of sex-farce, yet at the end we are neither amused nor titillated, but saddened and thoughtful. Mozart is not only a great musical craftsman; he is a great

psychologist and a great dramatist. He understands people down to their core as only a very few artists—Shakespeare, for one—do. Through his uncanny alchemy, he allows us to know what he knows about the pain of self knowledge. The contrast between the superficial nonsense of the ostensible plot and the deep truth that is revealed through the music makes that revelation all the more poignant.

I'll now fast-forward to the late 1980s when a trendy young director named Peter Sellars mounted controversial productions of Mozart's three great buffa operas, updating their settings to contemporary New York. Sellars was the perfect incarnation of what was then coming to be known as the postmodern sensibility—in other words, a knowing smart-aleck determined to deconstruct the life out of everything he touched. For my money, his stagings were wretched; their musical inadequacy alone doomed them. But what really riled me was the director's self-indulgent display of superficial knowingness. This was seen at its worst in Sellars' *Cosi*, which was set, if you can believe it, in a suburban diner, with all characters depicted as borderline psychotics. In numerous public statements, the director smugly insisted that in seeing through the comic exterior to the bitter inner reality, he was the first to understand the work deeply. This was, of course, nonsensical as well as arrogant. Sellars was hardly the first commentator to perceive the opera's autumnal sadness, merely the most vulgar and trivial. His knowingness was self-defeating; in discarding the farce, he also threw away the exquisite subtlety and the shimmering mystery of the piece. By presenting himself as smarter than Mozart, he proved himself an uncomprehending ass.

I mentioned Sellars and his mugging of Mozart because it was through this disagreeable episode that I first became aware that there was such a thing as postmodernism afoot in the land. Only later did it dawn on me that the academy had been deeply drawn into this dreadful vortex, with faculty (senior and junior) and graduate students by the thousands clamoring frantically to be let into the club. It was especially horrifying to realize that among the articles of faith required of postulants was the dogma that only through this creed could one enlist in the struggle against the social and political evils of the world; only by getting right with Foucault, Derrida, Lyotard, and Kristeva could one truly oppose racism, sexism, homophobia, imperialism, ethnocentrism, and all the attendant evils wrought by the capitalist West. Since my politics are those of my granddad—which is to say Debsian socialist—I was disconsolate that at the tail end of this horrid century the grand tradition of the engagé intellectual had deliquesced into this slobber. To the extent that I could unkink the prevailing rhetoric to see how its practitioners thought they might accomplish something in terms of real-world politics, the master-plan seemed to be this: if enough professors committed themselves to using bizarre, woolly, and pretentious language in books, papers, and lectures, then the contours of the world would shift, expelling all evils and inaugurating the reign of the just. This idea seemed pretty comical to me, although the joke was bitter, but it took many supposedly humanistic fields by storm, particularly literary criticism and related subjects. Frank Lentricchia, a repentant Duke English professor who was, until recently, a highly placed courtier in this little empire, put it this way:

> I believe what is now called literary criticism is a form of Xeroxing. Tell me your theory and I'll tell you in advance what you'll say about any work of literature, especially those you haven't read. Texts are not read, they are preread. All of literature is x and nothing but x, and literary study is the naming (exposure) of x. For x, read imperialism, sexism, homophobia, and so on. All of literary history is said to be a display of x, because human history is nothing but the structure of x. By naming x, we supposedly name the social order (ordure) as it is, and always has been. An advanced literature department is the place where you can write a dissertation on Wittgenstein and never have to face an examiner from the philosophy department. An advanced literature department is the place where you may speak endlessly about gender and never have to face the scrutiny of a biologist, because gender is just a social construction, and nature doesn't exist.

This comment is gratifying in that it pretty much summarizes what I've long believed about the weird course taken by lit-crits and the like in recent years; it's nice to hear it from a consummate insider. However, from my point of view, the antics of avant-garde English professors would merely have been part of the passing scene, and really none of my business, had not the infection spread to what used to be a sober, intelligent, and valuable discipline: the history, philosophy, and sociology of science. What emerged from this contagion is now usually called "science studies." It hasn't by any means completely obliterated traditional scholarship in the area, but it has become the most aggressively self-promoting and publicly visible branch. It has risen to prominence on the same current of enthusiasm for "postmodernism" and for ostensible political rectitude that has overwhelmed literature departments. It shares many of the current dogmas of literary studies, and colludes closely with academic manifestations of identity politics such as women's studies. It overlaps what is nowadays called cultural studies, a tendency that has effaced traditional scholarship in a number of areas, and it has absorbed many of the radically relativistic attitudes that predominate in postmodern cultural anthropology. The central doctrine of science studies is that science is "socially constructed" in a way that disallows traditional notions of scientific validity and objectivity. On this view, scientific theories are merely narratives peculiar to this culture and this point in its history. Their chief function is to create stories about the world consonant with dominant social and political values. Thus, they are no more "true," or even more reliable, than the myths, legends, and just-so stories of other cultures. All are equally culture-specific.

I can't claim that every would-be scholar connected with the science studies movement accepts this doctrine wholeheartedly in its most radical form. Yet it constitutes the ineluctable background assumption of most theorizing and discussion. It is the ultimate trump card in debate, and such misgivings as may exist tend to be expressed with exaggerated caution. To object too strongly is to invite the charge of collusion with Western intellectual hegemony and with the impermissibly universalistic claims of Western science and Western rationalism. Here, inviting comparison with Lentricchia's remarks on postmodern literary studies, is a disillusioned assessment of postmodern science studies by Meera Nanda, a scholar in that area who is, by the way, a leftist and feminist of nonwestern background:

> Indeed, constructionists admonish us to give up such outmoded notions of truth as a correspondence with a mind-independent reality. Rather, they insist that truth and falsity of knowledge claims be treated "symmetrically," that is, true knowledge to be contingent on social factors to the same degree as falsehoods are. In this remarkable feat of cognitive egalitarianism, one cannot say that true knowledge is true and preferable because it transcends social interests and describes the world as it is, for that would refute what sociologists set out to prove, namely, that *all* knowledge and not just ideology is constituted by social interests and power. . . . One not completely unintended consequence of their epistemological anti-realism is that constructionists have taken it upon themselves to try to wean working scien-

tists and ordinary people from their commonsensical distinction between truth and falsity as a better or worse match with an independent reality, a distinction the constructionists believe is itself a western social construct.

No less than in the circle of alien-abduction believers, knowingness rules the day for science critics, with the curious corollary that knowledge—that infinitely more precious substance—is tossed on the trash heap. "You can't dupe us!" cry the social constructionists, thereby duping themselves beyond hope of redemption.

Richard Olson's essay is an attempt to defend this rather indefensible cult as embodying a kind of cracker-barrel, commonsensical skepticism. I sense that his heart isn't completely in the project, and that he's rather uneasily aware that some of what he proposes to defend can't be defended but must be camouflaged instead. However that may be, his essay reveals, in a number of ways, the intellectual constipation that results when mere knowingness takes the place of analysis and inquiry. Since one of his points touches me personally, more or less, I'll begin with that one. Olson insists—and here he has a lot of company within the science studies confraternity—that the reason his cartel has come under heavy criticism from scientists is this: the end of the Cold War has diminished both popular enthusiasm and government backing for science; the era of the carte blanche is over. Chagrined scientists are therefore looking for scapegoats, and their ire has fastened upon the innocent science studies community, a clan of fellow scholars who are just doing their job.

This has a certain plausibility if cheap cynicism is your only benchmark. The problem is that it's simply untrue. Olson has been generous enough to point out that *Higher Superstition*, the book I co-authored with Paul R. Gross, was of some significance in triggering the counter-reaction of the scientific community. Thus it follows from his thesis that Paul and I must have been particularly obsessed with the post–Cold War shortfall in science funding, and that this sent us hunting for scapegoats. But this isn't so! Frankly, if someone had bothered to ask me at the time I started writing on these issues what I thought the end of the Cold War implied for science funding, I'd have answered that I expected at least a modest "peace dividend" for pure research in the basic sciences, even under a Republican administration. Alas, that's not how things worked out, but it's what I thought.

The simple truth is that I became a critic of the radical science-studies movement because it seemed so intellectually shallow and indefensible, and because its leading figures, a number of whom I had taken care to hear out, seemed to embody all the misplaced self-regard and self-certainty that make postmodernism so unappealing. In other words, the bumptious Peter Sellars and his unholy mangling of Mozart were much more to the front of my mind than the funding policies of the Pentagon, NASA, National Science Foundation, National Institute of Health, the Department of Energy, and so forth. Moreover, I can speak with some authority about the motives of other people who have become involved on my side of the issue. The "post–Cold War" hypothesis doesn't fit them either—for one thing, it's pretty clear to us all that a coterie of leftish professors, however fervent, doesn't have a hell of a lot of direct influence on high government policy or on popular opinion. Nor does it fit the mathematicians and physicists at the Institute for Advanced Study in Princeton who clobbered the proposed appointment of Bruno Latour, a character deified by science studies trendoids. There, the issue was whether charlatanry ought to be rewarded by tenure at the most prestigious scholarly institution in the country. I'm perfectly happy to stipulate that disciples of science studies don't have very much real-world political power. But that

should not immunize them from intellectual accountability.

While I'm on the subject of leftish politics and its connection with these issues, let me point out that Olson has it backwards on a related question. He specifically accuses my book of arguing that the practitioners of postmodern science-critique must be in error simply because they are on the left. This is not only a distortion, it's an absurdity. I'm pretty much on the left myself—I even have a couple of scars to prove it. What I really object to is the way a claim of left sympathies is used as a perpetual Get-Out-of-Jail-Free card, something that allows one to dismiss any criticism, however cogent, as the spite-work of diabolical reactionaries. If anyone bothers to check, it will be found that many of the points made by *Higher Superstition* have also been made by Noam Chomsky, clearly no "rightist" and clearly no fan of postmodern "theory" as it applies to science or anything else. Olson sheepishly acknowledges that most of the science studies gendarmerie has sort-of-leftish aims, but glosses this as merely implying an interest in socio-economic equality and increased democracy. That's not the problem. The problem is that the version of leftist thought that dominates is a sectarian offshoot, and a weird one at that. Peruse the literature, and you will easily find that "democracy," by these peculiar lights, is supposed to mean that all "ways of knowing" are to be accorded equal epistemic dignity, with the possible exception of scientific rationalism itself, which is naturally to be reviled as imperialistic, sexist, homophobic, and so forth. It seems to me that this view is not only silly, but of no particular use to progressive causes, as I understand them. It is, however, of some use to reactionary causes. The purveyors of biblical creationism, for instance, have their antennas up for useful bits of academic blather, and they have found a trove in the stock of catchphrases that science studies has coined to pooh-pooh actual science. In fact, they may have found actual allies, to judge by the statements one very prominent constructionist theorist has made within my hearing. To cite another instance, Meera Nanda has conclusively demonstrated that the impact of postmodernism, relativism, and anti-universalism on the Indian intellectual left was devastating. It paralyzed the fight against religious obscurantism and its attendant reactionary, misogynist politics. Simultaneously, it handed the Hindu fundamentalist movements a heap of useful slogans to deploy. One result has been the displacement of science and mathematics in many public schools by their "Vedantic" versions. The reaction of the science studies community has been telling, particularly in response to another outrage cited by Nanda. This concerns a powerful politician whose credulousness with respect to a superstitious practice called Vastu Shastra led directly to the destruction of a poor community. Nanda relates:

> I have tested this case on my social constructionist friends here in the U.S. While they do see the injustice of the situation, they do not see why I am so exercised by the irrationality that led to it. We have our superstitions in the West, they tell me. Did not Nancy Reagan consult astrologers? As for my suggestion that if we want justice, we must challenge the irrationality of the ideas that lead to injustice, I am told that there is no need for proving that Vastu Shastra is wrong and modern science correct. I am told that seeing the two culturally bound descriptions at par with each other is progressive in itself, for then neither can claim to know the absolute truth, and this tradition will lose its hold on people's minds. I am told that this desire to prove that the traditional knowledge is an incorrect representation of nature is a sign of a scientistic mindset, a hangover from my training in biology, that I must overcome it if I do not want to re-engineer the society of my birth on technocratic lines. Finally, I am told that I am an in-

corrigible modernist if I believe that Western science has any democracy-enhancing potential in the world.

Could there be any more pointed instance of smug, insular, airtight, infinitely condescending knowingness? Here we have a picture of sanctimonious science studies arrogance in full bloom. In my experience, it is quite characteristic.

Olson cites Sandra Harding as someone who is intent on "democratizing" science in order to make it "capable of producing a more nearly universal and objective knowledge." Perhaps he hasn't read her with particular care. What she says pretty much accords with the constructionist dogmatics cited above; she is horrified by the notion of universally valid knowledge. For a view of what she actually has in mind when she speaks of "democracy" and "objectivity," I recommend her essay in *Social Text* (no. 46/47). To wit:

> Most models of the scientific future . . . imagine "one true science." They do not imagine as existing or desirable many different, and in some respects conflicting representations of nature. Yet this vision is beginning to emerge in the new Northern [i.e., what is usually called Western] science studies.

No less than the constructionists cited by Nanda, she enthusiastically recommends regarding all local knowledge systems, of which standard science is but one instance, as equally mature and equally valid. As to objectivity, she seems to equate it with anything that serves her political goals.

Quite appropriately, perhaps, in that same issue of *Social Text* the mathematical physicist Alan Sokal published his now-famous hoax. Sokal induced the postmodern luminaries who edit that journal to publish a heap of double-talk under the pretext that it was a real live scientist's genuflection to the wisdom of postmodern sages. This illustrates the kind of trouble a supposed intellectual can get into by letting mere knowingness do the work of careful, critical thought. The editors approved of Sokal's pretended sentiments (including his fulminations against Gross and Levitt); they didn't understand the math or the physics, but they liked the postmodern slogans that surrounded the technical stuff; they really didn't understand the paper as a whole (you can't—it makes no sense) but it sounded like the kind of thing they assume one is supposed to pretend to take seriously. They invited disgrace, and it descended on them in spades. Goody! But the whole affair makes an important political point. Sokal is yet another opponent of postmodern science-critique who is himself a principled leftist. His prank brought dozens of such people out of the woodwork. Articles appeared in adamantly left publications like the *Nation* (Katha Pollitt), *In These Times* (Tom Frank), and *Z Magazine* (Michael Albert), praising Sokal's stunt and largely siding with him (and perforce with me) in the resulting doctrinal catfight.

It is either hopelessly naive or hopelessly disingenuous on Olson's part to imply that the quarrel between the science critics and "their" critics follows the standard Right-Left cleavage line. It doesn't—not even close.

Let us also consider one of Olson's more abstract philosophical points. At some length Olson defends, at least provisionally, the notion of anti-realism. Here, philosophical muddle clouds his efforts; he has confused the epistemological with the ontological. As the philosopher John Searle pointed out, ontological realism is a position virtually everyone takes automatically, while anti-realism is incoherent. For realism is not so much a formal doctrine as it is the unspoken ground of all discourse, all attempts at communication. Any sincere declarative utterance is an attempt to give a true account of something assumed to be real. Ol-

son himself, for instance, speaks of scientists, science studies scholars, and the relations between them. He assumes, ipso facto, that there are such things in the universe and that they may be meaningfully described. Thus, he is, malgre lui, as much an ontological realist as any physicist talking about quarks and leptons. We all are. Even a solipsist is a kind of straitened realist. This is not to say that we all agree on the same ontology or the same hierarchy of categories. Plainly we do not. The social constructionists, when they're not pretending to be anti-realist, hold that the socially real is really the really real, and that the scientist's reality is a figment. Thus they are realists after all, albeit screwy ones.

Olson does allude to real and perplexing philosophical questions. The ontological conundrum is a deep one: to what extent may we reify any of our theories about the world, even the most sophisticated, phenomenologically adequate theories? When, and with what justification, may we assert that the objects that seem natural in the context of these theories are the pristine entities underlying the real universe? This problem has been around for millennia, and it is surpassingly deep. In this connection, one may evoke names like Plato, Duns Scotus, William of Occam, Hume, Kant, Poincaré, Mach, Bohr, Carnap, Ayer, Quine, Bohm, Margenau, and even Penrose and Hawking. The problem largely stands apart, however, from problems of epistemology, especially those addressed by the social constructionists. Scientists, qua scientists, are basically interested in phenomenological adequacy and logical economy. Thus, a sensible theory of scientific epistemology must keep ontological questions pretty much in the background. They are not relevant to the "social construction" debate. In any case, despite their claims, the constructionists haven't made much of a contribution to the ontological problem—about the same, I'd say, as Barney the Purple Dinosaur. Talking about it is, however, a pretty good smokescreen for doubtful epistemology.

The besetting sin of social constructionism, and therefore of the science studies movement that blazons forth social construction on all its banners, is one of laziness. A few anemic truisms about how everything we do as human beings is "social" are cobbled together into a vague General Theorem. A fatal knowingness suffuses every corner of the enterprise. It licenses practitioners to talk endlessly about science without ever talking about science. Since one knows that scientific theories are mere transcriptions of social prejudices and social processes, all one has to do is tell a just-so story about social imagery or the like. One needn't bother with the inner logic of the theory, or with the evidence directly bearing on it, since these are, by assumption, mere illusions. This is a very forgiving methodology in practice; it seems to allow highly selective choice of evidence, procrustean treatment of such evidence as is cited, special pleading and, when all else fails, recourse to moralistic intimidation. Consequently, the "case studies" Olson alludes to as illustrating social construction in action are remarkably weak, and interesting only for what they tell us about the sovereign power of the bandwagon, even among supposed intellectuals with real Ph.D.'s.

The version of science studies Olson is trying to defend is really a changeling child. When the idea was first formulated about 20 years ago, the intention was to study the interaction between science and history, politics, social circumstances, philosophy, ethics, religion, and art. This was a worthy undertaking and a difficult one, requiring scholars at least moderately well versed in some branch of science in addition to whatever other specialized knowledge and methodology might be required. It wasn't intended to be slavishly admiring of each and every scientist, nor to disguise the difficult problems that a technology

often more powerful than wise imposes on us. But neither was it intended to minimize the intellectual strength and integrity of science, nor to "contextualize" it into a culture-bound tissue of prejudices. In short, it was an enterprise that required grown-ups. A funny thing happened, however. The infant discipline was whisked out of sight while a phalanx of postmodernist wiseacres put in its place a bizarre, misshapen, and antic creature, one which exhibited all the deformities of its cousins in literary studies, cultural anthropology, ethnic studies, and so on, as well as some peculiar organs all its own.

It may well be possible to return to the original intent and to create a discipline intellectually sound and with something important to contribute to the political, ethical, and even the esthetic, vision of our culture. Many scholars (perhaps including Olson himself) wish this were so. Alas, the faddists are still in charge, thanks largely to the imputation of deviation from political rectitude that awaits anyone who too skeptically challenges constructionist dogma. But questions are being raised and reluctant dragons prodded into battle. The caustic response of scientists has something to do with this. Nothing deflates a windbag like a horselaugh (for which reason Alan Sokal's drollery may well accelerate the process considerably). The adjustment may be painful for some young researchers who have been conned into thinking that they are on the cutting edge of enormous intellectual revolution. Science studies—the responsible version thereof—will enlighten, inform, and clarify in many respects, but it almost certainly won't produce earth-shattering epiphanies or mind-bending paradoxes. I suspect that it will deflect the course of science itself only modestly (though benevolently, I hope). To a generation that hoped to turn the world upside down, and was taught that the right jargon intoned in the proper style could do so, this no doubt will come as a disappointment. But perhaps maturity, together with an appropriately Darwinian winnowing of the field and a desacralization of smug smartasserie, will cushion the transition. I certainly hope so.

Knowingness doesn't work for scientists, not, at least, when they are practicing their trade. Knowingness invites you to cut corners, and when you do so, reality exhibits a most remarkable tendency to step right up and kick you in the tail. Knowingness simply gets in the way when it is knowledge you are after. Knowingness won't work for science studies either, not if one takes the long view. Olson's essay, like a number of other items, including the infamous issue of *Social Text*, erupts into view right now because, after years of relative immunity, the science studies racket is under scrutiny by intellectuals in and out of science who won't be put off by the usual line of patter or soothed by the standard aphorisms. Like any Mafia family when the indictments come down, science studies gets in touch with its lawyers and protestations of affronted virtue pour forth. Sorry. I don't think that sort of thing will work here. These days, the Tree of the Hesperides does not thrive in the Groves of Academe, for they are choked by postmodernist smog; such pomology brings forth apples not golden, but variously crab, sour, and just plain rotten. The word is out and it's getting hard to unload the crop at any price.

Face it, guys, the jig is up.

Olson Replies

I was deeply saddened to read Norman Levitt's response to my article because it seems to me to illustrate precisely the intensifying pattern of demonizing those who do not share every one of our assumptions and values that Lars Kluver so effectively pointed out and which I sought to discourage. Usually this process involves considerations which Professor Levitt identifies with the term knowingness—a stance which "dispenses one from having to look too closely at details or take complexity and fine distinctions into account. Thus, it rapidly becomes formulaic, perfunctory, and extremely closed minded." It is not clear to me that anyone would want to disagree with Levitt's antagonism to knowingness, but just to be absolutely clear, I happen to share his irritation with those who do not look closely and carefully at details, who ignore complexity and fine distinctions, and who are proudly closed minded. Moreover, I am not really thrilled about those whose arguments contain fundamental logical fallacies either.

Because I do not pretend to the knowledge which Professor Levitt has about literary criticism and Mozart, I would like to focus on the concept of knowingness in connection with science studies in general and my position with respect to radical social constructionism in particular. Let me begin with an issue of logic which will move us onto broader concerns. Levitt asserts that because I suggested that the impact of *Higher Superstition* was symptomatic of trends in the relationship between the scientific community and the broader public which are related to the post–Cold War downturn in science funding, "it follows from [my] thesis that Paul and I must have been particularly obsessed with the post–Cold War shortfall in science funding. . . ." I very carefully did not say anything about the motives of the authors of *Higher Superstition*, nor do I believe for one minute that there is any legitimate logical strategy that can allow one to infer the motives of any author by considering the way in which readers use that author's words. Indeed, one major theme of my *Emergence of the Social Sciences* (Twayne, 1993) was that early works in the social sciences almost universally ended up serving interests diametrically opposed to those intended by their authors.

Certainly Levitt is not alone in seeing logical implications where there are none. Radical social constructionists are as likely—perhaps even more likely—to assume that because some argument is used for a given purpose it was intended for that purpose; and I do not applaud this tendency among social constructionists any more than I do among their antagonists. In both cases, it seems to me to arise from an unappealing kind of "knowingness." This brings me closer to a central claim of Levitt's, which is that my essay was "an attempt to defend this rather indefensible cult [presumably social constructionism, because that is the subject of the previous sentence]." At the risk of being boring, let me repeat just part of two sentences from my earlier essay: ". . . any insistence upon pure social constructivism seems as unwarranted as an insistence on pure realism. The transcultural applicability of many scientific knowledge claims suggests that there may at least be some species-common forms of experience and cognition." It seems to me that only by ignoring details and gross distinctions, let alone fine ones, can one claim that an argument which includes these lines is an attempt to defend radical social constructivism. (For a brief positive statement of my position on this issue, please refer to my response to letters from John Thaler and John Toomay in *Skeptic*, V. 4, #3, 23–24).

This failure to acknowledge or perceive complexity and fine distinctions, however, is not primarily important in connection with my position. It seems to me to be at the very heart of Levitt's strategy of lumping together a huge range of perspectives which he and Paul Gross openly admit share few characteristics except that they differ broadly from those of Gross and Levitt. Nearly all persons who accept the notion that cultures have any bearing on the content of science in any degree are caricatured by identifying their views with the most radical cultural constructionists, post-modernists, academic feminists, and ecologists.

Then, the views of these groups are further distorted by taking passages out of context and interpreting them in ways that are at best uncharitable and at worst, intentionally perverse.

Consider, for example, Levitt's use of the passage from Sandra Harding's essay in *Social Text* (no. 46/47), in which Harding suggests that in her vision of the scientific future, there may be "many different, and in some respects, conflicting representations of nature." From this statement, Levitt infers that "she enthusiastically recommends regarding all local knowledge systems, of which standard science is but one instance, as equally mature and equally valid."

Not only does the Levitt statement not follow from the Harding passage which he cites, it is contrary to any position I have read in any of Sandra Harding's works or heard her express either in public or in private. I am certainly not prepared to agree with all positions that she might hold; but she is quite open in saying that it would be absurd to try to use any knowledge system other than that of the modern exact sciences if one's goal is, for example, to send a rocket to Mars. What she does insist upon—and here I am convinced that she is correct—is that local knowledge systems often incorporate knowledge of local environmental conditions which are important for the health and sustainability of the local community, even if that knowledge is not articulated in the same propositional form in which Western science expresses its knowledge claims. Equally to the point is the fact that though a few scientists may hope for some eventual theory of everything, most of my scientific colleagues are inclined, like Harding, to accept and often emphasize the existence of different representations of natural phenomena associated with different disciplines.

I am inclined to agree completely with Levitt that it is "hopelessly naive or hopelessly disingenuous . . . to imply that the quarrel between the science critics and their critics follows the standard Right-Left cleavage line . . . ," but then I was not the person who subtitled a book "The Academic Left and Its Quarrels with Science." I do believe that many, but not all, science studies students have left political leanings (many of which I share) and, like Levitt, I think that to imply that all left-leaning academics quarrel with science is absurd. The only disagreement we seem to have on this issue is over which of us has encouraged (note, I did not say taken) the naive or disingenuous stance, and whether most left-leaning science studies professionals can reasonably be said to quarrel with science because they approach it from a perspective not shared by Norman Levitt.

There is a final extremely serious issue which sometimes seems to get confused with the issue of the undoubted instrumental success of the modern Western sciences. This issue is raised by Levitt's discussion of Meera Nanda's critiques of science studies because of the aid and comfort they have supposedly given to "religious obscurantism and its attendant reactionary, misogynist politics." It brings us back to the fundamental question of the degree of respect we are to offer to persons whose basic values are different from our own. Do we really want a democratic world culture in which other persons are free to hold beliefs of which we do not approve? It seems to me that this is fundamentally a moral, rather than an epistemic, question, although it is clear that epistemology is deeply implicated in many subjects over which people are willing to fight to the very death to impose their wills on others.

Even if we are totally convinced that Western science offers a knowledge system which is more powerful in controlling the physical world than any alternative, and even if we are convinced of the undesirability of the gender politics which attends the practice of Vastu Shastra, or the stunted intellectual life associated with those who promote biblical creationism, it is clear to me that we have neither an obligation nor a right to deny people the opportunity to make the "wrong" choice or to denigrate them for doing so without trying to understand why they choose as they do. Legitimate issues other than control of the physical world, gender equity, or intellectual stimulation may be at the heart of their choices. And I am certainly convinced that I would not want to live in a world in which I was not free to choose "wrongly" by someone else's standards. On this issue it seems to me there is little to choose from between the extreme self-proclaimed defenders of science-as-we-know-it and the extreme proponents of such movements as eco-feminism or fundamentalist Christianity. That each group should try and make its best case seems completely appropriate to me, but that they should do so by demonizing their opponents and by distorting their views seems to me to decrease the likelihood that we can sustain a relatively free, open, and non-coercive society.

5

HISTORICAL DOCUMENTS

Creationism

"Mr. Bryan's Address to the Jury in the Scopes' Case. The Speech Which Was Never Delivered."

by *William Jennings Bryan*

Why Creationists Fear Evolution: An Introduction to William Jennings Bryan's Last Speech Showing Nothing Has Changed Since Scopes

MICHAEL SHERMER

In the movie version of *Inherit the Wind*, about the 1925 Scopes' "Monkey Trial," in the middle of William Jennings Bryan's final moving speech he dramatically keels over dead in the courtroom, to the gasps of his faithful followers and the chagrin of his evolutionary opponents. The reality was perhaps a bit less dramatic, but the real speech is much more poignant (in the movie he is reduced to reciting by heart the books of the Bible). William Jennings Bryan's last speech was never delivered, and he died two days later rather unceremoniously. Bryan College in Dayton, Tennessee, still stands as a monument to an age gone by. Or has it?

Recent legislation in Tennessee, fortunately defeated, proposed that evolution be taught as a "mere" theory, and not as a fact of science, opening the door for other "theories" to be discussed in public school biology classes, such as the "theory" of special creation, AKA "Scientific Creationism," AKA Genesis. A few other states are moving toward trying to pass similar legislative proposals and creationists continue with their bottom-up strategy of electing school board members and influencing teachers and parents.

In my book *Why People Believe Weird Things*, I provided a thorough refutation of creationist arguments. I thought we would allow William Jennings Bryan to be the champion of the "other side" that thinks belief in the theory of evolution can actually lead to immoral behavior, and that acceptance of the theory has led to social ills. Bryan's argument in this speech is not an antiquated belief. On the following page is an illustration of the "Evolution Tree," in which evolution is shown to lead to all manner of evil, including Communism, Nazism, Imperialism, Monopolism, Humanism, Atheism, Amoralism, Scientism, Racism, Pantheism, Behaviorism, and Materialism; and "Evil Practices" including Promiscuity, Pornography, Genocide, Slavery, Abortion, Euthanasia, Chauvinism, Infanticide, Homosexuality, Child Abuse, Bestiality, and Drug Culture. As a brief rebuttal to their creationist tactic I wish to provide a short history to the creationist history and a brief response to Bryan's address.

For those not familiar with the history of the trial, John T. Scopes was a substitute teacher

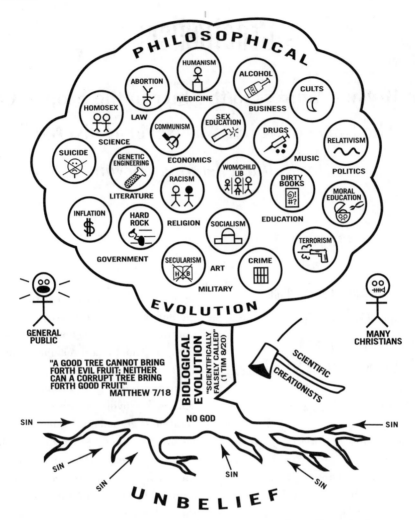

"Evolution Tree" from the Pittsburgh Creation Society. (R. G. Elmendorf)

who volunteered for the ACLU to be a test case to challenge Tennessee's "anti-evolution" law. It was the intention of the ACLU to take the case all the way to the U.S. Supreme Court. The most famous defense attorney of the day—Clarence Darrow—provided legal counsel for Scopes, and Bryan served as defender of the faith for the prosecution. Scopes was found guilty and fined $100 by Judge Raulston, but Tennessee law required that all fines above $50 must be set by a jury. Because of this technicality the defense was not able to appeal the case and it never was taken to the U.S. Supreme Court (though in 1987 an "equal time" law in

Louisiana was challenged and defeated by a 7–2 vote of the justices; see my 1991 "Science Defended, Science Defined" in *Science, Technology, & Human Values*, V. 16, #4; reprinted in *Why People Believe Weird Things*).

Most people think that Scopes, Darrow, and the scientific community scored a great victory in Tennessee. H. L. Mencken, covering the trial for the *Baltimore Sun*, summarized it and Bryan this way: "Once he had one leg in the White House and the nation trembled under his roars. Now he is a tinpot pope in the Coca-Cola belt and a brother to the forlorn pastors who belabor half-wits in galvanized iron tabernacles behind the railroad yards. . . . It is a tragedy, indeed, to begin life as a hero and to end it as a buffoon."

But, in fact, this was no victory for evolution. Bryan died, but he had the last laugh, as the controversy stirred by the trial made others, particularly textbook publishers and state boards of education, reluctant to deal with the theory of evolution in any manner. Judith Grabiner and Peter Miller conducted a comparison study of high school textbooks before and after the trial, concluding: "Believing that they had won in the forum of public opinion, the evolutionists of the late 1920s in fact lost on their original battleground—teaching of evolution in the high schools—as judged by the content of the average high school biology textbooks [which] declined after the Scopes trial." A trial that seems comical in retrospect was really a tragedy, as Mencken concluded:

Let no one mistake it for comedy, farcical though it may be in all its details. It serves notice on the country that Neanderthal man is organizing in these forlorn backwaters of the land, led by a fanatic, rid of sense and devoid of conscience. Tennessee, challenging him too timorously and too late, now sees its courts converted into camp meetings and its Bill of Rights made a mock of by its sworn officers of the law.

The speech that follows was vintage Bryan and should be read not just as a historical document and slice of fundamentalist Americana, it should toll a warning bell on the logic of faith and the power of rhetoric to move masses against reason and science. As Gould shows in "William Jennings Bryan's Last Campaign" (in *Bully for Brontosaurus*, Norton, 1991), Bryan's skepticism about evolution took a dramatic turn after the First World War when he became aware of the use of social Darwinism to justify militarism, imperialism, eugenics, and "paralyzing the hope of reform" through its

program of "scientific breeding, a system under which a few supposedly superior intellects, self-appointed, would direct the mating and the movements of the mass of mankind" (to quote from the speech). Bryan feared for his faith and his country, and it was obvious to him who the enemy was: Darwinism and evolutionary theory.

Forget Duane Gish's demand for one transitional fossil, his obsession with the Bombardier Beetle, or his claim that evolution violates the second law of thermodynamics. These arguments are secondary matter. What really disturbs Gish and the creationists, as it did Bryan, is the implication of evolution for ethics and religion, and the following speech is an excellent summary of their fear that somehow a belief in evolution undermines morality. How do we answer this fear? The study of evolutionary ethics and the application of secular morality show how one can construct a meaningful existence and a moral life without religion. A brief response to Bryan and the creationists might include the following points:

1. The use or misuse of a theory does not negate the validity of the theory itself. Marx once claimed he was not a Marxist. Darwin would undoubtedly be spinning in his grave if he knew the uses of his theory in the 20th century to justify all manner of ideologies. The fact that Hitler implemented a eugenics program does not negate the theory of genetics. Theories are neutral; the use of theories is not. They are two different things.

2. The creationists' list of social problems—promiscuity, pornography, abortion, infanticide, racism, etc.—obviously existed long before Darwin and the theory of evolution. To blame Darwin for our own social and moral problems is to misdirect us from a deeper analysis and true understanding of these complex social issues.

3. The social evils that creationists fear have been with us since the birth of civilization. Organized religion has had thousands of years to solve these problems. To blame science and evolutionary theory for moral shortcomings is to admit that 6,000 years of religion has failed to do the job.

4. It is not the goal of science to replace faith and religion with evolutionary theory. The theory of evolution is a scientific theory, not a religious doctrine. It stands or falls on evidence alone. Religious faith, by definition, depends on belief when evidence is absent or unimportant. To fear the theory of evolution is an indication of a shortcoming in one's faith. If creationists had true faith in their religion it should not matter what scientists think or say. The fact that creationists have tethered themselves to science, even calling themselves "creation scientists," means that they feel their faith is not enough. They want proof. But proof of God is not possible, as the last 700 years of attempts to do so have shown (from Aquinas on).

5. The scientific attempt to understand human psychology and moral development, and the application of evolutionary theory to the origin and evolution of ethical behavior, are in their infancy. Religion has had 6,000 years, science less than 100. This 10 order-of-magnitude difference in time is significant. How much greater will our understanding of humanity be 6,000 years from now if science is applied to human affairs, no one can say, but given the relative difference in the rate of cumulative knowledge between science and religion we should be optimistic for the future. Religion may provide hope for some people. But only science has proven it can deliver the hopeful goods.

May It Please the Court, and Gentlemen of the Jury

WILLIAM JENNINGS BRYAN

Demosthenes, the greatest of ancient orators, in his "oration on the crown," the most famous of his speeches, began by supplicating the favor of all the gods and goddesses of Greece. If, in a case which involved only his own fame and fate, he felt justified in petitioning the heathen gods of his country, surely we, who deal with the momentous issues involved in this case, may well pray to the ruler of the universe for wisdom to guide us in the performance of our several parts in this historic trial.

Let me in the first place, congratulate our cause that circumstances have committed the trial to a community like this and entrusted the decision to a jury made up largely of the yeomanry of the state. The book in issue in this trial contains on its first page two pictures contrasting the disturbing noises of a great city with the calm serenity of the country. It is a tribute that rural life has fully earned.

I appreciate the sturdy honesty and independence of these who come into daily contact with the earth, who living near to nature, worship nature's god and who, dealing with the myriad mysteries of earth and air, seek to learn from revelation about the Bible's wonder working God. I admire the stern virtues, the vigilance and the patriotism of the class from which the jury is drawn, and am reminded of the lines of Scotland's immortal bard, which, when changed but slightly, describe your country's confidence in you:

O, Scotia, my dear, my native soil!

For whom my warmest wish to heaven is
*   sent,*
Long may thy hardy sons of rustic toil
be blest with health, and peace, and sweet
*   content.*
And, Oh, may heaven their simple lives
*   present*
From luxury's contagion, weak and vile
Then, howe'er crowns and coronets be rent
A virtuous populace may rise the while,
And stand, a wall of fire, around their much
*   loved isle.*

Let us now separate the issues from the mis-representations, intentional and unintentional, that have obscured both the letter and the purpose of the law.

This is not an interference with freedom of conscience. A teacher can think as he pleases and worship God as he likes, or refuse to worship God at all. He can believe in the Bible or discard it; he can accept Christ or reject him. This law places no objections or restraints upon him. And so with freedom of speech, he can, so long as he acts as an individual, say anything he likes on any subject.

This law does not violate any rights guaranteed by any constitution to any individual. It deals with the defendant, not as an individual, but as an employee, an official or public servant, paid by the state, and therefore under instructions from the state.

The right of the state to control the public schools is affirmed in the recent decision in the Oregon case, which declares that the state can direct what shall be taught and also forbid the teaching of anything "manifestly inimical to the public welfare." The above decision goes even farther and declares that the parent not only has the right to guard the religious welfare of the child, but is in duty bound to guard it. That decision fits this case exactly. The state had a right to pass this law, and the law represents the determination of the parents to guard the religious welfare of their children.

It need hardly be added that this law did not have its origin in bigotry. It is not trying to force any form of religion on anybody. The majority is not trying to establish a religion or to teach it—it is trying to protect itself from the efforts of an insolent minority to force irreligion upon the children under the guise of teaching science. What right has a little irresponsible oligarchy of self-styled "intellectuals" to demand control of the schools of the United States, in which 25,000,000 of children are being educated at an annual expense of nearly $2,000,000,000?

Christians must, in every state of the union, build their own colleges in which to teach Christianity; it is only simple justice that atheists, agnostics and unbelievers should build their own colleges if they want to teach their own religious views or attack the religious views of others.

The statute is brief and free from ambiguity. It prohibits the teaching, in the public schools, of "any theology that denies the story of divine creation as taught in the Bible," and teaches, "instead, that man descended from a lower order of animals." The first sentence sets forth the purpose of those who passed the law. They forbid the teaching of any evolutionary theory that disputes the Bible record of man's creation and, to make sure that there shall be no misunderstanding, they place their own interpretation on their language and specifically forbid the teaching of any theory that makes man a descendant of any lower form of life.

The evidence shows that defendant taught, in his own language as well as from a book outlining the theory, that man descended from lower forms of life. Howard Morgan's testimony gives us a definition of evolution that will become known throughout the world as this case is discussed.

Howard, a 14-year-old boy, has translated the words of the teacher and the textbook into language that even a child can understand. As he recollects it, the defendant said "a little germ of one cell organism has formed in the sea; this kept evolving until it got to be a pretty good sized animal, then came on to be a land animal, and it kept evolving, and from this was man."

There is no room for difference of opinion here, and there is no need of expert testimony. Here are the facts, corroborated by another student, Harry Helton, and admitted to be true by counsel for defense. White, superintendent of schools, testified to the use of Hunter's civic biology, and to the fact that the defendant not only admitted teaching evolution, but declared that he could not teach it without violating the law. Robinson, the chairman of the school board, corroborated the testimony of Superintendent White in regard to the defendant's admissions and declaration. These are the facts; they are sufficient and undisputed; a verdict of guilty must follow.

But the importance of this case requires more. The facts and arguments presented to you must not only convince you of the justice of conviction in this case, but, while not necessary to a verdict of guilty, they should convince you of the righteousness of the purpose of the people of the state in the enactment of this law.

The state must speak through you to the outside world and repel the aspersions cast by the counsel for the defense upon the intelligence and the enlightenment of the citizens of Tennessee. The people of this state have a high appreciation of the value of education. The state constitution testifies to that in its demand that education shall be fostered and that science and literature shall be cherished. The continuing and increasing appropriations for public instruction furnish abundant proof that Tennessee places a just estimate upon the learning that is secured in its schools.

Religion is not hostile to learning; Christianity has been the greatest patron learning has ever had. But Christians know that "the fear of the Lord is the beginning of wisdom." Now, just as it has been in the past, and they therefore oppose the teaching of guesses that encourage Godlessness among the students.

Neither does Tennessee undervalue the service rendered by science. The Christian men and women of Tennessee know how deeply mankind is indebted to science for benefits conferred by the discovery of the laws of nature and by the designing of machinery for the utilization of these laws. Give science a fact and it is not only invincible, but it is of incalculable service to man.

If one is entitled to draw from society in proportion to the service that he renders to society, who is able to estimate the reward earned by those who have given to us the use of steam, the use of electricity, and enable us to utilize the weight of water that flows down the mountainside? Who will estimate the value of the service rendered by those who invented the radio? Or, to come more closely to our home life, how shall we recompense those who gave us the sewing machine, the tractor, the threshing machine, the tractor, the automobile and the method now employed in making artificial ice? The department of medicine also opens an unlimited field for invaluable service.

Typhoid and yellow fever are not feared as they once were. Diphtheria and pneumonia have been robbed of some of their terrors, and a high place on the scroll of fame still awaits the discoverer of remedies for arthritis, cancer, tuberculosis and other dread diseases to which mankind is heir.

Christianity welcomes truth from whatever source it comes, and is not afraid that any truth from any source can interfere with the divine truth that comes by inspiration from God Himself. It is not scientific truth to which Christians, therefore, can be scientific unless it is true.

Evolution is not truth; it is merely an hypothesis—is millions of guesses strung together.

It had not been proven in the day of Darwin; he expressed astonishment that with two or three million species, it had been impossible to trace any species to any other species. It had not been proven in the days of Huxley, and it has not been proven up to today. It is less than four years ago that Professor Bateson came all the way from London to Canada to tell the American scientists that every effort to trace one species to another had failed—every one.

He said he still had faith in evolution, but had doubts about the origin of species. But of what value is evolution, if it cannot explain the origin of species? While many scientists accept evolution as if it were a fact, they all admit, when questioned, that no explanation has been found as to how one species developed into another.

Darwin suggested two laws, sexual selection, and natural selection. Sexual selection has been laughed out of the class room, and natural selection is being abandoned, and no new explanation is satisfactory even to scientists. Some of the more rash advocates of evolution are wont to say that evolution is as firmly established as the law of gravitation, or the Copernican theory. The absurdity of such a claim is apparent when we remember that anyone can prove the law of gravitation by throwing a weight into the air, and that anyone can prove the roundness of the earth by going around it, while no one can prove evolution to be true in any way whatever.

Chemistry is an insurmountable obstacle in the path of evolution. It is one of the greatest of the sciences; it separates the atoms—isolates them and walks about them so to speak. If there were in nature a progressive force, an eternal urge, chemistry would find it. But it is not there.

All of the 92 original elements are separate and distinct; they combine in fixed and permanent proportions. Water is H_2O, as it has been from the beginning. It was here before life appeared and has never changed; neither can it be shown that anything else has materially changed.

Man a Special Creation

There is no more reason to believe that man descended from some inferior animal than there is to believe that a stately mansion had descended from a small cottage. Resemblances are not proof, they simply put us on inquiry.

As one fact, such as the absence of the accused from the scene of the murder, outweighs all resemblances that a thousand witnesses could swear to, so the inability of science to trace any one of the millions of species to another species, outweighs all the resemblances upon which evolutionists rely to establish man's blood relationship with the brutes.

But while the wisest scientists can not prove a pushing power, such as evolution is supposed to be, there is a lifting power that any child can understand. The plant lifts the mineral up into a higher world, and the animal lifts the plants up into a world still higher. So, it has been reasoned by analogy, man rises, not by a power within him, but only when drawn upward by a higher power.

There is a spiritual gravitation that draws all souls toward heaven, just as surely as there is a physical force that draws all matters on the surface of the earth towards the earth's center. Christ is our drawing power; he said, "I, if I be lifted from the earth, will draw all men unto Me," and his promise is being fulfilled daily all over the world.

It must be remembered that the law under consideration in this case does not prohibit the teaching of evolution up to the line that separates man from the lower form of animal. The law might well have gone farther than it does and prohibit the teaching of evolution in lower forms of life; the law is a very conservative statement of the people's opposition to an anti-Biblical hypothesis. The defendant was not content to teach what the law permitted; he, for reasons of his own, persisted in teaching that which was forbidden for reasons entirely satisfactory to the law makers.

Many of the people who believe in evolution do not know what evolution means. One of the science books taught in the Dayton high schools has a chapter on "The Evolution of Machinery." This is a very common misuse of the term. People speak of the evolution of the telephone, the automobile, and the musical instrument. But these are merely illustrations of man's power to deal intelligently with inanimate matter; there is no growth from within in the development of machinery.

Equally improper is the use of the word "evolution" to describe the growth of a plant from a seed, the growth of a chicken from an egg, or the development of any form of animal life from a single cell. All these give us a circle, not a change from one species to another.

Evolution—the evolution involved in this case, and the only evolution that is a matter of controversy anywhere—is the evolution taught by defendant, set forth in the books now prohibited by the new state law, and illustrated in the diagram printed on page 194 of *Hunter's Civic Biology*.

The author estimates the number of species in the animal kingdom at 518,900. These are then divided into 18 classes, and each class indicated on the diagram by a circle, proportioned in size to the number of species in each class and attached by a stem to the trunk of the tree. It begins at protozoa and ends with mammals.

Passing over the classes with which the average man is unfamiliar, let me call your attention to a few of the larger and better known groups. The insects are numbered at 360,000, over two-thirds of the total number of species in the animal world. The fishes are numbered at 13,000, the amphibians at 1,400, the reptiles at 3,500, and the birds at 13,000, while 3,500 mammals are crowded together in a little circle that is barely higher than the bird circle. No circle is reserved for man alone.

He is, according to the diagram, shut up in the little circle entitled "mammals," with 3,499 other species of mammals. Does it not seem a little unfair not to distinguish between man and lower forms of life? What shall we say of the intelligence, not to say religion of those who are so particular to distinguish between fishes and reptiles and birds, but put a man with an immortal soul in the same circle with the wolf, the hyena, and the skunk? What must be the impressions made upon children by such a degradation of man?

In the preface of this book, the author explains that it is for children, and adds that "the boy or girl of average ability upon admission to the secondary school is not a thinking individual." Whatever may be said in favor of teaching evolution to adults, it surely is not proper to teach it to children who are not yet able to think.

The evolutionist does not undertake to tell us how protozoa, moved by interior and resident forces, sent life up through all the various species, and can not prove that there was actually any such compelling power at all. And yet, the school children are asked to accept their guesses and build a philosophy of life upon them. If it were not so serious a matter, one might be tempted to speculate upon the various degrees of relationship that, according to evolutionists, exist between man and other forms of life.

It might require some very nice calculation to determine at what degree of relationship the killing of a relative ceases to be murder and the eating of one's kin ceases to be cannibalism. But it is not a laughing matter when one considers that evolution not only offers no suggestion as to a creator but tends to put the creative act so far away to cast doubt upon creation itself. And, while it is shaking faith in God as a beginning, it is also creating doubt as to heaven at the end of life.

Evolutionists do not feel that it is incumbent upon them to show how life began or at what point, in their long drawn out scheme of changing species man became endowed with hope and promise of immortal life.

God may be a matter of indifference to the evolutionists, and a life beyond may have no charm for them, but the mass of mankind will continue to worship their Creator and continue to find comfort in the promise of their Saviour that he has gone to prepare a place for them. Christ has made of death a narrow, starlit strip between the companionship of yesterday and the reunion of tomorrow, and evolution strikes out the stars and deepens the gloom that enshrouds the tomb.

If the results of evolution were unimportant, one might require less proof in support of the hypothesis, but before accepting a new philosophy of life, built upon a materialistic foundation, we have reason to demand something more than guess; "we may well suppose" is not a sufficient substitute for "thus saith the Lord."

If you, your honor, and you, gentlemen of the jury would have an understanding of the sentiment that lies back of the statute against the teaching of evolution, please consider these facts: First, as to the animals to which evolutionists would have us trace our ancestry. The following is Darwin's family tree, as you will find it set forth on pages 180–181 of his "Descent of Man."

The most ancient progenitors in the kingdom of vertebrata, at which we are able to obtain an obscure glance, apparently consisted of a group of marine animals, resembling the larvae of existing asidians. These animals probably gave rise to a group of fishes, as lowly organized as the lancelot; and from these the canoids, and other fishes like the lepidosiren, must have been developed. From such fish a very small advance would carry us on to the amphibians. We have seen that birds and reptiles were once intimately connected together; and the monotrematata now connect mammals with reptiles in a slight degree. But no one can at present say by what line of descent the three higher and related classes, namely, mammals, birds and reptiles, were derived from the two lower vertebrate classes, namely, amphibians and fishes.

In the class of mammals the steps are not difficult to conceive which led from the ancient monotremata to the ancient marsupials; and from these to the early progenitors of the placental mammals. We may thus ascend to the lemuridae; and the interval is not very wide from these to the simiadac. The simiadae then branched off into two great stems, the new world and the old world monkeys; and from the latter, at a remote period, man, the wonder and glory of the universe, proceeded. Thus we have given to man a pedigree of prodigious length, but not, it may be said, of noble quality.

Darwin, on page 171 of the same book, tries to locate his first man, that is, the first man to come down out of the trees, in Africa. After leaving man in company with gorillas and chimpanzees, he says: "But it is useless to speculate on this subject." If he had only thought of this earlier, the world might have been spared much of the speculation that his brute hypothesis has excited.

On page 79 Darwin gives some fanciful reasons for believing that man is more likely to have descended from the chimpanzee than from the gorilla. His speculations are an excellent illustration of the effect that the evolutionary hypothesis has in cultivating the imagination. Professor J. Arthur Thomson says that the "idea of evolution is the most potent thought economizing formula the world has yet known." It is more than that; it dispenses with thinking entirely and relies on the imagination.

On page 141 Darwin attempts to trace the mind of man back to the mind of lower animals. On pages 118 and 114 he endeavors to trace man's moral nature back to the animals. It is all animal, animal, animal, with never a thought of God or religion.

Our first indictment against evolution is that it disputes the truth of the Bible account of man's creation and shakes faith in the Bible as the word of God. This indictment we prove by comparing the process described as evolutionary with the text Genesis. It not only contradicts the Mosaic record as to the beginning of human life, but it disputes the Bible doctrines of reproduction according to kin—the greatest scientific principle known.

Evolution Incompatible with Faith

Our second indictment is that the evolutionary hypothesis carried to its logical conclusion, disputes every vital truth of the Bible. Its tendency, naturally, if not inevitably, is to lead those who really accept it, first to agnosticism and then to atheism. Evolutionists attack the truth of the Bible, not openly at first, but by using weasel-words like "poetical," "symbolical," and "allegorical" to search out the meaning of the inspired record of man's creation.

We call as our first witness Charles Darwin. He began life as a Christian. On page 39, volume 1, of the life and letters of Charles Darwin, by his son, Francis Darwin, he says, speaking of the period of 1828 to 1831, "I did not then in the least doubt the strict and literal truth of every word in the Bible." On page 412 of volume 2, of the same publication, he says, "when I was collecting facts for 'The Origin' my belief

in what is called a personal God was firm as that of Doctor Puzey himself."

It may be a surprise to your honor, and to you, gentlemen of the jury, as it was to me, to learn that Darwin spent three years at Cambridge studying for the ministry.

This was Darwin as a young man, before he came under the influence of doctrine that man was from a lower order of animals. The change wrought in his religious views will be found in a letter written to a German youth in 1879, and printed on page 277 of volume 1 of the life and letters above referred to. The letter begins:

> I am much engaged, an old man, and out of health, and I can not spare time to answer your questions fully, nor indeed can they be answered. Science has nothing to do with Christ, except insofar as the habit of scientific research makes a man cautious in admitting evidence. For myself, I do not believe that there ever has been any revelation. As for a future life, every man must judge for himself between conflicting vague probabilities.

Note that "science has nothing to do with Christ, except insofar as the habit of scientific research makes a man cautious in admitting evidence," stated plainly, that simply means that "the habit of scientific research" makes one cautious in accepting the only evidence that we have of Christ's existence, mission, teaching, crucifixion, and resurrection, namely the evidence found in the Bible.

To make this interpretation of his words the only possible one, he adds "for myself, I do not believe that there ever has been any revelation." In rejecting the Bible as a revelation from God he rejects the Bible's conception of God, and he rejects also the supernatural Christ of whom the Bible, and the Bible alone, tells. And, it will be observed, he refuses to express any opinion as to a future life.

Now let us follow with his son's exposition of his father's views as they are given in extracts from a biography written in 1876. Here is Darwin's language as quoted by his son:

During these two years (October, 1838, to January, 1839) I was led to think much about religion. Whilst on board the Beagle I was quite orthodox, and I remember being heartily laughed at by several of the officers (though themselves orthodox) for quoting the Bible as an unanswerable authority on some point of morality. When thus reflecting I felt compelled to look for a first cause, having an intelligent mind, in some degree analogous to man; and I deserved to be called an atheist. This conclusion was strong in my mind about the time, as far as I can remember, when I wrote the "Origin of Species." It is since that time that it has very gradually, with many fluctuations, become weaker. Then arises the doubt, can the mind of man, which has, as I fully believe, been developed from a mind as low as that possessed by the lowest animals, be trusted when it draws such grand conclusions?

I can not pretend to throw the least light on such abstruse problems. The mystery of the beginning of all things is insolvable by us; and I, for one, must be content to remain an agnostic.

When Darwin entered upon his scientific career he was "quite orthodox and quoted the Bible as an unanswerable authority on some point of morality." Even when he wrote "Origin of Species," the thought of "a first cause, having an intelligent mind, in some degree analogous to man," was strong in his mind. It was after that time that "very gradually, with many fluctuations, his belief in God became weaker." He traces this decline for us and concludes by telling us that he can not pretend to throw the least light on such abstruse problems—the religious problems above referred to. Then comes the flat statement that he "must be content to remain an agnostic," and, to make clear what he means by the word agnos-

tic, he says that "the mystery of the beginning of all things is insolvable by us"—not by him alone but by everybody. Here we have the effect of evolution upon its most distinguished exponent; it led him from an orthodox Christian, believing every word of the Bible and in a personal God, down and down to helpless and hopeless agnosticism.

But there is one sentence upon which I reserve comment—it throws light upon its downward pathway: "Then arises the doubt, can the mind of man, which has, as I fully believe, been developed from a mind as low as that possessed by the lowest animals, be trusted when it draws such grand conclusions?"

Here is the explanation; he drags man down to the brute levels, and then, judging man by brute standards he questions "'whether man's mind can be trusted to deal with God and immortality.'"

How can any teacher tell his students that evolution does not tend to destroy his religious faith? How can an honest teacher conceal from his students the effect of evolution upon Darwin himself? And is it not stranger still that preachers who advocate evolution never speak of Darwin's loss of faith, due to his belief in evolution? The parents of Tennessee have reason enough to fear the effect of evolution upon the mind of their children. Belief in evolution can not bring to those who hold such a belief any compensation for the loss of faith in God, trust in the Bible and belief in the supernatural character of Christ. It is belief in evolution that has caused so many scientists and so many Christians to reject the miracles of the Bible, and then give up, one after another, every vital trust in Christianity. They finally cease to pray and sunder the tie that binds them to their Heavenly Father.

The miracle should not be a stumbling block to anyone. It raises but three questions: First, could God perform a miracle? Yes, the God who created the universe can do anything he wants to do with it. He can temporarily suspend any law that he has made or he may employ higher laws that we do not understand.

Second: Would God perform a miracle? To answer that question in the negative one would have to know more about God's plans and purposes than a finite mind can know and yet some are so wedded to evolution that they deny that God would perform a miracle merely because a miracle is inconsistent with evolution.

If we believe that God can perform a miracle and might desire to do so, we are prepared to consider with open mind the third question, namely: Did God perform the miracles recorded in the Bible? The same evidence that establishes the authority of the Bible establishes the truth of miracles performed.

Now let me read of one of the most pathetic confessions that has come to my notice. George John Romanes, a distinguished biologist, sometimes called the successor of Darwin, like Darwin, was reared in the orthodox faith, and like Darwin, was led away from it by evolution.

For 25 years he could not pray. Soon after he became an agnostic, he wrote a book entitled, "A Candid Examination of Theism," publishing it under the assumed name "Physicus." In his book he says:

> And for so much as I am far from being able to agree with those who affirm that the twilight doctrine in the "new faith" is a desirable substitute for the waning splendor of "the old" I am not ashamed to confess that with this virtual negation of God the universe to me has lost its soul of loveliness; and although from hence the precept "work while it is day" will doubtless but gain an intensified force from the terribly intensified meaning of the words that "the night cometh when no man can work," yet when at times I think, as think at times I must, of the appalling contrast between the hallowed glory of that creed which once was mine, and the lonely mystery of existence as now I find it—at such times I shall ever feel

it impossible to avoid the sharpest pang of which my nature is susceptible.

Do these evolutionists stop to think of the crime they commit when they take faith out of the hearts of men and women and lead them out into a starless night? What pleasure can they find in robbing a human being of "the hallowed glory of that creed" that Romanes once cherished, and in substituting the "lonely mystery of existence" as he found it? Can the fathers and mothers of Tennessee be blamed for trying to protect their children from such a tragedy?

If any one has been led to complain of the severity of the punishment that hangs over the defendant, let him compare this crime and its mild punishment with the crimes for which a greater punishment is ascribed. What is the taking of a few dollars from one in day or night in comparison with the crime of leading one away from God and away from Christ?

He who spake as never man spake, thus describes the crimes that are committed against the young: "It is impossible but that offenses will come: but woe unto him through whom they come. It were better for him that a millstone were hanged about his neck and he be cast into the sea than he should offend one of these little ones."

Christ did not overdraw the picture. Who is able to set a price upon the life of a child—a child into whom a mother poured her life and for whom a father has labored? What may a noble life mean to the child itself, to the parents and to the world?

And, it must be remembered that we can measure the effect on only that part of life which is spent on earth; we have no way of calculating the effect on that infinite circle of life which existence here is but a small arc. The soul is immortal and religion deals with the soul; the logical effect of the evolutionary hypothesis is to undermine religion and thus affect the soul. I recently received a list of questions that were to be discussed in a prominent eastern school for women. The second question in the list read: "Is religion an obsolescent function that should be allowed to atrophy quietly, without arousing the passionate prejudice of outworn superstitions?" The real attack of evolution, it will be seen, is not upon orthodox Christianity or even upon Christianity, but upon religion—the most basic fact in man's existence and the most practical thing in life.

James H. Leuba, a professor of psychology at Bryn Mawr college, Pennsylvania, published a few years ago a book entitled, "Belief in God and Immortality." In this book he relates how he secured the opinions of scientists as to the existence of a personal God and a personal immortality. He issued a volume entitled, "American Men of Science," which he says, included the names of "practically every American who may properly be called a scientist."

There are 5,500 names in the book. He selected 1,000 names as representative of the 5,500, and addressed them personally. Most of them, he said, were teachers in schools of higher learning. The names were kept confidential. Upon the answer received, he asserts that over half of them doubt or deny the existence of a personal God and a personal immortality, and he asserts that unbelief being greatest among the most prominent. Among biologists, believers in a personal God numbered less than 31 per cent while unbelievers in a personal immortality numbered only 37 per cent.

He also questioned the students in nine colleges of high rank and from 1,000 answers received, 97 per cent of which were from students between 18 and 20, he found that unbelief increased from 15 per cent in the Freshman class up to 40 to 45 per cent among the men who graduated. On page 280 of this book, we read "the students' statistics show that young people enter college, possessed of

the beliefs still accepted, more or less perfunctorily, in the average home of the land, and gradually abandon the cardinal Christian beliefs." This change from belief to unbelief he attributed to the influence of the persons "of high culture under whom they studied."

The people of Tennessee have been patient enough; they acted none too soon. How can they expect to protect society, and even the church, from the deadening influence of agnosticism and atheism if they permit the teachers employed by taxation to poison the mind of the youth with this destructive doctrine? And remember, that the law has not heretofore required the writing of the word "poison" on poisonous doctrines. The bodies of our people are so valuable that the druggists and physicians must be careful to properly label all poisons; why not be as careful to protect the spiritual life of our people from the poisons that kill the soul?

There is a test that is sometimes used to ascertain whether one suspected of mental infirmity is really insane. He is put into a tank of water and told to dip the tank dry while a stream of water flows into the tank. If he has not sense enough to turn off the stream he is adjudged insane. Can parents justify themselves if, knowing the effect of belief in evolution, they permit irreligious teachers to inject skepticism and infidelity in the minds of their children?

Do bad doctrines corrupt the morals of students? We have a case in point. Mr. Darrow, one of the most distinguished criminal lawyers in our land, was engaged about a year ago in defending two rich men's sons who were on trial for as dastardly a murder as was ever committed. The older one, "Babe" Leopold, was a brilliant student, 19 years old. He was an evolutionist and an atheist. He was also a follower of Nietzsche, whose books he had devoured and whose philosophy he had adopted. Mr. Darrow made a plea for him, based upon the influence that Nietzsche's philosophy had exerted on the boy's mind. Here are extracts from his speech:

Babe took to philosophy. . . . He grew up in this way; he became enamored of the philosophy of Nietzsche. Your honor, I have read almost everything that Nietzsche ever wrote. A man of wonderful intellect; the most original philosopher of the last century. A man who made a deeper imprint on philosophy than any other man within a hundred years. In a way he has reached more people, and still he has been a philosopher of what we might call the intellectual cult.

He wrote one book called "Beyond Good and Evil," which was a criticism of all moral precepts, as we understood them, and a treatise that the intelligent was beyond good and evil; that the laws for good and the laws for evil did not apply to anybody who approached the superman. He wrote on the will to power.

I have just made a few short extracts from Nietzsche that show the things that he (Leopold) has read, and these are short and almost taken at random. It is not how this would affect you. It is not how it would affect me. The question is, how it would affect the impressionable, visionary, dreamy mind of a boy—a boy who should never have seen it—too early for him.

Quotations from Nietzsche: "Why so soft, oh my brethren? Oh why so soft, so unresisting and yielding? Why is there so much disavowal and abnegation, in your heart? Why is there so little faith in your looks? For all creators are hard and it must seem blessedness unto you to press your hand upon millenniums and upon wax. This new table, ah, my brethren, I put over you; become hard. To be obsessed by moral consideration presupposes a very low grade of intellect. We should substitute for morality the will to our own end and consequently to the means to accomplish that. A great man, a man whom nature has built up and invented in a grand style, is colder, harder,

less cautious and more free from the fear of public opinion. He does not possess the virtues which are compatible with respectability with being respected, nor any of these things which are counted among the virtues of the herd.

Mr. Darrow says: That the superman, a creation of Nietzsche, has permeated every college and university in the civilized world.

There is not any university in the world where the professor is not familiar with Nietzsche, not one. . . . Some believe it and some do not believe it. Some read it as I do and take it as a theory, a dream, a vision, mixed with good and bad but not in any way related to human life. Some take it seriously. . . . There is not a university in the world of any high standing where the professors do not tell you about Nietzsche and discuss him or where the books are not there.

If this boy is to blame for this, where did he get it? Is there any blame attached because somebody took Nietzsche's philosophy seriously and fashioned his life upon it? And there is no question in this case but what that is true. Then who is to blame? The university would be more to blame than he is; the scholars of the world would be more to blame than he is. The purposes of the world . . . are more to blame than he is. Your honor, it is hardly fair to hang a 19 year-old boy for the philosophy that was taught him at the university. It does not meet my ideas of justice and fairness to visit upon his head the philosophy that has been taught by university men for 25 years.

In fairness to Mr. Darrow, I think I ought to quote two more paragraphs. After this bold attempt to excuse the student on the ground that he was transformed from a well-meaning youth into a murderer by the philosophy of an atheist, and on the further ground that his philosophy was in the libraries of all the colleges and discussed by the professors—some adopting the philosophy and some rejecting it—on these two grounds, he denied that the boy should be held responsible for the taking of human life. He charges that the scholars in the universities were more responsible than the boy, and that the universities were more responsible than the boy, because they furnished such books to the students, and then he proceeds to exonerate the universities and scholars, leaving nobody responsible. Here is Mr. Darrow's language:

> Now I do not want to be misunderstood about this. Even for the sake of saving, the lives of my clients, I do not want to be dishonest and tell the court something that I do not honestly think in this case. I do not think that the universities are to blame. I do not think they should be held responsible. I do think however, that they are too large and that they should keep a closer watch, if possible, upon, the individual.
>
> But you can not destroy thought, because forsooth, some brain may be deranged by thought. It is the duty of the university as I conceive it, to be the greatest storehouse of the wisdom of the ages, and to have its students come there and learn, choose. I have no doubt but that it has meant the death of many, but that we can not help.

This is a damnable philosophy, and yet it is the flower that blossoms on the stalk of evolution. Mr. Darrow thinks the universities are in duty bound to feed out this poisonous stuff to their students, and when the students become stupefied by it and commit murder, neither they nor the universities are to blame. I protest against the adoption of any such a philosophy in the state of Tennessee. A criminal is not relieved from responsibility merely because he found Nietzsche's philosophy in a library which ought not to contain it. Neither is the university guiltless if it permits such corrupting nourishment to be fed to the souls that are entrusted to its care. But, go a step farther, would the state be blameless if it permitted the universities under its control to be turned into training schools for murder? When you get back to the root of this question, you will find that the legislature not only had a right to protect the students from the evolutionary hypothesis, but was in duty bound to do so.

While on this subject, let me call your attention to another proposition embodied in Mr. Darrow's speech. He said that Dickey Loeb, the younger boy, had read trashy novels, of the blood and thunder sort. He even went so far as to commend an Illinois statute which forbids minors reading stories of crime. Here is what Mr. Darrow said:

> We have a statute in this state, passed only last year, if I recall it, which forbids minors reading stories of crime. Why? There is only one reason; because the legislature in its wisdom, thought it would have a tendency to produce these thoughts and this life in the boys who read them.

If Illinois can protect her boys, why can not this state protect the boys of Tennessee? Are the boys of Illinois any more precious than yours?

But to return to the philosophy of an evolutionist, Mr. Darrow said:

> I say to you seriously that the parents of Dickey Loeb are more responsible than he, and yet few boys had better parents.

Again he says:

> I know that one of two things happened to this boy: That this terrible crime was inherent in his organism and came from an ancestor or that it came through his education and his training after he was born.

He thinks the boy was not responsible for anything; his guilt was due, according to this philosophy, either to heredity or environment. But let me complete Mr. Darrow's philosophy based on evolution. He says:

> I do not know what remote ancestor may have sent down the seed that corrupted him, and I do not know through how many ancestors it may have passed until it reached Dickey Loeb. All I know, it is true, and there is not a biologist in the world who will not say I am right.

Psychologists who build upon the evolutionary hypothesis teach that man is nothing but a bundle of characteristics inherited from brute ancestors. This is the philosophy which Darrow applied to his celebrated criminal case. "Some remote ancestor"—he does not know how remote—"sent down the seed that corrupted him." You can not punish the ancestor—he is not only dead, but, according to the evolutionists, he was a brute and may have lived 1,000,000 years ago. And he says that all the biologists agree with him—no wonder so small a percent of the biologists, according to Leuba, believe in a personal God.

This is the quintessence of evolution, distilled for us by one who follows that doctrine to its logical conclusion. Analyze this dogma of darkness and death. Evolutionists say that back in the twilight of life a beast, name and nature unknown, planted a murderous seed and that the impulse that originated in that seed throbs forever in the blood of the brute's descendants, inspiring killings innumerable, for which murderers are not responsible because coerced by a fate fixed by the laws of heredity. It is an insult to reason and shocks the heart. That doctrine is as deadly as leprosy; it may aid a lawyer in a criminal case, but it would, if generally adopted, destroy all sense of responsibility and menace the morals of the world. A brute, they say, can predestine a man to crime, and yet they deny that God-incarnated flesh can release a human being from his bondage or save him from ancestral sins. No more repulsive doctrine was ever proclaimed by man; if all the biologists of the world teach this doctrine—as Darrow says they do—then may Heaven defend the youth of our land from their impious babblings.

We Must Not Forget God

Our third indictment against evolution is that it diverts attention from pressing problems of great importance to trifling speculation. While one evolutionist is trying to imagine what happened in the dim past, another is trying to pry open the door of the distant future. One recently grew eloquent over ancient worms, and another predicted that 75,000 years hence everyone will be bald and toothless. But those who endeavor to clothe our remote ancestors with hair and those who endeavor to remove the hair from the heads of our remote descendants ignore the present with its imperative demands. The science of "how to live" is the most important of all the sciences. It is desirable to know the physical sciences, but it is necessary to know how to live. Christians desire that their children shall be taught all the sciences, but they do not want them to lose sight of the rock of ages while they study the age of the rocks; neither do they desire them to become so absorbed in measuring the distance between the stars that they will forget Him who holds the stars in his hand.

While not more than two per cent of our population are college graduates, these, because of enlarged powers, need a "heavenly vision," even more than those less learned, both for their own restraint and to assure society that their enlarged powers will be used for the benefit of society and not against the public welfare.

Evolution is deadening to spiritual life of a multitude of students. Christians do not desire less education, but they desire that religion shall be entwined with learning so that our boys and girls will return from college with their hearts aflame with love of God and love of fellow men, and prepared to lead in the altruistic work that the world so sorely needs. The cry in the business world, in the industrial, even in the religious world—is for consecrated talents—for ability plus a passion for service.

Our fourth indictment against the evolutionary hypothesis is that, by paralyzing the hope of reform, it discourages those who labor for the improvement of man's condition. Every upward-looking man or woman seeks to lift the level upon which mankind stands, and they trust that they will see beneficent changes during the brief span of their own lives. Evolution chills their enthusiasm by substituting aeons for years. It obscures all beginnings in the midst of endless ages. It is represented as a cold and heartless process, beginning with time and ending in eternity, and acting so slowly that even the rocks can not preserve a record of the imaginary changes through which it is credited with having carried an original germ of life that appeared sometime from somewhere. Its only program for man is scientific breeding, a system under which a few supposedly superior intellects, self-appointed, would direct the mating and the movements of the mass of mankind—an impossible system. Evolution, disputing the miracle and ignoring the spiritual in life, has no place for the regeneration of the individual. It recognizes no cry of repentance and scoffs at the doctrine that one can be born?

It is thus the tolerant and unrelenting enemy of the only process that can redeem society through the redemption of the individual. An evolutionist would never write such a story as the Prodigal Son; it contradicts the whole theory of evolution. The two sons inherited in the same parents, and through their parents from the same ancestors, proximate and remote. And these sons were reared at the same fireside and were surrounded by the same environment during all the days of their youth; and yet they were different.

If Mr. Darrow is correct in the theory applied to Loeb, namely, that his crime was due either to inheritance or to environment, how will he explain the difference between the elder brother and the wayward son? The evolutionist may understand from observation, if not by experience, even though he can not explain why one of these boys was guilty of every immorality, squandered the money that the father had laboriously earned, and brought disgrace upon the family name; but his theory does not explain why a wicked man underwent a change of heart, confessed his sins and begged forgiveness, and because the evolutionist can not understand this fact, one of the most important in the human life, he can not understand the infinite love of the Heavenly Father who stands ready to welcome home any repentant sinner, no matter how far he has wandered, how often he has failed, or how deep he has sunk in sin.

Your honor has quoted from a wonderful poem written by a great Tennessee poet, Walter Malone. I venture to quote another stanza which puts into exquisite language the new opportunity which a merciful God gives everyone who will turn from sin to righteousness:

Tho' deep in mire wring not your hands and
  weep,
I lend my arm to all who say "I can."
No shamefaced outcast ever sank so deep,
But he might rise and be a man.

There are no lines like these in all that evolutionists have ever written. Darwin says that science has nothing to do with the Christ who taught the spirit embodied in the words of Walter Malone, and yet this spirit is the only hope of human progress. A heart can be changed in the twinkling of an eye, and, a change in the life follows a change in the heart. If one heart can be changed, then a world can be born in a day. It is the fact that inspires all who labor for man's betterment. It is because Christians believe in individual regeneration and in the regeneration of society through the regeneration of individuals that they pray: "Thy Kingdom come, Thy will be done in earth as it is in heaven." Evolution makes a mockery of the Lord's prayer!

To interpret the words to mean that the improvement desired must come slowly through unfolding ages—a process with which each generation could have little to do—is to defer hope, and hope deferred makes the heart sick.

Evolution Demoralizing & Deadly

Our fifth indictment of the evolutionary hypothesis is that if taken seriously and made the basis of a philosophy of life, it would eliminate love and carry man back to a struggle of tooth and claw. The Christians who have allowed themselves to be deceived into believing that evolution is a beneficent, or even a rational, process have been associating with those who either do not understand its application or dare not avow their knowledge of these implicators. Let me give you some authority on this subject. I will begin with Darwin, the high priest of evolution, to whom all evolutionists bow.

On pages 149 and 150, in "The Descent of Man," already referred, he says:

With savages, the weak in body or mind are soon eliminated and those that survive commonly exhibit a vigorous state of health. We civilized men, on the other hand, do our utmost to check the process of elimination, we build asylums for the imbecile, the maimed and the sick; we institute poor laws; and our medical men exert their utmost skill to save the life of every one to the last moment. There is reason to believe that vaccination has preserved thousands who from a weak constitu-

tion would formerly have succumbed to smallpox. Thus the weak members of civilized society propagate their kind. No one who has attended to the breeding of domestic animals will doubt that this must be highly injurious to the race of man. It is surprising how soon a want of care, or care wrongly directed, leads to the degeneration of a domestic race, but, excepting in the case of man himself, hardly a one is so ignorant as to allow his worst animals to breed.

The aid which we feel impelled to give to the helpless is mainly an incidental result of the instinct of sympathy, which was originally acquired as part of the social instincts, but subsequently rendered in the manner previously indicated, more tender and more widely diffused. Nor could we check our sympathy, even at the urging of hard reason, without deterioration in the noblest part of nature. . . . We must therefore, bear the undoubtedly bad effects of the weak surviving and propagating their kind.

Darwin reveals the barbarous sentiment that runs through evolution and dwarfs the moral nature of those who become obsessed with it. Let us analyze the quotation just given. Darwin speaks with approval of the savage custom of eliminating the weak so that only the strong will survive and complains that "we civilized men do our utmost to check the process of elimination." How inhuman such a doctrine as this! He thinks it injurious to "build asylums for the imbecile, the maimed and the sick." Or to care for the poor. Even the medical men come in for criticism because they "exert their utmost skill to save the life of everyone to the last moment," and then note his hostility to vaccination because it has "preserved thousands who, from a weak constitution, would, but for vaccination, have succumbed to smallpox." All of the sympathetic activities of civilized society are condemned because they enable "the weak members to propagate their kind." Then he drags mankind down to the level of the brute and compares the freedom given to man unfavorably with the restraint that we put on barnyard beasts.

The second paragraph of the above quotation shows that his kindly heart rebelled against the cruelty of his doctrine. He says that we "feel impelled to give to the helpless," although he traces it to a sympathy which he thinks is developed by evolution; he even admits that we could not check this sympathy "even at the urging of hard reason, without deterioration of the noblest part of our nature." "We therefore bear," what he regards as "the undoubtedly bad effect of the weak surviving and propagating their kind." Could any doctrine be more destructive of civilization? And what a commentary on evolution! He wants us to believe that evolution develops a human sympathy that finally becomes so tender that it repudiates the law that created it and thus invites a return to a level where the extinguishing of pity and sympathy will permit the brutal instincts to again do their progressive work.

Let no one think that this acceptance of barbarism, as the basic principle of evolution, died with Darwin. Within three years a book has appeared whose author is even more frankly brutal than Darwin. The book is entitled "The New Decalogue of Science," and has attracted wide attention.

One of our most reputable magazines has recently printed an article by him defining the religion of a scientist. In his preface he acknowledges indebtedness to 21 prominent scientists and educators, "nearly all of them doctors" and "professors."

One of them who has recently been elevated to the head of a great state university read the manuscript over twice and made many valuable suggestions. The author describes Nietzsche, who, according to Mr. Darrow, made a murderer out of Babe Leopold, as the bravest soul since Jesus.

He admits Nietzsche was "gloriously wrong," but he affirms that Nietzsche was "gloriously right in his fearless questioning of the universe and of his own soul."

In another place the author says:

Most of our morals today are jungle products.

And then he affirms that:

It would be safer, biologically, if they were more so.

Now, after these two samples of his views, you will not be surprised when I read you the following:

Evolution is a bloody business, but civilization tries to make it a pink tea. Barbarism is the only process by which man has ever organically progressed and civilization is the only process by which he has ever organically declined.

Civilization is the most dangerous enterprise on which man ever set out. For when you take man out of the bloody, brutal, but beneficent hand of natural selection you place him at once in the soft, daintily gloved, but far more dangerous hand of artificial selection.

And unless you call science to your assistance and make this artificial selection as efficient as the rude methods of nature, you bungle the whole task.

This aspect of evolution may amaze some of the ministers who have not been permitted to enter the inner circle of the iconoclasts whose theories menace all the ideals of civilized society. Do these ministers know that evolution is a "bloody business"? Do they know that barbarism is the only process by which man has ever organically progressed, and "that civilization is the only process by which he has ever organically declined"?

Do they know that the bloody, brutal hand of natural selection is beneficent and the artificial selection "found in civilization is dangerous"? What shall we think of the distinguished educators and scientists who read the manuscript before publication and did not protest against this pagan doctrine?

To show that this is a worldwide matter, I now quote from a book issued from the press in 1918, seven years ago. The title of the book is "The Science of the Power," and its author, Benjamin Kidd, being an Englishman, could not have any national prejudice against Darwin. On pages 46 and 47 we find Kidd's interpretation of evolution:

Darwin's presentation of the evolution of the world as the product of natural selection in never-ceasing war, as a product that is to say, of a struggle in which the individual efficient in the fight for his own interests was always the winning type—touched the profoundest depths of the psychology of the west.

The idea seemed to present the whole order of progress in the world as the result of a purely mechanical and materialistic process resting on force. In so doing it was a conception which reached the springs of that heredity born of the unmeasured ages of conquest out of which the western mind has come. Within half a century the "Origin of Species" had become the Bible of the doctrine of the omnipotence of force.

Kidd goes so far as to charge that "Nietzsche recited the interpretation of the popular Darwinism, delivered with the fury and intensity of genius." And yet Nietzsche denounced Christianity as the "doctrine of the degenerate," and mercy as "the refuge of weaklings."

Kidd says that Nietzsche gave Germany the doctrine of Darwin's efficient animal in the voice of his sermon, and that Bernhardi and the military textbooks in due time gave Germany the doctrine of the superman translated into the national policy of the superstate aiming at world power.

And what else but the spirit of evolution can account for the popularity of the selfish doctrine, "each one for himself, and the devil take the hindmost," that threatens the very existence of the doctrine of brotherhood?"

In 1900—25 years ago, while an international peace congress was in session at Paris, the following editorial appeared in L'Univers:

The spirit of peace has fled the earth because evolution has taken possession of it. The plea for peace in past years has been inspired by faith in the divine nature and the divine origin of man; men were then looked upon as children of one father and war therefore was fratricide. But now that men are looked upon as children of apes, what matters it whether they were slaughtered or not?

When there is poison in the blood, no one knows on what part of the body it will break out, but we can be sure that it will break out unless the blood is purified.

One of the leading universities of the south (I love the state too well to mention its name) publishes a monthly magazine entitled, "Journal of Social Forces." In the January issue of this year a contributor has a lengthy article on "Zoology and Ethics," in the course of which he says:

No attempt will be made to take up the matter of the good or evil of sexual intercourse among humans aside from the matter of conscious procreation, but as an historian it might be worth while to ask the exponents of the impurity complex to explain the fact that without exception the great herds of cultural afflorescence have been those characterized by a large amount of freedom in sex relations and that those of the greatest cultural degradation and decline have been accompanied with greater sex repression and purity.

No one charges or suspects that all or any large percentage of the advocates of evolution sympathize with this loathsome application of evolution to social life, but it is worth while to inquire why those in charge of a great institution of learning allow such filth to be poured out for the stirring of the passions of its students.

Just one more quotation: "The Southeastern Christian Advocate" of June 25, 1925, quotes five eminent college men of Great Britain as joining in answer to the question: "Will civilization survive?"

Their reply is that "Greatest danger to our civilization is the abuse of the achievements of science. Mastery over the forces of nature has endowed the twentieth century man with a power which he is not fit to exercise. Unless the development of morality catches up with the development of technique, humanity is bound to destroy itself."

Can any Christian remain indifferent? Science needs religion to direct its energies and to inspire with lofty purpose those who employ the forces that are unloosed by science. Evolution is at war with religion because religion is supernatural, it is therefore the relentless foe of Christianity which is a revealed religion.

Let us, then, hear the conclusion of the whole matter. Science is a magnificent material for force, but is not a teacher of morals. It is perfect machinery, but it adds no moral restraints to protect society from the misuse of the machine. It can also build gigantic intellectual ships, but it constructs no moral rudders for control of storm tossed human vessels.

It not only fails to supply the spiritual element needed, but some of its unproven hypotheses rob the ship of its compass and thus endanger its cargo.

In war, science has proven itself an evil genius, it has made war more terrible than it ever was before. Man used to be content to slaughter his fellowman on a single plane—the earth's surface.

Science has taught him to go down into the water and shoot up; to go up into the clouds and shoot down from above, thus making the battlefield three times as bloody as it was before; but science does not teach brotherly love.

Science has made war so hellish that civilization has but to commit suicide; and now we are told that newly discovered instruments of destruction will make the cruelties of the late war seem trivial in comparison with the cruelties of war that may come in the future.

If civilization is to be saved from the wreckage threatened by intelligence not consecrated by love, it must be saved by the moral code of the meek and lowly Nazarene. His teachings and His teachings alone can solve the problems that vex the heart and perplex the world.

The world needs a saviour more than it ever did, and His is the only name under Heaven whereby we must be saved. It is this name that evolution degrades, for carried to its logical conclusion, it robs Christ of the glory of a virgin birth, of the majesty of His deity and mission, and of the triumph of His resurrection. It also disputes the doctrine of the atonement.

It is for the jury to determine whether this attack upon the Christian religion shall be permitted in the public schools of Tennessee by teachers employed by the state and paid out of the public treasury.

This case is no longer local; the defendant ceases to play an important part.

The case assumes the proportions of a battle royal between unbelief that attempts to speak through so called science and the defenders of the Christian faith, speaking through the legislators of Tennessee.

It is again a choice between God and Baal.

It is a renewal of the issue in Pilate's court. In that historic trial—the greatest in history—force, impersonated by Pilate, occupied the throne.

Behind it was the Roman government, mistress of the world, and behind the Roman government were the legions of Rome.

Before Pilate stood Christ, the apostle of love.

Force triumphed, they nailed Him to the tree and those who stood around mocked and jeered and said, "Christ is dead." But from that day the power of Caesar waned and the power of Christ increased.

In a few centuries the Roman government was gone and its legions forgotten; while the crucified and risen Lord is the greatest fact in history and the growing figure of all time.

Again love and force meet face to face and again, "What Shall I Do With Jesus" must be answered. A bloody doctrine, evolution demands, as the rabble did 1,900 years ago, that He be crucified.

This can not be the answer of the jury representing a Christian state and sworn to uphold the laws of Tennessee. Your answer will be heard throughout the world; it is eagerly awaited by a praying multitude.

If the law is nullified there will be rejoicing where ever God is repudiated, the Saviour scoffed at and the Bible ridiculed. Every unbeliever of every kind and degree will be happy.

If, on the other hand, the law is upheld and the religion of the school children protected, millions of Christians will call you blessed, and with hearts full of gratitude to God will again sing that old song of triumph:

Faith of our fathers, living still,
In spite of dungeon, fire and sword,
Oh, how our hearts beat high with joy,
Whene'er we hear that glorious word:—
Faith of our fathers—holy faith,
We will be true to thee till death.

David Hume's "Of Miracles"

An Enquiry Concerning Human Understanding, 1758

Introduction

MICHAEL SHERMER

The importance of skeptical publications in this New Age resurgence of interest in miracles and various claims of the paranormal cannot be overstated. Yet it is equally important to remember our historical antecedents and how they analyzed and critiqued such claims in their own time. One of the greatest skeptics of the Modern Age is the Scottish philosopher David Hume (1711–1776), whose work, *An Enquiry Concerning Human Understanding,* is a classic in skeptical analysis. The book was originally published anonymously in London in 1739, as *A Treatise of Human Nature,* but, in Hume's words, "fell dead-born from the press, without reaching such distinction as even to excite a murmur among the zealots." (An author's biggest fear is not being panned; it is being ignored.)

Hume blamed his own writing style and reworked the manuscript into *An Abstract of a Treatise of Human Nature* in 1740, and again in 1748, as *Philosophical Essays Concerning the Human Understanding.* The work still gained Hume no recognition, so in 1758 he brought it out in a final version as *An Enquiry Concerning Human Understanding,* which comes down to us today as his greatest philosophical work. Ironically, when Hume finally did achieve fame and position, his critics often attacked his earlier works, a practice Hume found "very contrary to all rules of candour and fair-dealing, and a strong instance of those polemical artifices, which a bigotted zeal thinks itself authorized to employ," as he wrote in an "Advertisement" to the final publication!

In Section XII, "Of the Academical or Sceptical Philosophy," Hume distinguished between "antecedent skepticism," such as Descartes's method of doubting everything, that has no "antecedent" infallible criterion for belief; and "consequent skepticism," the method Hume employed that recognizes the "consequences" of our fallible senses, but corrects them through reason: "A wise man proportions his belief to the evidence." Wiser words could not be chosen for a skeptical motto.

For the modern skeptic, Hume's Section X, "Of Miracles," provides a generalized, when-all-else-fails analysis of miraculous claims. That is, when one is confronted by a true believer whose apparently supernatural or paranormal claim has no immediately apparent natural explanation, Hume gives us an argument that even he thought was so important (and Hume was not a modest man) that he placed his own words in quotes and called it a maxim. I think it is so useful an argument that it bears repetition, as *Hume's Maxim:*

The plain consequence is (and it is a general maxim worthy of our attention), "That no testimony is sufficient to establish a miracle, unless the testimony be of such a kind, that its falsehood would be more miraculous than the fact which it endeavours to establish."

When anyone tells me that he saw a dead man restored to life, I immediately consider with myself whether it be more probable, that this person should either deceive or be deceived, or that the fact, which he relates, should really have happened. I weigh the one miracle against the other; and according to the superiority, which I discover, I pronounce my decision, and always reject the greater miracle. If the falsehood of his testimony would be more miraculous than the event which he relates; then, and not till then, can he pretend to command my belief or opinion.

So to honor *Hume's Maxim,* and to give the reader the full context of Hume's analysis, we present below the entirety of Section X "Of Miracles."

Section X. Of Miracles.

DAVID HUME

Part I

THERE is, in Dr. Tillotson's writings, an argument against the *real presence,* which is as concise, and elegant, and strong as any argument can possibly be supposed against a doctrine, so little worthy of a serious refutation. It is acknowledged on all hands, says that learned prelate, that the authority, either of the scripture or of tradition, is founded merely in the testimony of the apostles, who were eye-witnesses to those miracles of our Saviour, by which he proved his divine mission. Our evi-

dence, then, for the truth of the *Christian* religion is less than the evidence for the truth of our senses; because, even in the first authors of our religion, it was no greater; and it is evident it must diminish in passing from them to their disciples; nor can any one rest such confidence in their testimony, as in the immediate object of his senses. But a weaker evidence can never destroy a stronger; and therefore, were the doctrine of the real presence ever so clearly revealed in scripture, it were directly contrary to the rules of just reasoning to give our assent to it. It contradicts sense, though both the scripture and tradition, on which it is supposed to be built, carry not such evidence with them as sense; when they are considered merely as external evidences, and are not brought home to every one's breast, by the immediate operation of the Holy Spirit.

Nothing is so convenient as a decisive argument of this kind, which must at least *silence* the most arrogant bigotry and superstition, and free us from their impertinent solicitations. I flatter myself, that I have discovered an argument of a like nature, which, if just, will, with the wise and learned, be an everlasting check to all kinds of superstitious delusion, and consequently, will be useful as long as the world endures. For so long, I presume, will the accounts of miracles and prodigies be found in all history, sacred and profane.

Though experience be our only guide in reasoning concerning matters of fact; it must be acknowledged, that this guide is not altogether infallible, but in some cases is apt to lead us into errors. One, who in our climate, should expect better weather in any week of June than in one of December, would reason justly, and conformably to experience; but it is certain, that he may happen, in the event, to find himself mistaken. However, we may observe, that, in such a case, he would have no cause to complain of experience; because it commonly informs us beforehand of the uncertainty, by that contrariety of events, which we may learn from a diligent observation. All effects follow not with like certainty from their supposed causes. Some events are found, in all countries and all ages, to have been constantly conjoined together: Others are found to have been more variable, and sometimes to disappoint our expectations; so that, in our reasonings concerning matter of fact, there are all imaginable degrees of assurance, from the highest certainty to the lowest species of moral evidence.

A wise man, therefore, proportions his belief to the evidence. In such conclusions as are founded on an infallible experience, he expects the event with the last degree of assurance, and regards his past experience as a full *proof* of the future existence of that event. In other cases, he proceeds with more caution: He weighs the opposite experiments: He considers which side is supported by the greater number of experiments: to that side he inclines, with doubt and hesitation; and when at last he fixes his judgement, the evidence exceeds not what we properly call *probability*. All probability, then, supposes an opposition of experiments and observations, where the one side is found to overbalance the other, and to produce a degree of evidence, proportioned to the superiority. A hundred instances or experiments on one side, and fifty on another, afford a doubtful expectation of any event; though a hundred uniform experiments, with only one that is contradictory, reasonably beget a pretty strong degree of assurance. In all cases, we must balance the opposite experiments, where they are opposite, and deduct the smaller number from the greater, in order to know the exact force of the superior evidence.

To apply these principles to a particular instance; we may observe, that there is no species of reasoning more common, more useful, and even necessary to human life, than that which is derived from the testimony of men, and the reports of eye-witnesses and spectators. This species of reasoning, perhaps, one may deny to be founded on the relation of cause and effect. I shall not dispute about a word. It will be sufficient to observe that our assurance in any argument of this kind is derived from no other principle than our observation of the veracity of human testimony, and of the usual conformity of facts to the reports of witnesses. It being a general maxim, that no objects have any discoverable connexion together, and that all the inferences, which we can draw from one to another, are founded merely on our experience of their constant and regular conjunction; it is evident, that we ought not to make an exception to this maxim in favour of human testimony, whose connexion with any event seems, in itself, as little necessary as any other.

Were not the memory tenacious to a certain degree; had not men commonly an inclination to truth and a principle of probity; were they not sensible to shame, when detected in a falsehood: Were not these, I say, discovered by *experience* to be qualities, inherent in human nature, we should never repose the least confidence in human testimony. A man delirious, or noted for falsehood and villany, has no manner of authority with us.

And as the evidence, derived from witnesses and human testimony, is founded on past experience, so it varies with the experience, and is regarded either as a *proof* or a *probability*, according as the conjunction between any particular kind of report and any kind of object has been found to be constant or variable. There are a number of circumstances to be taken into consideration in all judgements of this kind; and the ultimate standard, by which we determine all disputes, that may arise concerning them, is always derived from experience and observation. Where this experience is not entirely uniform on any side, it is attended with an unavoidable contrariety in our judgements, and with the same opposition and mutual destruction of argument as in every other kind of evidence. We frequently hesitate concerning the reports of others. We balance the opposite circumstances, which cause any doubt or uncertainty; and when we discover a superiority on any side, we incline to it; but still with a diminution of assurance, in proportion to the force of its antagonist.

This contrariety of evidence, in the present case, may be derived from several different causes; from the opposition of contrary testimony; from the character or number of the witnesses; from the manner of their delivering their testimony; or from the union of all these circumstances. We entertain a suspicion concerning any matter of fact, when the witnesses contradict each other; when they are but few, or of a doubtful character; when they have an interest in what they affirm; when they deliver their testimony with hesitation, or on the contrary, with too violent asseverations. There are many other particulars of the same kind, which may diminish or destroy the force of any argument, derived from human testimony. Suppose, for instance, that the fact, which the testimony endeavours to establish, partakes of the extraordinary and the marvellous; in that case, the evidence, resulting from the testimony, admits of a diminution, greater or less, in proportion as the fact is more or less unusual. The reason why we place any credit in witnesses and historians, is not derived from any *connexion,* which we perceive *a priori,* between testimony and reality, but because we are accustomed to find a conformity between them. But when the fact attested is such a one as has seldom fallen under our observation, here is a contest of two opposite experiences; of which the one destroys the other, as far as its force goes, and the superior can only operate on the mind by the force, which remains. The very same principle of experience, which gives us a certain degree of assurance in the testimony of witnesses, gives us also, in this case, another degree of assurance against the fact, which they endeavour to establish; from which contradiction there necessarily arises a counterpoize, and mutual destruction of belief and authority.

I should not believe such a story were it told me by Cato, was a proverbial saying in Rome, even during the lifetime of that philosophical patriot. The incredibility of a fact, it was allowed, might invalidate so great an authority. The Indian prince, who refused to believe the first relations concerning the effects of frost, reasoned justly; and it naturally required very strong testimony to engage his assent to facts, that arose from a state of nature, with which he was unacquainted, and which bore so little analogy to those events, of which he had had constant and uniform experience. Though they were not contrary to his experience, they were not conformable to it.

But in order to encrease the probability against the testimony of witnesses, let us suppose, that the fact, which they affirm, instead of being only marvellous, is really miraculous; and suppose also, that the testimony considered apart and in itself, amounts to an entire proof; in that case, there is proof against proof, of which the strongest must prevail, but still with a diminution of its force, in proportion to that of its antagonist.

A miracle is a violation of the laws of nature; and as a firm and unalterable experience has established these laws, the proof against a miracle, from the very nature of the fact, is as entire as any argument from experience can possibly be imagined. Why is it more than probable, that all men must die; that lead cannot, of itself, remain suspended in the air; that fire consumes wood, and is extinguished by water; unless it be, that these events are found agreeable to the laws of nature, and there is required a violation of these laws, or in other words, a miracle to prevent them? Nothing is esteemed a miracle, if it ever happen in the common course of nature. It is no miracle that a man, seemingly in good health, should die on a sudden: because such a kind of death, though more unusual than any other, has yet been frequently observed to happen. But it is a miracle, that a dead man should come to life; because that has never been observed in any age or country. There must, therefore, be a uniform experience against every miraculous event, otherwise the event would not merit that appellation. And as a uniform experience amounts to a proof, there is here a direct and full *proof*, from the nature of the fact, against the existence of any miracle; nor can such a proof be destroyed, or the miracle rendered credible, but by an opposite proof, which is superior.

The plain consequence is (and it is a general maxim worthy of our attention), 'That no testimony is sufficient to establish a miracle, unless the testimony be of such a kind, that its falsehood would be more miraculous, than the fact, which it endeavours to establish; and even in that case there is a mutual destruction of arguments, and the superior only gives us an assurance suitable to that degree of force, which remains, after deducting the inferior.' When anyone tells me, that he saw a dead man restored to life, I immediately consider with myself, whether it be more probable, that this person should either deceive or be deceived, or that the fact, which he relates, should really have happened. I weigh the one miracle against the other; and according to the superiority, which I discover, I pronounce my decision, and always reject the greater miracle. If the falsehood of his testimony would be more miraculous, than the event which he relates; then, and not till then, can he pretend to command my belief or opinion.

Part II

In the foregoing reasoning we have supposed, that the testimony, upon which a miracle is founded, may possibly amount to an entire proof, and that the falsehood of that testimony would be a real prodigy: But it is easy to shew, that we have been a great deal too liberal in our concession, and that there never was a miraculous event established on so full an evidence. For *first*, there is not to be found, in all history, any miracle attested by a sufficient number of men, of such unquestioned good-sense, education, and learning, as to secure us against all delusion in themselves; of such undoubted integrity, as to place them beyond all suspicion of any design to deceive others; of such credit and reputation in the eyes of mankind, as to have a great deal to lose in case of their being detected in any falsehood; and at the same time, attesting facts performed in such a public manner and in so celebrated a part of the world, as to render the detection unavoidable: All which circumstances are requisite to give us a full assurance in the testimony of men.

Secondly. We may observe in human nature a principle which, if strictly examined, will be found to diminish extremely the assurance, which we might, from human testimony, have, in any kind of prodigy. The maxim, by which we commonly conduct ourselves in our reasonings, is, that the objects, of which we have no experience, resemble those, of which we have; that what we have found to be most usual is always most probable; and that where there is an opposition of arguments, we ought to give the preference to such as are founded on the greatest number of past observations. But though, in proceeding by this rule, we readily reject any fact which is unusual and incredible in an ordinary degree; yet in advancing farther, the mind observes not always the same rule; but when anything is affirmed utterly absurd and miraculous, it rather the more readily admits of such a fact, upon account of that very circumstance, which ought to destroy all its authority. The passion of *surprise* and *wonder*, arising from miracles, being an agreeable emotion, gives a sensible tendency towards the belief of those events, from which it is derived. And this goes so far, that even those who cannot enjoy this pleasure immediately, nor can believe those miraculous events, of which they are informed, yet love to partake of the satisfaction at second-hand or by rebound, and place a pride and delight in exciting the admiration of others.

With what greediness are the miraculous accounts of travellers received, their descriptions of sea and land monsters, their relations of wonderful adventures, strange men, and uncouth manners? But if the spirit of religion join itself to the love of wonder, there is an end of common sense; and human testimony, in these circumstances, loses all pretensions to authority. A religionist may be an enthusiast, and imagine he sees what has no reality: he may know his narrative to be false, and yet persevere in it, with the best intentions in the world, for the sake of promoting so holy a cause: or even where this delusion has not place, vanity, excited by so strong a temptation, operates on him more powerfully than on the rest of mankind in any other circumstances; and self-interest with equal force. His auditors may not have, and commonly have not, sufficient judgement to canvass his evidence: what judgement they have, they renounce by principle, in these sublime and mysterious subjects: or if they were ever so willing to employ it, passion and a heated imagination disturb the regularity of its operations. Their credulity increases his impudence: and his impudence overpowers their credulity.

Eloquence, when at its highest pitch, leaves little room for reason or reflection; but addressing itself entirely to the fancy or the affections, captivates the willing hearers, and subdues their understanding. Happily, this pitch it seldom attains. But what a Tully or a Demosthenes could scarcely effect over a Roman or Athenian audience, every *Capuchin*, every itinerant or stationary teacher can perform over the generality of mankind, and in a higher degree, by touching such gross and vulgar passions.

The many instances of forged miracles, and prophecies, and supernatural events, which, in all ages, have either been detected by contrary evidence, or which detect themselves by their absurdity, prove sufficiently the strong propensity of mankind to the extraordinary and the marvellous, and ought reasonably to beget a suspicion against all relations of this kind. This is our natural way of thinking, even with regard to the most common and most credible events. For instance: There is no kind of report which rises so easily, and spreads so quickly, especially in country places and provincial towns, as those concerning marriages; insomuch that two young persons of equal condition never see each other twice, but the whole neighbourhood immediately join them together. The pleasure of telling a piece of news so interesting, of propagating it, and of being the first reporters of it, spreads the intelligence. And this is so well known, that no man of sense gives attention to these reports, till he find them confirmed by some greater evidence. Do not the same passions, and others still stronger, incline the generality of mankind to believe and report, with the greatest vehemence and assurance, all religious miracles?

Thirdly. It forms a strong presumption against all supernatural and miraculous relations, that they are observed chiefly to abound among ignorant and barbarous nations; or if a civilized people has ever given admission to any of them, that people will be found to have received them from ignorant and barbarous ancestors, who transmitted them with that inviolable sanction and authority, which always attend received opinions. When we peruse the first histories of all nations, we are apt to imagine ourselves transported into some new world; where the whole frame of nature is disjointed, and every element performs its operations in a different manner, from what it does at present. Battles, revolutions, pestilence, famine and death, are never the effect of those natural causes, which we experience. Prodigies, omens, oracles, judgements, quite obscure the few natural events, that are intermingled with them.

But as the former grow thinner every page, in proportion as we advance nearer the enlightened ages, we soon learn, that there is nothing mysterious or supernatural in the case, but that all proceeds from the usual propensity of mankind towards the marvellous, and that, though this inclination may at intervals receive a check from sense and learning, it can never be thoroughly extirpated from human nature.

It is strange, a judicious reader is apt to say, upon the perusal of these wonderful historians, *that such prodigious events never happen in our days.* But it is nothing strange, I hope, that men should lie in all ages. You must surely have seen instances enough of that frailty. You have yourself heard many such marvellous relations started, which, being treated with scorn by all the wise and judicious, have at last been abandoned even by the vulgar. Be assured, that those renowned lies, which have spread and flourished to such a monstrous height, arose from like beginnings; but being sown in a more proper soil, shot up at last into prodigies almost equal to those which they relate.

It was a wise policy in that false prophet, Alexander, who though now forgotten, was once so famous, to lay the first scene of his impostures in Paphlagonia, where, as Lucian tells us, the people were extremely ignorant and stupid, and ready to swallow even the grossest delusion. People at a distance, who are weak enough to think the matter at all worth enquiry, have no opportunity of receiving better information. The stories come magnified to them by a hundred circumstances. Fools are industrious in propagating the imposture; while the wise and learned are contented, in general, to deride its absurdity, without informing themselves of the particular facts, by which it may be distinctly refuted. And thus the impostor above mentioned was enabled to proceed, from his ignorant Paphlagonians, to the enlisting of votaries, even among the Grecian philosophers, and men of the most emi-

nent rank and distinction in Rome: nay, could engage the attention of that sage emperor Marcus Aurelius; so far as to make him trust the success of a military expedition to his delusive prophecies.

The advantages are so great, of starting an imposture among an ignorant people, that, even though the delusion should be too gross to impose on the generality of them (*which, though seldom, is sometimes the case*) it has a much better chance for succeeding in remote countries, than if the first scene had been laid in a city renowned for arts and knowledge. The most ignorant and barbarous of these barbarians carry the report abroad. None of their countrymen have a large correspondence, or sufficient credit and authority to contradict and beat down the delusion. Men's inclination to the marvellous has full opportunity to display itself. And thus a story, which is universally exploded in the place where it was first started, shall pass for certain at a thousand miles distance. But had Alexander fixed his residence at Athens, the philosophers of that renowned mart of learning had immediately spread, throughout the whole Roman empire, their sense of the matter; which, being supported by so great authority, and displayed by all the force of reason and eloquence, had entirely opened the eyes of mankind. It is true; Lucian, passing by chance through Paphlagonia, had an opportunity of performing this good office. But, though much to be wished, it does not always happen, that every Alexander meets with a Lucian, ready to expose and detect his impostures.

I may add as a *fourth* reason, which diminishes the authority of prodigies, that there is no testimony for any, even those which have not been expressly detected, that is not opposed by an infinite number of witnesses; so that not only the miracle destroys the credit of testimony, but the testimony destroys itself. To make this the better understood, let us consider, that, in matters of religion, whatever is different is contrary; and that it is impossible the religions of ancient Rome, of Turkey, of Siam, and of China should, all of them, be established on any solid foundation. Every miracle, therefore, pretended to have been wrought in any of these religions (and all of them abound in miracles), as its direct scope is to establish the particular system to which it is attributed; so has it the same force, though more indirectly, to overthrow every other system. In destroying a rival system, it likewise destroys the credit of those miracles, on which that system was established so that all the prodigies of different religions are to be regarded as contrary facts, and the evidences of these prodigies, whether weak or strong, as opposite to each other. According to this method of reasoning, when we believe any miracle of Mahomet or his successors, we have for our warrant the testimony of a few barbarous Arabians: And on the other hand, we are to regard the authority of Titus Livius, Plutarch, Tacitus, and, in short, of all the authors and witnesses, Grecian, Chinese, and Roman Catholic, who have related any miracle in their particular religion; I say, we are to regard their testimony in the same light as if they had mentioned that Mahometan miracle, and had in express terms contradicted it, with the same certainty as they have for the miracle they relate. This argument may appear over subtile and refined; but is not in reality different from the reasoning of a judge, who supposes, that the credit of two witnesses, maintaining a crime against any one, is destroyed by the testimony of two others, who affirm him to have been two hundred leagues distant, at the same instant when the crime is said to have been committed.

One of the best attested miracles in all profane history, is that which Tacitus reports of Vespasian, who cured a blind man in Alexandria, by means of his spittle, and a lame man by the mere touch of his foot; in obedience to a vision of the god Serapis, who had enjoined them to have recourse to the Emperor, for these miraculous cures. The story may be seen in that fine historian; where every circumstance seems to add weight to the testimony, and might be displayed at large with all the force of argument and eloquence, if any one were now concerned to enforce the evidence of that exploded and idolatrous superstition. The gravity, solidity, age, and probity of so great an emperor, who, through the whole course of his life, conversed in a familiar manner with his friends and courtiers, and never affected those extraordinary airs of divinity assumed by Alexander and Demetrius. The historian, a cotemporary writer, noted for candour and veracity, and withal, the greatest and most penetrating genius, perhaps, of all antiquity; and so free from any tendency to credulity, that he even lies under the contrary imputation, of atheism and profaneness: The persons, from whose authority he related the miracle, of established character for judgement and veracity, as we may well presume; eye-witnesses of the fact, and confirming their testimony, after the Flavian family was despoiled of the empire, and could no longer give any reward, as the price of a lie. *Utrumque, qui interfuere, nunc quoque memorant, postquam nullum mendacio pretium.* To which if we add the public nature of the facts, as related, it will appear, that no evidence can well be supposed stronger for so gross and so palpable a falsehood.

There is also a memorable story related by Cardinal de Retz, which may well deserve our consideration. When that intriguing politician fled into Spain, to avoid the persecution of his enemies, he passed through Saragossa, the capital of Arragon, where he was shewn, in the cathedral, a man, who had served seven years as a doorkeeper, and was well known to every body in town, that had ever paid his devotions at that church. He had been seen, for so long a time, wanting a leg; but recovered that limb by the rubbing of holy oil upon the stump; and the cardinal assures us that he saw him with two legs. This miracle was vouched by all the canons of the church; and the whole company in town were appealed to for a confirmation of the fact; whom the cardinal found, by their zealous devotion, to be thorough believers of the miracle. Here the relater was also cotemporary to the supposed prodigy, of an incredulous and libertine character, as well as of great genius; the miracle of so *singular* a nature as could scarcely admit of a counterfeit, and the witnesses very numerous, and all of them, in a manner, spectators of the fact, to which they gave their testimony. And what adds mightily to the force of the evidence, and may double our surprise on this occasion, is, that the cardinal himself, who relates the story, seems not to give any credit to it, and consequently cannot be suspected of any concurrence in the holy fraud. He considered justly, that it was not requisite, in order to reject a fact of this nature, to be able accurately to disprove the testimony, and to trace its falsehood, through all the circumstances of knavery and credulity which produced it. He knew, that, as this was commonly altogether impossible at any small distance of time and place; so was it extremely difficult, even where one was immediately present, by reason of the bigotry, ignorance, cunning, and roguery of a great part of mankind. He therefore concluded, like a just reasoner, that such an evidence carried falsehood upon the very face of it, and that a miracle, supported by any human testimony, was more properly a subject of derision than of argument.

There surely never was a greater number of miracles ascribed to one person, than those, which were lately said to have been wrought in France upon the tomb of Abbé Paris, the famous Jansenist, with whose sanctity the people were so long deluded. The curing of the sick, giving hearing to the deaf, and sight to the blind, were every where talked of as the usual effects of that holy sepulchre. But what is more extraordinary; many of the miracles were immediately proved upon the spot, before judges

of unquestioned integrity, attested by witnesses of credit and distinction, in a learned age, and on the most eminent theatre that is now in the world. Nor is this all: a relation of them was published and dispersed every where; nor were the *Jesuits*, though a learned body, supported by the civil magistrate, and determined enemies to those opinions, in whose favour the miracles were said to have been wrought, ever able distinctly to refute or detect them. Where shall we find such a number of circumstances, agreeing to the corroboration of one fact? And what have we to oppose to such a cloud of witnesses, but the absolute impossibility or miraculous nature of the events, which they relate? And this surely, in the eyes of all reasonable people, will alone be regarded as a sufficient refutation.

Is the consequence just, because some human testimony has the utmost force and authority in some cases, when it relates the battle of Philippi or Pharsalia for instance; that therefore all kinds of testimony must, in all cases, have equal force and authority? Suppose that the Caesarean and Pompeian factions had, each of them, claimed the victory in these battles, and that the historians of each party had uniformly ascribed the advantage to their own side; how could mankind, at this distance, have been able to determine between them? The contrariety is equally strong between the miracles related by Herodotus or Plutarch, and those delivered by Mariana, Bede, or any monkish historian.

The wise lend a very academic faith to every report which favours the passion of the reporter; whether it magnifies his country, his family, or himself, or in any other way strikes in with his natural inclinations and propensities. But what greater temptation than to appear a missionary, a prophet, an ambassador from heaven? Who would not encounter many dangers and difficulties, in order to attain so sublime a character? Or if, by the help of vanity and a heated imagination, a man has first made a convert of himself, and entered seriously into the delusion; who ever scruples to make use of pious frauds, in support of so holy and meritorious a cause? The smallest spark may here kindle into the greatest flame; because the materials are always prepared for it. The *avidum genus auricularum*, the gazing populace, receive greedily, without examination, whatever sooths superstition, and promotes wonder.

How many stories of this nature have, in all ages, been detected and exploded in their infancy? How many more have been celebrated for a time, and have afterwards sunk into neglect and oblivion? Where such reports, therefore, fly about, the solution of the phenomenon is obvious; and we judge in conformity to regular experience and observation, when we account for it by the known and natural principles of credulity and delusion. And shall we, rather than have a recourse to so natural a solution, allow of a miraculous violation of the most established laws of nature?

I need not mention the difficulty of detecting a falsehood in any private or even public history, at the place, where it is said to happen; much more when the scene is removed to ever so small a distance. Even a court of judicature, with all the authority, accuracy, and judgement, which they can employ, find themselves often at a loss to distinguish between truth and falsehood in the most recent actions. But the matter never comes to any issue, if trusted to the common method of altercation and debate and flying rumours; especially when men's passions have taken part on either side.

In the infancy of new religions, the wise and learned commonly esteem the matter too inconsiderable to deserve their attention or regard. And when afterwards they would willingly detect the cheat, in order to undeceive the deluded multitude, the season is now past, and the records and witnesses, which might clear up the matter, have perished beyond recovery.

No means of detection remain, but those which must be drawn from the very testimony itself of the reporters: and these, though always sufficient with the judicious and knowing, are commonly too fine to fall under the comprehension of the vulgar.

Upon the whole, then, it appears, that no testimony for any kind of miracle has ever amounted to a probability, much less to a proof; and that, even supposing it amounted to a proof, it would be opposed by another proof; derived from the very nature of the fact, which it would endeavour to establish. It is experience only, which gives authority to human testimony; and it is the same experience, which assures us of the laws of nature. When, therefore, these two kinds of experience are contrary, we have nothing to do but subtract the one from the other, and embrace an opinion, either on one side or the other, with that assurance which arises from the remainder. But according to the principle here explained, this subtraction, with regard to all popular religions, amounts to an entire annihilation; and therefore we may establish it as a maxim, that no human testimony can have such force as to prove a miracle, and make it a just foundation for any such system of religion.

I beg the limitations here made may be remarked, when I say, that a miracle can never be proved, so as to be the foundation of a system of religion. For I own, that otherwise, there may possibly be miracles, or violations of the usual course of nature, of such a kind as to admit of proof from human testimony; though, perhaps, it will be impossible to find any such in all the records of history. Thus, suppose, all authors, in all languages, agree, that, from the first of January 1600, there was a total darkness over the whole earth for eight days: suppose that the tradition of this extraordinary event is still strong and lively among the people: that all travellers, who return from foreign countries, bring us accounts of the same tradition, without the least variation or contradiction: it is evident, that our present philosophers, instead of doubting the fact, ought to receive it as certain, and ought to search for the causes whence it might be derived. The decay, corruption, and dissolution of nature, is an event rendered probable by so many analogies, that any phenomenon, which seems to have a tendency towards that catastrophe, comes within the reach of human testimony, if that testimony be very extensive and uniform.

But suppose, that all the historians who treat of England, should agree, that, on the first of January 1600, Queen Elizabeth died; that both before and after her death she was seen by her physicians and the whole court, as is usual with persons of her rank; that her successor was acknowledged and proclaimed by the parliament; and that, after being interred a month, she again appeared, resumed the throne, and governed England for three years: I must confess that I should be surprised at the concurrence of so many odd circumstances, but should not have the least inclination to believe so miraculous an event. I should not doubt of her pretended death, and of those other public circumstances that followed it: I should only assert it to have been pretended, and that it neither was, nor possibly could be real. You would in vain object to me the difficulty, and almost impossibility of deceiving the world in an affair of such consequence; the wisdom and solid judgement of that renowned queen; with the little or no advantage which she could reap from so poor an artifice: All this might astonish me; but I would still reply, that the knavery and folly of men are such common phenomena, that I should rather believe the most extraordinary events to arise from their concurrence, than admit of so signal a violation of the laws of nature.

But should this miracle be ascribed to any new system of religion; men, in all ages, have been so much imposed on by ridiculous stories of that kind, that this very circumstance would be a full proof of a cheat, and sufficient, with all men of sense, not only to make them reject the fact, but even reject it without farther examination. Though the Being to whom the miracle is ascribed, be, in this case, Almighty, it does not, upon that account, become a whit more probable; since it is impossible for us to know the attributes or actions of such a Being, otherwise than from the experience which we have of his productions, in the usual course of nature. This still reduces us to past observation, and obliges us to compare the instances of the violation of truth in the testimony of men, with those of the violation of the laws of nature by miracles, in order to judge which of them is most likely and probable. As the violations of truth are more common in the testimony concerning religious miracles, than in that concerning any other matter of fact; this must diminish very much the authority of the former testimony, and make us form a general resolution, never to lend any attention to it, with whatever specious pretence it may be covered.

Lord Bacon seems to have embraced the same principles of reasoning. 'We ought,' says he, 'to make a collection or particular history of all monsters and prodigious births or productions, and in a word of every thing new, rare, and extraordinary in nature. But this must be done with the most severe scrutiny, lest we depart from truth. Above all, every relation must be considered as suspicious, which depends in any degree upon religion, as the prodigies of Livy: And no less so, every thing that is to be found in the writers of natural magic or alchimy, or such authors, who seem, all of them, to have an unconquerable appetite for falsehood and fable.'

I am the better pleased with the method of reasoning here delivered, as I think it may serve to confound those dangerous friends or disguised enemies to the *Christian Religion*, who have undertaken to defend it by the principles of human reason. Our most holy religion is founded on *Faith*, not on reason; and it is a sure method of exposing it to put it to such a trial as it is, by no means, fitted to endure. To make this more evident, let us examine those miracles, related in scripture; and not to lose ourselves in too wide a field, let us confine ourselves to such as we find in the *Pentateuch*, which we shall examine, according to the principles of these pretended Christians, not as the word or testimony of God himself, but as the production of a mere human writer and historian. Here then we are first to consider a book, presented to us by a barbarous and ignorant people, written in an age when they were still more barbarous, and in all probability long after the facts which it relates, corroborated by no concurring testimony, and resembling those fabulous accounts, which every nation gives of its origin. Upon reading this book, we find it full of prodigies and miracles. It gives an account of a state of the world and of human nature entirely different from the present: Of our fall from that state: Of the age of man, extended to near a thousand years: Of the destruction of the world by a deluge: Of the arbitrary choice of one people, as the favourites of heaven; and that people the countrymen of the author: Of their deliverance from bondage by prodigies the most astonishing imaginable:

I desire any one to lay his hand upon his heart, and after a serious consideration declare, whether he thinks that the falsehood of such a book, supported by such a testimony, would be more extraordinary and miraculous than all the miracles it relates; which is, however, necessary to make it be received, according to the measures of probability above established.

What we have said of miracles may be applied, without any variation, to prophecies; and indeed, all prophecies are real miracles, and as such only, can be admitted as proofs of any revelation. If it did not exceed the capacity of nature to foretell future events, it would be absurd to employ any prophecy as an argument for a divine mission or authority from heaven. So that, upon the whole, we may conclude, that the *Christian Religion* not only was at first attended with miracles, but even at this day cannot be believed by any reasonable person without one. Mere reason is insufficient to convince us of its veracity: And whoever is moved by *Faith* to assent to it, is conscious of a continued miracle in his own person, which subverts all the principles of his understanding, and gives him a determination to believe what is most contrary to custom and experience.

Mesmerism

"Report of the Commissioners Charged by the King to Examine Animal Magnetism, Printed on the King's Order Number 4 in Paris from the Royal Printing House"

by Benjamin Franklin and Antoine Lavoisier

Introduction

MICHAEL SHERMER

In 1991, about the time we were creating and organizing the Skeptics Society and *Skeptic* magazine, I read an essay by Stephen Jay Gould entitled "The Chain of Reason Versus the Chain of Thumbs," in *Bully for Brontosaurus* (1991, W. W. Norton). It is the story of an 18th-century scientific investigation of an extraordinary claim—mesmerism—commissioned by King Louis XVI of France and conducted by such scientific luminaries as Benjamin Franklin and Antoine Lavoisier. The result of that investigation was the Report of the Commissioners Charged by the King to Examine Animal Magnetism, "Printed on the King's Order Number 4 in Paris from the Royal Printing House" in 1784, just five years before the demise of the ancien régime. Gould called the report "an enduring testimony to the power and beauty of reason," a "key document in the history of human reason," and said that "it should be rescued from its current obscurity, translated into all languages, and reprinted by organizations dedicated to the unmasking of quackery and the defense of rational thought" (188–189).

I kept that challenge in the back of my mind for the next five years, awaiting the time when we would have the space to allocate for the resurrection of this "key document" (it runs 18 pages, making it the third longest piece we have ever run). It is not a waste of space because the history of skepticism and the skeptical movement should be tracked and recorded as any field should be, and this is the first scientific investigation that we know of into what would today be considered a paranormal or pseudoscientific claim. No one else has taken up Gould's challenge, so in the pages to come we present you with this delightful piece of science and reasoning, with thanks to Steve Gould for providing a copy from the original in Harvard's Houghton Library, and to my friend and colleague Charles Salas and his wife Danielle for the translation; both write and speak fluent French (plus Charles is an intellectual historian of the period).

The historical context for the report is given in great detail by the renowned intellectual historian Robert Darnton, in his 1968 book *Mesmerism and the End of the Enlightenment in France* (Harvard University Press). The German physician Franz Anton Mesmer was the "discoverer" of animal magnetism, and he has ever since been remembered whenever we are "mesmerized" by something that seems to draw us to it like a magnet. The analogy is appropriate, for Mesmer reasoned that just as an invisible force of gravity binds the planets together, and an invisible force of electricity flows through various substances, and an invisible force of magnetism draws iron shavings to a lodestone, so an invisible force—animal magnetism—flows through living beings. To Mesmer these forces were actually manifestations of a single fluid flowing throughout the universe, the blockage of which can cause disease. Cure comes through releasing the blockage (similar to what is claimed for Chi power, acupuncture and acupressure, therapeutic touch, and other modern nostrums). Mesmer's technique involved facing the patient, touching fingers, and staring for prolonged periods into her eyes. By most accounts Mesmer was, well, rather mesmerizing, especially to his female patients, who would shake, groan, scream, and even faint (is this beginning to sound familiar to those who have ever witnessed a faith healing?).

Group healings involved everyone surrounding a "baquet," or vat, filled with "magnetized" water and placed in the center of the room. "Magnetized" rods protruding from the vat were grabbed by the patients who, with their other hand, held each other's thumbs between their thumb and forefinger and squeezed at the appropriate time to allow the magnetism to flow evenly through the group. To ensure proper conductivity in this "mesmeric chain," Mesmer looped a rope around them (without knots, for this might impede flow).

Mesmerism became all the rage, triggering a skeptical response by the medical establishment, which, along with other concerned scientists, persuaded King Louis XVI to establish a Royal Commission to test Mesmer's claims. (In the film *Jefferson in Paris*, the vat and rods are depicted, along with a skeptical Thomas Jefferson.) Franklin, the world's leading authority on electricity, was in Paris as a U.S. representative;

Lavoisier, one of the founders of modern chemistry, lived there. The others on the Commission were respected scientists and medical doctors, including Dr. Guillotin, inventor of the device that would cut off Lavoisier's head, along with many others, over the course of the next decade of revolutionary mayhem.

The problem for the Commission, as the report reveals, is that animal magnetism is invisible. No problem, so is gravity. They would test its effects on objects, which was the basis for Mesmer's claims of curative power. (James Randi is fond of stating that it doesn't matter whether there is a scientific basis to astrology, ESP, and other psychic forces; the only thing that matters is if they actually work, which they don't.) The problem was that "cures" take too long for an experiment and may be caused by other conditions anyway (Franklin suspected that Mesmer's patients were cured by staying away from medical doctors!). Mesmer, however, did not take the test; his top student, Charles Deslon, took his place, which subsequently led to Mesmer disputing the findings. The experimenters began by trying to magnetize themselves—joined by rods, rope, and thumbs with Deslon giving proper instruction—to no effect. They then tried seven people from the lower classes and compared their results against seven people from the upper classes (recall the importance of class in prerevolutionary France). Only three, all from the lower classes, experienced anything significant, so the Commission concluded it was due to the power of suggestion.

To test the null hypothesis that magnetism is really just a placebo effect, Franklin and Lavoisier devised a test whereby some subjects would be deceived into thinking they were receiving the experimental treatment (magnetism) when they really were not, while others did receive the treatment and were told that they had not. The results were clear: the effects were due to the power of suggestion only.

To reinforce this conclusion, Franklin had

Deslon magnetize a tree in his garden. The experimental subject—allegedly "sensitive" to the magnetic effect but not told which tree was affected—then walked around the garden hugging trees until he declared he had sensed it. He collapsed in a fit in front of the fourth tree, but it was the fifth one that was "magnetized." Undaunted, Deslon claimed that all trees carry some magnetism and therefore the test was invalid (not unlike the excuses of failed water dowsers and other modern mystics). In test after test, Deslon failed. One woman was blindfolded and told that Deslon was "influencing" her, causing her to collapse in a mesmeric "crisis." He wasn't. Another woman could supposedly sense "magnetized" water. Lavoisier filled several cups with water, only one of which was "magnetized." After touching an unmagnetized cup she collapsed in a fit, upon which Lavoisier gave her the "magnetized" one, which "she drank quietly & said she felt relieved. Therefore the cup & magnetism missed their marks, because the crisis was quieted rather than exacerbated." Q.E.D.

The Commission concluded that "nothing proves the existence of Animal-magnetism fluid; that this fluid with no existence is therefore without utility; that the violent effects observed at the group treatment belong to touching, to the imagination set in action & to this involuntary imitation that brings us in spite of ourselves to repeat that which strikes our senses." In other words, the effect is mental, not magnetic.

The control of intervening variables and the testing of specific claims, without resort to unnecessary hypothesizing about what is behind the "power," is the lesson modern skeptics should take from this historical masterpiece. The other historical lesson is clear as well—true believers remain unaffected by contradictory evidence, in the 18th century as well as today. So why bother testing? Because the vast majority of people are neither true believers nor skeptics, but just intellectually curious and looking for a natural explanation for an apparently supernatural phenomenon.

Report of the Commissioners on Mesmerism

Translation by Danielle and Charles Salas

On March 12, 1784, the King appointed Physicians chosen from the Paris Faculté, *Messieurs* Borie, Sallin, d'Arcet, Guillotin, to examine & report on Animal magnetism practiced by *Monsieur* Deslon; & as requested by these four Physicians, His Majesty has appointed five of the Members of the Royal Academy of Sciences to conduct this examination with them: Messieurs Franklin, le Roy, Bailly, de Bory, Lavoisier. As M. Borie died at the beginning of the Commissioners' work, His Majesty chose M. Majault, a Doctor from the Faculté, to replace him.

The agent that M. Mesmer claims to have discovered, which he has made known under the name Animal magnetism, is, as he characterizes it himself & according to his own words,

a universally spread fluid; it is the means of a mutual influence between celestial bodies, the earth, & living bodies; it is continuous so as not to permit any vacuum; it is incomparably subtle; it is capable of receiving, spreading, & communicating all the sensations of movement; it is sensitive to flux & reflux. The physical body feels the effects of this agent; &, when it insinuates itself into the substance of nerves, it affects them immediately. One recognizes particularly in the human body, properties similar to those of the magnet. One distinguishes two diverse & opposed poles. The action & property of Animal magnetism may be transmitted from one body to another, animate & inanimate: This action operates from a distance, without the help of any intermediary body; it is increased when reflected by mirrors, communicated, spread, & increased by sound; this property may be accumulated, concentrated, transported. Although this fluid is universal, all animated bodies are not equally susceptible. There are some, albeit few, in whom the polar property is so strong that their mere presence destroys all the effects of this fluid in other bodies.

Animal magnetism may itself cure nervous disorders & be a medium for curing others; it improves the action of medications; it induces & guides crises in such a way that disorders can be understood & mastered. In this way, the Physician knows the state of health of each individual & determines with certainty the origin, nature, & progress of even the most complicated of diseases; he prevents their spread & reaches a cure without ever exposing the patients to dangerous effects or unfortunate consequences, regardless of age, temperament & sex. Nature offers in Magnetism a universal means of healing and protecting people.

Such is the agent that the Commissioners have been charged to examine & whose properties are attested to by M. Deslon, who endorses all of M. Mesmer's principles. This theory is the basis of a paper read May 9 at the home of M. Deslon in the presence of the Lieutenant General of Police & the Commissioners. In the paper it is claimed that there is but one nature, one disease, one remedy; & this remedy is Animal magnetism. In instructing the Commissioners about the theory & action of magnetism, this Physician also taught them practical exercises, indicating where the poles are, how patients are to be touched & the manner in which this magnetic fluid is to be trained upon them.

M. Deslon pledged with the Commissioners, 1. to ascertain the existence of Animal magnetism; 2. to make known their findings; 3. to prove the usefulness of these findings & of Animal magnetism in the cure of diseases.

Having been introduced to the theory & techniques of Animal magnetism, it was time to learn about the effects. The Commissioners visited (& all of them more than once) the place where M. Deslon had his practice. In the middle of a large room they saw a circular vat, made of oak & raised a foot or a foot & a half, called a *baquet*. The covering of this vat has many holes from which protrude bent, flexible metal rods. The patients are arranged in rows around this vat, one rod to a person which because it is bent may be applied directly to the afflicted area of the body; the patients are chained together by a rope looped around their bodies; sometimes a second chain is created by touching hands, which is to say, the thumb is pressed between a neighbor's thumb & index finger, & squeezed; the sensation received from the left is sent through the right, & it circulates all around.

There is a pianoforte in the corner on which different tunes with various movements are played; sometimes the sounds of voice & singing are added.

All those who magnetize hold a metal rod ten to twelve inches long.

M. Deslon declared to the Commissioners, 1. that this rod conducts magnetism; this rod has the advantage of concentrating magnetism in the tip, & making the emanations more powerful. 2. Sound, in accordance with M. Mesmer's principle, is also a conductor of magnetism, & to communicate the fluid to the pianoforte, it is enough to bring the metal rod closer; the person in contact with the instrument also provides some fluid, & magnetism is transmitted through sound to near-by patients. 3. The rope wrapped around the patients is intended, like the chain of thumbs to augment the effects through communication.

4. The inside of the vat is made so as to concentrate magnetism. It is a large basin from which magnetism is spread through the metal rods dipped within it.

The Commissioners used an electrometer & a non-magnetic, metal needle to check that the vat did not contain any electrical or charged matter; & upon the declaration of M. Deslon regarding the composition of the inside of the vat, they agreed that no physical agent capable of contributing to the reported effect of magnetism was present.

A large number of patients arranged in several rings around the vat receive magnetism simultaneously therefore through these means: through the metal rods that transmit the magnetism from the vat; through the rope intertwined about the body, & by the union of thumbs communicating that of their neighbors; through the sound of the pianoforte, or through a pleasant voice that spreads it through the air. Patients are directly magnetized as well by passing the finger & the metal rod in front of the face, on top of or behind the head, & on afflicted areas, always maintaining the distinction of the poles; sight, staring at them, activates the effects. But above all patients are magnetized by the laying of hands & the pressure of fingers on the hypochondria & lower abdominal areas; the contact often maintained for a considerable time, sometimes a few hours.

Patients then display a variety of reactions depending on the different states they find themselves in. Some are calm, quiet, & feel nothing; others cough, spit, feel slight pain, a warmth either localized or all over, & perspire; others are agitated & tormented by convulsions. These convulsions are extraordinary in their number, duration, & strength. As soon as a convulsion begins, many others follow. The Commissioners have seen some lasting for more than three hours; convulsions are accompanied by murky & viscous expectorations drawn out by the violence of the exertions.

Sometimes the expectorations contain streaks of blood; there is a young male patient, in particular, who spit out blood in abundance. These convulsions are characterized by quick, involuntary movements of limbs & the entire body, by a tightening of the throat, by the twitching of the hypochondria & epigastric area, by blurred & unfocused vision, by piercing shrieks, tears, hiccups & excessive laughter. They are preceded or followed by a state of languor & dreaminess, of a kind of prostration & even sleepiness. The slightest unexpected noise causes shivers; & it has been noticed that the change of tone & measure in the pieces played on the pianoforte had an influence on the patients—a faster movement, for example, agitated them more & renewed the intensity of their convulsions.

There is a padded room, intended primarily for patients racked by convulsions, a room named *des Crises*; but M. Deslon does not deem its usage necessary, & all patients, regardless of condition, are gathered together in the group treatment rooms. Nothing is more astonishing than the spectacle of these convulsions; without seeing it, it cannot be imagined: & in watching it, one is equally surprised by the profound repose of some of these patients & the agitation that animates others; the various reactions that are repeated, the fellow-feeling that sets in. One sees patients specifically searching for others & while rushing towards each other, smile, speak with affection & mutually soothe their crises. All submit to the magnetizer; even though they may appear to be asleep, his voice, a look, a signal pulls them out of it. Because of these constant effects, one cannot help but acknowledge the presence of a great power which moves & controls patients, & which resides in the magnetizer.

This convulsive state is improperly called Crisis in the theory of Animal magnetism: in this doctrine, the crisis is considered healthy, like those brought about by Nature or by the skillful physician to facilitate the cure of diseases. The Commissioners will adopt this term hence forward in this report, & when they make use of the word *crisis*, they will always mean the state of either the convulsions or the lethargy produced by the processes of Animal magnetism.

The Commissioners noticed that out of the number of patients in crisis, there were always many women & few men; that these crises took one to two hours to build; & that as soon as one was established, all the others would start successively soon after. This having been remarked upon, the Commissioners soon came to the conclusion that group treatment rooms could not be the setting for their experiments. The multiplicity of effects is a first obstacle; one sees too many things at once to see particular things clearly. Moreover, distinguished patients who come to the treatment for their health could be bothered by the questioning; being so carefully observed could inconvenience or displease them; the Commissioners themselves would be hindered by their concern for discretion. They then decided that their constant attendance not being necessary to the treatment, it sufficed that a few of them should come from time to time to confirm the preliminary general observations, to make new ones if necessary, & to report to the assembled commission.

The effect of group treatment having been observed, the next task was to unravel the causes & to search for proofs of the existence & the utility of magnetism. The question of existence is primary; the question of utility is not to be addressed until the first has been fully resolved. Animal magnetism may well exist without being useful but it cannot be useful if it does not exist.

In consequence, the principal purpose of the Commissioners' examination & the essential goal of their first experiments had to be to make certain of that existence. This purpose was still very broad & needed to be simplified. Animal magnetism embraces the whole of Nature; it is said to be the means by which celestial bodies influence us; the Commissioners thought that they should first set aside this mighty influence, to consider only the part of this fluid diffused upon the earth without bothering with whence it comes, & to ascertain the action it has upon us, around us & before our eyes, before considering its relations with the Universe.

The most reliable way to ascertain the existence of Animal-magnetism fluid would be to make its presence tangible; but it did not take long for the Commissioners to recognize that this fluid escapes detection by all the senses. Unlike electricity, it is neither luminescent nor visible. Its action does not manifest itself visibly as does the attraction of a magnet; it is without taste or smell; it spreads noiselessly & envelops or penetrates you without your sense of touch warning you of its presence. Therefore, if it exists in us & around us, it does so in an absolutely undetectable manner. Among those who profess magnetism, there are some who claim that it may occasionally be seen emanating from the tips of fingers serving as conductors or who believe that they feel its passage when the finger is moved back & forth in front of the face & over the hand. In the first instance, the visible emanation is only that of perspiration which becomes easily visible when magnified under a solar microscope; in the second, the feeling of cold or coolness that one feels, a feeling more noticeable the warmer one is, is caused by the finger disturbing the air which is always colder than body temperature. On the other hand, if the finger is brought close to the skin of the face, which is colder than the finger, & left there, one is made to feel a sensation of heat, which is communicated body heat.

It is also claimed that this fluid has an odor & that it is detectable when the finger or conducting rod is held under the nose; it is even said that these sensations are different under the two nostrils depending on the polar positioning of the finger or rod. M. Deslon has experimented upon several Commissioners; the Commissioners have repeated the experiment upon several subjects; none has felt this difference in sensation between one nostril & the other: & if by paying close attention, some odor is recognized, it is in the case of the iron rod, that is of the rod itself warmed & rubbed, & in the case of the finger, that of the emanation of perspiration, an odor often mixed with that of iron with which the finger is imprinted. These effects have been mistakenly attributed to magnetism, they all belong to known, natural causes.

In addition, M. Deslon never emphasized these fleeting sensations; he didn't think it necessary to have to produce them as proofs; &, on the contrary, he has expressly declared to the Commissioners that he could only prove the existence of magnetism through the action of this fluid, creating changes in animate bodies. This existence becomes even more difficult to ascertain through demonstrable effects whose causes are not unequivocal; through authenticated facts upon which mental circumstances have no influence; finally through proofs capable of impressing & convincing the mind, the only proofs that could satisfy enlightened Physicians.

The action of magnetism on animate bodies may be observed two different ways; either by prolonged action & its curative effects on the treatment of diseases, or by its temporary effects on the economy of the human body & by the observable changes it produces. M. Deslon insisted that the first of these methods be principally & almost exclusively used. The Commissioners did not believe they had to do so & here are their reasons:

Most diseases are seated inside the body. The long experience of a great many centuries has made the symptoms that precede & characterize these diseases well-known. That same experience has indicated their method of treatment. What is it in this method that is the goal of the Physician's effort? It is neither to oppose nor tame Nature, it is to help it in its operations. Nature heals the sick, said the Father of Medicine; but sometimes it meets obstacles that hinder its course, obstacles that needlessly consume its strength. The Physician is Nature's Minister; attentive observer, he studies its course. If that course is steady, sure, level & without deviations, the Physician observes it in silence & is careful not to disturb it with remedies at best useless; if this course is hampered, he facilitates it; if it is too slow or too fast, he accelerates it or slows it down. He sometimes limits himself to regulating diet to fulfill his goal; sometimes he uses medications. The action of medication in the human body is a new force that combines with the great force that sustains life: if the remedy follows the same paths already opened by this force, it is salutary & useful in expelling disease; if it tends to open contrary paths & divert this inner action, it is harmful. However, it must be agreed that this very real effect, salutary or harmful, may often escape common observation. The physical history of mankind offers very peculiar phenomena in this regard. We see that the most different diets have not prevented the attainment of old age. We see men seemingly stricken by the same disease who are healed while following opposite diets, & while taking entirely different remedies; Nature is therefore powerful enough to maintain life in spite of a bad diet & to triumph over both the disease & the remedy. If it has this power to resist remedies, all the more reason that it has the power to operate without them. The experience of their effectiveness, therefore, always carries some degree of uncertainty; in the case of magnetism, there is an extra degree of uncertainty: the question of its existence. For, how can one ascertain, by the treatment of diseases, the action of an agent the existence of which is in dispute when one can doubt the effect of medications the existence of which is not in question?

The cure cited the most in favor of the existence of magnetism is that of M. le Baron de

* * *, of which both the Court & the city have been informed. We will not enter herein to a discussion of the facts; we will not examine whether the remedies previously used may have contributed to that cure. On the other hand, we acknowledge that the state of the patient was grave &, on the other, the ineffectiveness of all the means of ordinary medicine; magnetism was used & M. le Baron de * * * fully recovered. But could not a natural occurrence alone have been responsible for this recovery? A woman of the people & very poor, living at Gros-caillou, was struck in 1779 by a malevolent fever of well known characteristics; she consistently refused any help, asking only that a water pitcher by her bedside be kept full. She stayed quietly on her bed of straw, drinking water all day & doing nothing else. The sickness progressed, passed successively through its different stages, & ended with complete recovery.

Mademoiselle G *** living at the Petite-sécuries of the King had two glands on the right breast that worried her very much; a surgeon advised her to use Painter's water, an excellent dissolving agent, stating that, if the remedy did not succeed within a month, the glands would have to be removed. The frightened young lady consulted M. Sallin who deemed the glands treatable. M. Bouvart, consulted later, gave the same opinion. She was encouraged to seek entertainment & distractions before beginning treatment; fifteen days later, she suffered a violent coughing crisis at the Opera & expectorated so abundantly that she had to be brought back home; in four hours she spit out three pints of phlegm; one hour later M. Sallin examined the breast & could no longer find any trace of the glands. M. Bouvart, who was called the next day, verified the felicitous effect of this natural crisis. If Mlle. G *** had taken Painter's water, then Painter's water would have had to be credited for the cure.

Observations over the centuries prove & Physicians themselves recognize, that Nature alone & without the help of medical treatment cures a great number of patients. If magnetism were inefficacious, using it to treat patients would be to leave them in the hands of Nature. In trying to ascertain the existence of this agent, it would be absurd to choose a method that, in attributing to the agent all of Nature's cures, would tend to prove that it has a useful & curative action, even though it would have none.

The Commissioners are in agreement on this with M. Mesmer. He rejected the cure of diseases when this way of proving magnetism was proposed to him by a Member of the Académie des Sciences: *it is*, said he, *a mistake to believe that this kind of proof is irrefutable; nothing conclusively proves that the Physician or Medicine heals the sick.*

The treatment of diseases, therefore can only furnish results that are always uncertain & often misleading; this uncertainty could not be evaded, & all cause of illusion offset, except by an infinity of cures & perhaps the experience of a few centuries. The purpose & importance of the Commission require means more prompt. The Commissioners have had to confine themselves to purely physical proofs, that is, to the temporary effects of the fluid on the Animal body, by stripping these effects of all illusions possibly mixed up with them, & making sure that they cannot be due to any cause other than Animal magnetism.

They set out to experiment on isolated subjects, who were willing to participate in a variety of experiments imagined by the Commissioners; & who, some through their naivete, others through their intelligence, would be able to give a truthful & exact account of what they experienced. These experiments will not be presented here chronologically but in the order of the facts that they ought to clarify.

The Commissioners resolved to begin by experimenting upon themselves, & to submit themselves to the action of magnetism. They were very curious to experience through their own senses the reported effects of this agent.

They therefore submitted themselves to these effects with the determination not to be angered by the injuries or upsets to their health known to be produced by magnetism, putting themselves in a position to resolve this important question on the spot by means of their own evidence. But in submitting themselves to magnetism in this way, the Commissioners had to take a necessary precaution. There is no individual, even in the best of health who, if he listened to himself attentively, would not feel within himself an infinity of the movements & variations of either warmth or very minor pain in various areas of the body; these variations which can occur at any time are independent from magnetism. It may not be inconsequential to bring & sustain attention upon oneself in this way. There are so many connections, by whatever means, between the will of the soul & body movements that it is impossible to gauge the effect of attentiveness, which seems only to be a sequence of intentions directed towards the same object with perseverance & without interruption. When one considers that the will moves the arm at pleasure, how can one be certain that the attention focused upon an interior part of the body cannot excite slight movements there, bring warmth there, & make modifications so as to produce new sensations there? The first concern of the Commissioners was necessarily not to pay too much attention to what was happening inside themselves. If magnetism is a real & powerful agent, it does not require to be thought about to be manifest; it must, so to speak, force itself upon the attention & make itself noticeable even by a mind disturbed by design.

But in deciding to make experiments upon themselves, the Commissioners unanimously agreed to make them amongst themselves without allowing any stranger other than M. Deslon to magnetize them or other persons of their own choosing; they also promised each other not to magnetize in group treatment, so that they could freely discuss their observations, & be in all cases the only, or at least the first, judges of what they would be observing.

In consequence, a separate room & particular vat were set aside for them at M. Deslon's, & once a week they sat there; they stayed for two to two & a half hours at a time, the iron rod resting on the left hypochondrium, & themselves surrounded by the rope of communication, & from time to time making the chain of thumbs. They were magnetized, either by M. Deslon or a disciple sent in his place, some for a longer time & more often than others, & these should have appeared to be the most sensitive; they were magnetized, sometimes with the finger & iron rod held & moved over various parts of the body, sometimes by applying hands & finger pressure to either the hypochondria or on the pit of the stomach.

None of them felt a thing, or at least, nothing that could be attributed to the action of magnetism. A few of the Commissioners have robust constitutions; others have weaker constitution & are subject to discomforts: one of these felt a slight pain in the pit of the stomach, following strong finger pressure there. This pain lasted all day & the next day, accompanied by a feeling of fatigue & uneasiness. A second felt a slight irritation of the nerves, which he is susceptible to, on the afternoon of one of the days he was touched. A third, endowed with a greater sensitivity, & especially an extreme instability in the nerves, felt more pain & more intense irritations; but these slight mishaps are the consequence of incessant & ordinary variations in the state of health &, consequently, foreign to magnetism, or they follow from the pressure exerted on the stomach. The Commissioners only mention these minor details out of a desire for scrupulous accuracy; they report them because they have imposed on themselves the rule of always telling the truth in all things.

The Commissioners could not help but be struck by the difference between group treatment & private treatment at the vat. Calm &

silence in one, movement & agitation in the other; there, multiple effects, violent crises, the normal state of body & spirit interrupted & troubled, Nature overstrung; here the body without pain, the spirit without trouble, Nature conserving its equilibrium & natural course, in a word, the absence of all effects; one cannot find this great power so astonishing in the group treatment; magnetism without energy appeared to be devoid of all sensible action.

The Commissioners, who at first went to the vat only once a week, wanted to test whether continuity might produce something; they went three days in a row, but their lack of sensibility was the same & they obtained no result whatsoever. This experiment, done & repeated on eight subjects at a time, a few of whom have habitual discomforts, suffices to conclude that magnetism has little or no effect on a state of health, & even on a state of slight infirmity. It was resolved to experiment on really sick subjects, & they were chosen from the class of commoners.

Seven patients were brought in Passy at the home of M. Franklin; they were magnetized in front of him & in front of the other Commissioners by M. Deslon.

The widow Saint-Amand, an asthmatic with swollen abdomen, thighs & legs; & the woman Anseaume, who had a lump on her thigh, felt nothing; little Claude Renard, a child of six years, scrofulous, almost emaciated, with a swollen knee & a crooked leg with an almost unmovable joint, an interesting child & more reasonable than his age would dictate, also felt nothing, & also Geneviève Leroux, nine years old, subject to convulsions & a disease somewhat similar to what is called *chorea sancti Viti*. François Grenet felt some effects; his eyes are diseased, especially the right one with which he can hardly see & where there is a large tumor. During the magnetization on the left eye, by bringing the thumb closer & moving it back & forth at close range & for a long time, he felt pain in the eyeball & tears appeared. When the right eye, the sicker of the two, was magnetized, he felt nothing; he felt the same pain in the left eye, & nothing elsewhere.

The woman Charpentier, knocked to the ground against a wooden beam by a cow two years ago, suffered various after effects: she lost her eyesight, then recovered it partially, but has stayed in a habitual state of infirmity; she claimed to have had two prolapses, & an abdomen of such sensitivity that she cannot bear to tie her skirt belts; this sensitivity is a matter of nerves being irritated and set into motion; the slightest pressure on the abdomen can get this motion underway &, by the correspondence of nerves, produce effects throughout the whole body.

This woman was magnetized like the others, by application & finger pressure; this pressure was painful to her; then as the finger was directed towards the area of prolapse, she complained of a headache; with the finger placed in front of her face, she said she was short of breath. With repeated movements of the finger from high to low, she had quick movements of the head & shoulders such as one has when feeling surprise mixed with fear, & similar to those of a person whose face has been splashed with drops of cold water. It seemed that she felt the same movements with her eyes closed. Fingers were placed under her nose while her eyes were closed & she said she thought that she was going to faint if that continued. The seventh patient, Joseph Ennuyé felt similar effects, but to a much lesser degree.

Out of these seven patients, four felt nothing & three felt some effects. These effects were worthy of the Commissioners' attention & warranted a scrupulous exam.

To enlighten themselves & fix their ideas on this matter, the Commissioners decided to experiment with patients from other circumstances, patients chosen from high society who could not be suspected of ulterior motives & whose intelligence would permit them to discuss their own sensations & report on them. Mmes. de B** & de V**, Ms. M** & R** were admitted to the Commissioners' private vat; they were asked to observe what they felt, but without giving it too much attention. M. M** & Mme. de V** were the only ones to feel something. M. M** has a cold tumor over the entire knee joint & his patella is painful. After having been magnetized, he declared he felt nothing anywhere in his body except when the finger was moved in front of the bad knee; he thought he then felt a slight warmth at the place where he usually has pain. Mme. de V**, suffering from a nervous condition, was many times on the point of falling asleep while being magnetized. Magnetized without interruption for one hour & nineteen minutes, most often by the laying of hands, she felt only some agitation & uneasiness. These two patients came only once to the vat. M. R** sick from an unresolved liver congestion, following from an obstruction improperly healed, came three times & felt nothing. Mme. de B** suffering obstructions sat constantly with the Commissioners, she felt nothing; & it must be said that she submitted to magnetism with perfect calm, which stemmed from a great incredulity.

Various patients were tested on other occasions but not around the vat. One of the Commissioners struck by migraine was magnetized by M. Deslon for half an hour; one of the symptoms of this migraine is excessive coldness in the feet. M. Deslon brought his foot close to that of the patient, the foot was not warmed, the migraine lasted its usual length, & the patient after sitting down by the fireplace felt the salutary effects that heat has always provided, without having felt during the day or the next night any of the effects of magnetism.

Even though inconveniences prevented M. Franklin from being in Paris & witnessing the experiments, he was himself magnetized by M. Deslon, who visited him at his home in Passy. The gathering there was numerous; all those present were magnetized. A few patients who

had accompanied M. Deslon felt the effects of magnetism, as they usually did during group treatment, but Mme. de B**, M. Franklin, his two parents, his secretary, an American officer, felt nothing, even though one parent of M. Franklin was convalescing, & the American officer sick at the time with a low grade fever.

These different experiments furnish facts worthy of being collected & compared, & from which the Commissioners have been able to draw conclusions. Out of fourteen patients, five seemed to have felt effects, & nine none at all. The Commissioner who had the migraine & ice cold feet felt no relief from magnetism, & his feet were not warmed. Therefore this agent does not have the property, attributed to it, of communicating heat to the feet. Magnetism is also heralded as indicating the type & especially the seat of disease through the pain that the action of this fluid inevitably brings there. This advantage would be precious; the fluid, indicator of disease, would be a great tool in the hands of the physician, often confounded by equivocal symptoms; but François Grenet only had sensation & some pain in the eye that was less sick. Had the other eye not been red & swollen, one would have believed it to be undamaged judging by the effect of magnetism. M. R** & Mme. de B**, both sick with obstructions, & Mme. de B** quite seriously, having felt nothing, would not have been made aware of either the seat or the type of their disease. & yet, obstructions are diseases claimed to be especially susceptible to the action of magnetism; because according to the new theory, free & fast circulation of this fluid through the nerves is a way to clear up channels & destroy obstacles, that is to say, the blockages that it meets. At the same time it is said that magnetism is the cornerstone of health. If M. R** & Mme. de B** had not felt discomforts & suffering inseparable from the obstructions, they would have firmly believed that they were in the best state of health in the world. The same should be said of the American officer:

magnetism, heralded as an indicator of disease, has therefore entirely missed its mark.

The heat that M. M** felt on the patella is too subtle & too fleeting to lead to any conclusion. We may suspect that it comes from the cause described above, that is, from too much attention paid to observing oneself: the same attention would find similar feelings at any other moment when magnetism was not in use. The drowsiness felt by Mme. de V** probably comes from the invariability & boredom of the same situation; if she has had a certain light movement, we know that the nature of nervous conditions depends heavily on the attention paid to them; it is enough to think about them or to hear about them to regenerate them. It can be judged what will happen to a woman whose nerves are very jittery, & who is magnetized for an hour & nineteen minutes, during which time she has no other thought than that of her habitual ailments. It would have not been surprising had she suffered a more considerable nervous crisis.

Of the effects that could appear to have to do with magnetism, only those on the woman Charpentier, on François Grenet & on Joseph Ennuyé remain. But then in comparing these three particular cases to all the others, the Commissioners were surprised that these three patients from the lower class were the only ones who had felt something, while those of a higher class, more enlightened, more able to give account of their feelings, felt nothing at all. No doubt François Grenet felt pain in his eye & cried because the thumb was brought so close to it; the woman Charpentier complained that when her stomach was touched, the pressure corresponded to the prolapse; & this pressure may have produced a part of the effects that this woman felt; but the Commissioners suspected that these effects had been augmented by mental circumstances.

Let us take the standpoint of a commoner, for that reason ignorant, struck by disease & desiring to get well, brought with great show before a large assembly composed in part of physicians, where a new treatment is administered which the patient is persuaded will produce amazing results. Let us add that the patient's cooperation is paid for, & that he believes that it pleases us more when he says he feels effects, & we will have a natural explanation for these effects; at the least, we will have legitimate reasons to doubt that the real cause of these effects is magnetism.

Moreover, one can ask why magnetism had these effects on those people who knew what was done to them, who may have believed they had an interest in saying what they said, whereas it had no hold over little Claude Renard, over this delicate organization of childhood, so fickle & so sensitive! The reason & ingenuity of this child guarantees the truth of his testimony. Why did this agent produce no effect upon Geneviève Leroux, who was in a perpetual state of convulsions? Her nerves were certainly jittery, why did magnetism not manifest itself, either by augmenting or diminishing her convulsions? Her indifference & impassibility lead to the conclusion that she felt nothing, because the lack of reason did not permit her to judge that she should have felt nothing.

These facts permitted the Commissioners to observe that magnetism has seemed to be worthless for those patients who submitted to it with a measure of incredulity; that the Commissioners, even when those with jittery nerves deliberately focused their attention elsewhere, having been armed with philosophical doubt that ought to accompany every examination, did in no way feel the impressions felt by the three lower-class patients, & they must have suspected that these impressions, even supposing them all to be real, followed from an anticipated conviction, & could have been an effect of the imagination. From this has resulted another plan of experiment. From now on, their research is going to be directed toward a new object; it is a question of disproving or confirming this suspicion, of determining up to what point the imagination can influence feelings & establishing whether it can be the cause of all or part of the effects attributed to magnetism.

Next the Commissioners heard about the experiments done at the home of the Dean of the Faculté by M. Jumelin, Doctor of Medicine; they requested to see these experiments & they met with him at the home of one of the Commissioners, M. Majault. M. Jumelin declared that he was not a follower of M. Mesmer or of M. Deslon, that he had learned nothing from them about Animal magnetism; & from what he had heard said on the subject he conceived principles & carried out proceedings. His principles consist of regarding Magnetic Animal fluid as a fluid circulating in the body, & which emanates from it, but which is essentially the same as that which produces body heat; a fluid that like all others, tending toward equilibrium, passes from the body which has the most to the body which has the least. His methods are equally different from those of M. Mesmer & M. Deslon; he magnetizes as they do using the finger & the metal rod as conductors, & by the laying of hands, but without making any distinction between poles.

First, eight men & two women were magnetized & felt nothing; finally a woman who is the door-keeper at the home of M. Alphonse le Roy, Doctor of Medicine, having been magnetized on her forehead, but without contact, said she felt heat while M. Jumelin was moving his hand, & with the tips of his five fingers next to the woman's face, she said she felt as if a moving flame were coming from it; magnetized on the stomach, she said she felt heat there; magnetized on the back, she said she felt the same heat there: she declared furthermore that she felt warm all over & had a headache.

The Commissioners, seeing that out of eleven persons subjected to the experiment only one was sensitive to the magnetism of M. Jumelin, thought that this person felt something only because she was doubtless more im-

pressionable; the occasion was favorable for shedding light on the matter. The sensitivity of the woman being well established, it was only a question of protecting her from her imagination, or at least of getting it out of the way. The Commissioners proposed to blindfold her so that they could observe the nature of her sensations while experimenting without her knowledge. She was blindfolded & magnetized; whereupon the phenomena no longer corresponded to the places where the magnetism was directed. Magnetized successively over the stomach & the back, the woman felt heat in her head, pain in her right leg, her left eye & left ear.

The blindfold was removed, & M. Jumelin having applied his hands on the hypochondria, she said she felt heat; then after a few minutes she said she was going to faint &, in fact, did. When she recovered, she was again used as a subject, she was blindfolded, M. Jumelin was moved aside, the room was made silent & the woman was made to believe that she was magnetized. The results were the same, even though nothing was done to her from near or afar; she felt the same heat, the same pain in her eyes & ears; she also felt heat in her back & loins.

After a quarter of an hour, M. Jumelin was signaled to magnetize her over her stomach, she felt nothing, the same thing with her back. Sensations diminished instead of increasing. The headache remained, the heat in the back & loins came to an end.

One sees that there have been effects produced & that these effects are similar to those felt by the three patients mentioned above. But the former & the latter were obtained by different methods. It follows that the methods of proceeding play no role whatsoever. The method of Ms. Mesmer & Deslon & an opposite method give the same results. The distinction between the poles, therefore, is chimerical.

One can observe that when the woman could see, she placed her sensations precisely on the magnetized area; whereas when she could not see, she placed them haphazardly & in areas far from those being magnetized. It was natural to conclude that these sensations, true or false, were determined by the imagination. We became convinced of this when we saw that this woman, having rested, not feeling anything & being blindfolded, felt all the same effects even though she was not magnetized; but the demonstration was completed when, after a fifteen minute experiment and her imagination probably tired & cooled off, the effects diminished instead of increasing at the very moment she was really being magnetized.

If she fainted, that is a mishap that happens frequently to women when they are bothered by clothes that are too tight. The laying of hands on the hypochondria may have produced the same effect in an excessively sensitive woman; but this cause is not even needed to explain what happened. It was very hot, the woman no doubt felt strong emotions in those first moments as she prepared to submit to a new, unknown experiment, & after such a prolonged effort, it is not out of the ordinary to feel weak.

This swooning, therefore, has a natural & known cause, but the sensations she experienced when not magnetized, can only be the effect of the imagination. The same results were obtained in similar experiments made by M. Jumelin at the same place, on the following day, in the presence of the Commissioners, on a blindfolded man & a woman with eyes uncovered; it was clear that their answers were determined by the questions that were posed. The question indicated where the sensation ought to be; instead of directing the magnetism towards them, it was only their imagination that was being heightened & directed. A child of five years, magnetized afterwards, felt only the heat generated beforehand in play.

These experiments appeared important enough to the Commissioners to be repeated in order to shed new light & M. Jumelin graciously agreed to participate. It would be pointless to object that M. Jumelin's method is bad; for at this moment it was not magnetism being put to the test but the imagination.

The Commissioners agreed to blindfold the subjects being tested, to not magnetize them most of the time, & to skillfully question them in such a way as to lead them to answers. The point was not to induce error, only to mislead their imaginations. Indeed, when not being magnetized, the sole response ought to be that they feel nothing; & when they are being magnetized, it is the heartfelt sensation that ought to dictate their response, & not the manner in which they are questioned.

The Commissioners, having accordingly moved to the home of M. Jumelin, began by putting his servant to the test. A specially designed blindfold, the same that was used in all subsequent experiments, was placed over his eyes. This blindfold was composed of two rubber crowns, the concave side of which was filled with eiderdown; all this was enclosed in two pieces of cloth sewn into a round shape. These two pieces were attached to one another; they had cords that tied behind. Placed over the eyes, they left a gap for the nose so that the subject could breathe freely without being able to see a thing, not even daylight, through, above, or under the blindfold. These precautions having been taken to secure the comfort of the subjects & the certainty of the results, M. Jumelin's servant was persuaded that he was magnetized. He then felt an almost overwhelming warmth, stirrings in his abdomen, his head became heavier; little by little he began to nod & appeared on the point of falling asleep. All of which proves, as we said earlier, that this effect is due to the situation, to boredom, & not to magnetism.

Magnetized next with eyes uncovered, he feels tingling in his forehead when the metal rod is brought close to it; blindfolded again, he feels no tingling when the rod is brought close; & when it is not, & he is questioned whether he does not feel something on his forehead, he declares he feels something there moving back & forth across it.

M. B**, an educated man, particularly in the field of medicine, blindfolded, offers the same spectacle; feeling effects when there is no action taking place, often feeling nothing when there is. These effects were such that even before being magnetized in any way, but believing he had been for ten minutes, he felt a warmth in his loins that he compared to the warmth of a stove. It is obvious that M. B** had a strong sensation because to describe it, he had to resort to such a comparison; & this sensation was entirely due to the imagination, which alone was acting upon him.

The Commissioners, especially the Physicians, conducted numerous experiments on different subjects whom they magnetized themselves, or whom they led to believe had been magnetized. The Commissioners magnetized randomly with opposite poles or like poles in either sense, & in every instance, they obtained the same results; there was not in all those experiments any variation other than that of the degree of imagination.

They were therefore convinced by facts that the imagination on its own can produce various sensations & make one feel pain, heat, even a substantial amount of heat in all parts of the body, & they have concluded that for many the imagination plays a necessary role in the effects attributed to Animal magnetism. But one must agree that the practice of magnetism produces in animated bodies changes more pronounced & upsets more substantial than the ones which have just been reported. So far none of the subjects who believed that they were magnetized were moved to the point of having convulsions; it therefore was a new type of experiment to test, if by shaking the imagination alone, one could produce crises similar to the ones taking place at the group treatment.

This idea then led to several experiments. When a tree has been touched following principles & methods of magnetism, anyone who stops beside it ought to feel the effect of this agent to some degree; there are some who even lose consciousness or feel convulsions. We spoke of this to M. Deslon who replied that the experiment ought to succeed so long as the subject was very sensitive, & we came to agreement with him to conduct this experiment in Passy, in the presence of M. Franklin. The necessity that the subject be sensitive made the Commissioners think that in order to make the experiment decisive & unquestionable, it must be made on a person chosen by M. Deslon, a person whose sensitivity to magnetism had already been proved. M. Deslon consequently brought with him a young man of about twelve; in the garden orchard, an isolated apricot tree, fit to conserve the magnetism that would be impressed upon it, was marked. M. Deslon was led to it by himself so he could magnetize it, the young man staying in the house in the presence of someone who did not leave his side. One would have wished that M. Deslon not be present during the experiment, but he declared that it could miss the mark if he did not direct his cane & his attention to that tree to amplify the action. It was reluctantly decided to keep M. Deslon as far away as possible & to place the Commissioners between him & the young man in order to ensure that he could make no signals & attest to the fact that no information was exchanged. These precautions, in an experiment that is to be authentic, are necessary without being offensive.

The young man was then brought in, blindfolded & made to stand in front of four trees that had not been magnetized, & asked to hug them each for two minutes as prescribed by M. Deslon himself.

M. Deslon, present & at some distance, pointed the cane at the tree that was really magnetized.

At the first tree, the young man, questioned after one minute, declared that he was perspiring profusely; he coughed, spit & said he felt a slight pain on the head; the distance to the magnetized tree was approximately twenty-seven feet.

At the second tree, he felt giddy with the same pain on the head; the distance was thirty-six feet.

At the third tree, the dizziness increases & the headache as well; he says he thinks he is getting closer to the magnetized tree; it was then about thirty-eight feet away.

Finally, at the fourth non-magnetized tree, & at about twenty-four feet from the magnetized one, the young man had a crisis; he lost consciousness, his limbs stiffened & he was carried to a nearby lawn where M. Deslon gave him first aid & revived him.

The result of this experiment is totally contrary to magnetism. M. Deslon tried to explain what happened by saying that all trees are naturally magnetized & that their own magnetism was strengthened by his presence. But in that case, anyone sensitive to magnetism could not chance going into a garden without incurring the risk of convulsions, an assertion contradicted by everyday experience. M. Deslon's presence did nothing more than it had in the coach in which he arrived with the young man, who sat across from him & felt nothing. Had the young man not felt anything, even under the magnetized tree, it could have been said that he was not sensitive enough, at least on that day: but the young man fell into a crisis under a non-magnetized tree; consequently, it is an effect which has no physical cause whatsoever, no outside cause, & which can have no cause other than the imagination. The experiment is therefore absolutely conclusive: the young man knew he was being led to a magnetized tree, his imagination was struck, successively heightened, & at the fourth tree it rose to the degree necessary to produce the crisis.

Other experiments support this one, & yield the same result. One day the Commissioners met in Passy at M. Franklin's with M. Deslon, having requested the latter to bring some patients with him & choose from amongst the poor being treated those who would be the most sensitive to magnetism. M. Deslon brought two women; & while he was busy magnetizing M. Franklin & several people in another apartment, these two women were separated & placed in two different rooms.

One of them, the woman P**, has leukoma; but as she is able to see a little, her eyes were covered with the blindfold described above. She was persuaded that M. Deslon had been brought in to magnetize her; silence was insisted upon, three Commissioners were present, one to question her, the other to take notes, the third to represent M. Deslon. They acted as if they were addressing M. Deslon, asking him to begin, but the woman was not magnetized at all; the three Commissioners remained quiet, occupied only in observing what was going to happen. After three minutes, the patient started to feel a nervous shiver; then in succession she felt pain in the back of her head, in her arms, pins & needles in her hands, that's the expression she used; she stiffened, clapped her hands, got up from her chair, tapped her feet: the crisis was well defined. Two other Commissioners in the next room with the door closed heard the clapping of hands & tapping of feet &, without seeing anything, were witnesses to this loud affair.

Those two Commissioners were with the other patient, a Mlle. B**, suffering from a nervous ailment. With her eyes left uncovered, her sight was unimpeded; she was seated in front of a closed door & persuaded that M. Deslon was on the other side in the process of magnetizing her. It was barely a minute of sitting there in front of that door before she began to feel shivers. A minute after that she started to chatter even though she felt generally warm; finally, after the third minute, she fell into a complete crisis. Her breathing was racing, she stretched both arms behind her back, twisting them strongly & bending her body forward; her whole body shook. The chatter of teeth was so loud that it could be heard from outside; she bit her hand hard enough to leave teeth marks.

It is well to observe that these two patients were not touched in any way; not even their pulses were felt so that it could not be said that magnetism had been communicated to them, & nonetheless the crises were full blown. The Commissioners, who wanted to know the effect of the workings of the imagination & appreciate what role it could have in the crises of magnetism, obtained all that they had wanted. It is impossible to see the effect of these workings more overtly or in a more evident way than in these two experiments. If the patients have claimed that their crises are stronger during treatment, it is because the shaking of nerves is catching & in general everyone's own individual emotion is increased by the spectacle of similar emotions.

We had an opportunity to test the woman P** a second time & to realize the extent to which she was ruled by her imagination. We wished to conduct the experiment of the magnetized cups: this experiment consists of choosing from amongst a number of cups one that is magnetized. The cups are presented one after the other to a patient sensitive to magnetism; he ought to have a crisis or at least sense some effect when the magnetized cup is presented; he ought to be indifferent to all the others that are not. It is only necessary that, as recommended by M. Deslon, the direct pole be presented so that the person handling the cup does not magnetize the patient, & that no effect other than the cup's magnetism be involved. The woman P** was summoned to M. Lavoisier's Arsenal where M. Deslon was present; she started falling into shock in the anteroom, before having seen either M. Deslon or the Commissioners; but she knew she should be seeing him, & that is a striking effect of the imagination.

After the crisis had abated, the woman was led to the site of the experiment. Several cups not at all magnetized were presented to her; the second cup started to affect her, & at the fourth, she fell completely into a crisis. It can be said that her actual state was that of a nervous crisis that had begun in the anteroom & began again on its own; but what is crucial is that having asked for a drink, it was given to her in the cup magnetized by M. Deslon himself; she drank quietly & said she felt relieved. Therefore the cup & magnetism missed their marks, because the crisis was quieted rather than exacerbated.

Sometime later, while M. Majault was examining her leukoma, the magnetized cup was brought close to the back of her head & held there for twelve minutes; she noticed nothing & felt no effect whatsoever, she was even calmer than at any other time because her imagination was distracted & occupied by the eye examination being made.

The Commissioners were told that this woman, left alone in the anteroom, suffered renewed convulsions when approached by several persons who had nothing to do with magnetism. It was pointed out to her that she was not being magnetized; but her imagination was so excited that she replied: if you were not doing anything to me, I would not be in the state I am in. She knew she had come to be the subject of experiment; someone's approach, the least noise drew her attention, awakening the idea of magnetism & renewing the convulsions.

In order to act powerfully, the imagination often needs to be stimulated in different ways simultaneously. The imagination responds to all the senses; its reaction must be proportional to the number of senses that move it & the feelings received: this is what the Commissioners realized following an experiment that they are about to describe. M. Jumelin had told them of a young lady, age 20, whose speech he had removed by the power of magnetism; the Commissioners repeated this experiment at his house, and the young lady agreed to it & agreed to be blindfolded.

First we tried to obtain the same result without magnetizing her; but whether she felt or believed she felt the effects of magnetism, we were unable to stimulate her imagination enough for the experiment to succeed. When she was really magnetized with eyes blindfolded, we were not more successful. The blindfold was removed; then the imagination was stimulated by sight as well as by hearing, the effects were more noticeable; but even though her head began to droop, even though she felt pressure at the base of the nose & many of the symptoms that she had felt the first time, she did not however lose her ability to speak. What she asked for was done, & in three fourths of a minute she became mute; only a few inarticulate sounds could be heard despite the visible efforts of the throat to push out sounds & those of the tongue & lips to enunciate. This state lasted only a minute: one can see that finding itself in precisely the same circumstances, the seduction of the mind & its effects on the organs of speech were the same. But it was not enough that the spoken word alerted her to the fact that she had been magnetized, it was necessary that the sense of sight make a stronger impression capable of stirring the imagination; it was necessary also that it be a known gesture to revive her ideas. It seems that this experiment shows wonderfully how the imagination works, being heightened by degree & requiring extra outside help in order to be stimulated more effectively.

This power that sight has over the imagination explains the effects that the doctrine of magnetism attributes to it. It is preeminently sight that has the power to magnetize; signs & gestures employed are ordinarily useless, the Commissioners were told, unless the subject has already been taken hold of by being glanced upon. The reason is simple; it is in the eyes where the most expressive traits of the passions are, & it is there that all that is most important & most seductive in character is unfolded. Therefore, the eyes must have a great power over us; but they have this power because they stir the imagination, & in a manner more or less exaggerated according to the strength of that imagination. It is therefore sight that gets all the work of magnetism underway; & the effect is so powerful, its origins so deep, that a woman newly arrived at M. Deslon's, coming out of a crisis & meeting the gaze of the disciple of Deslon who magnetized her, stared at him for three quarters of an hour. For a long time she was hounded by this look; she kept seeing before her that same eye intent on watching her; & she constantly carried it in her imagination for three days, whether asleep or awake. One sees all that can be produced by an imagination able to preserve the same impression for such a long time, the same impression, that is to say, able to revive by its own power the same feeling for three days.

The experiments just reported are consistent & also decisive; they authorize the conclusion that the imagination is the real cause of the effects attributed to magnetism. But the supporters of this new agent will perhaps reply that the identity of the effects does not always prove the identity of the causes. They will allow that the imagination may excite these impressions without magnetism; but they will maintain that magnetism can also excite them without the help of the imagination. The Commissioners could easily destroy this assertion by using reason & the principles of Physics: first & foremost, new causes are not to be postulated unless absolutely necessary. When the effects observed can have been produced by an existing cause, already manifested in other phenomena, sound Physics teaches that the effect observed must be attributed to it; & when one announces the discovery of a cause hitherto unknown, sound Physics also demands that it be established, demonstrated by effects that cannot be attributed to any known cause, & that can only be explained by the new cause. It would thus be up to the followers of magnetism to present other proofs & to look for effects that were entirely stripped of the illusion of the imagination. But as facts are more conclusive than reasoning & provide more striking evidence, the Commissioners wanted to put to the test what magnetism would be when the imagination was not at work.

An apartment with adjacent rooms & a communicating door was prepared. The door was removed & replaced by a frame, covered with two layers of paper. In one of these rooms was one of the Commissioners there to write down all that would happen, & a lady introduced as being from the provinces & in need of a seamstress. Mlle. B**, a seamstress who had already been used during the experiments in Passy & whose sensitivity to magnetism was known, was asked to come over. When she arrived, all was arranged so that there was only one chair where she could sit & this chair was situated in the embrasure of the communicating door where she found herself as in a nook.

The Commissioners were in the other room, & one of them, a Physician trained to magnetize & having already produced effects, was put in charge of magnetizing Mlle. B** through the paper frame. It is a principle of the theory of magnetism that this agent passes through wooden doors, walls, etc. A paper frame could not be an obstacle; moreover, M. Deslon has positively established that magnetism passes through paper; & Mlle. B** was magnetized as if she had been in the open & in his presence.

For a half-hour, from a distance of a foot & a half, she was magnetized with opposite poles, following all the procedures which had been taught by M. Deslon, & which the Commissioners saw practiced at his home. During all this time, Mlle. B** was conversing cheerfully; asked about her health, she answered freely that she felt quite well: in Passy she had fallen into a crisis after three minutes; here she endured magnetism for thirty minutes without any effect. It is just that here she did not know she was magnetized, & in Passy she believed that she was. One sees therefore that the imag-

ination alone produces all the effects attributed to magnetism; & when the imagination does not act, there are no more effects.

But one objection can be made to this experiment; that Mlle. B** could have been ill disposed & found herself less sensitive at that time to magnetism. The Commissioners anticipated the objection & consequently conducted the following experiment. As soon as one ceased to magnetize through the paper, the same Physician-Commissioner moved to the other room; it was easy to induce Mlle. B** to be magnetized. He then commenced magnetizing her, being careful, as in the preceding experiment, to stand at a distance of one & a half feet from her, to use only the gestures & movements of the index finger & the metal rod, for had he applied his hands & touched her hypochondria, it could have been said that magnetism had acted through this closer contact. The only difference between these two experiments is that in the first, he magnetized with opposite poles, following the rules, whereas in the second, he magnetized with direct poles & backwards. Acting in this way, by the theory of magnetism, no effect at all should have been produced.

However after three minutes, Mlle. B** felt ill at ease & short of breath; then followed interspersed hiccups, chattering of the teeth, a tightening of the throat & a bad headache; she anxiously stirred on her chair; she complained about lower back pain; she occasionally tapped her feet rapidly on the floor; she then stretched her arms behind her back, twisting them strongly as in Passy; in a word, a complete & perfectly characteristic convulsive crisis. She suffered all this in twelve minutes whereas the same treatment employed for thirty minutes found her insensitive. The only thing added here is the imagination; it is therefore to it that these effects are due.

If the imagination started the crisis, it is also the imagination that made it stop. The Commissioner who magnetized her said it was time to finish; crossing his two index fingers, he presented them to her; & it is well to observe that by this he was magnetizing her with direct poles as he had done so far; nothing therefore had changed, the same treatment should have continued the same impressions. But the intention was enough to calm the crisis; the heat & headache dissipated. The areas that hurt were attended to one after the other, while announcing that the pain would disappear. In this way, the voice, by directing the imagination, caused the pain in the neck to stop, then in succession the irregularities in the chest, stomach & arms. It took only three minutes; after which Mlle. B** declared that she no longer felt anything & was absolutely back in her natural state.

These last experiments along with several done at the home of M. Jumelin have the double advantage of simultaneously demonstrating the power of the imagination & the nullity of magnetism in the effects produced.

If the effects are even more marked & crises seemingly more violent during group treatment, it is because several causes concur with the imagination to multiply & magnify the effects. The process begins with staring to take hold of the mind; touching & applying hands soon follow; & it is appropriate here to develop an exposition of the physical effects.

These effects are more or less substantial; the lesser are the hiccups, stomach upsets, purges; the more substantial are convulsions which are called crises. The place where touching occurs is the hypochondria, at the pit of the stomach, & sometimes on the ovaries when it is women who are touched. Hands, fingers press & more or less squeeze these different areas.

The colon, one of the large intestines, runs across both regions of the hypochondria & the epigastric area that separates them. It is placed directly under the tegument. It is therefore on this intestine that touching takes place, on this sensitive & very irritable intestine. Movement alone, repeated movements without any other agent, excite the muscular action of the intestine & sometimes results in evacuations. Nature seems to indicate, as by instinct, this maneuvering to hypochondriacs. The practice of magnetism is nothing more than this very maneuvering; & the purges which it can produce are facilitated further in the magnetic treatment by the frequent & almost habitual use of a real purgative, diluted cream of tartar.

But when this movement principally excites the irritability of the colon, this intestine presents other phenomena. It swells more or less, & sometimes to a considerable volume. It then communicates to the diaphragm such an irritation that this organ enters more or less into convulsions & this is what we call *crisis* in the treatment of Animal magnetism. One of the Commissioners has seen a lady subject to a kind of spasmodic vomiting repeated several times a day. The efforts produced only a cloudy & viscous fluid similar to that vomited by patients in crisis during the practice of magnetism. The convulsion had its seat in the diaphragm; & the region of the colon was so sensitive that the slightest touching of that area, a strong disturbance of the air, the surprise caused by an unexpected noise, sufficed to stimulate the convulsion. Thus this woman had crises without magnetism due solely to the irritability of the colon & the diaphragm, & women who are magnetized have their crises due to the same cause & by this irritability.

The laying of hands on the stomach has physical effects equally remarkable. The application is made directly upon this organ. Sometimes compression there is strong & continuous, sometimes light & repeated; sometimes vibrations are transmitted to this part by rotating the metal rod; lastly, thumbs are sometimes passed along there quickly & successively one after the other. These maneuvers quickly bring to the stomach an irritation strong & more or less lasting depending on whether the subject is more or less sensitive & irritable. Compressing the stomach predisposes it to this irritation.

This compression allows it to act on the diaphragm, & to communicate to it the impressions it receives. It cannot become irritated unless the diaphragm is irritated, & from there, as by the action of the colon, result the nervous symptoms we have just talked about.

With sensitive women, if one has put pressure on the two hypochondria without making any movement, the stomach tightens & these women faint. This is what happened to the woman magnetized by M. Jumelin; & what often happens without any other cause when the clothes of women are too tight; there is then no crisis, because the stomach is squeezed without being irritated, & because the diaphragm remains in its natural state. These same maneuvers practiced on the ovaries, aside from the effects that are particular to them, produce the same symptoms even more powerfully. The influence & the power of the uterus on animal economy is well known.

The intimate relation between the colon, the stomach & the uterus with the diaphragm is one of the causes of the effects attributed to magnetism. The lower abdominal regions, subjected to various touches, respond to a different plexus that constitutes a veritable nervous center, by means of which, aside from all other systems, it very likely excites a sympathy, a communication, a correspondence between all parts of the body, an action & a reaction such that the sensations excited in this center shake the other parts of the body; & vice versa such that a sensation felt in one part gets the nervous system going, which often transmits this impression to all the other parts.

This explains not only the effects of magnetic touching but also the physical effects of the imagination. It has always been observed that the affections of the soul make their first impression on this nervous center, which leads to the common saying that one has a weight on the stomach & that one feels suffocated. The diaphragm joins in, from which come sighs, tears & laughter. Next a reaction is felt on the viscera of the lower abdomen; & that is how we can make sense of physical disorders produced by the imagination. A sudden chill occasions colic, fear causes diarrhea, sadness gives rise to jaundice. The history of Medicine contains infinite examples of the power of the imagination & the influence of the soul. The fear of fire, a violent desire, a strong & lasting hope, a crisis of anger return the use of legs to a man crippled by gout, to a paralytic; an intense & unexpected joy dissipates a quartan fever two months old; a strong attentiveness brings a halt to hiccups; accidental mutes recover speech following a strong emotion of the soul. History shows that this emotion suffices to recover speech, & the Commissioners saw that striking the imagination was enough to cause its loss. The action & the reaction of the physical upon the mental & of the mental upon the physical have been demonstrated since observation has been part of Medicine, that is, from its origin. Crises arise from touching & from the imagination.

Tears, laughter, coughs, hiccups, & in general all the effects observed during what are called the crises of the group treatment arise therefore from either the functions of the diaphragm disturbed by physical means, such as touching & pressure, or from the power of the imagination so gifted for acting upon this organ & disturbing its functions.

If it were objected that touching is not always necessary for these effects, the reply would be that the imagination may possess enough resources to manufacture everything by itself—especially the imagination acting in a group treatment, doubly excited therefore by its own movement & that of the surrounding imaginations. We have seen what it produced in the experiments made by the Commissioners on isolated subjects; one can judge of its multiplied effects on patients brought together in the group treatment. These patients are assembled in a tight place, relative to their number: the air is warm, although care is taken to renew it; & it is always more or less laden with mephitic gas the action of which particularly affects the head & the nervous system. If there is music, it is another means of acting upon nerves & of stimulating them.

Several women are magnetized simultaneously & at first feel only effects similar to those noted by the Commissioners in several of their experiments. They have recognized that even during the group treatment, it is more often only after two hours that the crises begin. Little by little, impressions are communicated & reinforce each other, as one may notice at theatrical spectacles where the impressions are greater when there are many spectators, & especially in the places where one is at liberty to applaud. This indication of particular emotions establishes a general emotion which each shares to the extent to which he is susceptible. It is this that one observes also in armies on the day of battle, when the enthusiasm of courage as well as the panic of terror spread with so much rapidity. The sound of the drum & of the military music, the noise of the cannon, the musket fire, the cries, the disorder rattle the organs, give to the mind the same movement & heighten imaginations to the same degree. In this drunken unity, one impression manifested becomes universal; it encourages a charge or determines flight. The same cause gives birth to revolts; the imagination governs the multitude: men gathered in numbers are more taken by their senses, reason has less hold on them; & when fanaticism presides over these assemblies, it gives rise to the Tremblers of the Cevennes.

It is in order to stop such disturbances which can spread so easily that gatherings are forbidden in seditious towns. The mind is everywhere influenced by example. Mechanical imitation brings the physical into play: by isolating individuals, one can quiet their minds; by separating them, one can stop convulsions, naturally always contagious: we have a recent example of this in the young girls of Saint-Roch, who when separated were healed of the convulsions they suffered from when together.

Thus we meet again with magnetism, or rather with the theatrical play of the imagination, in the army, in large gatherings like that around the vat, acting by different means, but producing the same effects. The vat is surrounded by a new crowd of patients: sensations are continuously communicated & returned; in the end the exercise wears out the nerves; they become irritated & the woman who is most sensitive gives the signal. At that point the cords, all pulled to the same degree & in unison, respond, & the crises multiply; they mutually reinforce each other; they become violent. At the same time, the men witnessing these emotions share them to the degree of their nervous sensibility, & those whose sensibility is greater & more easily affected fall into a crisis themselves. This great affectability, in part natural & in part acquired, in men as well as women, becomes habitual. Having felt these sensations once or several times, it is only a question of recalling their memory to stimulate the imagination to the degree necessary to create the same effects. This is something always easy to do by placing the subject in the same circumstances. Then there is no need for group treatment, one has only to touch the hypochondria, to pass the finger & the metal rod in front of the face; the gestures are known. It is not even necessary that they be employed, it suffices that patients, eyes blindfolded, believe that the gestures are being repeated, that they are persuaded they are being magnetized; the ideas awake, the sensations reproduce themselves, the imagination employing familiar means, & taking the same paths, makes the same phenomena reappear. It is this that happens to the patients of M. Deslon, who fall into crisis without a vat, & without being excited by the spectacle of group treatment.

Touching, imagination, imitation, these then are the real causes of the effects attributed to this new agent, known under the name Animal magnetism, to this fluid said to circulate in the body & to spread from individual to individual; such is the result of the experiments by the Commissioners, & the observations that they made on the methods employed, & on the effects produced. This agent, this fluid does not exist, but as chimerical as it is, the idea of it is not new. A few authors, a few physicians from the last century have expressly dealt with it in several works. The curious & interesting researches of M. Thouret prove to the group that the theory, the processes, the effects of Animal magnetism, proposed in the last century, closely resembled those being taken up again in this one. Magnetism therefore is only an old error. This theory is being presented today with a more impressive apparatus, necessary in a more enlightened century; but it is not for that reason less false. Man seizes, abandons, takes up again the error that gratifies him. There are errors which will be eternally dear to humanity. How many times has astrology not reappeared upon the earth! Magnetism draws us to return to it. The desire has been to link it to celestial influences so as to make it more captivating & attract men with the double hopes that touch them most, the hope of knowing their futures, & the hope of prolonging their days.

There is reason to believe that the imagination is the most important of the three causes that we have just assigned to magnetism. We have seen by the experiments cited that it suffices on its own to produce crises. Pressure, touching appear therefore to serve it as preparations; it is through touching that the nerves are unsettled, imitation communicates & spreads the sensations. But the imagination is this terrible, active power that produces the great effects one observes with astonishment in the group treatment. These effects are astonishing in the eyes of everyone, while the cause is obscure & hidden. When it is considered that in the last centuries these effects have captivated

men esteemed for their merit, their knowledge, & even genius, such as Paracelsus, Vanhelmont, Kirker, etc., it should not be surprising if today, persons who are educated, enlightened, if even a great number of Physicians have been taken in. The Commissioners admitted only to the group treatment where there is neither time nor the ability to conduct decisive experiments could themselves have been led into error. The freedom to isolate the effects was necessary in order to distinguish the causes; one must like them have seen the imagination work, partially in some way, to produce its effects separately & in detail, so as to conceive of the accumulation of these effects, to get an idea of its total power & take account of its wonders. But such examination requires a sacrifice of time, & much follow-up research which one does not always have the leisure to pursue for the purpose of instruction or satisfying one's own curiosity, or which one does not have even the right to undertake unless one is like the Commissioners charged by the King's orders, & honored with the group trust.

M. Deslon does not stray from his principles. He declared at the committee meeting held at the home of M. Franklin on June 19 that he believed he could in fact lay down the principle that the imagination had the greatest part in the effects of Animal magnetism; he said that this new agent may be only the imagination itself, the power of which is so great that it is little understood: at the same time he certifies that he has constantly been cognizant of this power in the treatment of his patients, & he certifies also that several have been healed or remarkably relieved. He has remarked to the Commissioners that the imagination directed in this way toward the relief of human suffering, would be a great blessing in the practice of Medicine; & persuaded of the truth of the imagination's power, he invited them to study its workings & effects at his home. If M. Deslon is still attached to the first idea that these effects are due to the action of a fluid that is communicated from person to person through touching or under the direction of a conducting agent, it will not take him long to recognize with the Commissioners that all that is needed is one cause for one effect, & that because the imagination is sufficient, the fluid is useless. No doubt we are surrounded by a fluid that belongs to us, imperceptible perspiration forms around us an atmosphere of vapors equally imperceptible; but this fluid acts only like the atmospheres, can only be communicated in infinitely small quantities through touching, is not directed either by conductors, or by sight, or by intention, is not at all spread by sound, nor reflected in mirrors, & is in no way admitting of the effects attributed to it.

It remains to examine whether the crises or the convulsions produced by the processes of this so-called magnetism, in the gathering around the vat, can be useful in healing or relieving the sick. No doubt the imagination of patients often has an influence upon the cure of their maladies. The effect is only known through a general experiment & was not determined by positive experiments but it does not appear that we can doubt it. It is a well-known adage that in medicine faith saves; this faith is the product of the imagination: the imagination therefore acts only through gentle means; through spreading calm through the senses, through reestablishing order in functions, in reanimating everything through hope. Hope is the life of man; what can give him the one contributes to him the other. But when the imagination produces convulsions, it acts through violent means; these means are almost always destructive. In a few very rare cases, they can be useful; there are some desperate cases where all must be disturbed in order to be put in order anew. These dangerous upsets may only be used in Medicine the way poisons are. It must be necessity that dictates their use & economy that controls it. This need is momentary, the upset must be unique. Far from repeating it, the wise physician busies

himself with repairing the damage it has necessarily produced; but at the group treatment of magnetism, crises repeat themselves everyday, they are long, violent; the situation of these crises being harmful, making a habit of them can only be disastrous. How can one conceive that a woman whose chest is affected may without danger have bouts of convulsive coughing, of forced expectorations; & by violent & repeated efforts, tire & perhaps tear the lung where one has so much difficulty bringing balm & soothing? How can one imagine that a man, whatever his disease, in order to cure it must fall into crises where sight appears to be lost, where limbs stiffen, where with furious & involuntary movements he batters his own chest; crises that end with an abundant spitting up of mucus & blood! This blood is neither polluted nor corrupted; this blood comes from vessels torn by the efforts & from whence it comes contrary to the wish of Nature. These effects therefore are real afflictions & not curative ones; they are maladies added to the disease whatever it may be.

These crises still have another danger. Man is constantly controlled by habit; habit modifies Nature by successive degrees, but it disposes it so strongly that it often changes it entirely & makes it unrecognizable. Who can tell whether that crisis-state, at first impressed upon the will, will not become habitual? Whether this habit, thus acquired, would often reproduce the same incidents against one's will, & almost without the help of the imagination, which would be the lot of an individual subjected to these violent crises, physically & morally tormented by their unhappy impression, whose days would be divided between apprehensiveness & pain, & whose life would be only a lasting torture? These afflictions of the nerves, when they are natural, are the scourge of Physicians; it should not be the place of art to produce them. This art is disastrous, disturbing the functions of animal economy, pushing Nature to deviate, & multiplying the victims of its disordering. This art is especially dangerous in that not only does it aggravate nervous disorders by bringing the accidents back to mind, by making them degenerate into habits, but if this malady is contagious, as one may suspect, the practice of provoking nervous convulsions, & exciting them publicly during the treatments, is a means of spreading them in large cities; & even of afflicting the generations to come because the ills & habits of parents are transmitted to their posterity.

The Commissioners, having recognized that this Animal-magnetism fluid cannot be perceived by any of our senses, that it had no action whatsoever, neither on themselves, nor on patients submitted to it; having certified that pressure & touching occasion changes rarely favorable to animal economy & perturbations always distressing in the imagination; having finally demonstrated by decisive experiments that the imagination without magnetism produces convulsions, & that magnetism without imagination produces nothing; they have unanimously concluded, on the question of the existence & utility of magnetism, that nothing proves the existence of Animal-magnetism fluid; that this fluid with no existence is therefore without utility; that the violent effects observed at the group treatment belong to touching, to the imagination set in action & to this involuntary imitation that brings us in spite of ourselves to repeat that which strikes our senses, & at the same time, they feel obliged to add, as an important observation, that the touchings, the repeated action of the imagination in producing crises can be dangerous; that the witnessing of these crises is equally dangerous because of this imitation which Nature seems to have made a law; & that, consequently, all group treatment in which the means of magnetism will be used, can in the long run have only disastrous effects.

In Paris, this August eleven one thousand seven hundred & eighty four.

Signed B. Franklin, Majault, le Roy, Sallin, Bailly, d'Arcet, de Bory, Guillotin, Lavoisier

What Ever Happened to N-Rays?

Robert Wood's 1904 N-Ray Letter in *Nature*

Editor's note: This essay is the third in a series of classic historical pieces in skeptical and pseudoscience literature. Following William Jennings Bryan's never-delivered "Address to the Jury in the Scopes Case" on "The Most Powerful Argument against Evolution Ever Made" and Benjamin Franklin's and Antoine Lavoisier's investigation of Mesmerism for King Louis XVI of France. Here we republish Robert W. Wood's famous letter in *Nature* that blew apart the chimerical search for n-rays, with an introduction by psychologist and skeptical investigator Terence Hines.

A Classic in Skeptical History

TERENCE HINES

In early 1903, the news of the discovery of a new type of radiation in France spread through the international physics community. Rene Blondlot, one of the most famous physicists in the world, had made the discovery at the University of Nancy. He named the new radiation n-rays in honor of the university and city. The discovery of a new form of radiation was certainly not an unprecedented event at the start of the 20th century. Several other types of radiation had been reported in the dozen or so years previously (including x-rays). But none would be more controversial than n-rays.

N-rays were supposedly a form of radiation exhibited by any number of substances, with the bizarre exceptions of green wood and "anesthetized" metal (metal soaked in ether or chloroform). Within less than a year of its announced "discovery," no fewer than 30 papers were published confirming the existence of the new rays. Other laboratories, however, using more sophisticated methods were unable to replicate the findings. Blondlot's measuring instrument was a spectroscope with an aluminum-coated prism and thread on the inside. The n-rays were refracted by the prism and spread out into a spectrum. The only way to see the normally invisible n-rays was to cause them to hit a treated thread (e.g., one coated in calcium sulfide). Moving the thread across the gap between the prism and n-ray source caused the thread to become illuminated and this is what was reported as a "detection."

In 1903 *Nature* sent Johns Hopkins University physicist Robert W. Wood, who was attending a scientific conference in Britain, to

Nancy, France, to investigate. During a series of experiments, when the lights were out, Wood secretly removed the prism from the spectroscope, after which n-rays were still detected, clearly an impossible result since the prism was supposedly critical for refracting the rays. In short, what Wood's little experiment proved was that n-rays didn't exist. Blondlot's use of a purely subjective methodology, as opposed to an objective one, led him to believe in the reality of the new rays, as it did in several other laboratories, mostly in France. (There may have been some nationalistic bias here since the Germans had discovered x-rays).

Wood was an extraordinary individual whose wide-ranging areas of interest included many in physics, as well as non-traditional areas such as investigating spiritualistic mediums and the use of scientific methodology in crime detection. Following his visit to Blondlot's laboratory, Wood reported his findings in the September 29, 1904, issue of *Nature*, then, as it is today, one of the leading scientific publications in the world. This letter, reprinted here, is a classic in skeptical literature. After its appearance in *Nature*, it was quickly published in French in the *Revue Scientifique* (Vol. 2, Oct. 22, 1904, 536–538) and in German in the *Physikalische Zeitschrift* (Vol. 1, 1904, 789–791).

The letter seems to have had quite an effect. According to M. Nye, whose excellent history of the n-ray affair should be consulted for further details ("N-rays: An Episode in the History and Psychology of Science." *Historical Studies in the Physical Sciences*, 1980, 125–156), "only one confirming account of n-rays was presented to the [French] Academy" in the following years. Thus, Wood's letter signaled the beginning of the end of the n-ray episode. The debate would simmer on for a few more years and Blondlot, who retired in 1909, continued his n-ray quest, but to no avail.

It is worth noting that nowhere in Wood's letter did he specify at which laboratory it was that he made his observations. But everyone in the field knew.

The n-Rays

By Robert W. Wood

Nature, *September 29, 1904, pp. 530–531*

The inability of a large number of skillful experimental physicists to obtain any evidence whatever of the existence of the n-rays, and the continued publication of papers announcing new and still more remarkable properties of the rays, prompted me to pay a visit to one of the laboratories in which the apparently peculiar conditions necessary for the manifestation of this most elusive form of radiation appear to exist. I went, I must confess, in a doubting frame of mind, but with the hope that I might be convinced of the reality of the phenomena, the accounts of which have been read with so much scepticism.

After spending three hours or more in witnessing various experiments, I am not only unable to report a single observation which appeared to indicate the existence of the rays, but left with a very firm conviction that the few experimenters who have obtained positive results have been in some way deluded.

A somewhat detailed report of the experiments which was shown to me, together with my own observations, may be of interest to the many physicists who have spent days and weeks in fruitless efforts to repeat the remarkable experiments which have been described in the scientific journals of the past year.

The first experiment which it was my privilege to witness was the supposed brightening of a small electric spark when the n-rays were concentrated on it by means of an aluminum lens. The spark was placed behind a small screen of ground glass to diffuse the light, the luminosity of which was supposed to change when the hand was interposed between the spark and the source of the n-rays.

It was claimed that this was most distinctly noticeable, yet I was unable to detect the slightest change. This was explained as due to a lack of sensitiveness of my eyes, and to test the matter I suggested that the attempt be made to announce the exact moments at which I introduced my hand into the path of the rays, by observing the screen. In no case was a correct answer given, the screen being announced as bright and dark in alternation when my hand was held motionless in the path of the rays, while the fluctuations observed when I moved my hand bore no relation whatever to its movements.

I was shown a number of photographs which showed the brightening of the image, and a plate was exposed in my presence, but they were made, it seems to me, under conditions which admit of many sources of error. In the first place, the brilliancy of the spark fluctuates all the time by an amount which I estimated at 25 per cent, which alone would make accurate work impossible.

Secondly, the two images (with n-rays and without) are built of "installment exposures" of five seconds each, the plate holder being shifted back and forth by hand every five seconds. It appears to me that it is quite possible that the difference in the brilliancy of the images is due to a cumulative favoring of the exposure of one of the images, which may be quite unconscious, but may be governed by the previous knowledge of the disposition of the apparatus. The claim is made that all accidents of this nature are made impossible by changing the conditions, i.e., by shifting the positions of the screens; but it must be remembered that the experimenter is aware of the change, and may be unconsciously influenced to hold the plate holder a fraction of a second longer on one side than on the other. I feel

very sure that if a series of experiments were made jointly in this laboratory by the originator of the photographic experiments and Profs. Rubens and Lummer, whose failure to repeat them is well known, the source of the error would be found.

I was next shown the experiment of the deviation of the rays by an aluminum prism. The aluminum lens was removed, and a screen of wet cardboard furnished with a vertical slit about 3 mm. wide put in its place. In front of the slit stood the prism, which was supposed not only to bend the sheet of rays, but to spread it out into a spectrum. The positions of the deviated rays were located by a narrow vertical line of phosphorescent paint, perhaps 0.5 mm. wide, on a piece of dry cardboard, which was moved along by means of a small driving engine. It was claimed that a movement of the screw corresponding to a motion of less than 0.1 of a millimeter was sufficient to cause the phosphorescent line to change in luminosity when it was moved across the n-ray spectrum, and this with a slit 2 or 3 mm. wide. I expressed surprise that a ray bundle 3 mm. in width could be split up into a spectrum with maxima and minima less than 0.1 of a millimeter apart, and was told that this was one of the inexplicable and astonishing properties of the rays. I was unable to see any change whatever in the brilliancy of the phosphorescent line as I moved it along, and I subsequently found that the removal of the prism (we were in a dark room) did not seem to interfere in any way with the location of the maxima and minima in the deviated (!) ray bundle.

I then suggested that an attempt be made to determine by means of the phosphorescent screen whether I had placed the prism with its refracting edge to the right or the left, but neither the experimenter nor his assistant determined the position correctly in a single case (three trials were made). This failure was attributed to fatigue.

I was next shown an experiment of a different nature. A small screen on which a number of circles had been painted with luminous paint was placed on the table in the dark room. The approach of a large steel file was supposed to alter the appearance of the spots, causing them to appear more distinct and less nebulous. I could see no change myself, though the phenomenon was described as open to no question, the change being very marked. Holding the file behind my back, I moved my arm slightly towards and away from the screen. The same changes were described by my colleague. A clock face in a dimly lighted room was believed to become much more distinct and brighter when the file was held before the eyes, owing to some peculiar effect which the rays emitted by the file exerted on the retina. I was unable to see the slightest change, though my colleague said that he could see the hands distinctly when he held the file near his eyes, while they were quite invisible when the file was removed. The room was dimly lit by a gas jet turned down low, which made blank experiments impossible. My colleague could see the change just as well when I held the file before his face, and the substitution of a piece of wood of the same size and shape as the file in no way interfered with the experiment. The substitution was of course unknown to the observer.

I am obliged to confess that I left the laboratory with a distinct feeling of depression, not only having failed to see a single experiment of a convincing nature, but with the almost certain conviction that all the changes in the luminosity or distinctness of sparks and phosphorescent screens (which furnish the only evidence of n-rays) are purely imaginary. It seems strange that after a year's work on the subject not a single experiment has been devised which can in any way convince a critical observer that the rays exist at all. To be sure the photographs are offered as an objective proof of the effect of the rays upon the lumi-

nosity of the spark. The spark, however, varies greatly in intensity from moment to moment, and the manner in which the exposures are made appears to me to be especially favourable to the introduction of errors in the total time of exposure which each image receives. I am unwilling also to believe that a change of intensity which the average eye cannot detect when the n-rays are flashed "on" and "off" will be brought out as distinctly in photographs as is the case on the plates exhibited.

Experiments could easily be devised which would settle the matter beyond all doubt; for example, the following: Let two screens be prepared, one composed of two sheets of thin aluminum with a few sheets of wet paper between, the whole hermetically sealed with wax along the edges. The other screen to be exactly the same, containing, however, dry paper.

Let a dozen or more photographs be taken with the two screens, the person exposing the plates being ignorant of which screen was used in each case. One of the screens being opaque to n-rays, the other transparent, the resulting photographs would tell the story. Two observers would be required, one to change the screens and keep a record of the one used in each case, the other to expose the plates.

The same screen should be used for two or three successive exposures, in one or more cases, and it should be made impossible for the person exposing the plates to know in any way whether a change had been made or not.

I feel very sure that a day spent on some such experiment as this would show that variations in the density on the photographic plate had no connection with the screen used.

Why cannot the experimenters who obtain results with n-rays and those who do not try a series of experiments together, as was done only last year by Cremieu and Pender, when doubt had been expressed about the reality of the Rowland effect?

R. W. Wood, Brussels, September 22

Scientific Study of Unidentified Flying Objects

Introduction

M ICHAEL S HERMER

The *Scientific Study of Unidentified Flying Objects* was conducted at the University of Colorado between 1966 and 1968, with physics professor Edward U. Condon as its primary investigator. It is commonly known as the "Condon Report" or the "Colorado Project Report." The publication represents the largest single scientific project ever undertaken in relation to the UFO question. The *Scientific Study of Unidentified Flying Objects* was originally copyrighted in 1968 by the Regents of the University of Colorado, a body corporate. It was subsequently published in reports of the United States Air Force and other governmental agencies and was published commercially by Bantam Books, but is currently out of print.

Because of the historical importance of this document, the National Capital Area Skeptics, with the permission of the Regents of the University of Colorado, republished the *Scientific Study of Unidentified Flying Objects* on their web page. Under the direction of Jim Giglio, who worked for more than a year to bring this document to the web, and with the permission of the National Capital Area Skeptics, we present these excerpts—the first two sections of the publication—as a slice of twentieth-century history related to UFOs.

My own skepticism about the UFO phenomenon stems from a simple observation involving evolutionary biology: the extra-terrestrial inhabitants of UFOs are invariably described as remarkably similar to terrestrial primates—bilaterally symmetrical with two legs, two arms, two eyes, two ears, fingers and toes, a nose and a mouth. The probability of such creatures being anything like primates, let alone humans, is so remote as to not be worthy of further consideration. Of the hundreds of millions of species to have roamed the earth over the past three billion years, only gorillas, orangutans, chimps, bonobos, and humans have survived as living great apes, and only one species—us—has reached a level of intelligence and culture to achieve space flight. Is it really possible that the evolution of life on some other planet would so resemble ours as to produce another primate-like creature? No.

There is an additional problem, and that is the question of technological evolution. I first addressed this question in my January 2002 column in *Scientific American,* in an essay entitled "Shermer's Last Law." It is based on the famous three "laws" of the science fiction writer Arthur C. Clarke:

Clarke's First Law: "When a distinguished but elderly scientist states that something is possible he is almost certainly right. When he states that something is impossible, he is very probably wrong."

Clarke's Second Law: "The only way of discovering the limits of the possible is to venture a little way past them into the impossible."

Clarke's Third Law: "Any sufficiently advanced technology is indistinguishable from magic."

This last observation stimulated me to think more on the impact the discovery of an Extra-Terrestrial Intelligence (ETI) would have on civilization. To that end I have immodestly proposed Shermer's Last Law (I don't believe in naming laws after oneself, so as the good book warns, the last shall be first and the first shall be last): *Any sufficiently advanced ETI is indistinguishable from God.*

God is typically described by Western religions as omniscient and omnipotent. Since we are far from the mark on these traits, how could we possibly distinguish a God who has them absolutely, from an ETI who has them in relatively (to us) copious amounts? Thus, we would be unable to distinguish between absolute and relative omniscience and omnipotence. But if God were only relatively more knowing and powerful than us, then by definition it *would* be an ETI! Consider two observations and one deduction:

1. Biological evolution operates at a snail's pace compared to technological evolution (the former is Darwinian and requires generations of differential reproductive success, the latter is Lamarckian and can be implemented within a single generation). 2. The cosmos is very big and space is very empty (*Voyager I,* our most distant spacecraft, hurtling along at over 38,000 mph, will not reach the distance of even our sun's nearest neighbor, the Alpha Centauri system that it is *not* even headed toward, for over 75,000 years). Ergo, the probability of an ETI who is only slightly more advanced than us and also makes contact is virtually nil. If we ever do find ETI it will be as if a million-year-old *Homo erectus* were dropped into the middle of Manhattan, given a computer and cell phone, and instructed to

communicate with us. ETI would be to us as we would be to this early hominid—godlike.

Science and technology have changed our world more in the past century than it changed in the previous hundred centuries. It took 10,000 years to get from the cart to the airplane, but only 66 years to get from powered flight to a lunar landing. Moore's Law of computer power doubling every eighteen months continues unabated and is now down to about a year. Ray Kurzweil, in *The Age of Spiritual Machines,* calculates that there have been thirty-two doublings since World War II, and that the Singularity point may be upon us as early as 2030. The Singularity (as in the center of a black hole where matter is so dense that its gravity is infinite) is the point at which total computational power will rise to levels that are so far beyond anything that we can imagine that they will appear near infinite and thus, relatively speaking, be indistinguishable from omniscience (note the suffix!).

When this happens the world will change more in a decade than it did in the previous thousand decades. Extrapolate that out a hundred thousand years, or a million years (an eye blink on an evolutionary time scale and thus a realistic estimate of how far advanced ETI will be, unless we happen to be the first space-faring species, which is unlikely), and we get a gut-wrenching, mind-warping feel for just how godlike these creatures would seem.

In Clarke's 1953 novel *Childhood's End,* humanity reaches something like a Singularity (with help from ETIs) and must make the transition to a higher state of consciousness in order to grow out of childhood. One character early in the novel opines that "science can destroy religion by ignoring it as well as by disproving its tenets. No one ever demonstrated, so far as I am aware, the nonexistence of Zeus or Thor, but they have few followers now."

Although science has not even remotely destroyed religion, Shermer's Last Law predicts that the relationship between the two will be profoundly affected by contact with ETI. To find out how we must follow Clarke's Second Law, venturing courageously past the limits of the possible and into the unknown. Ad astra!

This is best done, in my opinion, through the SETI program, the Search for Extra-Terrestrial Intelligence using radio telescopes in the hopes of detecting a signal from an ETI, rather than a close encounter of the third kind. Thus, I agree with the final conclusion of the Condon report, as summarized in "Section I Conclusions and Recommendations":

We believe that the existing record and the results of the Scientific Study of Unidentified Flying Objects of the University of Colorado, which are presented in detail in subsequent sections of this report, support the conclusions and recommendations which follow.

As indicated by its title, the emphasis of this study has been on attempting to learn from UFO reports anything that could be considered as adding to scientific knowledge. Our general conclusion is that nothing has come from the study of UFOs in the past 21 years that has added to scientific knowledge. Careful consideration of the record as it is available to us leads us to conclude that further extensive study of UFOs probably cannot be justified in the expectation that science will be advanced thereby.

It has been argued that this lack of contribution to science is due to the fact that very little scientific effort has been put on the subject. We do not agree. We feel that the reason that there has been very little scientific study of the subject is that those scientists who are most directly concerned, astronomers, atmospheric physicists, chemists, and psychologists, having had ample opportunity to look into the matter, have individually decided that UFO phenomena do not offer a fruitful field in which to look for major scientific discoveries.

. . .

The question remains as to what, if any-thing, the federal government should do about the UFO reports it receives from the general public. We are inclined to think that nothing should be done with them in the expectation that they are going to contribute to the advance of science.

This question is inseparable from the question of the national defense interest of these reports. The history of the past 21 years has repeatedly led Air Force officers to the conclusion that none of the things seen, or thought to have been seen, which pass by the name of UFO reports, constituted any hazard or threat to national security.

. . .

It has been contended that the subject has been shrouded in official secrecy. We conclude otherwise. We have no evidence of secrecy concerning UFO reports. What has been miscalled secrecy has been no more than an intelligent policy of delay in releasing data so that the public does not become confused by premature publication of incomplete studies of reports.

The subject of UFOs has been widely misrepresented to the public by a small number of individuals who have given sensationalized presentations in writings and public lectures. So far as we can judge, not many people have been misled by such irresponsible behavior, but whatever effect there has been has been bad.

Scientific Study of Unidentified Flying Objects

DR. EDWARD U. CONDON
SCIENTIFIC DIRECTOR

Conducted by the University of Colorado under contract No. 44620-67-C-0035 with the United States Air Force

Section II Summary of the Study

1. Origin of the Colorado Project. The decision to establish this project for the Scientific Study of Unidentified Flying Objects stems from recommendations in a report dated March 1966 of an Ad Hoc Committee of the Air Force Scientific Advisory Board set up under the chairmanship of Dr. Brian O'Brien to review the work of Project Blue Book. Details of the history of work on UFOs are set forth in Section V, Chapter 2. (See also Appendix A.)

The recommendation was:

It is the opinion of the Committee that the present Air Force program dealing with UFO sightings has been well organized, although the resources assigned to it (only one officer, a sergeant, and a secretary) have been quite limited. In 19 years and more than 10,000 sightings recorded and classified, there appears to be no verified and fully satisfactory evidence of any case that is clearly outside the framework of presently known science and technology. Nevertheless, there is always the possibility that analysis of new sightings may provide some additions to scientific knowledge of value to the Air Force. Moreover, some of the case records at which the Committee looked that were listed as "identified" were sightings where the evidence collected was too meager or too indefinite to permit positive listing in the identified category. Because of this the Committee recommends that the present program be strengthened to provide opportunity for scientific investigation of selected sightings in more detail than has been possible to date.

To accomplish this it is recommended that:

A. Contracts be negotiated with a few selected universities to provide scientific teams to investigate promptly and in depth certain selected sightings of UFO's. Each team should include at least one psychologist, preferably one interested in clinical psychology, and at least one physical scientist, preferably an astronomer or geophysicist familiar with atmospheric physics. The universities should be chosen to provide good geographical distribution, and should be within convenient distance of a base of the Air Force Systems Command (AFSC).

B. At each AFSC base an officer skilled in investigation (but not necessarily with scientific training) should be designated to work with the corresponding university team for that geographical section. The local representative of the Air Force Office of Special Investigations (OSI) might be a logical choice for this.

C. One university or one not-for-profit organization should be selected to coordinate the work of the teams mentioned under A above, and also to make certain of very close communication and coordination with the office of Project Blue Book.

It is thought that perhaps 100 sightings a year might be subjected to this close study, and that possibly an average of 10 man days might be required per sighting so studied. The information provided by such a program might bring to light new facts of scientific value, and would almost certainly provide a far better basis than we have today for decision on a long term UFO program.

These recommendations were referred by the Secretary of the Air Force to the Air Force Office of Scientific Research for implementation, which, after study, decided to combine recommendations A and C so as to have a single contracting university with authority to subcontract with other research groups as needed. Recommendation B was implemented by the issuance of Air Force Regulation 80-17 (Appendix B) which establishes procedures for handling UFO reports at the Air Force bases.

In setting up the Colorado project, as already stated in Section I, the emphasis was on whether deeper study of unidentified flying objects might provide some "additions to scientific knowledge."

After considering various possibilities, the AFOSR staff decided to ask the University of

Colorado to undertake the project (see Preface). Dr. J. Thomas Ratchford visited Boulder in late July 1966 to learn whether the University would be willing to undertake the task. A second meeting was held on 10 August 1966 in which the scope of the proposed study was outlined to an interested group of the administrative staff and faculty of the University by Dr. Ratchford and Dr. William Price, executive director of AFOSR. After due deliberation, University officials decided to undertake the project.

The contract provided that the planning, direction and conclusions of the Colorado project were to be conducted wholly independently of the Air Force. To avoid duplication of effort, the Air Force was ordered to furnish the project with the records of its own earlier work and to provide the support of personnel at AF bases when requested by our field teams.

We were assured that the federal government would withhold no information on the subject, and that all essential information about UFOs could be included in this report. Where UFO sightings involve classified missile launchings or involve the use of classified radar systems, this fact is merely stated as to do more would involve violation of security on these military subjects. In our actual experience these reservations have affected a negligible fraction of the total material and have not affected the conclusions (Section I) which we draw from our work.

The first research contract with AFOSR provided $313,000 for the first 15 months from 1 November 1966 to 31 January 1968. The contract was publicly announced on 7 October 1966. It then became our task to investigate those curious entities distinguished by lack of knowledge of what they are, rather than in terms of what they are known to be, namely, unidentified flying objects.

2. Definition of an UFO. An unidentified flying object (UFO, pronounced OOFO) is here defined as the stimulus for a report made by one or more individuals of something seen in the sky (or an object thought to be capable of flight but when landed on the earth) which the observer could not identify as having an ordinary natural origin, and which seemed to him sufficiently puzzling that he undertook to make a report of it to police, to government officials, to the press, or perhaps to a representative of a private organization devoted to the study of such objects.

Defined in this way, there is no question as to the existence of UFOs, because UFO reports exist in fairly large numbers, and the stimulus for each report is, by this definition, an UFO. The problem then becomes that of learning to recognize the various kinds of stimuli that give rise to UFO reports.

The UFO is "the stimulus for a report . . ." This language refrains from saying whether the reported object was a real, physical, material thing, or a visual impression of an ordinary physical thing distorted by atmospheric conditions or by faulty vision so as to be unrecognizable, or whether it was a purely mental delusion existing in the mind of the observer without an accompanying visual stimulus.

The definition includes insincere reports in which the alleged sighter undertakes for whatever reason to deceive. In the case of a delusion, the reporter is not aware of the lack of a visual stimulus. In the case of a deception, the reporter knows that he is not telling the truth about his alleged experience.

The words "which he could not identify" are of crucial importance. The stimulus gives rise to an UFO report precisely because the observer could not identify the thing seen. A woman and her husband reported a strange thing seen flying in the sky and reported quite correctly that she knew "it was unidentified because neither of us knew what it was."

The thing seen and reported may have been an object as commonplace as the planet Venus, but it became an UFO because the observer did not know what it was. With this usage it is clear that less well informed individuals are more likely to see an UFO than those who are more knowledgeable because the latter are better able to make direct identification of what they see. A related complication is that less well informed persons are often inaccurate observers who are unable to give an accurate account of what they believe that they have seen.

If additional study of a report later provides an ordinary interpretation of what was seen, some have suggested that we should change its name to IFO, for identified flying object. But we have elected to go on calling it an UFO because some identifications are tentative or controversial, due to lack of sufficient data on which to base a definite identification. A wide variety of ordinary objects have through misinterpretation given rise to UFO reports. This topic is discussed in detail in Section VI, Chapter 2. (The Air Force has published a pamphlet entitled, "Aids to Identification of Flying Objects" [USAF, 1968] which is a useful aid in the interpretation of something seen which might otherwise be an UFO.)

The words "sufficiently puzzling that they undertook to make a report" are essential. As a practical matter, we can not study something that is not reported, so a puzzling thing seen but not reported is not here classed as an UFO.

3. UFO Reports. In our experience, the persons making reports seem in nearly all cases to be normal, responsible individuals. In most cases they are quite calm, at least by the time they make a report. They are simply puzzled about what they saw and hope that they can be helped to a better understanding of it. Only a very few are obviously quite emotionally disturbed, their minds being filled with pseudo-scientific, pseudo-religious or other fantasies. Cases of this kind range from slight disturbance to those who are manifestly in need of psychiatric care. The latter form an extremely small minority of all the persons encountered in this study. While the existence of a few mentally unbalanced persons among UFO observers is part of the total situation, it is completely incorrect and unfair to imply that all who report UFOs are "crazy kooks," just as it is equally incorrect to ignore the fact that there are mentally disturbed persons among them.

Individuals differ greatly as to their tendency to make reports. Among the reasons for not reporting UFOs are apathy, lack of awareness of public interest, fear of ridicule, lack of knowledge as to where to report and the time and cost of making a report.

We found that reports are not useful unless they are made promptly. Even so, because of the short duration of most UFO stimuli, the report usually can not be made until after the UFO has disappeared. A few people telephoned to us from great distances to describe something seen a year or two earlier. Such reports are of little value.

Early in the study we tried to estimate the fraction of all of the sightings that are reported. In social conversations many persons could tell us about some remarkable and puzzling thing that they had seen at some time in the past which would sound just as remarkable as many of the things that are to be found in UFO report files. Then we would ask whether they had made a report and in most cases would be told that they had not. As a rough guess based on this uncontrolled sample, we estimate that perhaps 10% of the sightings that people are willing to talk about later are all that get reported at the time. This point was later covered in a more formal public attitude survey (Section III, Chapter 7) made for this study in which only 7% of those who said they had seen an UFO had reported it previously. Thus if all people reported sightings that are like those that some people do report, the number of reports that would be received would be at least ten times greater than the number actually received.

At first we thought it would be desirable to undertake an extensive publicity campaign to try to get more complete reporting from the public. It was decided not to do this, because about 90% of all UFO reports prove to be quite plausibly related to ordinary objects. A tenfold increase in the number of reports would have multiplied by ten the task of eliminating the ordinary cases which would have to be analyzed. Our available resources for field study enabled us to deal only with a small fraction of the reports coming in. No useful purpose would have been served under these circumstances by stimulating the receipt of an even greater number.

Study of records of some UFO reports from other parts of the world gave us the strong impression that these were made up of a mix of cases of similar kind to those being reported in the United States. For example, in August 1967 Prof. James McDonald of Arizona made a 20-day trip to Australia, Tasmania and New Zealand in the course of which he interviewed some 80 persons who had made UFO reports there at various times. On his return he gave us an account of these experiences that confirmed our impression that the reports from these other parts of the world were, as a class, similar to those being received in the United States. Therefore we decided to restrict our field studies to the United States and to one or two cases in Canada. (See Section III, Chapter 1.) This was done on the practical grounds of reducing travel expense and of avoiding diplomatic and language difficulties. The policy was decided on after preliminary study had indicated that in broad generality the spectrum of kinds of UFO reports being received in other countries was very similar to our own.

4. Prologue to the Project.   Official interest in UFOs, or "flying saucers" as they were called at first dates from June 1947. On 24 June, Kenneth Arnold, a business man of Boise, Idaho was flying a private airplane near Mt. Rainier, Washington. He reported seeing a group of objects flying along in a line which he said looked "like pie plates skipping over the water." The newspaper reports called the things seen "flying saucers" and they have been so termed ever since, although not all UFOs are described as being of this shape.

Soon reports of flying saucers were coming in from various parts of the country. Many received prominent press coverage (Bloecher, 1967). UFOs were also reported from other countries; in fact, more than a thousand such reports were made in Sweden in 1946.

The details of reports vary so greatly that it is impossible to relate them all to any single explanation. The broad range of things reported is much the same in different countries. This means that a general explanation peculiar to any one country has to be ruled out, since it is utterly improbable that the secret military aircraft of any one country would be undergoing test flights in different countries. Similarly it is most unlikely that military forces of different countries would be testing similar developments all over the world at the same time in secrecy from each other.

Defense authorities had to reckon with the possibility that UFOs might represent flights of a novel military aircraft of some foreign power. Private citizens speculated that the UFOs were test flights of secret American aircraft. Cognizance of the UFO problem was naturally assumed by the Department of the Air Force in the then newly established Department of Defense. Early investigations were carried on in secrecy by the Air Force, and also by the governments of other nations.

Such studies in the period 1947–52 convinced the responsible authorities of the Air Force that the UFOs, as observed up to that time, do not constitute a threat to national security. In consequence, ever since that time, a minimal amount of attention has been given to them.

The year 1952 brought an unusually large

number of UFO reports, including many in the vicinity of the Washington National Airport, during a period of several days in July. Such a concentration of reports in a small region in a short time is called a "flap." The Washington flap of 1952 received a great deal of attention at the time (Section III, Chapters).

At times in 1952, UFO reports were coming in to the Air Force from the general public in such numbers as to produce some clogging of military communications channels. It was thought that an enemy planning a sneak attack might deliberately stimulate a great wave of UFO reports for the very purpose of clogging communication facilities. This consideration was in the forefront of a study that was made in January 1953 by a panel of scientists under the chairmanship of the late H. P. Robertson, professor of mathematical physics at the California Institute of Technology (Section V, Chapter 2). This panel recommended that efforts be made to remove the aura of mystery surrounding the subject and to conduct a campaign of public education designed to produce a better understanding of the situation. This group also concluded that there was no evidence in the available data of any real threat to national security.

Since 1953 the results of UFO study have been unclassified, except where tangential reasons exist for withholding details, as, for example, where sightings are related to launchings of classified missiles, or to the use of classified radar systems.

During the period from March 1952 to the present, the structure for handling UFO reports in the Air Force has been called Project Blue Book. As already mentioned the work of Project Blue Book was reviewed in early 1966 by the committee headed by Dr. Brian O'Brien. This review led to the reaffirmation that no security threat is posed by the existence of a few unexplained UFO reports, but the committee suggested a study of the possibility that something of scientific value might

come from a more detailed study of some of the reports than was considered necessary from a strictly military viewpoint. This recommendation eventuated in the setting up of the Colorado project.

The story of Air Force interest, presented in Section V, Chapter 2, shows that from the beginning the possibility that some UFOs might be manned vehicles from outer space was considered, but naturally no publicity was given to this idea because of the total lack of evidence for it.

Paralleling the official government interest, was a burgeoning of amateur interest stimulated by newspaper and magazine reports. By 1950 popular books on the subject began to appear on the newsstands. In January 1950 the idea that UFOs were extraterrestrial vehicles was put forward as a reality in an article entitled "Flying Saucers are Real" in *True* magazine written by Donald B. Keyhoe, a retired Marine Corps major. Thereafter a steady stream of sensational writing about UFOs has aroused a considerable amount of interest among laymen in studying the subject.

Many amateur organizations exist, some of them rather transiently, so that it would be difficult to compile an accurate listing of them. Two such organizations in the United States have a national structure. These are the Aerial Phenomena Research Organization (APRO), with headquarters in Tucson, Arizona, claiming about 8000 members; and the National Investigations Committee for Aerial Phenomena (NICAP) with headquarters in Washington, D.C., and claiming some 12,000 members. James and Coral Lorenzen head APRO, while Keyhoe is the director of NICAP, which, despite the name and Washington address is not a government agency. Many other smaller groups exist, among them Saucers and Unexplained Celestial Events Research Society (SAUCERS) operated by James Moseley.

Of these organizations, NICAP devotes a considerable amount of its attention to attacking the Air Force and to trying to influence members of Congress to hold hearings and in other ways to join in these attacks. It maintained a friendly relation to the Colorado project during about the first year, while warning its members to be on guard lest the project turn out to have been "hired to whitewash the Air Force." During this period NICAP made several efforts to influence the course of our study. When it became clear that these would fail, NICAP attacked the Colorado project as "biased" and therefore without merit.

The organizations mentioned espouse a scientific approach to the study of the subject. In addition there are a number of others that have a primarily religious orientation.

From 1947 to 1966 almost no attention was paid to the UFO problem by well qualified scientists. Some of the reasons for this lack of interest have been clearly stated by Prof. Gerard P. Kuiper of the University of Arizona (Appendix C). Concerning the difficulty of establishing that some UFOs may come from outer space, he makes the following cogent observation: "The problem is more difficult than finding a needle in a haystack; it is finding a piece of extraterrestrial hay in a terrestrial haystack, often on the basis of reports of believers in extra-terrestrial hay."

5. Initial Planning. A scientific approach to the UFO phenomenon must embrace a wide range of disciplines. It involves such physical sciences as physics, chemistry, aerodynamics, and meteorology. Since the primary material consists mostly of reports of individual observers, the psychology of perception, the physiology of defects of vision, and the study of mental states are also involved.

Social psychology and social psychiatry are likewise involved in seeking to understand group motivations which act to induce belief in extraordinary hypotheses on the basis of what most scientists and indeed most laymen would regard as little or no evidence. These

problems of medical and social psychology deserve more attention than we were able to give them. They fell distinctly outside of the field of expertise of our staff, which concentrated more on the study of the UFOs themselves than on the personal and social problems generated by them.

Among those who write and speak on the subject, some strongly espouse the view that the federal government really knows a great deal more about UFOs than is made public. Some have gone so far as to assert that the government has actually captured extraterrestrial flying saucers and has their crews in secret captivity, if not in the Pentagon, then at some secret military base. We believe that such teachings are fantastic nonsense, that it would be impossible to keep a secret of such enormity over two decades, and that no useful purpose would be served by engaging in such an alleged conspiracy of silence. One person with whom we have dealt actually maintains that the Air Force has nothing to do with UFOs, claiming that this super-secret matter is in the hands of the Central Intelligence Agency which, he says, installed one of its own agents as scientific director of the Colorado study. This story, if true, is indeed a well kept secret. These allegations of a conspiracy on the part of our own government to conceal knowledge of the existence of "flying saucers" have, so far as any evidence that has come to our attention, no factual basis whatever.

The project's first attention was given to becoming familiar with past work in the subject. This was more difficult than in more orthodox fields because almost none of the many books and magazine articles dealing with UFOs could be regarded as scientifically reliable. There were the two books of Donald H. Menzel, director emeritus of the Harvard College Observatory and now a member of the staff of the Smithsonian Astrophysical Observatory (Menzel, 1952 and Boyd, 1963). Two other useful books were *The UFO Evidence* (1964), a compilation of UFO cases by Richard Hall, and *The Report on Unidentified Flying Objects* by E. J. Ruppelt (1956), the first head of Project Blue Book. In this initial stage we were also helped by "briefings" given by Lt. Col. Hector Quintanilla, the present head of Project Blue Book, Dr. J. Allen Hynek, astronomical consultant to Project Blue Book, and by Donald Keyhoe and Richard Hall of NICAP.

Out of this preliminary study came the recognition of a variety of topics that would require detailed attention. These included the effects of optical mirages, the analogous anomalies of radio wave propagation as they affect radar, critical analysis of alleged UFO photographs, problems of statistical analysis of UFO reports, chemical analysis of alleged material from UFOs, and reports of disturbances to automobile ignition and to headlights from the presence of UFOs. Results of the project's study of these and other topics are presented in this section and in Sections III and VI of this report.

6. Field Investigations.   Early attention was given to the question of investigation of individual cases, either by detailed critical study of old records or by field trip investigation of current cases. From this study we concluded that there was little to be gained from the study of old cases, except perhaps to get ideas on mistakes to be avoided in studies of new cases. We therefore decided not to make field trips to investigate cases that were more than a year old, although in a few cases we did do some work on such cases when their study could be combined with a field investigation of a new case.

At first we hoped that field teams could respond to early warning so quickly that they would be able to get to the site while the UFO was still there, and that our teams would not only get their own photographs, but even obtain spectrograms of the light of the UFO, and make radioactive, magnetic, and sound measurements while the UFO was still present.

Such expectations were found to be in vain. Nearly all UFO sightings are of very short duration, seldom lasting as long as an hour and usually lasting for a few minutes. The observers often become so excited that they do not report at all until the UFO has gone away. With communication and travel delays, the field team was unable to get to the scene until long after the UFO had vanished.

This was, of course, a highly unsatisfactory situation. We gave much thought to how it could be overcome and concluded that this could only be done by a great publicity campaign designed to get the public to report sightings much more promptly than it does, coupled with a nationwide scheme of having many trained field teams scattered at many points across the nation. These teams would have had to be ready to respond at a moment's notice. Even so, in the vast majority of the cases, they would not have arrived in time for direct observation of the reported UFO. Moreover, the national publicity designed to insure more prompt reporting would have had the effect of arousing exaggerated public concern over the subject, and certainly would have vastly increased the number of nonsense reports to which response would have had to be made. In recruiting the large number of field teams, great care would have had to be exercised to make sure that they were staffed with people of adequate scientific training, rather than with persons emotionally committed to extreme pro or con views on the subject.

Clearly this was quite beyond the means of our study. Such a program to cover the entire United States would cost many millions of dollars a year, and even then there would have been little likelihood that anything of importance would have been uncovered.

In a few cases some physical evidence could be gathered by examination of a site where an UFO was reported to have landed. In such a case it did not matter that the field team arrived after the UFO had gone. But in no case did we obtain any convincing evidence of this kind although every effort was made to do so. (See below and in Section III, Chapters 3 and 4.)

Thus most of the field investigation, as it turned out, consisted in the interviewing of persons who made the report. By all odds the most used piece of physical equipment was the tape recorder.

The question of a number of investigators on a field team was an important one. In most work done in the past by the Air Force, UFO observers were interviewed by a single Air Force officer, who usually had no special training and whose freedom to devote much time to the study was limited by the fact that he also had other responsibilities. When field studies are made by amateur organizations like APRO or NICAP, there are often several members present on a team, but usually they are persons without technical training, and often with a strong bias toward the sensational aspects of the subject.

Prof. Hynek strongly believes that the teams should have four or more members. He recommends giving each report what he calls the "FBI treatment," by which he means not only thorough interviewing of the persons who made the report, but in addition an active quest in the neighborhood where the sighting occurred to try to discover additional witnesses. Against such thoroughness must be balanced the consideration that the cost per case goes up proportionately to the number of persons in a team, so that the larger the team, the fewer the cases that can be studied.

The detailed discussions in Section III, Chapter 1 and in Section IV make it clear that the field work is associated with many frustrations. Many of the trips turn out to be wild goose chases and the team members often feel as if they are members of a fire department that mostly answers false alarms.

We found that it was always worthwhile to do a great deal of initial interviewing by long distance telephone. A great many reports that

seem at first to be worthy of full field investigation could be disposed of in this way with comparatively little trouble and expense. Each case presented its own special problems. No hard-and-fast rule was found by which to decide in advance whether a particular report was worth the trouble of a field trip.

After careful consideration of these various factors, we decided to operate with two-man teams, composed whenever possible of one person with training in physical science and one with training in psychology. When the study became fully operational in 1967 we had three such teams. Dr. Roy Craig describes the work of these teams in Section III, Chapters 1, 3, and 4. Reports of field investigations are presented in Section IV.

7. Explaining UFO Reports. By definition UFOs exist because UFO reports exist. What makes the whole subject intriguing is the possibility that some of these reports cannot be reconciled with ordinary explanations, so that some extraordinarily sensational explanation for them might have to be invoked. A fuller discussion of some misinterpretations of ordinary events by Dr. W. K. Hartmann is given in Section VI, Chapter 2.

A great many reports are readily identified with ordinary phenomena seen under unusual circumstances, or noted by someone who is an inexperienced, inept, or unduly excited observer. Because such reports are vague and inaccurate, it is often impossible to make an identification with certainty.

This gives rise to controversy. In some cases, an identification that the UFO was "probably" an aircraft is all that can be made from the available data. After the event no amount of further interviewing of one or more witnesses can usually change such a probable into a certain identification. Field workers who would like to identify as many as possible are naturally disposed to claim certainty when this is at all possible, but others who desire to have a residue of unexplained cases in order to add mystery and importance to the UFO problem incline to set impossibly high standards of certainty in the evidence before they are willing to accept a simple explanation for a report.

This dilemma is nicely illustrated by a question asked in the House of Commons of Prime Minister Harold Wilson, as reported in *Hansard* for 19 December 1967:

> Unidentified Flying Objects. Question 14. Sir J. Langford-Holt asked the Prime Minister whether he is satisfied that all sightings of unidentified flying objects which are reported from service sources are explainable, what inquiries he has authorized into these objects outside the defense aspect, and whether he will now appoint one Minister to look into all aspects of reports.
>
> The Prime Minister: The answers are "Yes, except when the information given is insufficient," "None" and "No."

Obviously there is a nice bit of semantics here in that the definition of "when the information is sufficient" is that it is sufficient when an explanation can be given.

Discussions of whether a marginal case should be regarded for statistical purposes as having been explained or not have proved to be futile. Some investigators take the position that, where a plausible interpretation in terms of commonplace events can be made, then the UFO is regarded as having been identified. Others take the opposite view that an UFO cannot be regarded as having been given an ordinary identification unless there is complete and binding evidence amounting to certainty about the proposed identification.

For example, in January 1968 near Castle Rock, Colo., some 30 persons reported UFOs, including spacecraft with flashing lights, fantastic maneuverability, and even with occupants presumed to be from outer space. Two days later it was more modestly reported that two high school boys had launched a polyethylene hot-air balloon.

Locally that was the end of the story. But there is a sequel. A man in Florida makes a practice of collecting newspaper stories about UFOs and sending them out in a mimeographed UFO news letter which he mails to various UFO journals and local clubs. He gave currency to the Castle Rock reports but not to the explanation that followed. When he was chided for not having done so, he declared that no one could be *absolutely* sure that *all* the Castle Rock reports arose from sightings of the balloon. There might also have been an UFO from outer space among the sightings. No one would dispute his logic, but one may with propriety wonder why he neglected to tell his readers that at least *some* of the reports were actually misidentifications of a hot-air balloon.

As a practical matter, we take the position that if an UFO report can be plausibly explained in ordinary terms, then we accept that explanation even though not enough evidence may be available to prove it beyond all doubt. This point is so important that perhaps an analogy is needed to make it clear. Several centuries ago, the most generally accepted theory of human disease was that it was caused by the patient's being possessed or inhabited by a devil or evil spirit. Different diseases were supposed to be caused by different devils. The guiding principle for medical research was then the study and classification of different kinds of devils, and progress in therapy was sought in the search for and discovery of means for exorcising each kind of devil.

Gradually medical research discovered bacteria; toxins and viruses, and their causative relation to various diseases. More and more diseases came to be described by their causes.

Suppose now that instead, medicine had clung to the devil theory of disease. As long as there exists one human illness that is not yet fully understood in modern terms such a theory cannot be disproved. It is always possible, while granting that some diseases are caused by viruses, etc. to maintain that those that are not yet understood are the ones that are really caused by devils.

In some instances the same sort of UFO is observed night after night under similar circumstances. In our experience this has been a sure sign that the UFO could be correlated with some ordinary phenomenon.

For example, rather early in our work, a Colorado farmer reported seeing an UFO land west of his farm nearly every evening about 6:00 p.m. A field team went to see him and quickly and unambiguously identified the UFO as the planet Saturn. The nights on which he did not see it land were those in which the western sky was cloudy.

But the farmer did not easily accept our identification of his UFO as Saturn. He contended that, while his UFO had landed behind the mountains on the particular evening that we visited him, on most nights, he insisted, it landed in front of the mountains, and therefore could not be a planet. The identification with Saturn from the ephemeris was so precise that we did not visit his farm night after night in order to see for ourselves whether his UFO ever landed in front of the mountains. We did not regard it as part of our duty to persuade observers of the correctness of our interpretations. In most cases observers readily accepted our explanation, and some expressed relief at having an everyday explanation available to them.

We sought to hold to a minimum delays in arriving at the site of an UFO report, even where it was clear that it was going to be impossible to get there in time actually to see the reported UFO. Once an observer made a report, the fact of his having done so usually becomes known to friends and neighbors, local newspapermen, and local UFO enthusiasts. The witness becomes the center of attention and will usually have told his story over and over again to such listeners, before the field team can arrive. With each telling of the story it is apt to be varied and embellished a little. This need not be from dishonest motives. We all like to tell an interesting story. We would rather not bore our listeners if we can help it, so embellishment is sometimes added to maximize the interest value of the narration.

It is not easy to detect how a story has grown under retelling in this way. Listeners usually will have asked leading questions and the story will have developed in response to such suggestions, so that it soon becomes impossible for the field team to hear the witness's story as he told it the first time. In some cases when the witness had been interviewed in this way by local UFO enthusiasts, his story was larded with vivid language about visitors from outer space that was probably not there in the first telling.

Another kind of difficulty arises in interviewing multiple associated witnesses, that is, witnesses who were together at the time that all of them saw the UFO. Whenever several individuals go through an exciting experience together, they are apt to spend a good deal of time discussing it afterward among themselves, telling and retelling it to each other, unconsciously ironing out discrepancies between their various recollections, and gradually converging on a single uniform account of the experience. Dominant personalities will have contributed more to the final version than the less dominant. Thus the story told by a group of associated witnesses who have had ample opportunity to "compare notes" will be more uniform than the accounts these individuals would have given if interviewed separately before they had talked the matter over together.

One of the earliest of our field trips (December 1966) was made to Washington, D.C. to interview separately two air traffic control operators who had been involved in the great UFO flap there in the summer of 1952. Fourteen years later, these two men were still quite annoyed at the newspaper publicity they had received, because it had tended to ridicule their reports. Our conclusion from this trip was that these men were telling in 1966 stories that were thoroughly consistent with the main points of their stories as told in 1952. Possibly this was due to the fact that because of their strong emotional involvement they had recounted the incident to many persons at many times over the intervening years. Although it was true that the stories had not changed appreciably in 14 years, it was also true for this very reason that we acquired no new material by interviewing these men again. (See Section III, Chapter 5.)

On the basis of this experience we decided that it was not profitable to devote much effort to re-interviewing persons who had already been interviewed rather thoroughly at a previous time. We do not say that nothing can be gained in this way, but merely that it did not seem to us that this would be a profitable way to spend our effort in this study.

In our experience those who report UFOs are often very articulate, but not necessarily reliable. One evening in 1967 a most articulate gentleman told us with calm good manners all of the circumstances of a number of UFOs he had seen that had come from outer space, and in particular went into some detail about how his wife's grandfather had immigrated to America from the Andromeda nebula, a galaxy located 2,000,000 light years from the earth.

In a few cases study of old reports may give the investigator a clue to a possible interpretation that had not occurred to the original investigator. In such a case, a later interview of the witness may elicit new information that was not brought out in the earlier interview. But we found that such interviews need to be conducted with great care as it is easily possible that the "new" information may have been generated through the unconscious use of leading questions pointing toward the new interpretation, and so may not be reliable for that reason.

8. Sources of UFO Reports. Usually the first report of an UFO is made to a local police officer or to a local news reporter. In some cases, members of UFO study organizations are sufficiently well known in the community that reports are made directly to them. In spite of the very considerable publicity that has been given to this subject, a large part of the public still does not know of the official Air Force interest.

Even some policemen and newsmen do not know of it and so do not pass on the UFO report. In other cases, we found that the anti–Air Force publicity efforts of some UFO enthusiasts had persuaded observers, who would otherwise have done so, not to report to the Air Force. We have already commented on the fact that for a variety of reasons many persons who do have UFO experiences do not report promptly.

Ideally the entire public would have known that each Air Force base must, according to AFR 80-17, have an UFO officer and would have reported promptly any extraordinary thing seen in the sky. Or, if this were too much to expect, then all police and news agencies would ideally have known of Air Force interest and would have passed information along to the nearest Air Force base. But none of these ideal things were true, and as a result our collection of UFO reports is extremely haphazard and incomplete.

When a report is made to an Air Force base, it is handled by an UFO officer whose form of investigation and report is prescribed by APR 80-17 (Appendix A). If the explanation of the report is immediately obvious and trivial— some persons will telephone a base to report a contrail from a high-flying jet that is particularly bright in the light of the setting sun—the UFO officer tells the person what it was he saw, and there the matter ends. No permanent record of such calls is made. As a result there is no record of the total number of UFO reports made to AF bases. Only those that require more than cursory consideration are reported to Project Blue Book. Air Force officers are human, and therefore interpret their duty quite differently. Some went to great lengths not to submit a report. Others took special delight in reporting all of the "easy" ones out of a zealous loyalty to their service, because the more "identifieds" they turned in, the higher would be the over-all percentage of UFO reports explained. When in June 1967 Air Force UFO officers from the various bases convened in Boulder some of them quite vigorously debated the relative merits of these two different extreme views of their duty.

Many people have from time to time tried to learn something significant about UFOs by studying statistically the distribution of UFO reports geographically, in time, and both factors together. In our opinion these efforts have proved to be quite fruitless. The difficulties are discussed in Section VI, Chapter 10.

The geographical distribution of reports correlates roughly with population density of the non-urban population. Very few reports come from the densely populated urban areas. Whether this is due to urban sophistication or to the scattering of city lights is not known, but it is more probably the latter.

There apparently exists no single complete collection of UFO reports. The largest file is that maintained by Project Blue Book at Wright-Patterson Air Force Base, Ohio. Other files are maintained by APRO in Tucson and NICAP in Washington. The files of Project Blue Book are arranged by date and place of occurrence of the report, so that one must know these data in order to find a particular case. Proposals have been made from time to time for a computer-indexing of these reports by various categories but this has not been carried out. Two publications are available which partially supply this lack: one is *The UFO Evidence* (Hall, 1964) and the other is a collection of reports called *The Reference for Outstanding UFO Reports* (Olsen, n.d.).

We have already mentioned the existence of flaps, that is, the tendency of reports to come in clusters at certain times in certain areas. No quantitative study of this is available, but we believe that the clustering tendency is partly due to changing amounts of attention devoted to the subject by the news media. Publicity for some reports stimulates more reports, both because people pay more attention to the sky at such a time, and because they are more likely to make a report of something which attracts their attention.

In the summer of 1967 there was a large UFO flap in the neighborhood of Harrisburg, Pa. This may have been in part produced by the efforts of a local NICAP member working in close association with a reporter for the local afternoon newspaper who wrote an exciting UFO story for his paper almost daily. Curiously enough, the morning paper scarcely ever had an UFO story from which we conclude that one editor's news is another's filler. We stationed one of our investigators there during August with results that are described in Case 27.

Many UFO reports were made by the public to Olmsted Air Force Base a few miles south of Harrisburg, but when this base was deactivated during the summer UFO reports had to be made to McGuire Air Force Base near Trenton, N.J. This required a toll call, and the frequency of receipt of UFO reports from the Harrisburg area dropped abruptly.

For all of these various reasons, we feel that the fluctuations geographically and in time of UFO reports are so greatly influenced by sociological factors, that any variations due to changes in underlying physical phenomena are completely masked.

In sensational UFO journalism the statement is often made that UFOs show a marked tendency to be seen more often near military installations. There is no statistically significant evidence that this is true. For sensational writers, this alleged but unproven concentration of UFO sightings is taken as evidence that extraterrestrial visitors are reconnoitering our military defenses, preparatory to launching a military attack at some time in the future. Even if a slight effect of this kind were to be established by careful statistical studies, we feel that it could be easily accounted for by the fact that at every base men stand all night guard duty and so unusual things in the sky are more likely to be seen. Moreover civilians living near a military base are more likely to make a report to the base than those living at some distance from it.

AFR 80-17a directed UFO officers at each base to send to the Colorado project a duplicate of each report sent to Project Blue Book. This enabled us to keep track of the quality of the investigations and to be informed about puzzling uninterpreted cases. Such reporting was useful in cases whose study extended over a long period, but the slowness of receipt of such reports made this arrangement not completely satisfactory as a source of reports on the basis of which to direct the activity of our own field teams. A few reports that seemed quite interesting to Air Force personnel caused them to notify us by teletype or telephone. Some of our field studies arose from reports received in this way.

To supplement Air Force reporting, we set up our own Early Warning Network, a group of about 60 active volunteer field reporters, most of whom were connected with APRO or NICAP. They telephoned or telegraphed to us intelligence of UFO sightings in their own territory and conducted some preliminary investigation for us while our team was en route. Some of this cooperation was quite valuable. In the spring of 1968, Donald Keyhoe, director of NICAP, ordered discontinuation of this arrangement, but many NICAP field teams continued to cooperate.

All of these sources provided many more quickly reported, fresh cases than our field teams could study in detail. In consequence we had to develop criteria for quickly selecting which of the cases reported to us would be handled with a field trip (See Section III, Chapter 1.)

9. Extra-terrestrial Hypothesis. The idea that some UFOs may be spacecraft sent to Earth from another civilization, residing on another planet of the solar system, or on a planet associated with a more distant star than the Sun, is called the Extra-terrestrial Hypothesis (ETH). Some few persons profess to hold a stronger level of belief in the *actuality* of UFOs being visitors from outer space, controlled by intelligent beings, rather than merely of the *possibility*, not yet fully established as an observational fact. We shall call this level of belief ETA, for extraterrestrial actuality.

It is often difficult to be sure just what level of belief is held by various persons, because of the vagueness with which they state their ideas.

For example, addressing the American Society of Newspaper Editors in Washington on 22 April 1967, Dr. McDonald declared: "There is, in my present opinion, no sensible alternative to the utterly shocking hypothesis that the UFOs are extraterrestrial probes from somewhere else." Then in an Australian broadcast on 20 August 1967 McDonald said: ". . . you find yourself ending up with the seemingly absurd, seemingly improbable hypothesis that these things may come from somewhere else."

A number of other scientists have also expressed themselves as believers in ETH, if not ETA, but usually in more cautious terms.

The general idea of space travel by humans from Earth and visitors to Earth from other civilizations is an old one and has been the subject of many works of fiction. In the past 250 years the topic has been widely developed in science fiction. A fascinating account of the development of this literary form is given in *Pilgrims through Space and Time—Trends and Patterns in Scientific and Utopian Fiction* (Bailey, 1947).

The first published suggestion that some UFOs are visitors from other civilizations is contained in an article in *True*, entitled "Flying Saucers are Real" by Donald E. Keyhoe (1950).

Direct, convincing and unequivocal evidence of the truth of ETA would be the greatest single scientific discovery in the history of mankind. Going beyond its interest for science, it would undoubtedly have consequences of surpassing significance for every phase of human life. Some persons who have written speculatively on this subject, profess to believe that the supposed extraterrestrial visitors come with beneficent motives, to help humanity clean up the terrible mess that it has made. Others say they believe that the visitors are hostile. Whether their coming would be favorable or unfavorable to mankind, it is almost certain that they would make great changes in the conditions of human existence.

It is characteristic of most reports of actual visitors from outer space that there is no corroborating witness to the alleged incident, so that the story must be accepted, if at all, solely on the basis of belief in the veracity of the one person who claims to have had the experience. In the cases which we studied, there was only one in which the observer claimed to have had contact with a visitor from outer space. On the basis of our experience with that one, and our own unwillingness to believe the literal truth of the Villas-Boas incident, or the one from Truckee, Calif. reported by Prof. James Harder (see Section V, Chapter 2), we found that no direct evidence whatever of a convincing nature now exists for the claim that any UFOs represent spacecraft visiting Earth from another civilization.

Some persons are temperamentally ready, even eager, to accept ETA without clear observational evidence. One lady remarked, "It would be so wonderfully exciting if it were true!" It certainly would be exciting, but that does not make it true. When confronted with a proposition of such great import, responsible scientists adopt a cautiously critical attitude toward whatever evidence is adduced to support it. Persons without scientific training, often confuse this with basic opposition to the idea, with a biased desire or hope, or even of willingness to distort the evidence in order to conclude that ETA is not true.

The scientists' caution in such a situation does not represent opposition to the idea. It represents a determination not to accept the proposition as true in the absence of evidence that clearly, unambiguously and with certainty establishes its truth or falsity.

Scientifically it is not necessary—it is not even desirable—to adopt a position about the truth or falsity of ETA in order to investigate the question. There is a widespread misconception that scientific inquiry represents some kind of debate in which the truth is adjudged to be on the side of the team that has scored the most points. Scientists investigate an undecided proposition by seeking to find ways to get decisive observational material. Sometimes the ways to get such data are difficult to conceive, difficult to carry out, and so indirect that the rest of the scientific world remains uncertain of the probative value of the results for a long time. Progress in science can be painfully slow—at other times it can be sudden and dramatic. The question of ETA would be settled in a few minutes if a flying saucer were to land on the lawn of a hotel where a convention of the American Physical Society was in progress, and its occupants were to emerge and present a special paper to the assembled physicists, revealing where they came from, and the technology of how their craft operates. Searching questions from the audience would follow.

In saying that thus far no convincing evidence exists for the truth of ETA, no prediction is made about the future. If evidence appears soon after this report is published, that will not alter the truth of the statement that we do not *now* have such evidence. If new evidence appears later, this report can be appropriately revised in a second printing.

10. Intelligent Life Elsewhere.

Whether there is intelligent life elsewhere (ILE) in the Universe is a question that has received a great deal of serious speculative attention in recent years. A good popular review of thinking on the subject is *We Are Not Alone* by Walter Sullivan (1964). More advanced discussions are *Interstellar Communications*, a collection of papers edited by A. G. W. Cameron (1963), and *Intelligent Life in the Universe* (Shklovskii and Sagan, 1966). Thus far we have no observational evidence whatever on the question, so therefore it remains open. An early unpublished discussion is a letter of 13 December 1948 of J. E. Lipp to Gen. Donald Putt (Appendix D). This letter is Appendix D of the Project Sign report dated February 1949 from Air Materiel Command Headquarters No. F-TR-2274-IA.

The ILE question has some relation to the ETH or ETA for UFOs as discussed in the preceding section. Clearly, if ETH is true, then ILE must also be true because some UFOs have then to come from some unearthly civilization. Conversely, if we could know conclusively that ILE does not exist, then ETH could not be true. But even if ILE exists, it does not follow that the ETH is true.

For it could be that the ILE, though existent, might not have reached a stage of development in which the beings have the technical capacity or the desire to visit the Earth's surface. Much speculative writing assumes implicitly that intelligent life progresses steadily both in intellectual and in its technological development. Life began on Earth more than a billion years ago, whereas the known geological age of the Earth is some five billion years, so that life in any form has only existed for the most recent one-fifth of the Earth's life as a solid ball orbiting the Sun. Man as an intelligent being has only lived on Earth for some 5,000

years, or about one-millionth of the Earth's age. Technological development is even more recent. Moreover the greater part of what we think of as advanced technology has only been developed in the last 100 years. Even today we do not yet have a technology capable of putting men on other planets of the solar system. Travel of men over interstellar distances in the foreseeable future seems now to be quite out of the question (Purcell, 1960; Markowitz, 1967).

The dimensions of the universe are hard for the mind of man to conceive. A light-year is the distance light travels in one year of 31.56 million seconds, at the rate of 186,000 miles per second, that is, a distance of 5.88 million million miles. The nearest known star is at a distance of 4.2 light-years.

Fifteen stars are known to be within 11.5 light-years of the Sun. Our own galaxy, the Milky Way, is a vast flattened distribution of some 10^{11} stars about 80,000 light-years in diameter, with the Sun located about 26,000 light-years from the center. To gain a little perspective on the meaning of such distances relative to human affairs, we may observe that the news of Christ's life on Earth could not yet have reached as much as a tenth of the distance from the Earth to the center of our galaxy.

Other galaxies are inconceivably remote. The faintest observable galaxies are at a distance of some two billion light-years. There are some 100 million such galaxies within that distance, the average distance between galaxies being some eight million light-years.

Authors of UFO fantasy literature casually set all of the laws of physics aside in order to try to evade this conclusion, but serious consideration of their ideas hardly belongs in a report on the scientific study of UFOs.

Even assuming that difficulties of this sort could be overcome, we have no right to assume that in life communities everywhere there is a steady evolution in the directions of both greater intelligence and greater technological competence. Human beings now know enough to destroy all life on Earth, and they may lack the intelligence to work out social controls to keep themselves from doing so. If other civilizations have the same limitation then it might be that they develop to the point where they destroy themselves utterly before they have developed the technology needed to enable them to make long space voyages.

Another possibility is that the growth of intelligence precedes the growth of technology in such a way that by the time a society would be technically capable of interstellar space travel, it would have reached a level of intelligence at which it had not the slightest interest in interstellar travel. We must not assume that we are capable of imagining now the scope and extent of future technological development of our own or any other civilization, and so we must guard against assuming that we have any capacity to imagine what a more advanced society would regard as intelligent conduct.

In addition to the great distances involved, and the difficulties which they present to interstellar space travel, there is still another problem: If we assume that civilizations annihilate themselves in such a way that their effective intelligent life span is less than, say, 100,000 years, then such a short time span also works against the likelihood of successful interstellar communication. The different civilizations would probably reach the culmination of their development at different epochs in cosmic history. Moreover, according to present views, stars are being formed constantly by the condensation of interstellar dust and gases. They exist for perhaps 10 billion years, of which a civilization lasting 100,000 years is only 1/100,000 of the life span of the star. It follows that there is an extremely small likelihood that two nearby civilizations would be in a state of high development at the same epoch.

Astronomers now generally agree that a fairly large number of all main-sequence stars are probably accompanied by planets at the right distance from their Sun to provide for habitable conditions for life as we know it. That is, where stars are, there are probably habitable planets. This belief favors the possibility of interstellar communication, but it must be remembered that even this view is entirely speculation: we are quite unable directly to observe any planets associated with stars other than the Sun.

In view of the foregoing, we consider that it is safe to assume that no ILE outside of our solar system has any possibility of visiting Earth in the next 10,000 years.

This conclusion does not rule out the possibility of the existence of ILE, as contrasted with the ability of such civilizations to visit Earth. It is estimated that 10^{21} stars can be seen using the 200-inch Hale telescope on Mount Palomar. Astronomers surmise that possibly as few as one in a million or as many as one in ten of these has a planet in which physical and chemical conditions are such as to make them habitable by life based on the same kind of biochemistry as the life we know on Earth. Even if the lower figure is taken, this would mean there are 10^{15} stars in the visible universe which have planets suitable for an abode of life. In our own galaxy there are 10^{11} stars, so perhaps as many as 10^8 have habitable planets in orbit around them.

Biologists feel confident that wherever physical and chemical conditions are right, life will actually emerge. In short, astronomers tell us that there are a vast number of stars in the universe accompanied by planets where the physical and chemical conditions are suitable, and biologists tell us that habitable places are sure to become inhabited (Rush, 1957).

An important advance was made when Stanley L. Miller (1955) showed experimentally that electrical discharges such as those in natural lightning when passed through a mixture of methane and ammonia, such as may have been present in the Earth's primitive atmosphere, will initiate chemical reactions which yield various amino acids. These are the raw materials from which are constructed the proteins that are essential to life. Miller's work has been followed up and extended by many others, particularly P. H. Abelson of the Carnegie Institution of Washington.

The story is by no means fully worked out. The evidence in hand seems to convince biochemists that natural processes, such as lightning, or the absorption of solar ultraviolet light, could generate the necessary starting materials from which life could evolve. On this basis they generally hold the belief that where conditions make it possible that life could appear, there life actually will appear.

It is regarded by scientists today as essentially certain that ILE exists, but with essentially no possibility of contact between the communities on planets associated with different stars. We therefore conclude that there is no relation between ILE at other solar systems and the UFO phenomenon as observed on Earth.

There remains the question of ILE within our solar system. Here only the planets Venus and Mars need be given consideration as possible abodes of life.

Mercury, the planet nearest the Sun, is certainly too hot to support life. The side of Mercury that is turned toward the Sun has an average temperature of 660°F. (Mercury rotates in 59 days and the orbital period is 88 days, so there is a slow relative motion.) Since the orbit is rather eccentric this temperature becomes as high as 770°F, hot enough to melt lead, when Mercury is closest to the Sun. The opposite side is extremely cold, its temperature not being known. Gravity on Mercury is about one-fourth that on Earth. This fact combined with the high temperature makes it certain that Mercury has no atmosphere, which is consistent with observational data on this point. It is quite impossible that life as found on Earth could exist on Mercury.

Jupiter, Saturn, Uranus, Neptune and Pluto are so far from the Sun that they are too cold for life to exist there.

Although it has long been thought that Venus might provide a suitable abode for life, it is now known that the surface of Venus is also too hot for advanced forms of life, although it is possible that some primitive forms may exist. Some uncertainty and controversy exist about the interpretation of observations of Venus because the planet is always enveloped in dense clouds so that the solid surface is never seen. The absorption spectrum of sunlight coming from Venus indicates that the principal constituent of the atmosphere is carbon dioxide. There is no evidence of oxygen or water vapor. With so little oxygen in the atmosphere there could not be animal life there resembling that on Earth.

Although it is safe to conclude that there is no intelligent life on Venus, the contrary idea is held quite tenaciously by certain groups in America. There are small religious groups who maintain that Jesus Christ now sojourns on Venus, and that some of their members have traveled there by flying saucers supplied by the Venusians and have been greatly refreshed spiritually by visiting Him. There is no observational evidence in support of this teaching.

In the fantasy literature of believers in ETH, some attention is given to a purely hypothetical planet named Clarion. Not only is there no direct evidence for its existence, but there is conclusive indirect evidence for its non-existence. Those UFO writers who try not to be totally inconsistent with scientific findings, recognizing that Venus and Mars are unsuitable as abodes of life, have invented Clarion to meet the need for a home for the visitors who they believe come on some UFOs.

They postulate that Clarion moves in an orbit exactly like that of the Earth around the Sun, but with the orbit rotated through half a revolution in its plane so that the two orbits have the same line of apsides, but with Clarion's perihelion in the same direction from the Sun as the Earth's aphelion. The two planets, Earth and Clarion, are postulated to move in their orbits in such a way that they are always opposite each other, so that the line Earth-Sun-Clarion is a straight line. Thus persons on Earth would never see Clarion because it is permanently eclipsed by the Sun.

If the two orbits were exactly circular, the two planets would move along their common orbit at the same speed and so would remain exactly opposite each other. But even if the orbits are elliptical, so that the speed in the orbit is variable, the two planets would vary in speed during the year in just such a way as always to remain Opposite each other and thus continue to be permanently eclipsed.

However, this tidy arrangement would not occur in actuality because the motion of each of these two planets would be perturbed by the gravitational attractions between them and the other planets of the solar system, principally Venus and Mars. It is a quite complicated and difficult problem to calculate the way in which these perturbations would affect the motion of Earth and Clarion.

At the request of the Colorado project, Dr. R. L. Duncombe, director of the Nautical Almanac office at U.S. Naval Observatory in Washington, D.C., kindly arranged to calculate the effect of the introduction of the hypothetical planet Clarion into the solar system. The exact result depends to some extent on the location of the Earth-Sun-Clarion line relative to the line of apsides and the computations were carried out merely for one case (see Appendix E).

These calculations show that the effect of the perturbations would be to make Clarion become visible from Earth beyond the Sun's limb after about thirty years. In other words, Clarion would long since have become visible from Earth if many years ago it were started out in such a special way as has been postulated.

The computations revealed further that if Clarion were there it would reveal its presence indirectly in a much shorter time. Its attraction on Venus would cause Venus to move in a different way than if Clarion were not there. Calculation shows that Venus would pull away from its otherwise correct motion by about 1 second of arc in about three months' time. Venus is routinely kept under observation to this accuracy, and therefore if Clarion were there it would reveal its presence by its effect on the motion of Venus. No such effect is observed, that is, the motion of Venus as actually observed is accurately in accord with the absence of Clarion, so therefore we may safely conclude that Clarion is nonexistent. (These calculations assume Clarion's mass roughly equal to that of the Earth.)

In his letter of transmittal Dr. Duncombe comments "I feel this is definite proof that the presence of such a body could not remain undetected for long. However, I am afraid it will not change the minds of those people who believe in the existence of Clarion."

We first heard about Clarion from a lady who is prominent in American political life who was intrigued with the idea that this is where UFOS come from. When the results of the Naval Observatory computations were told to her she exclaimed, "That's what I don't like about computers! They are always dealing death blows to our fondest notions."

[So we need consider Clarion no further.]

Mars has long been considered as a possible abode of life in the solar system. There is still no direct evidence that life exists there, but the question is being actively studied in the space research programs of both the United States and Soviet Russia, so it may well be clarified within the coming decade.

At present all indications are that Mars could not be the habitation of an advanced civilization capable of sending spacecraft to visit the Earth. Conditions for life there are so harsh that it is generally believed that at best

Mars could only support the simpler forms of plant life.

An excellent recent survey of the rapidly increasing knowledge of Mars is *Handbook of the Physical Properties of the Planet Mars* compiled by C. M. Michaux (NASA publication SP-3030, 1967). A brief discussion of American research programs for study of life on Mars is given in *Biology and Exploration of Mars*, a 19-page pamphlet prepared by the Space Science Board of the National Academy of Sciences, published in April 1965.

The orbit of Mars is considerably more eccentric than that of the Earth. Consequently the distance of Mars from the Sun varies from 128 to 155 million miles during the year of 687 days. The synodic period, or mean time between successive oppositions, is 800 days.

The most favorable time for observation of Mars is at opposition, when Mars is opposite the Sun from Earth. These distances of closest approach of Mars and Earth vary from 35 to 60 million miles. The most recent favorable time of closest approach was the opposition of 10 September 1956, and the next favorable opposition will be that of 10 August 1971. At that time undoubtedly great efforts will be made to study Mars in the space programs of the U.S.S.R. and the United States.

Some of the UFO literature has contended that a larger than usual number of UFO reports occur at the times of Martian oppositions. The contention is that this indicates that some UFOs come from Mars at these particularly favorable times. The claimed correlation is quite unfounded; the idea is not supported by observational data (Vallee and Vallee, 1966, 138).

Mars is much smaller than Earth, having a diameter of 4,200 miles, in comparison with 8,000 miles. Mars' mass is about one-tenth the Earth's, and gravity at Mars' surface is about 0.38 that of Earth. The Martian escape velocity is 3.1 mile/sec.

At the favorable opposition of 1877, C. V.

Schiaparelli, an Italian astronomer, observed and mapped some surface markings on Mars which he called "canali," meaning "channels" in Italian. The word was mistranslated as "canals" in English and the idea was put forward, particularly vigorously by Percival Lowell, founder of the Lowell Observatory of Flagstaff, Arizona, that the canals on Mars were evidence of a gigantic planetary irrigation scheme, developed by the supposed inhabitants of Mars (Lowell, 1908). These markings have been the subject of a great deal of study since their discovery. Astronomers generally now reject the idea that they afford any kind of indication that Mars is inhabited by intelligent beings.

Mars has two moons named Phobos and Deimos. These are exceedingly small, Phobos being estimated at ten miles in diameter and Deimos at five miles, based on their brightness, assuming the reflecting power of their material to be the same as that of the planet. The periods are 7h39m for Phobos and 30h18m for Deimos. They were discovered in August 1877 by Asaph Hall using the then new 26-inch refractor of the U.S. Naval Observatory in Washington. An unsuccessful search for moons of Mars was made with a 48-inch mirror during the opposition of 1862.

I. S. Shklovskii (1959) published a sensational suggestion in a Moscow newspaper that these moons were really artificial satellites which had been put up by supposed inhabitants of Mars as a place of refuge when the supposed oceans of several million years ago began to dry up (Sullivan, 1966, 169). There is no observational evidence to support this idea. Continuing the same line of speculation Salisbury (1962), after pointing out that the satellites were looked for in 1862 but not found until 1877, then asks, "Should we attribute the failure of 1862 to imperfections in existing telescopes, or may we imagine that the satellites were launched between 1862 and 1877?" This is a slender reed indeed with which to prop up so sensational an inference, and we reject it.

11. Light Propagation and Visual Perception.

Most UFO reports refer to things seen by an observer. Seeing is a complicated process. It involves the emission or scattering of light by the thing seen, the propagation of that light through the atmosphere to the eye of the observer, the formation of an image on the retina of the eye by the lens of the eye, the generation there of a stimulus in the optic nerve, and the perceptual process in the brain which enables the mind to make judgments about the nature of the thing seen.

Under ordinary circumstances all of these steps are in fairly good working order with the result that our eyes give reasonably accurate information about the objects in their field of view. However, each step in the process is capable of malfunctioning, often in unsuspected ways. It is therefore essential to understand these physical and psychological processes in order to be able to interpret all things seen, including those reported as UFOs.

The study of propagation of light through the atmosphere is included in atmospheric optics or meteorological optics. Although a great deal is known about the physical principles involved, in practice it is usually difficult to make specific statements about an UFO report because not enough has been observed and recorded about the condition of the atmosphere at the time and place named in the report.

Application of the knowledge of atmospheric optics to the interpretation of UFO reports has been especially stressed by Menzel (1952; Menzel and Boyd, 1963). A valuable treatise on atmospheric effects on seeing is Middleton's *Vision through the Atmosphere* (1952). A survey of the literature of atmospheric optics with emphasis on topics relevant to understanding UFO reports was prepared for the Colorado project by Dr. William Viezee of the Stanford Research Institute (Section VI, Chapter 4).

Coming to the observer himself, Menzel stressed in consulting visits to the Colorado project that more ought to be known about defects of vision of the observer. He urged careful interviews to determine the observers' defects of vision, how well they are corrected, and whether spectacles were being worn at the time the UFO sighting was made. Besides the defects of vision that can be corrected by spectacles, inquiry ought to be made where relevant into the degree of color blindness of the observer, since this visual defect is more common than is generally appreciated.

Problems connected with the psychology of perception were studied for the Colorado project by Prof. Michael Wertheimer of the Department of Psychology of the University of Colorado. He prepared an elementary presentation of the main points of interest for the use of the project staff (Section VI, Chapter 1).

Perhaps the commonest difficulty is the lack of appreciation of size-distance relations in the description of an unknown object. When we see an airplane in the sky, especially if it is one of a particular model with which we are familiar, we know from prior experience approximately what its size really is. Then from its apparent size as we see it, we have some basis for estimating its distance. Conversely, when we know something about the distance of an unknown object, we can say something about its size. Although not usually expressed this way, what is really "seen" is the size of the image on the retina of the eye, which may be produced by a smaller object that is nearer or a larger object that is farther away. Despite this elementary fact, many people persist in saying that the full moon looks the same size as a quarter or as a washtub. The statement means nothing. Statements such as that an object looks to be of the same size as a coin *held at arm's length* do, however, convey some meaningful information.

Another limitation of normal vision that is often not appreciated is the color blindness of the dark-adapted eye. The human eye really has two different mechanisms in the retina for the conversion of light energy into nerve stimulus. Photopic vision is the kind that applies in the daytime or at moderate levels of artificial illumination. It involves the cones of the retina, and is involved in color vision. Scotopic vision is the kind that comes into play at low levels of illumination. It involves the rods of the retina which are unable to distinguish colors, hence the saying that in the dark all cats are gray. The transition from photopic to scotopic vision normally takes place at about the level of illumination that corresponds to the light of the full moon high in the sky. When one goes from a brightly lighted area into a dark room he is blind at first but gradually dark adaptation occurs and a transition is made from photopic to scotopic vision. The ability to see, but without color discrimination, then returns. Nyctalopia is the name of a deficiency of vision whereby dark adaptation does not occur and is often connected with a Vitamin A dietary deficiency.

If one stares directly at a bright light which is then turned off, an afterimage will be seen; that is, the image of the light, but less bright and usually out of focus, continues to be seen and gradually fades away. Positive afterimages are those in which the image looks bright like the original stimulus, but this may reverse to a negative afterimage which looks darker than the surrounding field of view. Afterimages have undoubtedly given rise to some UFO reports.

The afterimage is the result of a temporary change in the retina and so remains at a fixed point on the retina. When one then moves his eyes to look in a different direction, the afterimage seems to move relative to the surroundings. If it is believed by the observer to be a real object it will seem to him to have moved at an enormous velocity. A light going out will seem to shrink and move away from the observer as it does so. If one light goes on while another is going off, it may appear as if the light that is going off is moving to the place where the other light is going on.

Autokinesis is another property of the eye which needs to be understood by persons who are interested in looking for UFOs. A bright light in a field of view which has no reference objects in it, such as a single star in a part of the sky which has very few other stars in it, will appear to move when stared at, even though it is in reality stationary. This effect has given rise to UFO reports in which observers were looking at a bright star and believed that it was rapidly moving, usually in an erratic way.

12. Study of UFO Photographs. The popular UFO literature abounds with photographs of alleged strange objects in the sky, many of which are clearly in the form of flying saucers. Some of these have been published in magazines of wide circulation. The editors of *Look*, in collaboration with the editors of United Press International and Cowles Communications, Inc. published a *Look* "Special" in 1967 that is entirely devoted to "Flying Saucers," which contains many examples of UFO pictures.

Photographic evidence has a particularly strong appeal to many people. The Colorado study therefore undertook to look into the available photographs with great care. Chapter 2 of Section III gives the story of most of this work and Chapter 3 of Section IV gives the detailed reports on individual cases.

It is important to distinguish between photographic prints and the negatives from which they are made. There are many ways in which an image can be added to a print, for example, by double-printing from two negatives. Negatives, on the other hand, are somewhat more difficult to alter without leaving evidence of the fact. We therefore decided wherever possible to concentrate our study of photographic case upon the negatives. This was not, of course, possible in every instance examined.

A barber whose shop is in Zanesville, Ohio, but whose home is in the suburb of Roseville, has made a widely publicized pair of UFO photographs. He did not attempt to exploit them in a big way. He merely exhibited them for local interest (and stimulation of his barbering business) in the window of his shop. There they remained for more than two months until they were discovered by a big city newspaperman from Columbus, Ohio, who arranged to sell them to the Associated Press. They were distributed in February 1967 and have been often printed in various magazines after their original presentation in many newspapers.

Early in the project we became acquainted with Everitt Merritt, photogrammetrist on the staff of the Autometrics Division of the Raytheon Company of Alexandria, Virginia. He undertook to do an analysis of the photographs. A pair of prints was supplied to Merritt by NICAP.

Each of the pair shows the home of the photographer, a small bungalow, with a flying saucer flying over it. The flying saucer looks like it might be almost as large as the house in its horizontal dimension. The photographer says that he was leaving home with a camera when he chanced to look back and see the saucer flying over his home. He says he quickly snapped what we call picture A. Thinking the UFO was about to disappear behind a tree, he ran to the left about 30 feet and snapped picture B, having spoiled one exposure in between. He estimated that there was less than a two minute interval between the two pictures, with A followed by B.

Merritt studied the negatives themselves by quantitative photogrammetric methods, and also did some surveying in the front yard of the Roseville home, as a check on the calculations based on the photographs. From a study of the shadows appearing in the picture, he could show conclusively that actually picture B was taken earlier than picture A, and that the time interval between the two pictures was more than an hour, rather than being less than two minutes as claimed.

The photographic evidence contained in the negatives themselves is therefore in disagreement with the story told by the man who took the pictures. Two letters written to him by the Colorado project requesting his clarification of the discrepancy remain unanswered.

We made arrangements with Merritt for his services to be available for photogrammetric analysis of other cases. These methods require a pair of pictures showing substantially the same scene taken from two different camera locations. Unfortunately this condition is seldom met in UFO photographs. Only one other pair came to our attention which met this criterion. These were the much publicized pictures taken on 11 May 1950 near McMinnville, Ore. (Case 46). But in this case the UFO images turned out to be too fuzzy to allow worthwhile photogrammetric analysis.

Other photographic studies were made for the Colorado project by Dr. William K. Hartmann (Section III, Chapter 2).

Hartmann made a detailed study of 35 photographic cases (Section IV, Chapter 3) referring to the period 1966–68, and a selection of 18 older cases, some of which have been widely acclaimed in the UFO literature. This photographic study led to the identification of a number of widely publicized photographs as being ordinary objects, others as fabrications, and others as innocent misidentifications of things photographed under unusual conditions.

On p. 43 of the *Look* Special on "Flying Saucers" there is a picture of an allegedly "claw-shaped" marking on the dry sand of a beach. Some of the dark colored moist sand making up the "claw mark" was shipped to Wright-Patterson AFB and analyzed. The liquid was found to be urine. Some person or animal had performed an act of micturition there.

A report by Staff Sergeant Earl Schroeder which says "Being a native of this area and having spent a good share of my life hunting and fishing this area, I believe that the so-called 'monster' (if there was such) could very well have been a large black bear." His report also notes that "during the week of July 26 the local TV stations showed a program called *Lost in Space*. In this program there were two monsters fitting their description controlled by a human being."

Summarizing, the investigation report says, "There was food missing from the picnic table which leads to the belief that some animal was responsible for the black shape portion of the total sighting. There are numerous bears and raccoons in the area."

Another photograph presented in the *Look* Special is of a pentagonal image, though called hexagonal. Photographic images of this kind arise from a malfunctioning of the iris of the camera and are quite commonplace. It is hard to understand how the editors of a national illustrated magazine could be unfamiliar with this kind of camera defect.

13. Direct and Indirect Physical Evidence.

A wide variety of physical effects of UFOs have been claimed in the UFO literature. The most direct physical evidence, of course, would be the actual discovery of a flying saucer, with or without occupants, living or dead. None were found. Claims which we studied as direct evidence are those of the finding of pieces of material which allegedly came from outer space because it is a product of a different technology, so it is said, than any known on earth. Another kind of direct evidence studied was allegations that disturbance of vegetation on the ground, or of the soil was due to an UFO having landed at the place in question.

The claimed indirect physical evidence of the presence of an UFO is of the nature of effects produced at a distance by the UFO. Accounts of sounds, or the lack of sounds, associated with UFOs, even though reports of visual observation indicated speeds of the UFO far in excess of the velocity of sound were common. Whenever a terrestrial solid object travels through the atmosphere faster than the speed of sound, a sonic boom is generated. The argument has been advanced that the absence of a sonic boom associated with UFOs moving faster than cutoff Mach (see Section VI, Chapter 6) is an indication of their being a product of a technology more advanced than our own because we do not know how to avoid the generation of sonic booms. Another category of indirect physical effects is those associated with claims that UFOs possess strong magnetic fields, vastly stronger than those that would be produced by the strongest magnets that we know how to make.

There are many UFO reports in which it is claimed that an automobile's ignition failed and the motor stopped, and in some cases that the headlights failed also, and that after this happened, an UFO was seen nearby. Usually such reports are discussed on the supposition that this is an indication that the UFO had been the source of a strong magnetic field.

Reports of both direct and indirect physical evidence were studied by various staff members of the Colorado project, principally by Dr. Roy Craig, whose account of these studies is contained in Chapters 3 and 4 of Section III.

These studies resulted mostly in lack of substantiation of the claims that have been made. Claims of terrestrial magnetic disturbances at various Antarctic bases were either unconfirmed or seemed to be closely related to a practical joke that was played on a base commander.

During the period of field study of this project only one case of automobile engine malfunction came to our attention. There was some ground for skepticism about the report in that it was made by a diabetic patient who had been drinking and was returning home alone from a party at 3:00 a.m.

Some laboratory tests showed that engine failure due to the action of an external magnetic field on the car's ignition coil would require fields in excess of 20,000 gauss, at the coil. Owing to the magnetic shielding action of the sheet steel in the car body, the strength of the field outside the car would have to be considerably greater than this. But magnetic fields of such intensity would alter the state of magnetization of the car itself.

The process of forming car bodies by cold-forming the sheet steel introduces some quasi-permanent magnetization into all car bodies. Since all of the bodies of a given make in a given year are usually made with the same molds on the same presses they are all magnetized in the same pattern.

In the case in question we found that the car body that had been subjected to the presence of the UFO was magnetized. The pattern of magnetization quite closely resembled that of a car of the same make and year that was found a thousand miles away in a used car lot in Boulder, Colo. From this we can infer that the car that was supposedly near the UFO, had not been subjected to a strong magnetic field, otherwise this would have permanently changed the state of magnetization of the body of the exposed car.

In the area of direct physical evidence, probably the most interesting result of investigation was the analysis of a piece of metallic magnesium which was alleged to have come from an UFO that exploded over a stretch of tidal water at Ubatuba, São Paulo, Brazil in 1957. This was one of several pieces of magnesium from the same source that had been sent to the society editor of a Rio de Janeiro newspaper at the time.

Later one of the pieces was subjected to elaborate chemical analysis in government laboratories in Brazil. The results of the analysis are given in great detail in the first of the Lorenzen books (1962), the full account occupying some forty pages. The claimed result of these studies was that the laboratory work showed the metallic magnesium to be purer than any ever made by man on Earth. Therefore it could not have been a product of earthly technology, therefore it came from an extraterrestrial source.

Mrs. Lorenzen kindly supplied one of the magnesium specimens to the Colorado project. We arranged to have it studied by the method of neutron activation analysis in a laboratory in Washington, D.C. The result, which is presented in detail in Chapter 3 of Section III, was that the magnesium metal was found to be much less pure than the regular commercial metal produced in 1957 by the Dow Chemical Company at Midland, Michigan. Therefore it need not have come from an extraterrestrial source, leaving us with no basis for rational belief that it did.

14. Radar Sightings of UFOs. The public became generally aware of radar at the end of World War II when the story of its important use in that war was told, after having been kept secret for some 12 years. A good non-technical account of this development is given in R. M. Page, *The Origin of Radar* (1962).

The word radar is an acronym for *RA*dio *D*etection *A*nd *R*anging. Basically, most radar systems operate in the following way. A transmitter sends out short pulses of electromagnetic energy at regular intervals. These are sent out through an antenna designed to radiate a narrow beam within a small angle of its main direction. This beam of pulses travels outward at the speed of light. If it encounters an obstacle, which may be a metallic object like an airplane, a rain storm, or a bird or a flock of birds, it is partially scattered in all directions from the obstacle. In particular a part of the beam is scattered back toward the transmitter. When it arrives back at the transmitter it is received and indicated or displayed in various ways, depending on the special purpose for which the system was designed. By the fact of there being a returned signal at all, the function of detection is accomplished. By the time delay involved between the transmission of the outgoing signal and the return of the back-scattered signal, the distance of the scattering object is inferred, thus accomplishing the function of ranging.

To get a beam of sufficiently narrow distribution in angle as to enable inferring from what direction the scattered signal was returned, the antenna must have a diameter of the order of ten times the wavelength of the radio waves which it uses.

In the period since 1945 the technology has had an enormous development so that nowadays there are elaborate networks of land and ship based radar systems, as well as radar systems carried by most airplanes, which have become vitally necessary to the safe operation of civil and military aircraft. In addition to the use of radar in connection with navigation, it has become a valuable tool in meteorological work in that distant rain storms can be detected by radar. Also the trails of ionized air left by meteors can be detected and studied by radar, providing for the first time the means for observing meteors in the daytime.

There are many popular misconceptions about radar. It is important at the outset to realize that the returned radar signal does *not* give a sharply focused image or picture of the obstacle that has been detected. What one gets when it is displayed on a cathode-ray screen is simply a diffuse blob of light indicating that *something* is there, in the direction the antenna is pointed (with some exceptions) and at the distance indicated by the time delay between transmission and reception of the back-scattered pulse. Of course, a large airplane gives a more intense signal than a flock of small birds at the same range, and skilled op-

erators learn to make valid inferences about the nature of the object detected from other things that they know about the general situation together with the magnitude of the returned signal.

It is important also to recognize that the propagation of the outgoing and the back-scattered pulses is ordinarily assumed to be rectilinear and at the normal speed of light. But the actual propagation is affected by temperature and humidity difference in the air path along which the radio pulse travels. This can give rise to anomalous propagation that is analogous to but in detail not identical with the effects which give rise to mirages in the propagation of light through such an atmosphere. Usually the radar set operator does not know enough about the actual atmospheric conditions to make allowance for effects of this kind and, if they happen to be pronounced, can be led to make erroneous decisions. Another point is that, although the antenna sends out most of its energy in a single narrow beam, small amounts of energy go out in several other directions, known as sidelobes, so that a large or a nearby object in the direction of a sidelobe can give rise to a received signal that is indistinguishable from a small or distant object in the direction of the main beam.

The overall radar system is a rather complicated set of electronic equipment which can malfunction in various ways giving rise to internally generated signals which the operator will tend to regard as reflections made by outside obstacles which are in reality not there.

Usually the returned radar signals are displayed on the screen of a cathode ray tube and observed visually by the operator. On this account, subjective judgments of the operator enter into the final determination of what is seen, how it is interpreted and how it is reported. The data obtained from radar systems are thus not as completely objective as is often assumed. In some few instances subjectiveness is somewhat reduced by the fact that the cathode ray screen is photographed, but even when this is done there is a subjective element introduced at the stage where a human observer has to interpret the photograph of the radar screen.

Radar operators do report unidentified targets from time to time and so there exists a category of UFO cases in which the unidentified flying object was seen on a radar screen. In a few cases there is a close correlation between an unknown thing in the sky seen visually and something also displayed on radar.

However in view of the many difficulties associated with unambiguous interpretation of all blobs of light on a radar screen it does not follow directly and easily that the radar reports support or "prove" that UFOs exist as moving vehicles scattering the radio pulses as would a metallic object. The Colorado project engaged the services of the Stanford Research Institute to make a general study of the functioning of radar systems from the point of view of the relation of their indications to UFOs. The study which was carried out resulted in the production of Section VI, Chapter 5, by Dr. Roy H. Blackmer, Jr. and his associates, R. J. Allen, R. T. S. Collis, C. Herold and R. I. Presnell.

Studies of specific UFO radar reports and their interpretation are presented in Section III, Chapter 5 by Gordon Thayer. Thayer is a radio propagation specialist on the staff of the Environmental Science Services Administration in Boulder. In his chapter, Thayer presents a detailed analysis of some 35 cases, some of which are visual, others radar, and some are both. Both optical and radar phenomena are treated together because of the similarity in the wave propagation problems involved.

In his summary of results he says: ". . . there was no case where the meteorological data available tended to negate the anomalous propagation hypothesis . . ." However, Thayer points out that adequate meteorological data for a thorough interpretation is often lacking so that a great deal more observational mate-

rial of this kind would be needed in order to deal with a larger proportion of all of the reported UFO radar cases.

In view of the importance of radar to the safe operation of all aircraft, it is essential that further research be done leading to the more precise knowledge possible of anomalous propagation of radar signals. However, it is felt that this can best be done by a direct attack on the problem itself rather than by detailed field investigation of UFO cases.

15. Visual Observation made by U.S. Astronauts. The popular UFO literature makes occasional reference to UFOs seen by the U.S. astronauts in the space program operated by the National Aeronautics and Space Administration. We do not know of similar reports by Soviet astronauts but they may well have seen similar things.

In flights conducted between 12 April 1961 and 15 November 1966, thirty U.S. and Russian astronauts spent a total of 2,503 hours in orbit. The Colorado project was fortunate in that Dr. Franklin Roach, one of the principal investigators, has worked closely with the astronaut program in connection with their visual observations and so was already quite familiar with what they had seen and also was able to conduct further interviews with several of them on the basis of close personal acquaintances already established.

Roach presents a detailed account of what they saw as related to the UFO question in Section III, Chapter 6. Nothing was seen that could be construed as a "flying saucer" or manned vehicle from outer space. Some things were seen that were identified as debris from previous space experiments. Three sightings that are described in detail remain quite unidentified and are, Roach says, "a challenge to the analyst."

Roach emphasizes that the conditions for simple visual observation of objects near the satellite are not as good as might be naively supposed. As he describes them, "The conditions under which astronauts made their observations are similar to those which would be encountered by one or two persons in the front seat of a small car having no side or rear windows and a partially covered, very smudged windshield." Moreover, the astronauts were kept occupied with other observations and activities during their flight and so did not have extended periods of time in which to concentrate on visual observation of their surroundings. Most of the available visual observations therefore have to be regarded as a by product rather than a primary purpose of the program in which they were engaged.

The conclusion is that nothing definite relating to the ETH aspect of UFOs has been established as a result of these rather sporadic observations.

16. Public Attitudes Toward UFOs. Opinion polls are widely employed nowadays to measure public attitudes on various important and trivial issues. It is natural therefore to apply the same method to a determination of public attitudes toward various phases of the UFO question.

Studies of this sort are not studies of the UFOs themselves, but an attempt at determination of what the American public thinks about UFOs. Some UFOs either do or do not come from outer space, and the fact of the matter would not be determined by finding out what the opinion of the American people about it may be. Nevertheless we considered that public attitudes do play a role in policy formation in America, and therefore it was appropriate to carry on some work in this area.

In 1947, 1950 and 1966 brief surveys of public attitudes on UFOs or flying saucers were conducted by the American Institute of Public Opinion, popularly known as the Gallup poll. Arrangements were made by the Colorado project for a more detailed study to be made during the spring of 1968. This was

done for us by the Opinion Research Corporation. Findings of the earlier studies and of the study made for us are presented in Chapter 7 of Section III.

The first two studies indicated respectively that 90% and 94% of the American adult public had heard of flying saucers. The first of these results, taken within months of the original June 1947 sightings at Mt. Rainier indicates the extraordinary interest which the subject aroused from the outset. The 1966 survey indicated that 96% of the adult public had heard of flying saucers.

In the 1966 poll people were asked,

"Have you, yourself, ever seen anything you thought was a 'flying saucer'?"

The result was that 5% of the 96% who had heard of them answered yes to this question. The sample was designed to be representative of the American population, 21 years of age and older, of whom there are some 100 million. This is the basis of the oft-quoted statistic that five million Americans have said that they think they have seen a flying saucer.

In the same 1966 poll, 48% said they thought the things called flying saucers were "something real," and 31% said that they were "just people's imagination." The question does not distinguish between various kinds of "real" things, such as weather balloons, aircraft, planets, mirages, etc., so the result by no means indicated that 48% believe they are visitors from outer space. That question was not included in the 1966 poll.

The 1966 poll asked whether the person interviewed thinks "there are people somewhat like ourselves living on other planets in the universe." The question thus bears solely on ILE, not on whether such intelligences do in fact visit the Earth. Of the 1,575 interviewed 34% thought yes, 45% thought no, and 21% had no opinion.

There were no statistically significant regional differences between East, Midwest, South and West with regard to the proportion of the population which had heard of, had seen, or believed in the reality of flying saucers. However, as to belief in ILE, the existence of people on other planets, this belief was held by only 27% of southerners, as compared with 36% of easterners, 37% of mid-westerners and 36% of westerners. The lower proportion of southerners who believe in ILE is statistically significant, that is, outside the range of chance variation due to finite size of sample. Although statistically significant, it is causally unexplained.

Significant variation with age is shown in responses to belief in the reality of flying saucers, and to belief in intelligent life on other planets. About 50% of persons under 60 believe in the reality of flying saucers as compared with about 33% of persons over 60. On the other hand, a significantly smaller proportion of those under 50 believe in ILE, than do those over 50. On both of these points, the decline in the number of "believers" among older people is mostly due to the increase of those having "no opinion" rather than to an increase of the number of "non-believers." Here again the poll gives no basis for conclusions as to the reasons for these differences.

As to dependence on sex, 22% of men or women have no opinion as to the "reality" of flying saucers. Significantly more women than men believe in their reality:

	% Real	% Imaginary
Men	43	35
Women	52	26

The poll showed that increased amount of formal education is associated with an increased tendency to believe in the reality of flying saucers. Perhaps this result says something about how the school system trains students in critical thinking.

An interesting correlation is found between tendency to believe in UFO reality, and to believe in ILE with having had a personal experience of having seen an UFO. The results are:

	% Believing UFOs Are Real	% Believing in ILE
Sighters	76	51
Non-sighters	46	34

As before, causal relations are unexplored; we do not know whether seeing is believing, or believing is seeing.

In the 1968 study conducted for the Colorado project by the Opinion Research Corporation, 2,050 adults over 17 years of age, living in private households in the continental United States were interviewed. In addition teenagers in the same household with an adult who was interviewed were also interviewed to give a sample of their views. Separate studies of opinions held by college students were conducted. These are reported in Section III, Chapter 7.

In the 1968 survey, 3% of adults replied affirmatively to "Have you, yourself, ever seen an UFO?" This parallels the 5% who answered affirmatively in the 1966 Gallup poll to the similar question, "Have you ever seen anything that you thought was a 'flying saucer'?" One might think that the smaller number in 1968 could be explained by perhaps less familiarity of the public with the term UFO than with the term flying saucer. This seems hardly likely, however, in that the question was part of a total interview in which the meaning of the term UFO would have become clear from the general context of other questions in the interview. It seems to us therefore that this poll actually indicated a smaller percentage of sighters than the earlier one.

An important finding is that 87% of those who said that they had seen an UFO, also declared that they had reported it to no one, other than to family or friends, that is, to no one by which it would have received official attention. Thus only about one-eighth of sightings were reported anywhere, and not all of these were reported to the Air Force. Hence if all sightings were reported to the Air Force, this result indicates that the number of reports received would be more than eight times as many as are now being received. From the small fraction who did report to the Air Force, it seems a fair inference that most of these non-reporting sighters did not think that what they saw constituted a security hazard.

In contrast, 56% of the non-sighters declared that they would report it to the police if they saw an UFO. We find this rather large discrepancy between the promised reporting behavior of the non-sighters and the actual reporting behavior of the sighters quite puzzling.

17. Other Psychological Studies. Consideration was given to a variety of modes of conducting psychological and psychiatric research into the UFO phenomenon. The possibility that an "experimental UFO" might be launched and reports of its sighting studied was given serious consideration and rejected on three grounds: In view of the fact that this was a government-sponsored, university-based study, it was felt that experiments in which the public might regard itself as having been victimized by what amounted to a hoax were unwise. Such experiments also might give rise, we thought, to the erroneous notion that the study regarded UFO phenomena *solely* as the result of misinterpretation of natural or man-made phenomena. Finally, we were advised by some of our experts in the psychological disciplines, that a "mock-up" UFO would introduce unknown variables that would render inconclusive any results derived from the conduct of experiments with it (see Section VI, Chapter 10).

Turning to the realm of psychiatry, we decided to refrain from mounting a major effort in this area on the ground that such a study

could not be given priority over other investigations. This decision was buttressed by the evidence that we rapidly gathered, pointing to the fact that only a very small proportion of sighters can be categorized as exhibiting psychopathology and that, therefore, there is no reason to consider them any more suitable for study than psychotic or psychoneurotic individuals who belong to any other statistical class of the population as a whole (see Section VI, Chapter 3).

18. Instrumentation for UFO Searches. As remarked earlier, the short duration of most UFO sightings, the delays in reporting them and the delays caused by communication and travel, make it essentially impossible that investigators can bring physical observing equipment to a report site quickly enough to make UFO observations in that way. There is another way that is often proposed for getting better observational data than is now available; namely, to set up a permanently manned network of observing stations at various places in the country to observe such UFOs as might come within their range.

Such a network of stations might be set up solely for the purpose of UFO study, or it might be established in conjunction with one of the networks of stations which exist for other astronomical or meteorological purposes. This latter alternative, of course, would be much less expensive than the former, or could give a greater coverage for the same expenditure.

We gave considerable attention to the possibilities and difficulties in this direction (Section VI, Chapter 9). At first we hoped that some definite results could be obtained by such cooperation with existing stations in a way that would make results available for this report.

An all-sky camera was operated during most of August 1967 at Harrisburg, Penna. during an UFO flap in that locality (Case 25) but no interesting results were found on some 9,000 photographs. It would be quite expensive to operate a network of such cameras on a routine basis all over the United States. The likelihood of interesting images being recorded would be very small. Because of the short duration of an UFO appearance a proper plan for use of the all-sky camera would involve frequent processing and examination of the film, otherwise the presence of an UFO would not be recognized until long after it had disappeared. This would greatly increase the cost of operation of such a network.

Another suggestion that is often made is to make UFO studies in connection with the radar networks operating in this country for air traffic control under auspices of the Federal Aviation Agency. Consideration was given to this possibility and it was concluded that it is quite out of the question to burden this network with additional duties of any kind. The air traffic control operators are now heavily burdened with the work of safely guiding civil and military aviation. During the summer of 1968 especially, the heavy overloads that sometimes exist on the system were emphasized by troublesome traffic delays in the neighborhood of several of the nation's major airports. It would be quite out of the question to ask the air traffic controllers to assume the responsibility of watching for UFOs in addition to their primary responsibilities. It would likewise be impracticable for a separate group of personnel to be installed at these stations to watch the same radars for UFOs.

The Prairie Network is a group of camera stations operated in the mid-west by the Smithsonian Institution in connection with the Harvard Meteor Program. Its primary purpose is to detect and record meteor trails in such a way as to guide a search for actual meteoritic bodies that strike the earth's surface. The field headquarters of this network is at Lincoln, Nebraska.

We prepared a listing of reported UFO sightings since 1965 that fell within the geographic limits of this network and through the kind cooperation of the Smithsonian Institution obtained the records of the network for the times and locations of these sightings. About half of the sightings were so lacking in specific information that, Frederick Ayer reports (1229) "even if an object had been recorded by the film it would have been impossible to correlate it with the sighting." About one-third of the sightings could not be traced on the film because of overcast skies. Some 18% of all the UFO sightings were identified on the network's records with a fair degree of probability. Nearly all of these were identified as astronomical objects. Some consideration was given to the costs and likelihood of success of adapting the Prairie Network instruments to UFO searches without interfering with their primary purpose. We think that something might be done along this line at reasonable expense, but we do not make a positive recommendation that such a program be undertaken because of the inconclusiveness of the information that we believe would be gathered.

Another existing program that was studied for unrecognized UFO records was that of scanning the night sky for study of air glow from the upper atmosphere, and of zodiacal light. Detailed study was made of two records obtained from a station on the Hawaiian Islands. One of these remains unidentified but is thought to be related to an artificial satellite for which no information is readily available. The other was definitely identified as a suborbital missile launched from Vandenberg AFB on the coast of southern California. Mr. Ayer concludes that "because of their relatively extensive sky coverage, scanning photometers can be considered useful instruments in the conduct of UFO searches." This, however, is not to be construed as a recommendation that a network of scanning photometer stations be established for this purpose.

Consideration was also given to the adaptability to UFO search purposes of radars of the type used by the Weather Bureau, and the radar station of the Radar Meteor Project of the Smithsonian Institution located near Havana, Illinois.

Although frequent claims are made in the UFO popular literature of magnetic disturbances due to the presence of UFOs, a consideration of various official magnetometer records produced no evidence of an effect of this kind that, in our judgment would warrant the setting up of an observational program to look for UFOs by their alleged magnetic effects.

19. Conclusion. In our study we gave consideration to every possibility that we could think of for getting objective scientific data about the kind of thing that is the subject of UFO reports. As the preceding summary shows, and as is fully documented in the detailed chapters which follow, all such efforts are beset with great difficulties. We place very little value for scientific purposes on the past accumulation of anecdotal records, most of which have been explained as arising from sightings of ordinary objects. Accordingly in Section I we have recommended against the mounting of a major effort for continuing UFO study for scientific reasons.

This conclusion is controversial. It will not be accepted without much dispute by the UFO amateurs, by the authors of popular UFO books and magazine articles, or even by a small number of academic scientists whose public statements indicate that they feel that this is a subject of great scientific promise.

We trust that out of the clash of opinions among scientists a policy decision will emerge. Current policy must be based on current knowledge and estimates of the probability that further efforts are likely to produce further additions to that knowledge. Additions to knowledge in the future may alter policy judgments either in the direction of greater, or of

less attention being paid to UFO phenomena than is being done at present.

We hope that the critical analysis of the UFO situation among scientists and government officials that must precede the determination of official policy can be carried out on a strictly objective basis.

Attacks on the integrity of various individuals on either side of this controversy ought to be avoided. The question of an individual's integrity is wholly distinct from the issue of what science should do in the future about UFOs.

In the Congress of the United States concern about the UFO problem from a defense viewpoint is the province of the House Committee on Armed Services. Concern about it from the point of view of the nation's scientific research program comes under the House Committee on Science and Astronautics. Here there seems to be a valid situation of overlapping jurisdictions because the UFO problem can be approached from both viewpoints.

A particular interest in the UFO problem has been shown by Congressman J. Edward Roush of Indiana, who is a member of the House Committee on Science and Astronautics. He performed a valuable service by arranging for the holding of a "Symposium on Unidentified Flying Objects" in Washington on 29 July 1968 (see references). As pointed out by one of the symposium participants, Prof. Carl Sagan of the department of astronomy of Cornell University, the presentations made in that symposium incline rather strongly to the side of belief that large-scale investigations of the UFO phenomenon ought to be supported in the expectation that they would be justified by what some speakers called "scientific paydirt."

We studied the transcript of this symposium with great care to see whether we would be led thereby to any new material related to this study. We did not find any new data.

Several of the contributors to that symposium have become trenchant advocates in the past several years of a continuing major government investment in an UFO program. Several have long urged a greater degree of congressional interest in this subject. The symposium of 29 July afforded them an occasion on which with the utmost seriousness they could put before the Congress and the public the best possible data and the most favorable arguments for larger government activity in this field.

Hence it is fair to assume that the statements presented in that symposium represent the maximum case that this group feels could be made. We welcome the fact that this symposium is available to the public and expect that its data and arguments will be compared with those in their report of this study by those whose duty it is to make responsible decisions in this area.

We have studied this symposium record with great care and find nothing in it which requires that we alter the conclusions and recommendations that we have presented in Section I, nor that we modify any presentation of the specific data contained in other sections of this report.

References:

Bailey, J. O. *Pilgrims through Space and Time—Trends and Patterns in Scientific and Utopian Fiction*, New York: Argus Books, 1947.

Bloecher, T. E. *Report of the UFO Wave of 1947*, Washington (?), 1967.

Cameron, A. G. W. *Interstellar Communication*, New York: Benjamin, 1963.

Hall, Richard H. *The UFO Evidence*, Washington: NICAP, 1964.

Keyhoe, Donald E. "Flying Saucers Are Real," *True*, 1950.

Lorenzen, Coral B. *The Great Flying Saucer Hoax*, New York: William-Frederick Press, 1962.

Lowell, Percival H. *Mars and Its Canals*, New York: The Macmillan Company, 1908.

Markowitz, William. "The Physics and Metaphysics of Unidentified Flying Objects," *Science*, 157 (1967), 1274–79.

Menzel, Donald H. *Flying Saucers*, Cambridge: Harvard University Press, 1952.

Menzel, Donald H., and Lyle G. Boyd. *The World of Flying Saucers*, New York: Doubleday, 1963.

Miller, Stanley L. "Production of Organic Compounds under Possible Primitive Earth Conditions," *Journal American Chemical Society*, 77 (1955), 2351–61.

Olsen, T. *The Reference for Outstanding UFO Sighting Reports*, Ridenwood, Maryland: UFOIRC, Inc.

Page, R. M. *The Origin of Radar*, Garden City, New York: Doubleday, Anchor Books, 1962.

Purcell, Edwin. "Radioastronomy and Communication through Space," *Brookhaven Lecture Series No. 1*, Brookhaven National Laboratory, New York, 16 November 1960.

Ruppelt, B. J. *The Report on Unidentified Flying Objects*, New York: Doubleday and Company, Ace Books, 1956.

Rush, J. H. *The Dawn of Life*, New York: Doubleday & Co., Inc. 1957 (also Signet Library of Science, New American Library, N.Y. 1962).

Salisbury, Frank B. "Martian Biology," *Science*, 136 (1962), 17–26.

Shklovskii, I. S. *Artificial Satellites of Mars and Riddle of the Martian Satellites*, Moskow: Komsomal'skaya Pravda, 1 May and 31 May 1959, English translation, FTD-T[-62-488-1], Wright Patterson AFB, 18 May 1962.

Shklovskii, I. S., and Carl Sagan. *Intelligent Life in the Universe*, San Francisco: Holden-Day, 1966.

Sullivan, Walter. *We Are Not Alone*, New York: McGraw-Hill Book Co., 1964, New York: New American Library (paperback edition), 1966.

U.S. Ninetieth Congress, Second Session, Hearings before the Committee on Science and Astronautics, 29 July 1968. *Symposium on Unidentified Flying Objects*, Washington: Govt. Print. Off., 1968.

Vallee, Jacques, and Janine Vallee. *Challenge to Science—The UFO Enigma*, Chicago: Henry Regnery Co., 1966.

Epilogue

Let Us Reflect

Thoughtful Inquiry on Twenty-Five Years of Skepticism

MICHAEL SHERMER

Skepticism dates back to the ancient Greeks, well captured in Socrates' famous quip that all he knew was that he knew nothing. Skepticism as nihilism, however, gets us nowhere, and thankfully, almost no one embraces it. The word *skeptic*, in fact, comes from the Greek *skeptikos*, for "thoughtful"—far from modern misconceptions of the word as meaning "cynical" or "nihilistic." According to the *Oxford English Dictionary*, *skeptical* has also been used to mean "inquiring," "reflective," and, with variations in the ancient Greek, "watchman" or "mark to aim at." What a glorious meaning for what we skeptics do! We are thoughtful, inquiring, and reflective, and in a way, we are the watchers who guard against bad ideas—consumer advocates of good thinking who, through the guidelines of science, establish the mark to aim at.

Since the time of the Greeks, skepticism (in its various incarnations) has evolved along with other epistemologies and their accompanying social activists. The Enlightenment, on one level, was a century-long skeptical movement, for there were no beliefs or institutions that did not come under the critical scrutiny of such great thinkers as Voltaire, Denis Diderot, Jean-Jacques Rousseau, John Locke, Thomas Jefferson, and many others. Immanuel Kant in Germany and David Hume in Scotland were skeptics' skeptics in an age of skepticism, and their influence continues unwaned to this day (at least in academic philosophy and skepticism). Closer to our time, Charles Darwin and Thomas Huxley were skeptics par excellence, not only for the revolution they launched and carried on, respectively, against the dogma of creationism but also for their stand against the burgeoning Spiritualism movement that was sweeping across the United States, England, and the Continent. (Darwin worked quietly behind the scenes, whereas Huxley railed publicly against the movement, bemoaning it in one of the great one-liners in the history of skepticism: "Better live a crossing-sweeper than die and be made to talk twaddle by a 'medium' hired at a guinea a seance.") In the 1900s, Bertrand Russell and Harry Houdini stand out as representative of the skeptical thinkers and doers, respectively, of the century's first half, and in the first year of its second half, Martin Gardner's *Fads and Fallacies in the Name of Science* launched what we think of today as "the skeptics."

We are at an appropriate time for reflection with this two-volume encyclopedia on science, pseudoscience, and skepticism. I date the modern skeptical movement to 1950, with the publication of an essay by Gardner in the *Antioch Review* entitled "The Hermit Scientist." The essay is about what we would today call pseudoscientists, and it was Gardner's first-ever publication of a skeptical nature. It launched a lifetime of critical analysis of fringe claims, and in 1952 (at the urging of his literary agent, John T. Elliott), Gardner expanded the article into a book-length treatment of the subject under the title *In the Name of Science*, with the descriptive subtitle *An Entertaining Survey of the High Priests and Cultists of Science, Past and Present*. Published by Putnam, the book sold so poorly that it was quickly remaindered, and it lay dormant until 1957, when it was republished by Dover. It has come down to us as *Fads and Fallacies in the Name of Science*, still in print and arguably *the* skeptic classic of the past half century.

What caught the attention of a youthful Martin Gardner half a century ago? The "hermit scientist" who worked alone and was usually ignored by mainstream scientists: "Such neglect, of course, only strengthens the convictions of the self-declared genius," Gardner concluded in his original 1950 paper. "Thus it is that probably no scientist of importance will present the bewildered public with detailed proofs that the earth did not twice stop whirling in Old Testament times, or that neuroses bear no relation to the experiences of an embryo in the mother's womb" (referring to L. Ron Hubbard's dianetics theory that negative engrams are imprinted in the fetus's brain while in the womb).

Gardner was, however, half wrong in his prognostications: "The current flurry of discussion about (Immanuel) Velikovsky and Hubbard will soon subside, and their books will begin to gather dust on library shelves." While Velikovskians are a quaint few surviving in the interstices of fringe culture, Hubbard has been canonized by the Church of Scientology and deified as the founding saint of a world religion.

In the first chapter of *In the Name of Science*, Gardner picked up where he left off, noting that "tens of thousands of mentally ill people throughout the country entered 'dianetic reveries' in which they moved back along their 'time track' and tried to recall unpleasant experiences they had when they were embryos." More than fifty years later, Scientology has converted those reveries into a worldwide cult of personality surrounding L. Ron Hubbard that targets celebrities for membership and generates hundreds of millions of dollars in tax-free revenue as an IRS-approved "religion."

Today, UFOs are big business, but in 1950, Gardner could not have known that the nascent flying-saucer craze would turn into an alien industry, but it was off to a good start: "Since flying saucers were first reported in 1947, countless individuals have been convinced that the earth is under observation by visitors from another planet." Absence of evidence then was no more a barrier to belief than it is today, and believers proffered the same conspiratorial explanations for the dearth of proof, as Gardner explained: "I have heard many readers of the saucer books upbraid the government in no uncertain terms for its stubborn refusal to release the 'truth' about the elusive platters. The administration's 'hush-hush policy' is angrily cited as proof that our military and political leaders have lost all faith in the wisdom of the American people."

From his perspective in 1950, Gardner was even then bemoaning the fact that some beliefs never seem to go out of vogue, as he recalled H. L. Mencken's quip from the 1920s that "if you heave an egg out of a Pullman car window anywhere in the United States you are likely to hit a fundamentalist."

Gardner cautioned that when presumably

religious superstition should be on the wane, it is all too easy "to forget that thousands of high school teachers of biology, in many of our southern states, are still afraid to teach the theory of evolution for fear of losing their jobs." Today, Kansas and other states enjoin the fight as the creationist virus spreads northward.

I devote an entire chapter in my book *The Borderlands of Science* to Martin Gardner and his seminal work, but suffice it to say here that *Fads and Fallacies in the Name of Science* has been a cherished classic read by legions of skeptics and scientists, and it laid the foundation for a bona fide skeptical movement that found its roots in the early 1970s. There has been some debate (and much quibbling) about who gets what amount of credit for the founding of the Committee for the Scientific Investigation of Claims of the Paranormal (CSICOP) and its journal, *Skeptical Inquirer* (much of this played out in the pages of *Skeptic* magazine in our interviews with the major players). This is not the place to present a definitive history of the movement, but from what I have gleaned from first- and secondhand sources, Gardner, magician James Randi, psychologist Ray Hyman, and philosopher Paul Kurtz played key roles in the foundation and planning of the organization, with numerous others, such as Phil Klass and Marcello Truzzi, in important supporting roles.

The founding of the Skeptics Society by myself, Pat Linse, and Kim Ziel Shermer in 1992, then, was also not without precedent and historical roots, and though the history of this organization has yet to be written, it is clear that without the likes of Gardner, Randi, Hyman, and Kurtz, there would be no Skeptics Society and no *Skeptic* magazine. And what an experience it has been.

Twenty-five years ago, I was twenty years old and in my third year of college at Pepperdine University, a Church of Christ–based institution located in Malibu, California, and overlooking the Pacific Ocean. Although the site was certainly a motivating factor in my choice of a college, the primary reason I went there was that I was a born-again Christian who took his mission for Christ seriously. I thought I should attend a school where I could receive some serious theological training, and I did. I took courses in the Old and New Testaments, Jesus the Christ, and the writings of C. S. Lewis. I attended chapel twice a week (although, truth be told, attendance was required for all students). Dancing was not allowed on campus (the sexual suggestiveness might trigger already-inflamed hormone production to go into overdrive), and we were not allowed into the dorm rooms of members of the opposite sex.

Despite the restrictions, it was a good experience because I was a serious believer and thought that was the way we should behave anyway. But somewhere along the way, I found science, and that changed everything (although not overnight). I was thinking of majoring in theology, but then I discovered that a Ph.D. required proficiency in several dead languages (Hebrew, Greek, Aramaic, and Latin). Knowing that I was not especially good at learning live languages, let alone dead ones, I went into psychology and mastered one of the languages of science: statistics. There (and in research methodology courses), I discovered that many problems can be solved by establishing parameters to determine whether a hypothesis is probably right (i.e., rejecting the null hypothesis at the .01, or 99 percent, level of significance) or definitely wrong (i.e., not statistically significant). Instead of the rhetoric and disputation of theology, there were the logic and probabilities of science. What a difference this difference in thinking makes!

By the end of my first year of a graduate program in experimental psychology at the California State University, Fullerton, I had deconverted out of Christianity and removed my silver ichthus, replacing what was for me the stultifying dogmas of a 2,000-year-old religion with the worldview of an always changing, always fresh science. The passionate nature of this perspective was enthused most emphatically by my evolutionary biology professor, Bayard Brattstrom, particularly in his after-class discussions at a local bar that went into the wee hours of the morning. This is where the action was for me.

About that time (1975–1976), Uri Geller showed up on my radar screen. I recall *Psychology Today* and other popular magazines published glowing stories about him, and reports were afloat that experimental psychologists had tested the Israeli psychic and determined that he was genuine. My adviser—a strictly reductionistic Skinnerian behavioral psychologist named Doug Navarick—didn't believe a word of it, but I figured there might be something to the Geller phenomenon, especially in light of all the other interesting research being conducted on altered states of consciousness, hypnosis, dreams, sensory deprivation, dolphin communication (John C. Lilly), and the like. I took a course in anthropology from a woman who researched shamans of South America and their use of mind-altering plants. It all seemed entirely plausible to me, and, being personally interested in the paranormal (the Ouija board consistently blew my mind), I figured that this was rapidly becoming a legitimate subfield of psychological research. After all, Thelma Moss had a research laboratory devoted to studying the paranormal, and it was at the University of California, Los Angeles (UCLA), no less, which had one of the most highly regarded psychology programs in the country.

Enter James "the Amazing" Randi. I do not recall exactly when or where I first encountered him. I believe it was on the *Tonight Show* when he was demonstrating how to levitate tables, bend spoons, and perform psychic surgeries. He didn't convince me to become a full-fledged skeptic overnight, but he got me thinking that if some of the psychics were

fakes, perhaps they all were (and if not fakes, at least self-deceived). Herein lies an important lesson. There is little to no chance that we can convince True Believers of the errors of their thinking. Our purpose is to reach that vast middle ground between hard-core skeptics and dogmatic believers—people like me who thought that there might be something to these claims but had simply never heard a good counterexplanation. There are many reasons why people believe weird things, but certainly one of the most pervasive is simply that most people have never heard a good explanation for the weird things they hear and read about. Short of a good explanation, they accept the bad explanation that is typically proffered. This fact alone justifies all the hard work performed by skeptics toward the cause of science and critical thinking. It does make a difference.

Fast-forward ten years. My first contact with organized skepticism came in the mid-1980s through the famed aeronautics engineer and human-powered flight inventor Paul Mac-Cready. I originally met Paul through the International Human Powered Vehicle Association (IHPVA), as he was interested in designing these vehicles and I was interested in racing them (I had a ten-year career as an ultramarathon cyclist). One day, he phoned to invite me to a lecture at the California Institute of Technology being hosted by a group called the Southern California Skeptics (SCS). This was an offshoot of CSICOP and one of many groups that had spontaneously self-organized around the country throughout the 1980s. The lectures were fascinating, and because of my affiliation with Paul, I got to meet some of the insiders in what was rapidly becoming the "skeptical movement." Paul was a friend of such science megastars as Richard Feynman, Stephen Jay Gould, and Murray Gell-Mann, and with the likes of Randi and the magicians Penn and Teller affiliated with the movement, it seemed like it was a happening place to be.

In 1987, CSICOP hosted a convention at the Pasadena Civic Center that featured Carl Sagan as the keynote speaker, and he was so inspiring that I decided to return to graduate school to complete my doctorate.

By the end of the 1980s, however, the Southern California Skeptics folded, and the skeptical movement came to a grinding halt in the very place that so desperately needed it. In 1991, I completed my Ph.D., was teaching part-time at Occidental College, and was nosing around for something different to do. I had just published a paper in a science history journal on the Louisiana creationism trial; it featured the activities of SCS members who had organized the amicus curiae brief that was signed by seventy-two Nobel laureates (Murray Gell-Mann encouraged his fellow Nobelists) and was submitted to (and read by) the U.S. Supreme Court. One of SCS's former volunteer staff members, Pat Linse, heard about the paper, tracked me down, and dropped by to pick up a reprint of my article.

During that visit, she expressed her frustration—and that of many others—that skepticism in southern California had gone the way of the Neanderthals. Subsequent meetings with her and others inspired Kim, Pat, and me to jumpstart the skeptics movement again by launching a new group and inviting James Randi for our inaugural lecture in March 1992. The event was a smashing success, as well over 400 people crammed into a 300-seat hall to hear the amazing one astonish us all with his wit, wisdom, and magic.

With that successful event, we were off and running. I starting planning a newsletter, but when Pat saw a sample copy of a bicycle magazine I was publishing—*Ultra Cycling* magazine (the publication of the Ultra-Marathon Cycling Association and Race across America, which I had cofounded in the early 1980s), which was 64 pages long, perfect-bound, and with a duotone coated cover—she said that if we could splurge for a skeptical publication of that quality, she would provide the appropriate artwork and typography. Since Pat is a professional artist who was working for movie studios generating film posters, she was more than capable of backing up her offer, which I accepted.

Our original cover was to feature Randi, and Pat produced a striking portrait of him. But just before publication, Isaac Asimov died, so Pat generated a new cover portrait, and that became the cover of volume 1, number 1, of what we came to call *Skeptic* magazine. (My originally planned title—*The Journal of Rational Skepticism*—was voted down by Pat and my wife, Kim Ziel Shermer, who reasoned that shorter is better. They were right.)

Allow me to close this epilogue with a quote from one of my favorite skeptical books, Paul Kurtz's *The Transcendental Temptation* and his discussion of the meaning and goals of skepticism. It is an admonition we should all bear in mind, a passage to be read once a year:

> The skeptic is not passionately intent on converting mankind to his or her point of view and surely is not interested in imposing it on others, though he may be deeply concerned with raising the level of education and critical inquiry in society. Still, if there are any lessons to be learned from history, it is that we should be skeptical of all points of view, including those of the skeptics. No one is infallible, and no one can claim a monopoly on truth or virtue. It would be contradictory for skepticism to seek to translate itself into a new faith. One must view with caution the promises of any new secular priest who might emerge promising a brave new world—if only his path to clarity and truth is followed. Perhaps the best we can hope for is to temper the intemperate and to tame the perverse temptation that lurks within.

Amen, brother!

Contributors

John Adams (The Alien Archetype: The Origin of the "Grays") is a professor of history at Alabama A & M University. He has written an article titled "Outer Space and the New World in the Imagination of Eighteenth-Century Europeans." He teaches courses in ancient and modern world civilizations, British history, and Asian history, and has written a book on the dynamics between science fiction in early modern Europe and attitudes toward race and ethnicity among early Copernicans.

D. Alan Bensley (Pseudoscience and Science: A Primer in Critical Thinking) is an associate professor of psychology at Frostburg State University in Frostburg, Maryland. He is the author of the textbook *Critical Thinking in Psychology: A Unified Skills Approach* and has done extensive research on the improvement of thinking skills. His research and teaching interests are in research methods, sensation and perception, and cognition and critical thinking.

John Berger (Handwriting Analysis and Graphology) is an expert on handwriting analysis and graphology and a long-time investigator of unusual claims.

Susan J. Blackmore (Memes as Good Science, Out-of-Body Experiences, Near-Death Experiences) is a senior lecturer in psychology at the University of the West of England and a long-time researcher on the paranormal. She is the author of *The Adventures of a Parapsychologist, Beyond the Body, Dying to Live,* and *The Meme Machine.* She is one of the best known and most highly regarded skeptical investigators in the world today.

Jon Blumenfeld (Stock Market Pseudoscience) is Connecticut chapter chairman of the New England Skeptical Society, and is a regular contributor to its quarterly newsletter, *The New England Journal of Skepticism.* He has ten years of experience as a bond trader and commodity trading advisor and is currently an interest rate strategist for the United States' fixed income derivatives trading unit of a large European bank.

Chris Bonds (Synchronicity) teaches music at Wayne State College, Wayne, Nebraska. His interests include music, psychology, the paranormal, and the theory of evolution.

Rebecca Bradley (Tutankhamun's Curse) has a doctorate in archeology, specializing in the Nile Valley. Her other personas include fantasy writer (*The Gil Trilogy*), horror writer, and disaster voyeur.

Maarten Brys (Bermuda Triangle) studied the philosophy of science. He's a member of SKEPP and SKEPSIS, two skeptical organizations in Belgium and the Netherlands, and he is interested in finding scientific explanations for apparently paranormal phenomena.

Tim Callahan (Anastasia: A Case Study in the Myth of the Miraculous Survival) is the religion editor for *Skeptic* magazine and a longtime contributor to skeptical and humanist publications. He is the author of *Bible Prophecy: Failure or Fulfillment?* and his latest book is *The Secret Origins of the Bible*. His research interests are in comparative mythology, creationism, environmental issues, and biblical criticism.

Steuart Campbell (Ball Lightning) is a science writer from Edinburgh, Scotland, whose work has appeared in the *New Humanist* and *Skeptic*. He is also the author of *The UFO Mystery Solved* and *The Rise and Fall of Jesus*.

Al Carroll (Shamans and Shamanism) is in the Ph.D. program in American Indian history at Arizona State University. He received his master's degree from Purdue University. He is a Native American activist and co-founder of New Age Frauds Plastic Shamans (NAFPS), a watchdog organization devoted to warning the public about frauds impersonating as Native American medicine people. His research interests include Native American veterans, the modern practice of Native American beliefs, and Native American/New Age conflict.

John Casti (Science Is Just Beginning) is executive editor of the journal *Complexity*, a fellow of the Santa Fe Institute in Santa Fe, New Mexico, and a professor at the Technical University of Vienna. He is the author of *Searching for Certainty, Paradigms Lost, Complexification*, and other science books.

Drew Christie (Séance, Societies for Psychical Research) is a professor of philosophy at the University of New Hampshire, where he teaches environmental philosophy, logic, philosophy of law, and social and political philosophy. His research interests also encompass American pragmatism (old and new) and the philosophy of education. His recent work includes "Dewey and the Splintered Vision"; encyclopedia entries, "Richard Rorty" and "Chauncey Wright"; and reviews of websites devoted to the classical pragmatists Peirce, James, and Dewey. He is currently a member of the local school board and is working to meaningfully integrate computers into the K-12 curriculum.

Brad Clark (Spiritualism) has studied spiritualism and the spiritual movement in the United Kingdom and America.

Kevin Courcey (Prayer and Healing) is a registered nurse who has practiced for 22 years. He has spent 15 years as a psychiatric nurse and six years in phone triage answering questions about medical problems ranging from lacerations to fevers to chest pain. He has also chaired an 800-nurse bargaining unit and been a board member of the Oregon Nurses Association. He is a member of Freedom From Religion Foundation and is active in the Corvallis Secular Society in Oregon.

Chris Cunningham (The Shroud of Turin) is interested in applying science to miracles and to claims of the paranormal.

Geoffrey Dean (Astrology, Placebo Effect, Undeceiving Ourselves) coedited with Arthur Mather *Recent Advances in Natal Astrology: A Critical Review 1900–1976*, the first book-length critical review of scientific research into astrology. He and Mather have been collaborators since 1975 on critical articles, debates, surveys, and prize competitions for research in astrology. Dean is a freelance technical writer and editor in Perth, Western Australia.

Perry DeAngelis (Cults, Dowsing) is the executive director of the New England Skeptical Society. His interests are in field investigations of paranormal and pseudoscientific claims.

Tana Dineen (Psychotherapy as Pseudoscience) is a licensed psychologist with three decades of clinical experience. Early in her career she became concerned about the growing influence of mental health "experts" on society, which lead her to write her controversial book: *Manufacturing Victims: What the Psychology Industry Is Doing to People.*

Clayton J. Drees (Witches and Witchcraft) is associate professor of history and chair of the history department at Virginia Wesleyan College in Norfolk, Virginia. He teaches courses on the medieval and early modern periods in Europe and has published two books, *Authority and Dissent in the English Church* (1997) and *The Late Medieval Age of Crisis and Renewal* (2001).

Dan Dugan (Anthroposophy and Anthroposophical Medicine) is well known in the field of audio engineering as the inventor of the automatic microphone mixer. His patented equipment is used in thousands of churches, courtrooms (including the U.S. Supreme Court), and on television shows, including *The Late Show with David Letterman* and *Hollywood Squares*. In addition to engineering, Dan has a lively interest in philosophy, particularly skepticism, the philosophy of science, and current controversies about scientific paradigms and alternative medicine.

Chris Duva (Anomalous Psychological Experiences) is an assistant professor of biological psychology at Eastern Oregon University and an adjunct faculty member at Capella University. His research interests include false memory, brain damage-induced amnesia, and the physiological basis of drug addiction.

Jon Entine (Race and Sports as Good Science) wrote and produced a widely acclaimed 1989 NBC television special with Tom Brokaw on black athletes. This led to the publication of his controversial book *Taboo: Why Black Athletes Dominate Sports and Why We're Afraid to Talk about It*. His next two projects focused on genetics: *Jewish Genes* examines the effort to identify medical cures for diseases that disproportionately effect specific populations, including the social and political tempest stirred by such research; and *Creating Superboy (and Girl)*, which looks at the impact of genetic engineering on human performance in athletics and elsewhere.

Garrett G. Fagan (Alternative Archaeology) is associate professor of classics and ancient Mediterranean studies and history at Penn State University. Aside from the phenomenon of pseudoarchaeology, his research interests lie mainly in Roman history. His first book *Bathing in Public in the Roman World* was published in 1999.

Kenneth Feder (Ancient Astronauts, The Mars Face: Extraterrestrial Archaeology, Pseudoarchaeology: Native American Myths as a Test Case) is a professor of anthropology at Central Connecticut State University. He is the director of the Farmington River Archaeological Project and the author of several books including: *The Past in Perspective: An Introduction to Human Prehistory; A Village of Outcasts: Historical Archaeology and Documentary Research at the Lighthouse Site;* and *Frauds, Myths, and Mysteries: Science and Pseudoscience in Archaeology.*

Robert A. Forde (Hypnosis) is a chartered psychologist and over the last 30 years has worked in prisons and police services. He is now in private practice in North Somerset, England, specializing in forensic and health psychology. His special interests are researching suggestibility (especially in police interviews), psychological trauma, and malingering.

Ronald Fritze (Pseudoarchaeology: Precolumbian Discoverers of America as a Test

Case) is a professor of history at Lamar University in Beaumont, Texas. He received his Ph.D. from Cambridge University and is one of the authors of *Reference Sources in History, Reflections on Western Civilization*, and *Reflections on World Civilization*. He is also editor of *The Historical Dictionary of Stuart England*.

Diego Golombek (Biorhythms) is professor of physiology and a researcher at the National University of Quilmes (where he heads the Chronobiology Lab), the University of Buenos Aires, and the National Research Council (Buenos Aires, Argentina). He has published extensively on circadian rhythms and general science topics.

Gina Green (Facilitated Communication) was director of research at the New England Center for Autism and Associate Scientists in the behavioral sciences division of the E. K. Shriver Center for Mental Retardation. She has written extensively on facilitated communication and was one of the first scientists to submit facilitated communication to scientific analysis. The book she most recently edited is *Behavioral Intervention for Young Children with Autism: A Manual for Parents and Professionals*.

Diane Halpern (Race and I.Q. as Pseudoscience) is director of the Berger Institute for Work, Family, and Children and professor of psychology at Claremont McKenna College. She is the author of several hundred journal articles and many books, including *Thought and Knowledge: An Introduction to Critical Thinking and Sex Differences in Cognitive Abilities*. Her teaching and research have been recognized with many awards including the 2002 Outstanding Teaching Award from Western Psychological Association, the American Psychological Foundation Award for Distinguished Teaching, the American Psychological Association Award for Distinguished Career

Contributions to Education and Training, and the Outstanding Professor Award from California State University (state-wide).

Alan Harris (Tunguska) is a former scientist at NASA's Jet Propulsion Laboratory in Pasadena, California, and is now a senior research scientist with the Space Science Institute. His research specialty is studying small bodies of the solar system such as satellites, asteroids, comets, and meteors. His long-time interest lies in studying the risks of cosmic impacts on the Earth.

Steve B. Harris (Immortality: The Search for Everlasting Life) is an internist and experimental physiologist who is particularly interested in issues of life extension and the philosophy of science. He is a long-time member of the Skeptics Society's editorial board, and is chief of research at Critical Care Research, Inc., a southern California biotech company that is developing advanced resuscitation technologies.

Michael Heap (Ideomotor Effect [the "Ouija Board" Effect]) is a freelance clinical and forensic psychologist in Sheffield, England, and chairman of the Association for Skeptical Enquiry. He has a special interest in hypnosis and is the coauthor of *Hypnosis in Therapy* and *Hartland's Medical and Dental Hypnosis* and the coeditor of *Hypnosis: Current Clinical, Experimental and Forensic Practices*, and *Hypnotherapy: A Handbook* and *Hypnosis in Europe*.

John Hochman (Recovered Memory Therapy and False Memory Syndrome: A Psychiatrist's Perspective as a Test Case) is a practicing psychiatrist in Los Angeles, California. He specializes in the evaluation and treatment of victims of cultic entities and/or undue influence; the theoretical study of cult phenomena, psychiatry and the law; post-traumatic stress disorders, and multiple personality disorder, of which he is skeptical. He is a consultant and expert witness in courtroom cases involving abuse allegations, coercive persuasion, and psychotherapy cult involvement.

Samuel Homola (Chiropractic: Conventional or Alternative Healing?) retired in 1998 after 43 years of full-time practice as a chiropractor. He is the author of 12 books, including *Inside Chiropractic: A Patient's Guide*. He has written numerous articles for magazines and journals, including "Finding a Good Chiropractor," published in *Archives of Family Medicine*.

John Horgan (Science Is at an End) was a senior writer at *Scientific American* from 1986 to 1997 and is now a freelance writer whose work has appeared in the *New York Times*, *Time*, the *Washington Post*, *Science*, the *London Times*, the *New Republic*, *Discover*, *Slate*, and elsewhere. His books include T*he End of Science* (1996), T*he Undiscovered Mind* (1999), and *Rational Mysticism* (2003).

Satyam Jain (Magnetic Therapy) is a resident in psychiatry at Brown University and a research fellow in psychiatry at Creighton University Medical.

William Jarvis (Homeopathy) is a professor at Loma Linda University with dual appointments in the schools of medicine and public health and a secondary appointment in the school of dentistry. He is a consumer health education specialist and is involved in a wide variety of activities related to this field. He is president of the National Council Against Health Fraud, a nonprofit voluntary health agency that combats health misinformation, fraud, and quackery. He is also a member of the American Cancer Society's National Committee on Questionable Methods of Cancer Management and the California attorney general's Task Force on Health Fraud.

Simon Jones (Uri Geller) has written articles and interviews related to paranormal claims and fringe beliefs. His award-winning interview with Uri Geller can be found online at: www.simon-jones.org.uk.

Professor Ivan W. Kelly (Astrology, Placebo Effect, Undeceiving Ourselves) chairman of the Astrology Subcommittee of the United States-based Committee for the Scientific Investigation of Claims of the Paranormal, and author or coauthor of over one hundred scientific or philosophical articles. He is professor of educational psychology at the University of Saskatchewan, Saskatoon, Canada, and is especially interested in philosophical aspects of science.

Steven Korenstein (Electromagnetic Fields and Cell Phones) holds a master's degree in environmental and occupational health and works as a hazardous substances scientist for the California Environmental Protection Agency in the department of toxic substances control. He has recently published a study on the health of children in the *Journal of Environmental Health*. His research interests include the effects of exposure to environmental toxicants at the community level.

David J. W. Lauridsen Jr. (Fairies, Elves, Pixies, and Gnomes) is currently a technical analyst and web developer for Qwest Communications. He holds a bachelor's degree in communications from Ohio State University and is an increasingly ardent skeptic. An avid private pilot, David is excited by the philosophy of science and would like to expand the teaching of critical thinking skills to today's youth.

Bernard Leikind (Science and God) is a senior editor of *Skeptic* magazine. He lives in Encinitas, California, and works for a San Diego area software company. Previously, he worked as a physicist for General Atomics and as a plasma physics and fusion energy researcher at UCLA. He achieved notoriety through his investigation and explanation of firewalking, a stunt that he foolishly performed many times. In one imaginative and astonishing experiment, he demonstrated that raw steaks have the same mental powers as human firewalkers. His research interests also include unusual atmospheric phenomena and other unexplained anomalies.

Norman Levitt (The Science Wars: Deconstructing Science Is Pseudoscience) is a professor of mathematics at Rutgers University in New Brunswick, New Jersey. He specializes in geometric topology. He is the coauthor with Paul R. Gross of the controversial book *Higher Superstition: The Academic Left and Its Quarrels with Science*, and *The Flight from Science and Reason*.

Ricki Lewis (Dietary Supplements) is the author of *Human Genetics: Concepts and Applications*, coauthor of three other textbooks for McGraw-Hill Higher Education, and a contributing editor to *The Scientist*. She has a Ph.D. in genetics and is affiliated with the TIGR Center for the Advancement of Genomics.

Scott O. Lilienfeld (EMDR, Multiple Personality Disorder) is associate professor of psychology at Emory University, founder and editor-in-chief of the journal, *The Scientific Review of Mental Health Practice*, and past president of the Society for a Science of Clinical Psychology. His research interests include the causes and assessment of personality disorders, anxiety disorders, and dissociative disorders, and the problem of pseudoscience in clinical psychology and allied disciplines.

Andrew O. Lutes (Animal Mutilations) has a bachelor's degree in history from Northern Kentucky University and a master's in library science from Kent State University. He writes letters and essays constantly and reads every issue of both Skeptic and Skeptical Inquirer (which he indexes) cover to cover.

Steven Jay Lynn (Multiple Personality Disorder) is professor of psychology at the State University of New York at Binghamton. He edited a book series on trauma, memory, hypnosis, and dissociation for the American Psychological Association; was consulting editor for the *Journal of Abnormal Psychology*; and was guest editor for *Current Directions in Psychological Science*. He is on the editorial board of Scientific Review of Mental Health Practices and is a fellow of the American Psychological Association, the American Psychological Society, the American Association of Applied and Preventive Psychology, and the Society for Clinical and Experimental Hypnosis. He has published more than 200 books, articles, and chapters in the areas of hypnosis, memory, sexual abuse, risk prevention, dissociation and fantasy, and forensic psychology.

Kevin MacDonald (Psychoanalysis as Pseudoscience) received his Ph.D. in personality development at the University of Connecticut. He is a professor of psychology at California State University–Long Beach. His research emphasizes evolutionary perspectives in personality, child development, and ethnic relations. He is the author of *Social and Personality Development: An Evolutionary Synthesis, A People That Shall Dwell Alone, Separation and Its Discontents, Sociobiological Perspectives on Human Development,* and *Parent-Child Play.*

Barry Markovsky (UFOs) is professor and chair of the department of sociology at the University of South Carolina. In addition to his interest in how social factors influence paranormal beliefs, he has published research on social power, status processes, perceptions of justice, social influence, group solidarity, social networks, and methods for theory construction.

Juan Carlos Marvizon (Meditation) is assistant professor in the department of medicine, UCLA. He is an author of thirty research papers on neurotransmission and the physiology of pain, contributes to *Skeptic* magazine, and moderates the Skeptic Forum (http://forums.delphiforums.com/skepticforum/start). He has practiced different forms of meditation for 25 years. His interests are on topics related to the brain and the mind, including acupuncture, meditation and consciousness

Arthur Mather (Astrology, Undeceiving Ourselves) coedited with Geoffrey Dean *Recent Advances in Natal Astrology: A Critical Review 1900–1976,* the first book-length critical review of scientific research into astrology. He and Dean have been collaborators since 1975 on critical articles, debates, surveys, and prize competitions for research into astrology. Mather is in charge of technical training projects in Livingston, Scotland.

William F. McComas (Science and Its Myths) is an associate professor of science education at the Rossier School of Education of the University of Southern California where he is also the founding director of the Program to Advance Science Education. He teaches courses in educational research, issues in science education, and advanced science teaching methods. He maintains an active research program focusing on the improvement of laboratory instruction, evolution education, the impact of the philosophy of science on science teaching, and science learning in museums and field sites.

Richard J. McNally (EMDR) is professor of psychology in the department of psychology at Harvard University. He is the author of more than 165 publications, mostly concerning anxiety and traumatic stress disorders. McNally served with the American Psychiatric Association's subgroup on post-traumatic stress disorder for the 4th edition of the *Diagnostic and Statistical Manual.*

Jean Mercer (Attachment Therapy) has a Ph.D. in psychology from Brandeis University. She is professor of psychology at Richard Stockton College and president of the New Jersey Association for Infant Mental Health. Together with Larry Sarner and Linda Rosa, she recently completed a book on a death caused by attachment therapists, and has published several related journal articles.

Frank Miele (Evolutionary Psychology as Good Science) is senior editor of *Skeptic* magazine and author of *Jensenism and Skepticism.* His interviews of the major figures in and introductions to the IQ, evolutionary psychology, and environmental debates are featured regularly in *Skeptic* (and include E. O. Wilson, Richard Dawkins, Charles Murray, Jerry Brown, Lionel Tiger, and many others.) He is also a technical writer in the silicon valley.

Robert L. Miller (Christian Science as Pseudoscience) is a trial attorney in southern California, and runs a law firm called Robert Miller & Associates. He holds a Juris Doctor degree from Western State University College of Law and has written articles for various newspapers and magazines on a variety of subjects.

Richard Milner (Piltdown Man [Hoax]), contributing editor of *Natural History Magazine* at the American Museum of Natural History, is the author of *The Encyclopedia of Evolution: Humanity's Quest for Its Origins.* A historian of science and anthropology, he also wrote the acclaimed one-man musical Charles Darwin: Live & In Concert, which he performs all over the world.

Phil Molé (Carlos Castenada, Holistic Medicine: The Case of Caroline Myss) has a bachelor's degree in chemistry from DePaul University, where he minored in biology and mathematics. He earned a master's in public health from the University of Illinois at Chicago, and works at an environmental consulting company in Elmhurst, Illinois. He is a regular contributor to *Skeptic* magazine.

Douglas G. Mook (Observer Effects and Observer Bias) is professor of psychology emeritus at the University of Virginia, where he taught courses in research methodology for a number of years, and is now adjunct professor at Cooper Union College. He is author of *Motivation: The Organization of Action,* and *Psychological Research: The Ideas Behind the Methods.*

John L. Moore (Cryptozoology) is studying biology and geology at the University of Utah. He was formerly the associate editor of *The Cryptozoology Review,* and his research interests include invertebrate paleontology and archaeology.

David Morrison (Velikovsky: Cultures in Collision on the Fringes of Science) is a NASA research space scientist and was one of Carl Sagan's first doctoral students at Harvard University. His research interests include near-earth asteroids and how to detect them, as well as Immanuel Velikovsky and his influence on astronomy and the sciences.

John Mosley (Planetary Alignments) is an astronomer at the Griffith Observatory in Los Angeles where he supervises the educational programs. He has produced 50 public planetarium shows, including the *Star of Bethlehem.* He specializes in amateur astronomy and astronomical computer software.

Steve Novella (Cults, Dowsing) is an assistant professor of neurology at Yale University School of Medicine, president of the New England Skeptical Society and editor of the *New England Journal of Skepticism.* His interests are in medical fraud and skeptical philosophy.

Richard Olson (Witchcraft and The Origins of Science, The Science Wars: Deconstructing Science Is Good Science) is professor of history and Willard W. Keith Fellow in humanities at Harvey Mudd College and the 2002–2003 Hennebach Visiting Professor in humanities at the Colorado School of Mines. His publications include *Science Deified* (vol 1, 1982; vol. 2, 1990) and *The Emergence of the Social Sciences* (1993). He is currently working on a reference volume on science and religion in the Christian West: 1450–1900 and is series editor for a fourteen volume reference series on science and religion of which that work will be a part.

Laura Pasley (Recovered Memory Therapy and False Memory Syndrome: A Patient's Perspective as a Test Case) worked for the Dallas police department, retiring in January 1999 following a 25 year career. She was the first person to sue a therapist for inducing false memories and creating an unhealthy dependence. Her story was published in the book *True Stories of False Memories.*

Mark Pendergrast (Recovered Memory Therapy and False Memory Syndrome: A Father's Perspective as a Test Case) is an independent scholar and author living in Vermont. His books include *Victims of Memory, For God, Country and Coca-Cola,* and *Uncommon Grounds.* He is working on a history of mirrors.

Massimo Pigliucci (Science and Religion) is assistant professor in the departments of botany, ecology, and evolutionary biology at the University of Tennessee in Knoxville. His research focuses on the ecology and evolution of genotype-environment interactions. He is the author of several textbooks, as well as a book on creationism entitled *Evolution Denial*.

James W. Polichak (Memes as Pseudoscience) has a Ph.D. in experimental psychology at SUNY Stony Brook where his research focused on the comprehension of noun phrases and on auditory attention. He writes about science and education and their impacts on people's daily lives.

Gary P. Posner (Police Psychics: Noreen Renier as a Case Study) practiced internal medicine for 15 years. He founded the Tampa Bay Skeptics in 1988 and is editor of its newsletter. He is a consultant to the Committee for the Scientific Investigation of Claims of the Paranormal and is a member of the Board of Scientific and Policy advisers of the American Council on Science and Health.

Mark Pratarelli (Polygraph and Lie Detection) is associate professor of psychology at Colorado State University–Pueblo, the director of the Cognitive Neuroscience Laboratory, and author of *Niche Bandits*. His research interests include memory, language and the brain, as well as the evolution of human behavior.

Jon Puro (Feng Shui) is a computer programmer, freelance writer, and classical pianist and composer. He lived in Japan for over five years studying Japanese language and culture, and his research interests include Asian culture and history, philosophy, and the sociological and psychological implications of religious belief systems.

James Randi (The Liquefying "Blood" of St. Januarius, Pseudoscience and the Paranormal) 74, is a MacArthur Prize winner, a professional magician who has now turned his attention to the examination of paranormal, supernatural, and occult claims. He is president and founder of the James Randi Educational Foundation

(www.randi.org) and he lectures all over the world. His books, such as *Flim Flam!* and *The Faith Healers*, have been published in English, Chinese, Japanese, Korean, French, German, Italian, Spanish, Polish, Hungarian, and Norwegian.

Todd C. Riniolo (Psi and Psi-Missing) is an assistant professor of psychology at Medaille College in Buffalo, New York. His research interests include quantitative issues in psychophysiological research, the history of psychology, and teaching of psychology. His work has appeared in publications such as *Psychophysiology*, *Infant Behavior and Development*, *Teaching of Psychology*, and *Skeptic*.

Lance Rivers (Alien Abductions) is an assistant professor of English at Lake Superior State University in Sault Sainte Marie, Michigan, where he chairs the School of English and Speech's Writing Studies Committee. He has presented conference papers nationally on the misuse of scientific theories in literary and composition studies, especially postmodern misreadings of chaos theory. His research interests include the intersection between science and the study of composition, the rhetoric of reports of the paranormal, and alien abduction narratives as folklore.

Russell Robinson (Earthquake Prediction) is a senior seismologist at the New Zealand Institute of Geological and Nuclear Sciences. He holds a Ph.D. in geophysics from Stanford University and has published over 40 scientific papers. His research interests are in earthquake forecasting, seismicity and geologic structure of the New Zealand region, and computer modeling of seismicity.

Ben S. Roesch (Cryptozoology) is a B.Sc (Hons.) marine biology student at the University of Guelph and was formerly the editor of *The Cryptozoology Review*. His research interests include deep-sea biology, shark biology, and environmental and comparative physiology and biochemistry.

Gerald M. Rosen (EMDR) practices clinical psychology in Seattle, Washington and holds a joint appointment as clinical associate professor in the departments of psychology and psychiatry at the University of Washington. He received Level I and Level II training in EMDR from Dr. Shapiro, and has been writing commentaries and reviews on the method ever since. He has authored more than 50 scientific publications.

Rebecca Rush (Subliminal Perception and Advertising) teaches world studies and geography at Lockport Township High School. In addition, she has worked as a film researcher on numerous historical documentaries and is also an advocate for media literacy.

Charles Salas and Danielle Salas (Mesmerism: "Report of the Commissioners Charged by the King to Examine Animal Magnetism," by Benjamin Franklin and Antonie Lavoisier). Charles is research project analyst at the Getty Research Institute for the History of Art and the Humanities. He received his Ph.D. in modern intellectual history from the Claremont Graduate University. Both he and his wife, Danielle Salas, are particularly interested in eighteenth-century French studies.

Vince Sarich (Race and I.Q. as Good Science) has been a faculty member in the department of anthropology at U.C. Berkeley since 1966. He is best known for his work in molecular dating in which he found that the accumulation of immunological differences among albumins occurred as a regular function of time. His current research centers on racial variation within the human species in which he suggests that while the species may be relatively old, races are young with most of the in-terpopulational variation having developed within the last 15,000 to 20,000 years.

Larry Sarner (Therapeutic Touch) is a mathematician, cryptographer, and voting-machine inventor who resides in Loveland, Colorado. He cofounded the Front Range Skeptics and the National Therapeutic Touch Study Group, is a member of the National Council Against Health Fraud, and is coauthor of *Your Very Last Chance: How Attachment Therapists Killed Candace Newmaker.*

Thomas F. Sawyer (Clever Hans) is professor of psychology at North Central College in Naperville, Illinois. He received his Ph.D. from Bowling Green State University. He teaches the following courses in psychology: science of behavior, statistics, research design and experimentation, drugs and behavior, sensation and perception, physiological psychology, and history and systems of psychology. His research interests include: time perception; drug legislation/policy in the US; and behavioral genetics.

Theodore Schick Jr. (Do Extraordinary Claims Require Extraordinary Evidence?: A Reappraisal of a Classic Skeptics' Axiom) is a professor of philosophy at Muhlenberg College in Allentown, Pennsylvania. He has published articles on epistemology, philosophy of science, and philosophy of mind. He is coauthor of *How to Think About Weird Things.*

Henry Schlinger Jr. (Evolutionary Psychology as Pseudoscience) is a professor of psychology at Western New England College in Springfield, Massachusetts. He is the author of *A Behavior Analytic View of Child Development* and coauthor of *Psychology: A Behavioral Overview.* He has also published numerous theoretical articles on intelligence and artificial intelligence, the role of verbal behavior in learning, and child development.

Louis A. Schmidt (Psi and Psi-Missing) is an assistant professor of psychology at McMaster University in Ontario, Canada. His research interests include socioemotional development in infants and children, and developmental psychophysiology.

Rudolf Smit (Astrology) is secretary of the late professor H J Eysenck's Committee for Objective Research into Astrology, founding editor of what is now *Astrologie in Onderzoek* [Astrology under Scrutiny], and editor 1992–1999 of *Correlation*, the journal of research into astrology. Until late 2000 he was editor and translator for one of the Netherlands' leading scientific institutes.

Jorge Soto (Crop Circles) is a chemist by training, and an astronomer hobbyist. He did his graduate studies at Caltech (1983) and postgraduate studies at UCLA, both in chemistry. Jorge started to work at Dow Chemical in 1988 and moved to Midland, Michigan in 1993. Throughout his career, he has been involved in various projects related to making plastics, which have lead to numerous patents.

Bob Steiner (Cold Reading) is a CPA and magician; was the national president of The Society of American Magicians, of which he is chair of the Occult Investigation Committee; a fellow of The Committee for the Scientific Investigation of Claims of the Paranormal (CSICOP); a member of Professionals Against Confidence Crime; an associate of the Inner Magic Circle (London); and served on the board of directors of The National Council Against Health Fraud. Among his nine published books is *Don't Get Taken!*

David X. Swenson (Thought Field Therapy) is a licensed psychologist in Wisconsin and Minnesota, and a diplomate in forensic psychology. He teaches management courses at the College of St. Scholastica in Duluth, Minnesota, and has a small private practice in forensic and organizational psychology.

George A. Ulett (Acupuncture) has an M.D. and Ph.D. and has held professorships at the Missouri Institute of Mental Health, Washington University School of Medicine, St. Louis University School of Medicine, and was Chairman of the Department of Psychiatry at the University of Missouri Medical School. He is the author of over 270 scientific articles and books. He studied traditional Chinese acupuncture in the 1960s, received the first NIH grant to study acupuncture (1972) and has used the neuroelectric acupuncture method in his medical practice for many years. His 1992 book *Beyond Yin and Yang: How Acupuncture Really Works*, has been revised and updated. His latest book is *The Biology of Acupuncture*.

John van Wyhe (Phrenology) wrote his doctoral dissertation on the role of phrenology in the creation and spread of naturalism in nineteenth-century Britain. He is currently a senior research fellow at the National University of Singapore and a researcher at the department of history and philosophy of science at Cambridge. His general research interests include eighteenth- and nineteenth-century British and German intellectual/cultural history, as well as evolutionary thought, understandings of brain functions, science and religion, nature, and philosophies of materialism. He has published extensively on phrenology.

Jeffrey S. Victor (Satanic Ritual Abuse) is a professor of sociology at a branch of the State University of New York. He has published a book on human sexuality and many articles on rumor-panics and other sociological topics. He is the author of *Satanic Panic: The Creation of a Contemporary Legend*. He also studies the repressed memory movements, as well as the alien abduction movement.

Daniel R. Wilson (Magnetic Therapy) is professor and chairman of psychiatry and professor of anthropology at Creighton University Medical Center in Omaha. His research interests include evolutionary epidemiology, psychopharmacology, and forensic psychiatry.

Bill Wisdom (Skepticism and Credulity: Finding the Balance between Type 1 and Type 2 Errors) is emeritus professor of philosophy at Temple University in Philadelphia, where for more than thirty years he has taught formal logic, the philosophy of science, the philosophy of religion, and topics in the history of philosophy. He is the coauthor of a textbook in formal logic and metatheory, and has given lectures and published articles in the theory of knowledge, philosophy of religion, skepticism, and formal logic.

Eric Wojciehowski (Ancient Astronauts: Zecharia Sitchin as a Case Study) is a probation agent with the Michigan department of corrections currently working in the city of Detroit. He earned a bachelor's degree in psychology and has spent many years studying mythology, religion, history, and the general basis of paranormal beliefs. He is also a member of the Ancient Astronaut Society.

Roahn H. Wynar (Faster-Than-Light Travel, Laundry Balls) is an atomic physics researcher in the physics department at the University of Washington in Seattle. His interests include laser cooling and trapping and fundamental symmetries.

Julie Yau (Witchcraft and Magic) is a freelance writer and artist residing in Toronto. Her research interests include cultures and behaviors of the masses, and issues pertaining to the body. She is currently compiling research for a book on the fear of death.

Harry Ziel (Alternative Medicine v. Scientific Medicine) is emeritus clinical associate professor, Department of Ob/Gyn at the University of Southern California School of Medicine. He served as the director of Ob/Gyn at Kaiser Hospital, Los Angeles, from 1980–1991, as residency director from 1970–1980, and as medical education director from 1962–1970. He is a graduate of Harvard and attended the University of Pennsylvania medical school.

Index

About the Editors

Dr. Michael Shermer is the founding publisher of *Skeptic* magazine, the director of the Skeptics Society, contributing editor and monthly columnist for *Scientific American*, and the host of the Skeptics Lecture Series at Caltech. He is the author of *In Darwin's Shadow: The Life and Science of Alfred Russel Wallace*; *The Borderlands of Science: Where Sense Meets Nonsense*; *Denying History*; *How We Believe: The Search for God in an Age of Science*; and *Why People Believe Weird Things*. He is also the author of *Teach Your Child Science* and coauthored *Teach Your Child Math* and *Mathemagics*. According to

Stephen Jay Gould: "Michael Shermer, as head of one of America's leading skeptic organizations, and as a powerful activist and essayist in the service of this operational form of reason, is an important figure in American public life."

Dr. Shermer received his B.A. in psychology from Pepperdine University, M.A. in experimental psychology from California State Univesity–Fullerton, and his Ph.D. in the history of science from Claremont Graduate University. Since his creation of the Skeptics Society, *Skeptic* magazine, and the Skeptics Lecture Series at Caltech, he has appeared on such shows as *20/20*, *Dateline*, *Charlie Rose*, *Tom Snyder*, *Donahue*, *Oprah*, *Sally*, *Lezza*, *Unsolved Mysteries*, and other shows as a skeptic of weird and extraordinary claims, as well as on documentaries aired on A & E, Discovery, and The Learning Channel.

Pat Linse is an award winning illustrator specializing in film industry art. Long active in the skeptical movement, she is one of the founders of the Skeptics Society, *Skeptic* magazine, and *Jr. Skeptic* magazine, of which she is publisher and editor-in-chief. As *Skeptic's* art director, she has created most of the illustrations for both *Skeptic* and *Jr. Skeptic*. She is coauthor of the first *Baloney Detection Kit* and is presently working on a *Baloney Detection Kit* series of books for teaching children science and critical thinking.